CONTEMPORARY ISSUES
IN COMPARATIVE PSYCHOLOGY

CONTEMPORARY ISSUES IN COMPARATIVE PSYCHOLOGY

Edited by Donald A. Dewsbury
UNIVERSITY OF FLORIDA

SINAUER ASSOCIATES, INC. • Publishers
SUNDERLAND, MASSACHUSETTS

CONTEMPORARY ISSUES IN COMPARATIVE PSYCHOLOGY

Copyright © 1990 by Sinauer Associates Inc.

Library of Congress Cataloging-in-Publication Data

Contemporary issues in comparative psychology / edited by Donald A.
  Dewsbury.
      p.   cm.
    Bibliography: p.
    Includes index.
    ISBN 0-87893-137-6 (alk. paper) : $40.00 (est.).—ISBN
0-87893-138-4 (pbk. : alk. paper) : $27.50 (est.)
    1. Animal behavior.   2. Psychology, Comparative.   I. Dewsbury,
Donald A., 1939–
QL751.C665   1990   89-11501
591.51—dc20   CIP

This book is printed on paper that meets the guidelines for permanence
and durability of the Committee on Production Guidelines for Book Longevity
of the Council on Library Resources.

Printed in U.S.A.

5 4 3 2 1

*This book is respectfully dedicated
to the memory of*
FRANK AMBROSE BEACH
1911–1988

Contents

Preface   ix

Introduction   xi

The Contributors   xiii

Part I. Feeding and Other Behavior in Individual Animals   1

1. Learning, Memory, and Foraging Behavior   7
   ALAN C. KAMIL AND KEVIN C. CLEMENTS

2. Natural Learning in Laboratory Paradigms   31
   WILLIAM TIMBERLAKE

3. An Adaptionist Perspective on Social Learning,   55
   Social Feeding, and Social Foraging in Norway Rats
   BENNETT G. GALEF, JR.

4. Body Size, Allometry, and Comparative Psychology: 80
   Locomotion and Foraging
   DEL THEISSEN

5. The Behavior of the Brown Tree Snake: 101
   A Study in Applied Comparative Psychology
   DAVID A. CHISZAR

Part II. Mating Behavior   125

6. Deer Mice as a Case Study in the Operation of   129
   Natural Selection via Differential Reproductive Success
   DONALD A. DEWSBURY

7. Natural Selection and Reproduction: 149
   A Study of the Golden Orb-Weaving Spider
   TERRY E. CHRISTENSON

8. Ground Squirrel Reproductive Behavior   175
   and Mating Competition: A Comparative Perspective
   P. L. SCHWAGMEYER

9. The Role of Pavlovian Conditioning   197
   in Territorial Aggression and Reproduction
   KAREN L. HOLLIS

Part III. Parental Behavior and Development   221

10. Mechanisms Maintaining Monogamy in Monkeys   225
    CHARLES T. SNOWDON

11. Biological Timing Mechanisms with Special Emphasis   252
    on the Parental Behavior of Doves
    RAE SILVER

12. Comparative Development of Vertebrate Sexual Behavior: 278
    Levels, Cascades, and Webs
    CELIA L. MOORE

13. Littermate Influences on Behavioral   300
    and Physiological Development in Spiny Mice
    RICHARD H. PORTER

Part IV. Communication and Social Behavior   317

14. Variation In Species-Typical Behavior: 321
    A Contemporary Issue for Comparative Psychology
    ANDREW P. KING AND MEREDITH J. WEST

15. Avian Song Development: 340
    Methodological and Conceptual Issues
    LEWIS PETRINOVICH

16. The Evolution of Parent–Offspring Recognition   360
    in Swallows
    MICHAEL D. BEECHER

17. Chemical Communication in Golden Hamsters: 381
    From Behavior to Molecules and Neural Mechanisms
    ROBERT E. JOHNSTON

18. The Colony Model of Aggression and Defense   410
    D. CAROLINE BLANCHARD AND ROBERT J. BLANCHARD

Epilogue   431
Comparative Psychology: Retrospect and Prospect
DONALD A. DEWSBURY

Acknowledgements   449

Literature Cited   452

Index   497

Preface

In this book we bring together the work of various comparative psychologists whose work has one foot in traditional psychology and the other in the interdisciplinary mainstream of research in animal behavior. Our goal has been to summarize the current status of some important research in comparative psychology and to tie this work to general principles. Although we have tried to illustrate exciting approaches rather than to provide an exhaustive survey, we hope that this book also will be useful as a textbook for advanced courses in comparative psychology.

The approach to comparative psychology emphasized here entails a broad-based, biological approach to the study of behavior with an emphasis on the natural lives of animals. In a sense, this represents the realization of the "comparative behavioral science" envisaged by Frank Beach in a textbook he wrote in the late 1950s but which, regrettably, he chose not to publish. I thank all who played a role in the publication of this book. Most important are the authors who wrote it and who generally did so remarkably close to the schedule agreed upon. Pessimists sometimes bemoan the small number of comparative psychologists active today, but I believe we have an embarrassment of riches. I regret the extent to which we have had to limit the size of this volume, thus excluding some very fine comparative psychologists. From the standpoint of the viability of the field, however, this is a good problem to have. On the other hand, I am delighted with the group of psychologists who were willing to contribute chapters.

With the help of Chuck Snowdon and Susan Abrams, I was put in touch with Sinauer Associates. They were supportive of my idea for this volume, and Carl Brose and Peter Farley were most helpful as work progressed. My family, and, I'm sure, the families of the other authors, were most tolerant of the time spent at the word processor rather than with them. I hope that the result is a useful book in which comparative psychology, as many of us view it, is presented effectively.

DONALD A. DEWSBURY
Gainesville, Florida
August, 1989

Introduction

Although comparative psychology is a relatively small area within the overall field of psychology, it is a dynamic discipline; its practitioners are active and productive scientists. In this book, the authors and I have worked to bring together some of the accomplishments of comparative psychologists and to show that this exciting work is a vital part of both psychology and the broader study of animal behavior.

At least three strains of comparative psychology can be recognized. One area of important and valuable work that has had a recent renaissance is the study of learning, language acquisition, and cognition in non-human animals (e.g., Roitblat, 1987; Roitblat, Bever, & Terrace, 1984). Scientists working in this area have found capacities and processes unanticipated only a few years ago. Another group of comparative psychologists finds a core approach derived from the theoretical notions of approach–withdrawal theory, the levels concept, and other proposals of T. C. Schneirla (Greenberg & Tobach, 1984). A third, substantial group of psychologists is studying animal behavior in ways that blend contemporary zoological and psychological methods and contemporary knowledge to address a broader range of questions concerning the evolution, development, causation, and adaptive significance of behavior. They are working somewhat closer to the mainstream of the interdisciplinary study of animal behavior.

It is with this last approach that the current volume is primarily concerned. In such work it matters less that a scientist is a psychologist, zoologist, psychiatrist, or anthropologist than that the work be addressed at significant scientific questions in appropriate ways. Comparative psychologists of this type thus tie their work both to this interdisciplinary mainstream and to psychology itself. There have been few opportunities for these comparative psychologists to summarize and integrate their research in a forum that will reveal its breadth and depth, although the volume based on the 1987 Nebraska Symposium on Motivation (Leger, 1988) provided an excellent start in this direction. Here, we present a larger set of chapters illustrative of the substantial range and considerable quality of research in this area.

It can be argued that comparative psychology has always been part of an interdisciplinary effort and that today's field represents a logical development of trends that have occurred throughout the century (e.g., Dewsbury, 1984b). During this time there has been much debate within the field. However, debate and polemic can accomplish only so much. The best demonstration of the accomplishments of a field is to present its accomplishments (see Schrier, 1969). Thus, our objective in creating this volume has not been to assess the field, but rather to illuminate it.

As we assembled the volume, several key themes emerged that shed some light on important issues in contemporary comparative psychology. I shall state some briefly here; they are developed in the Epilogue. A key notion in the study of animal behavior is that of adaptation. As a result of the action of natural selection over generations and the interaction of genes and environment during ontogeny, animals become adapted to function effectively in their environments so that they survive, reproduce, and pass on their genetic material to future generations. The concept of adaptation cannot be applied to behavior loosely (see Williams, 1966). Applied with care, however, it provides a foundation for the study of animal behavior. Other themes include (1) the integration of the four questions of the study of animal behavior proposed by Tinbergen (1963) (i.e., immediate causation, development, evolutionary history, and adaptive significance), (2) the development of new applications and approaches in using the comparative method, (3) the interesting processes used in selecting study species, (4) the diversity of study species, (5) the impact of improved technology and new methods on the development of the field, (6) realization of the ubiquity of influence of the social context on behavior, (7) integration of information on the processes underlying learning and memory with research on the natural lives of animals, (8) new approaches to the study of the development of behavior, and (9) explorations of the implications of research for applied settings and in conservation.

In organizing the book, I have chosen to stress the functional categories of behavior that are relevant to adaptation. First, animals as individuals must do certain things to survive—eat, drink, breathe, avoid predators, and so forth. If an animal fails at these basic tasks, all, including the genome, is lost. However, an animal that survives, but fails to reproduce, will be as much of an evolutionary dead end as one that fails to survive. A second class of essential behavioral patterns is focused about mating behavior; effective mating behavior leads to the production of young. In many species parents care for their young, and the development of the young can be seen in their interaction with parents, siblings, and environmental factors; this is a third category. Finally, animals live in complex social organizations with shared codes of communication; these are the focus of the fourth category. Although a few chapters do not fit comfortably within this schema, I think that some important implications of others are brought out by placing them in these contexts.

This book thus is organized about these four categories of adaptive behavior—individual behavior, mating behavior, parental behavior and development, and communication and social behavior. Each part of the book is preceded by an introduction. Within each part is a set of chapters by contemporary comparative psychologists discussing their research and its relationship to general principles in the study of animal behavior. The focus is on in-depth treatments of specific problems that illustrate the activity of comparative psychologists. In the Epilogue, I try to tie the material together and reflect on the past and present of comparative psychology.

The Contributors

MICHAEL D. BEECHER, Department of Psychology, University of Washington, Seattle, WA 98195

D. CAROLINE BLANCHARD, Békésy Laboratory of Neurobiology, University of Hawaii, Honolulu, HI 96822

ROBERT J. BLANCHARD, Department of Psychology, University of Hawaii, Honolulu, HI 96822

DAVID A. CHISZAR, Department of Psychology, University of Colorado, Campus Box 345, Boulder, CO 80309

KEVIN C. CLEMENTS, Department of Psychology, University of Massachusetts, Amherst, MA 01003

TERRY E. CHRISTENSON, Department of Psychology, Tulane University, New Orleans, LA 70118

DONALD A. DEWSBURY, Department of Psychology, University of Florida, Gainesville, FL 32611

BENNETT G. GALEF, JR., Department of Psychology, McMaster University, Hamilton, Ontario, L8S 4K1, Canada

KAREN L. HOLLIS, Department of Psychology, Mount Holyoke College, South Hadley, MA 01075

ROBERT E. JOHNSTON, Department of Psychology, Cornell University, Uris Hall, Ithaca, NY 14853

ALAN C. KAMIL, Department of Psychology, University of Massachusetts, Amherst, MA 01003

ANDREW P. KING, Department of Psychology, Duke University, Durham, NC 27706

CELIA L. MOORE, Department of Psychology, University of Massachusetts/Boston, Boston, MA 02125

LEWIS PETRINOVICH, Department of Psychology, University of California, Riverside, Riverside, CA 92521

RICHARD H. PORTER, Department of Psychology and Human Development, George Peabody College of Vanderbilt University, Nashville, TN 37203

P. L. SCHWAGMEYER, Department of Psychology, University of Oklahoma, Norman, OK 73019

RAE SILVER, Psychology Department, Barnard College of Columbia University, 3009 Broadway, New York, NY 10027

CHARLES T. SNOWDON, Department of Psychology, University of Wisconsin, Madison, WI 53706

DEL THIESSEN, Department of Psychology, University of Texas, Austin, TX 78712

WILLIAM TIMBERLAKE, Department of Psychology, Psychology Building, Indiana University, Bloomington, IN 47405

MEREDITH J. WEST, Department of Psychology, University of North Carolina, Chapel Hill, NC 27514

PART I

Feeding and Other Behavior in Individual Animals

Each section of this book is focused on one of four functional categories of animal behavior: behavior characteristic of individuals, reproductive behavior, parental behavior and the development of young, and communication and social behavior. This section concerns behavioral patterns that characterize individual organisms. As will be apparent, these patterns do not occur in a social vacuum—Galef's work on social learning (Chapter 3) provides a case in point. Nevertheless, the emphasis in the following chapters is on behavior that is relevant to the sustenance and survival of the individual. The role of behavioral plasticity, the capacity to alter such behavior, also is considered.

The first three chapters are concerned with different aspects of the acquisition of food: foraging, learning, and social learning. Chapter 4 provides methodological guides for comparative study, such as that which characterizes much of the book, with an emphasis on locomotion and foraging. In the final chapter of this section the application of comparative psychology is discussed, with locomotion and feeding again providing a focus.

Animals depend on environmental resources, such as food, water, and shelter, for survival. These resources can be located, utilized, and depleted in various patterns, some of which may be more effective than others. It seems reasonable to assume that those animals that exploit resources most efficiently, with minimal effort and minimal exposure to predation and the elements, will reap the maximal returns, and will, in the long run, survive and reproduce more effectively than those using less effective patterns. Indeed, without an independent criterion of effectiveness, this could be considered a truism. Kamil and Clements (Chapter 1) present a discussion of optimal foraging strategies based on their studies of foraging behavior in birds. These laboratory studies are modeled after processes that occur as birds feed in nature; however, the powerful techniques and exquisite controls possible in the laboratory render this work especially enlightening.

Kamil and Clements focus on two aspects of birds' utilization of environmental resources in feeding. The first is the optimization of foraging patterns and, in

1

particular, the problem of patch departure timing. As an animal exploits a patch of food, the gain per unit of time decreases, and the animal must decide when to leave the patch and try another. Under the conditions simulated by Kamil and Clements, the timing of patch departure was affected by both the number of prey already obtained in the depleting patch and by the length of a "run of bad luck." The second aspect of foraging behavior upon which Kamil and Clements focus is the recovery of seeds from a stored cache. It is clear that some birds have memories that are well-adapted for locating previously cached food, and are able to exploit these stored resources efficiently. However, there is interspecific variation; among the species studied, the two most dependent upon cached food performed most accurately in Kamil and Clements's tests.

Animals appear to be selected to behave in ways that approach optimality. However, because they may not possess the wherewithal to perform the calculations of the animal behaviorist, animal behavior is often governed proximally by "rules of thumb"—serviceable decision rules which permit an animal to reach a reasonable approximation of optimal performance. Natural selection produces animals that can display effective performance within the range of capacities and proclivities characteristic of their makeup.

Kamil and Clements's work provides an excellent example of the utilization of powerful laboratory methods to gain insight into biologically important problems and to reveal the rules according to which animals appear to behave. In so doing, the ultimate functions of behavior become linked to proximal control, and an integrated picture of behavior can emerge.

At one level, Timberlake (Chapter 2) deals with the study of learning, and his work might have been placed in a different section of this volume. Timberlake's deeper message, however, is that the performance of an animal in a test situation is a manifestation of a hierarchical system of behavioral tendencies that the animal brings to the test situation; laboratory "learning" must be viewed, then, as an integrated part of the total behavioral repertoire of the animal. Timberlake thus helps to break down the barriers between the study of animal learning and of animal behavior by presenting studies of feeding behavior that occurs in situations psychologists have generally designed to study learning, and his work can thus be seen as bridging the two surrounding chapters.

Timberlake presents a "behavior system model," according to which an animal brings to the test situation a set of functional behavioral systems, hierarchical control structures, and processes that relate to particular needs and functions of the organism. The model has four levels: systems, subsystems, modes, and perceptual–motor modules. In essence, the animal has a structured set of control mechanisms that enable it to deal with situations it encounters, and its performance in tests of learning reflects the operation of these control structures. Timberlake emphasizes the form of behavior, its functions, and its ecological settings. He does not elaborate the model here, as he has done so elsewhere;

rather, he concentrates on its implications, dissolving the barriers between the study of animal learning and animal behavior.

Much of Timberlake's chapter consists of a presentation of the kinds of insights that can be achieved with a behavior system approach. He first considers traditional studies of maze learning and concludes that animal performance in these studies reflects a set of search routines that are guided by particular stimulus circumstances. This discussion is followed by similar analyses of superstitious behavior, adjunctive behavior, autoshaping, the role of conspecifics as cues to food, and the phenomena of operant conditioning. For example, rats' fascination with ball bearings, which were originally used to study performance in token economies, is viewed by Timberlake as reflecting predatory sequences appropriate for capturing, killing, and eating insect prey.

Timberlake shows that many apparently puzzling phenomena of laboratory learning can be viewed in relation to the kinds of structured response tendencies envisaged in the behavior system model. Timberlake also turns the argument around to show that standard paradigms used in the study of animal learning can be used to reveal the structure of the animal's natural behavior system. Finally, both of these phenomena should interact and enrich the study of learning in the laboratory. Timberlake's chapter is thus a study of learning, but of learning viewed from within the life history of the organism. It is a study of feeding behavior that is influenced by experience rather than a study of learning using food as an arbitrarily selected reinforcer.

The focus in Galef's work (Chapter 3) is *social* learning. Again, the problem examined is the effective location and utilization of food resources. Galef's focus, however, is not on the foraging strategies of individuals, but upon social interactions and their effect on foraging and eating in Norway rats. No rat is an island; rats live in colonies, and even the process of locating food can be highly social. Like most of the authors of this volume, Galef is an "adaptationist," and is concerned with the role of behavior in the adaptation of the organism. He seeks both to delineate the precise ways in which rats share information about foods in the environment and to consider the function of these interactions in promoting survival and reproduction.

The bulk of Galef's chapter concerns his research on the fine structure of the social interactions that affect the location of and choice of food by rats. First, he found that the foods eaten by "demonstrator" rats do indeed affect the choices of "observer" rats. He then set out to discover the ways in which this is accomplished. In a discussion of his beautifully integrated series of studies, Galef shows that the transmission of information about food is accomplished via olfaction, that live demonstrator rats are the most effective transmitters, and that their breath is implicated in the process. Remarkably, Galef shows that carbon disulfide (CS_2) is emitted in the breath of rats and appears to enhance preferences for odors encountered by rats.

Galef next turns to the task of relating these controlled studies of olfactory transmission of information to the natural setting by considering three ways in which socially acquired information might be of use to naive forager rats: it can provide cues to the location of food, to what kinds of food to eat, and to what kinds of food not to eat. He finds indications that all might occur. Rats may often live in situations in which given types of food occur periodically and unpredictably at fixed locations. They can use their fellow rats to orient feeding trips in a given direction, and they will even follow each other to food.

These studies show that animals do not function alone in determining effective ways in which to exploit food resources, but that individuals can utilize information from conspecifics to deal with the problem of food location more effectively than they could by themselves. Adaptation is flexible and opportunistic; many potential sources of information are used in shaping animals to deal efficiently with their environments.

A major goal of Thiessen's contribution (Chapter 4) is to provide grounds for some caution in the development of hypotheses and explanations about the adaptive nature of behavior. Comparative analyses often are focused on one aspect of animals' behavior. This is a necessary step for comparative psychologists as they begin analyses, because one cannot study everything at once. However, there is a risk of interpreting all characteristics as being adaptive in and of themselves. This need not be so; some characteristics may appear as secondary manifestations of other aspects of the animal's previous evolutionary history or in association with functions not under study in a particular line of research (see Gould & Lewontin, 1979).

Body size is an important determinant of behavior, and is both a product of the action of selection and a constraint on other adaptive characteristics for animals. As Thiessen points out, for example, movements are especially metabolically expensive in small animals, and, consequently, these animals may be adapted for finding and eating localized and predictable foods. Larger species can move more efficiently, and thus exhibit adaptations that are more compatible with the exploitation of patchy and unpredictable resources.

Thiessen first provides a description and interpretation of allometric scaling, and provides some examples that make use of this technique. He then applies allometric scaling to problems of food location and foraging strategies, showing that much of the cross-species variation in home- range size can be explained by body weight alone. Finally, Thiessen suggests that allometric methods can play an important role in comparative psychology by generating specific, testable hypotheses. He proposes the development of a dictionary of allometric equations that would allow researchers to make comparisons among a wide range of species and behavior patterns. Thiessen points to the need to view both the broad and the delicate strokes of evolution. His emphasis on the products of evolutionary history provides an appropriate complement to the emphasis on specific adaptations that is characteristic of many other researchers and of many of the authors in this book.

Behavioral patterns must interlock in an effective manner to produce a complete functioning organism. The organisms often interact in ways that create an organized society in which each can survive. Finally, different species interact to make a whole community. In Chiszar's chapter on brown tree snakes (Chapter 5) we get an appreciation of the complexity of these interspecies interactions. Brown tree snakes on the island of Guam have experienced an "ecological release," having been introduced into a habitat where the factors that normally control their population sizes appear to be missing. As a result, their impact on the environment is considerable, with the most prominent effects being a dramatic loss of avian fauna and the involvement of the snakes in a large number of power outages due to their climbing on power lines and infestation of transformers.

Chiszar's work with these snakes is first and foremost an example of applied comparative psychology; it shows how the powerful methods of the field can be used in the search for solutions to practical, everyday problems. In the process of searching for solutions, however, Chiszar has learned much about the snakes themselves and their place in the community of species. He describes, for example, a remarkable plasticity in their predatory behavior. The snakes can switch from visual to chemical cues while foraging, use constriction to subdue large prey, effectively swallow very large prey, and even forage on the ground. The snakes possess a flexibility not anticipated by the researchers. One lesson of this work may apply to the design of environments for behavioral studies. There is much value in designing test environments in which the natural environment is simulated as closely as possible, as this gives us the best insight into behavior as it is displayed under normal conditions. However, there may also be great value in studying animals in highly unusual environments because it is here that we see the range of variation in an animal's capacity to deal with new situations.

The attempt to control the access of brown tree snakes to power lines led Chiszar and his colleagues to perform a systematic study of the environmental substrates and motor patterns these snakes use in climbing. The attractiveness to the snakes of dark areas of refuge suggested that conical devices placed on power-line guy wires may limit their climbing, and the initial results of this strategy are encouraging. In this chapter, the reader can see a fine example of research designed to solve a practical problem yielding new and important information on the biology and plasticity of a species capable of having considerable impact on humans and other animals.

CHAPTER 1

LEARNING, MEMORY, AND FORAGING BEHAVIOR

Alan C. Kamil and Kevin C. Clements

The problem of obtaining food is probably the most important problem that animals confront. Without the energy and nutrients gained while foraging, other activities, such as obtaining a mate and reproducing, are impossible. As Hutchinson (1959) observed, " . . . food relations appear as one of the most important aspects of the system of animate nature" (p. 147). Thus, the study of foraging ecology is basic to the understanding of animals.

Two recent developments in behavioral ecology, one empirical and one theoretical, have clearly shown that the behavioral decisions of individual foragers play a crucial role in foraging ecology. The empirical development was a result of field studies in which the foraging behavior of marked individuals is followed over time (e.g., Gill & Wolf, 1977; Kamil, 1978; Mook, Mook, & Heikens, 1960; Tinbergen, 1960). Such studies have demonstrated that the foraging behavior of animals is extremely well organized and is sensitive to changes in the spatial and temporal distribution of food. At the same time, optimal foraging theory has shown that the ability of animals to respond adaptively to the characteristics of their food supply can have considerable effects on foraging efficiency and therefore, presumably, on fitness. Our purpose in this chapter is to show how the natural history and behavioral ecology of foraging animals can provide an excellent starting point for research on learning and memory. The results of such research, which integrates approaches from ecology, ethology, and psychology, can have important implications for all three disciplines.

FOOD IN PATCHES: A UBIQUITOUS PROBLEM

Much of the theory and research on foraging behavior has focused upon the use of patches of food. Many animals forage for food that is distributed in discrete

7

areas. For example, titmice search for larvae buried in pine cones (Gibb, 1960), hummingbirds take nectar from flowers (Armstrong, Gass, & Sutherland, 1987), and desert rodents find seeds that are unevenly distributed by the wind (Reichman, 1981). In fact, many situations that superficially appear to involve uniformly distributed food turn out on closer examination to involve clumped, patchy food distributions. For example, leaf-eating monkeys, like many herbivores, appear to have access to an abundance of uniformly distributed food, since leaves can be found throughout the forest. But many leaves contain poisonous secondary compounds, and at many times of the year there are few nutritious leaves available. Edible leaves can only be found on certain specific trees, which are, in effect, patches (Glander, 1981).

An animal foraging for patchily distributed food faces at least two decisions: when between patches, it must decide which patch to visit next, and when foraging within a patch, it must decide when to leave that patch and travel to the next. The most theoretical and empirical attention has been focused on the patch departure issue. This is partly because the marginal value theorem (Charnov, 1976), a model that predicts the optimal moment to leave a depleting patch, attracted enormous attention, especially after initial empirical tests produced results in agreement with its predictions (Cowie, 1977; Krebs, Ryan, & Charnov, 1974). But it has also become clear that patch departure is a general problem. Patch departure decisions are important in many different foraging contexts. For example, when hummingbirds take nectar from a flower, the rate at which the nectar can be extracted declines as the amount remaining declines (Hainsworth & Wolf, 1976). As blue jays hunt for cryptic prey, the probability of finding a prey item decreases as the amount of time spent in unsuccessful search increases (Kamil, Lindstrom, & Peters, 1985). As aquatic insects such as waterboatmen extract food from their prey, the rate of intake declines (Cook & Cockrell, 1978). In each of these cases, the observed patch departure behavior agrees at least qualitatively with the predictions of the marginal value theorem. Space limitations prevent us from presenting the details of the marginal value theorem, but a good discussion of it can be found in Stephens and Krebs (1986).

Although the logic and the mathematics of the marginal value theorem are sound given its assumptions, it has been subjected to considerable criticism. Some of this has been general criticism of the optimality approach (see Gray, 1987, and Schoener, 1987, for discussions of both sides of this issue). Other criticisms have addressed more specific issues. One of the specific criticisms is that the marginal value theorem assumes that the within-patch intake rate is a continuous function of time in the patch. Although this may be an appropriate assumption for some foragers, such as those that suck the nutrients from their patches, it is clearly inappropriate for many others. Foragers such as titmice, which search for larvae in pine cones, find their food in distinct lumps within patches. Thus, the curve relating time in patch to food obtained shows long flat periods between prey captures. As prey are depleted within a patch, the instantaneous rate of energy intake does not systematically decline, as the marginal value theorem assumes. Rather, the length of the flat (zero intake) periods between successive prey captures increases. Under such conditions, the mathematics of the marginal value theorem do not hold.

Another specific criticism has particularly strong implications for those interested in the behavioral mechanisms animals use to decide when to leave a patch. The marginal value theorem, like most optimal foraging models, assumes that the forager is omniscient and possesses all of the necessary relevant information to make its foraging decisions. This is unlikely to be the case very often, if at all. For example, the mathematics of the marginal value theorem require knowing both the expected within-patch rate of intake and the average rate of intake across all patches. But the forager is unlikely to have direct knowledge of either of these rates of intake. The forager's overall capture rate is a function of a series of non-random patch choices and residence times, and therefore the predator cannot have direct knowledge of the average capture rate provided by the entire foraging area (McNamara, 1982). These considerations suggest that animals may use simpler, more direct information when making decisions about patch departure.

For this reason, many researchers have sought to identify some relatively simple within-patch parameter, such as time since the last prey was found (Krebs et al., 1974), that may be used by a forager to determine when to leave a patch. Departure rules based on simple parameters are often called *rules of thumb*. In many cases, the foraging efficiency of an animal using a simple rule of thumb may closely approach the foraging efficiency of an omniscient predator (Green, 1987; McNamara, 1982).

There are a number of different within-patch characteristics to which an animal might be sensitive. These are generally composed of some combination of the number of prey found in the patch and their distribution in time, either measured from the moment of patch entry or from the time of last prey capture. For example, Gibb (1962) proposed that titmice "hunt by expectation" when searching for larvae that have burrowed beneath the surface of pine cones. He suggested that if the birds formed some expectation of the number of larvae they would find in a cone, they could leave after having found the expected number. Krebs et al. (1974), adapting the marginal value theorem to a situation involving artificial pine cones, found that time since the last prey capture could be used to predict patch departure. Krebs, Kacelnik, & Taylor (1978), studying a situation in which birds made discrete "perch-hopping" responses within a patch, suggested that a run of bad luck, that is, several consecutive hops producing no reward, might lead to patch departure. Lima (1983), studying a situation in which patch quality varied, suggested a fixed time-in-patch rule.

In these examples, investigators working with different situations have stressed the importance of different rules of thumb. This implies that animals may use different rules of thumb when patch characteristics vary. In fact, theoretical work has demonstrated that the rule which produces the highest rate of intake varies as a function of the type of distribution of prey within patches (Green 1987; Iwasa, Higashi, & Yamamura, 1981).

If animals do vary the rule of thumb that they use as conditions change, this raises many interesting psychological questions about how environmental conditions affect behavior. In order to begin to test the variables controlling patch departure decisions, we designed a discrete-trials operant procedure that simulated the patch depletion problem.

AN OPERANT SIMULATION OF PATCH DEPLETION

Before proceeding to a description of our experimental procedures, there is a general question that should be discussed: What constitutes a valid laboratory simulation of a natural situation? The goal of a laboratory simulation is not to replicate nature in exact detail, but to study the phenomenon in question under rigorously controlled experimental conditions. This requires that the field situation be simplified. But it is always possible that the simplification will result in the elimination of some important parameter.

Laboratory research and field research each have advantages and disadvantages. The laboratory offers the advantages of experimental control, which allows the determination of the causes of behavioral effects (internal validity), but it leaves one uncertain of the extent to which the results can be generalized to other situations, particularly those that occur in nature (external validity). Field work has the opposite characteristics: high external validity, but low internal validity (Kamil, 1988a). Thus, when naturalistic research suggests hypotheses about the mechanisms underlying behavior, these need to be regarded as hypotheses to be tested under experimental conditions. Similarly, when behavioral mechanisms are discovered in the laboratory, their generality and importance must be studied in the field.

In the case of our laboratory research on patch departure, we have started from the results of field work and ecological theory. Our goal was to select a species that regularly faces the problem of patchily distributed food, and to design a procedure that simulated nature in the sense that the consequences of the decisions the animals had to make were similar in form to the consequences that hold in nature.

The species we selected for these studies was the blue jay (*Cyanocitta cristata*). The blue jay is an appropriate choice because it is a notoriously omnivorous forager that feeds on a wide variety of food types (Bent, 1964). It is clear that jays encounter many different types of patchily distributed food and experience many different patterns of patch depletion in nature. In addition, the blue jay is a species well suited to laboratory studies of behavior.

Blue jays were trained to choose between two simulated patches in an operant conditioning chamber. Two sets of pecking keys were mounted on a panel on one wall of the chamber, one set on each side of a centrally placed food cup. Each set of keys represented a patch of food, and consisted of one large rectangular key situated above a smaller round key. The keys were made of a material onto which various stimuli could be projected from behind. Each large rectangular key had a Kodak Carousel slide projector mounted behind it to project slides onto the rectangular keys, and each round key had a small stimulus projector mounted behind it which projected colors and simple geometric stimuli onto the round keys. A perch, running the length of the wall, was located so that the eye level of a jay on the perch was just below the center of the rectangular keys.

We began each foraging session by placing the jay in the chamber with all keys dark. There were 36 trials per session. Each trial began with the illumination of both small round keys. The jay chose between the patches by pecking one of the round keys. The key not chosen went dark, and all subsequent events of that trial took place on the chosen side. The first peck at a round key initiated a travel-time delay, simulating the time between the decision to hunt in a patch and arrival in the patch. If the jay chose the same side it had chosen on the previous trial, the travel time was shorter than if it switched sides; as in nature, it was more time-consuming to switch between patches than to stay in the same area. When the travel-time delay was over, the display on the round key changed, and the next peck at the round key initiated the search phase of the trial: the round key changed color again, and a slide was projected onto the rectangular key.

Two types of slides were used, one showing a *Catocala* moth on a plain background, and the other showing only the background. The jay could end the search phase with either of two responses: a peck at the round key, which caused both keys to go dark and ended the trial, or a peck at the rectangular key, which caused the round key to go dark and began a 20-second handling-time delay. The first peck at the rectangular key after the handling time was over caused the key to darken, and, if there had been a moth in the slide, a piece of mealworm (*Tenebrio molitor* larva) was delivered into the food cup. The cup was illuminated for 3 seconds to allow the bird to eat the reward, then the trial ended. If there had been no moth in the slide, the trial ended without a reward being delivered. Following each trial, there was a 2-second intertrial interval (ITI) during which the slide projector behind the rectangular key advanced, then the next trial began. See Figure 1 for a flow diagram summarizing these within-trial events.

This complex sequence of events was designed to simulate the series of decisions that a jay foraging for moths in trees must make and the relative consequences that each decision would have in nature. A blue jay foraging within a tree hops from place to place looking for moths. Because the moths tend to be highly dispersed (Sargent, 1976), a maximum of one moth can be found in any

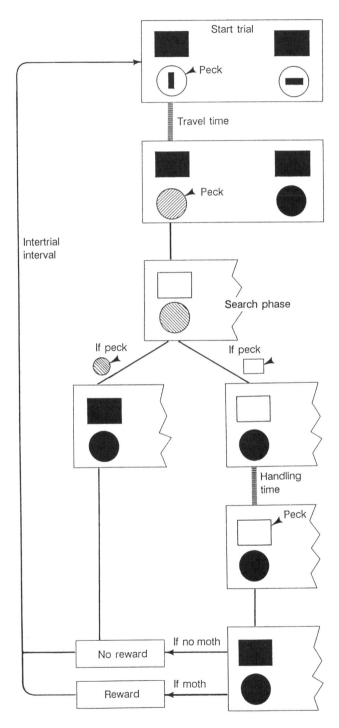

given place within a tree. After searching a place, the jay can either move to another place within the tree or switch to another tree. Switching trees will take longer than staying within a tree. Thus, in our simulation, each patch (set of keys) simulated a tree, while each slide simulated a place within the tree. Remaining in the same patch from trial to trial resulted in a shorter travel time than switching patches did. In nature, staying in a tree after all prey in that tree have been found results in a low rate of food intake, whereas switching to a new tree produces a higher intake rate. This is also true of our simulation (see below).

As a terminological convention, we will refer to each set of keys as a patch (tree), and to each specific slide as a subpatch (specific place within the tree). On each trial, the bird chose between patches and then visited one subpatch within the chosen patch. At the start of each trial, the jay was asked to choose between patches by choosing which round key to peck. Then, after "traveling" to the next subpatch within the chosen patch, the jay could search for a prey item, which might or might not be present on any given trial. If no prey was present, the jay could leave the subpatch immediately. If a prey item was present, the jay had to invest handling time in "attacking" the moth before receiving a reward. As in the previous research on prey detection upon which this procedure was based (Kamil, Lindstrom, & Peters, 1985; Pietrewicz & Kamil, 1977, 1979, 1987), the handling time requirement was sufficient to maintain accurate responding during the search phase. After initial training with these procedures, response accuracy during the search phase approached 100 percent.

In all of the experiments using these procedures, one of the patches was a uniform, nondepleting patch in which the probability of a prey item appearing in any given subpatch was a constant .25. The other patch was a depleting patch, in which the probability of any given subpatch containing prey at the beginning of each session was .50. This probability declined to zero in a single step part way through the session. With this single-step, "catastrophic" depletion, the point at which the depleting patch became less valuable than the nondepleting patch was unambiguous, making the most efficient point of departure unambiguous. The prey densities and distributions, the conditional probabilities of prey encounter, and the moment of depletion were all controlled simply by manipulating the order of the slides in the trays of the projectors behind the two rectangular keys.

Our first experiment (Kamil & Yoerg, 1985) was designed to evaluate the usefulness of these procedures while also testing an implication of the paper by Iwasa et al. (1981), who demonstrated that if the within-patch distribution of prey

◄FIGURE 1. Flow diagram for within-trial events in the sequence used for all the depletion experiments. The sequence begins at the top of the figure, showing the illumination of the two round keys. In this example, the bird chooses the left set of keys by pecking the vertical bar on the left round key. See the text for a description of these experiments.

is binomial, the best indicator of depletion is the number of prey already obtained within the patch. But if it is a Poisson distribution, then time spent in the patch is the best indicator.

Four jays were tested by Kamil and Yoerg. Two were exposed to a condition analogous to the Poisson distribution. For these birds, there were either five, six, or seven prey before depletion, and the last prey always occurred on the 12th trial in the depleting patch. Thus, the best rule for an omniscient predator would be to leave after a fixed number of trials, in this case, 12. In this discrete trials procedure, a fixed number of trials is analogous to a fixed amount of time. The other two birds were exposed to a condition analogous to the binomial distribution. There were always exactly six prey before depletion, but the trial in which the last prey was found varied from the 10th to the 14th. For these birds, the best rule was to always leave immediately after exactly six prey had been found. Of course, these rules for leaving the depleting patch would only apply if the birds hunted in it early in the foraging bout.

There are three different ways to look at the strategies available to the jays. First, the jays could behave so as to maximize the number of prey found per session. Any pattern of patch choice that involved always choosing the depleting patch exactly as many times as required to find the last prey in that patch would serve this function equally well. For the birds in the Poisson condition, always choosing the depleting patch exactly 12 times would maximize the number of prey per session, regardless of the order of choice of the two patches. Second, the jays could behave so as to maximize the rate of food intake during the session. Since the travel time cost of switching between patches was greater than that for staying within the same patch, food intake could be maximized by choosing the depleting patch exactly the "correct" number of times in succession. It would not matter whether these choices were made at the beginning or at the end of the session as long as there was only one switch between patches (minimizing travel time). Third, the jays could behave so as to capture as many prey as possible as quickly as possible, either because of discounting the value of future prey items (Houston, Kacelnik, & McNamara, 1982) or to minimize the average delay to reinforcement (Fantino, 1987). This would be achieved by choosing the depleting patch first, and staying in the depleting patch until depletion had taken place.

In fact, all four blue jays learned to begin the session in the depleting patch and switch to the nondepleting patch part way through the session. By the end of the experiment, the probability of choosing the depleting patch during the first 12 trials was about .90, but fell to less than .15 during the last 12 trials of the foraging session (Figure 2). There were no differences in patch choice between the birds receiving the Poisson type and the birds receiving the binomial-type prey distributions.

In order to maximize the number of prey obtained or the rate of prey capture, it was necessary for the birds to avoid choosing the depleting patch after depletion

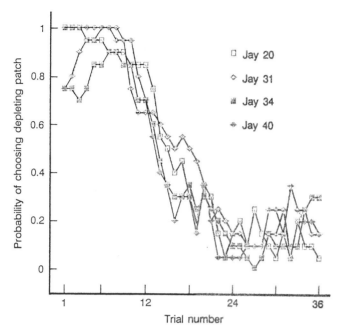

FIGURE 2. Mean probability of choosing the depleting patch for each jay on each trial of a session, averaged across the last 20 sessions of the first experiment.

had occurred. This did not happen. Even when the probability of choosing the depleting patch is plotted as a function of the number of trials since the last prey was found there (Figure 3), the decline in the choice of the depleting patch is gradual. Three trials after the last prey, the jays were choosing the depleted patch about half the time. In fact, the birds never completely stopped choosing the depleted patch, even very late in the session. Even on the last trial of the session, Trial 36, all birds chose the depleted patch at least occasionally (Figure 2). These choices of the depleted patch late in the foraging session generally involved the birds' periodically leaving the nondepleting patch for one or two trials in the depleted patch. These visits to the empty patch can be interpreted as sampling behavior. If the depleted patch became good again, such behavior would be necessary for the birds to discover its repletion.

It is clear that the birds treated the discrete trials operant procedure as a depleting patch problem. They also responded in an orderly and sensible fashion to the experimental conditions. It appeared that the birds were using different rules of thumb for switches in different directions. While switches from the depleting to the nondepleting patch were usually preceded by several trials during which no prey were found (a run of bad luck, or ROBL), switches from the

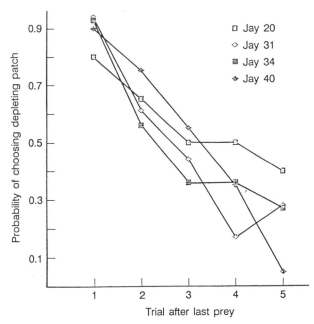

FIGURE 3. Mean probability of choosing the depleting patch for each jay, shown as a function of the number of trials since the last prey item in the depleting patch had been found, averaged across the last 20 sessions of the first experiment.

nondepleting to the depleting patch were usually preceded by a trial during which a moth was found.

   In order to more intensively study the rules used by the jays, particularly the rule used to decide when to leave the depleting patch, a second experiment was carried out (Kamil, Yoerg, & Clements, 1988). Five blue jays were trained with the same type of procedures as those used by Kamil & Yoerg. Throughout this experiment, the probability of a prey item appearing in the depleting patch before depletion on any particular trial was .50; after depletion, it was zero. The probability of a prey item appearing in the nondepleting patch was .25 throughout the experiment. During each stage of the experiment, the depleting patch always contained a fixed number of prey, and this number varied across four conditions. During the first 150 sessions, there were always nine prey in the depleting patch. During the next 120 sessions, there were six prey before depletion. During the next 100 sessions, there were three prey before depletion. Finally, during the last 50 sessions, there were nine prey again. By extensively testing the jays under several different conditions, several goals could be met. First, enough data were gathered under each condition to enable us to calculate conditional probabilities of patch departure as a function of various within-patch events. Second, by testing during several depletion conditions, we were able to observe how the birds reacted to environmental change. Third, we were able to determine whether the patch departure strategy of the jays changed as the number of prey in the depleting patch changed.

As in the previous study, the jays quickly learned to begin each foraging session in the depleting patch and to switch to the nondepleting patch after depletion had occurred. We used several measures to compare their behavior across the different conditions of the experiment. First, a relative measure of foraging efficiency was examined. The number of prey actually obtained by each jay was divided by the number of prey an omniscient jay (one that started in the depleting patch and stayed there until the last prey was found, then switched immediately to the nondepleting patch) would have obtained (Figure 4). Efficiency improved to high levels, generally above 90 percent within each condition. As the number of prey in the depleting patch decreased from the first to the third condition of the experiment, asymptotic levels of relative foraging efficiency increased.

These changes in efficiency were primarily due to changes in patch choice. In order to determine when a jay left the depleting patch, a critical switch measure was devised. This was necessary because, as in the Kamil & Yoerg experiment, the jays continued to visit the depleted patch occasionally late in foraging

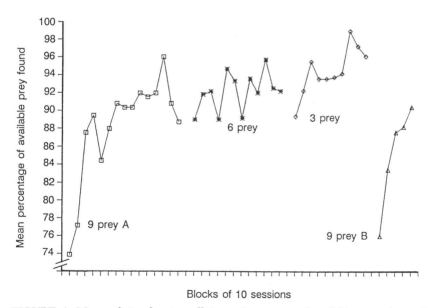

FIGURE 4. Mean relative foraging efficiency (percentage of available prey obtained) during each 10-session block in each condition, averaged across the subjects in the second experiment.

sessions. The critical switch trial was defined as the first trial in which a bird switched between patches after which it chose the nondepleting patch in more than 80 percent of the subsequent trials. At the beginning of each condition, the jays stayed in the depleting patch much too long. But as they learned about the new condition, their departure from the depleting patch came earlier in the session, closer to the optimal point (Figure 5). This can be seen most clearly by comparing the asymptotic values of critical switches across conditions. The rapid and dramatic increase during the last condition of the experiment, when the number of prey was increased from three to nine, was particularly impressive. The critical switch data clearly show that the birds adapted rapidly to changes in the number of prey in the depleting patch. This implies that the rule they used to leave the depleting patch must be one that allowed for this behavioral flexibility in the face of environmental change.

In order to determine the patch departure rules that the jays were using, the probability of leaving the depleting patch was calculated as a function of both the number of prey found and the number of consecutive nonprey trials experienced (that is, the length of the most recent ROBL) in the depleting patch. These probabilities were calculated for the last 30 sessions of each of the first three conditions of the experiment. The results clearly indicate that both number of prey found and ROBL length affected patch departure (Figure 6). As the length

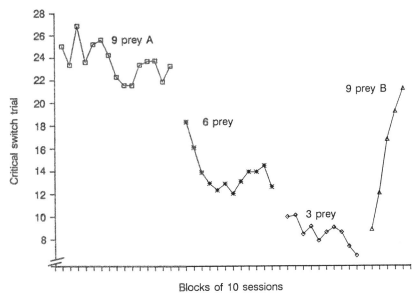

Blocks of 10 sessions

FIGURE 5. The mean critical switch trial during each 10-session block in each condition, averaged across the subjects in the second experiment.

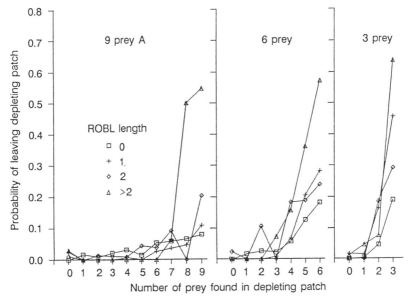

FIGURE 6. Mean probability of leaving the depleting patch as a joint function of the number of prey found and the length of the run of bad luck (ROBL), averaged across the subjects in the first three conditions of the second experiment.

of the ROBL increased, the probability of leaving the depleting patch generally increased. Furthermore, the probability of leaving increased in a nonlinear fashion as the number of prey found in the depleting patch increased. Perhaps the most important result of this experiment was a significant interaction between these two variables. This indicates that the jays did not simply use one parameter or the other in forming a departure rule. Rather, the jays combined both within-patch sources of information—number of prey captured and ROBL—to form the final departure rule. These two variables worked together so that, for example, a ROBL of 4 early in the session, when few prey had been found, was less likely to cause departure than the same ROBL later in the session, when more prey had been found.

In the past, these two within-patch parameters have been treated separately as possible sources for a departure rule (e.g., Krebs et al., 1974). This experiment provided the first evidence of which we are aware that suggests multiple information sources can be used in a single rule. In retrospect, it is clear that neither parameter alone can account for the patch choice patterns of the jays. Consider the behavior seen when the number of prey available in the depleting patch was changed between conditions. If the jays had been using a pure ROBL rule, then the critical switch trial should have decreased as soon as the number of available prey decreased at the start of the six-prey and three-prey conditions. But the data clearly show a gradual adjustment of the critical switch trial to each of these conditions; gradual because the previously expected number of prey still exerted its influence in the rule. Conversely, if a pure counting rule had been used, we would have expected a much slower adjustment than that seen when the number of available prey was increased at the start of the last condition. Birds using such a rule would have left the patch too early (after three prey) to discover the increase in patch quality.

In this light, the rule the jays used makes sense. The rule was not "optimal" for any individual condition when only the rate of prey intake is considered. However, staying past the point of depletion may have provided the jays with information concerning changes in patch quality between conditions. It is hard to imagine how a jay might have recovered efficiency when the number of prey was increased from three to nine if it had not been staying in the patch past the (expected) depletion point. A pure ROBL rule might have accomplished this goal. However, when conditions did not change, extra time spent in the patch was in fact wasted time relative to the optimal rule for a condition. The amount of time wasted might, however, be minimized by also hunting for an expected number of prey. The relative weighting of these two variables in the final rule seemed to change as the number of prey available in the depleting patch decreased. It may have been that as the number of available prey became easier to track (decreased), the ROBL exerted less influence in the final rule.

In optimization theory terms, the rule used by the jays was less than optimal within any single condition. But the loss of efficiency within a condition was due to behavior that allowed the jays to adapt efficiently to changes across conditions. This is an important distinction when one considers that animals do not forage in unchanging environments. Behaviors that appear less than optimal in the short run may allow the animal to be more efficient over a longer time.

In our next experiment (Yoerg, Clements, & Kamil, 1989), we examined jays' patch departure choices when neither the number of prey obtained nor the number of trials experienced (i.e., time spent in the patch) provided reliable cues for leaving the depleting patch. In the previous experiment, the number of prey was the same from session to session within conditions; yet even at asymptote, the jays used a departure rule dependent upon both number of prey and ROBL. We were interested in determining whether the birds would become more dependent on the ROBL if the number of prey available in the depleting patch and the trial on which the patch was depleted varied unpredictably from one foraging session to the next. During any given foraging session, we provided anywhere from three to nine prey in the depleting patch. Under these conditions, the birds could not function efficiently only by counting prey because number of prey obtained would be an unreliable predictor of patch quality on the next trial.

The method of presenting stimuli was changed for this experiment. Instead of presenting slides with and without prey items, artificial prey were presented on a color monitor using computer-generated graphics. Otherwise, conditions were similar to those of the previous experiment.

Four of the jays from the previous experiment were tested for 200 sessions, and data analyses concentrated on asymptotic behavior during the last 50 sessions. As in both previous experiments, the jays generally chose the depleting patch at the beginning of sessions, but chose the nondepleting patch most of the time late in the sessions. The jays usually stayed in the depleting patch beyond the point at which depletion occurred, as would be expected from a ROBL rule. However, each bird showed high variation in the ROBL length that preceded patch departure (Figure 7), implying the birds were not using a pure ROBL rule. This suggested that although the number of prey found in the depleting patch was not a reliable cue for patch departure, the jays may have been influenced by this parameter. Therefore, we again analyzed the probability of leaving the depleting

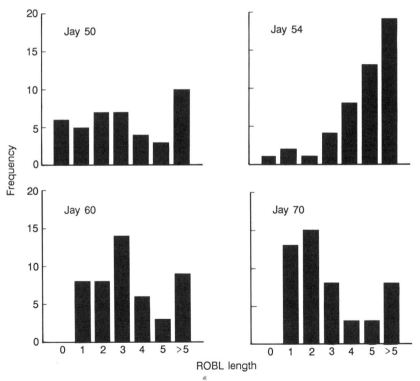

FIGURE 7. Frequency distributions for the length of the ROBL before leaving the depleting patch for each jay in the third experiment.

patch as a joint function of ROBL and number of prey obtained (Figure 8). As in the previous study, it turned out that the jays were using both factors to decide when to leave the depleting patch. However, it appeared that the ROBL played a larger role during this experiment than when the number of prey was consistent from session to session.

One indication that the ROBL played a larger role than the number of prey found when the number of prey in the depleting patch varied can be found by looking at how long after depletion the birds stayed in the depleting patch. The birds generally stayed longer in this study than they did in the previous study when there was a fixed number of prey in the depleting patch. Because exclusive use of number of prey found would result in leaving the patch immediately after the expected number of prey had been found, ROBLs greater than zero indicate that the ROBL is being used as a rule of thumb. Another indication of the larger role of ROBLs could be seen when we compared the proportion of the variance in the patch departure data explained by both the ROBL and the number of prey found (using treatment magnitude or Ω^2; Dodd & Schultz, 1973). When the number of prey varied across sessions, the number of prey found accounted for 24 percent of the variance, while the ROBL accounted for 18.4 percent. In the six-prey condition of the previous study, the number of prey found accounted for 20.2 percent, while the ROBL accounted for only 7.1 percent of the vari-

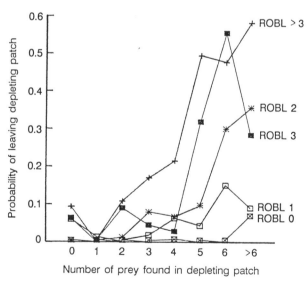

FIGURE 8. Mean probability of leaving the depleting patch as a joint function of the number of prey found and the length of the ROBL, averaged across the subjects in the third experiment.

ance. Thus, the influence of the number of prey found seemingly remained the same, while the ROBL became more influential when the number of prey varied across sessions.

It is not clear why the jays continued to use the number of prey found when it became less informative. One possibility is that because of the upper limit on prey number, there was still sufficient information value to encourage its use. Another possibility is that the jays were biased towards using the number of prey found, perhaps because of their extensive previous experience during which prey number was fixed for long periods of time. It is also possible that jays are innately biased towards using number of prey found. Further research with naive birds explicitly comparing conditions in which the two factors have differing informational value needs to be carried out. But it is clear that the jays used the ROBL more when number of prey became less reliable.

Summary: Patch depletion experiments

In summary, these experiments contribute to the understanding of the decision-making abilities of blue jays faced with the problem of patch depletion. The results clearly demonstrate that the decisions of the jays are affected by both the number of prey obtained in the depleting patch and the length of the ROBL. It also appears that the relative weights the jays give these two factors depends on their information value. The decision system the blue jays use when faced with this type of patch depletion problem is efficient and flexible. However, many aspects of this system remain unclear and merit further attention.

One important question is whether jays use this type of complex patch departure rule in nature. Our finding that they do so under laboratory conditions demonstrates that they are capable of doing so, but only direct observation in the field can determine whether this ability is used by wild jays. This may prove particularly difficult because ROBLs may be hard to define under natural conditions. We hope that our results will stimulate field workers to attempt to determine the extent to which animals use patch departure rules that depend on two or more parameters while foraging outside of the laboratory.

Another important question is how the jays gauge the reliability of different cues. When the ROBL is the best cue, they seem to give it more weight than the number of prey obtained. When the number of prey is the best cue, they weight it more heavily. Although neither cue ever exercised complete control over behavior, the relative weights changed. But how do the jays know which cue is best? In order to make this judgement, the jays must integrate information from many foraging bouts.

Another question with important implications for both ecology and psychology concerns the apparent sampling behavior of the jays. The consistent visits to the depleted patch late in foraging sessions, along with a general tendency to stay in the depleted patch somewhat longer than maximal efficiency would dictate, undoubtedly function to provide information to the forager. If the jays always left the depleted patch at exactly the optimal time based on the conditions they had experienced in the past, they would later be unable to detect changes in those conditions. This is most obvious when considering the last stage of the second experiment. When the number of prey present before depletion was increased from three to nine, the birds began staying in the patch longer almost immediately. This could only happen if the birds were visiting the patch after the third prey had been obtained.

This functional argument suggests that remaining in or revisiting a depleted patch is not necessarily best thought of as an "error." For example, in many choice experiments, animals continue to choose the incorrect alternative occasionally, even after extended training. Although these responses are commonly labeled errors, they could be important to behavioral flexibility should conditions change. This suggests that psychologists should be more concerned with dynamic, changeable situations. Although the control of behavior under unchanging conditions is an interesting topic, from which we have learned a great deal, animals do not live in unchanging worlds.

This raises an ecological issue which future research must address. There can be little doubt that animals need information about their worlds. A variety of informal naturalistic observations suggest that animals engage in behaviors that yield information about resource distribution. In addition, theoretical analyses (Stephens, in press) indicate that, at least under many conditions, information is a valuable commodity, worth investing energy to obtain.

However, despite the face validity of this concept, the anecdotal suggestions, and the theoretical calculations, the effects of information about the environment on behavior have not been widely studied. (There is a substantial literature on the effects of the informational value of stimuli in the context of classical and operant conditioning, e.g., Rescorla, 1988. This is a different application of the idea which may offer an arena for interesting interdisciplinary developments.) This is an issue that future research must address.

SPECIES DIFFERENCES IN FORAGING BEHAVIOR

The research on patch depletion provides a good example of using natural history and ecological theory as a guide to the design of experiments. In this section, we address a related issue, how natural history and ecology can be used to address another problem of comparative psychology, the selection of species for comparative study.

Biologists recognize two sources of similarities and differences among species: phylogeny and adaptation. If two species are similar, it may be because they are closely related and the similarities are due to common ancestry (homology). But the species may also be similar because of similar, or convergent, adaptations (analogy). Species differences may also be due to either phylogeny or adaptation (see Atz, 1970 for a discussion of applying these ideas to the study of behavior). Closely related species are usually more similar to one another than to distantly related species. But sometimes, closely related species may be very different from one another because of differences in adaptation. The beaks of Galapagos finches are probably the most famous example of such divergence.

This suggests two approaches to choosing species for study: one based on phylogenetic relationship, the other on adaptation. The phylogenetic approach of comparing species that are very distantly related has been the most common approach in the comparative psychology of learning (Bitterman, 1965). However, the phylogenetic strategy is extremely difficult to apply to behavior in a biologically meaningful way. Although sophisticated phylogenetic strategies are available (Hodos & Campbell, 1969), they are limited to relatively few species. Comparative psychologists must also pursue the alternative strategy, choosing species on the basis of adaptation and biological function. Closely related species that differ significantly in their adaptations to their environments may provide a particularly fertile arena for comparative psychological research (see Beecher, this volume).

The patch depletion problem could provide a basis for such comparative study if we knew more about the types of patch distributions animals face in nature: we could then compare closely related species that confront different types of patch depletion patterns in their natural habitat. One difficulty in following this strategy might be that patch depletion is such a widespread and common situation that species that never encounter depletion may be rare. Another possibility would be to look for species that specialize in different types of patches. Such species might differ in the rules they use to leave patches. For example, Reichman (1981) has suggested that the seeds upon which different desert rodents specialize may be distributed differently in space. However, we are unaware of any research attempting to compare the patch departure rules of such species under well-controlled conditions.

The strategy of comparing closely related species that differ in the natural history of their foraging behavior is being used to study species differences in spatial memory among food-storing birds of the crow, jay, and nutcracker family. Some of these species are extremely dependent on cached food for reproduction and survival. The two species of the *Nucifraga* genus, the Eurasian (*N. caryocatactes*) and Clark's (*N. columbiana*) nutcracker, offer particularly clear examples of this dependence. These birds live at high elevations year round. Every fall, nutcrackers cache large quantities of pine seeds. A single Clark's nutcracker will bury about 30,000 pine seeds in the ground, in about 5,000–6,000 separate caches. During the winter and spring, including the breeding season, the seeds cached during the previous fall provide virtually all of the food eaten by the bird and by its offspring, which fledge in early spring. These birds have been observed digging up seeds as long as 7 months after they were cached (Vander Wall & Hutchins, 1983). How do they locate these buried seeds?

A series of different field studies has shown that the probability that a nutcracker digging in the soil will find buried pine seeds is much higher than would be expected for any kind of random search (Tomback, 1980; Vander Wall & Hutchins, 1983). However, laboratory investigation under controlled conditions was necessary to determine the mechanisms responsible for this accurate cache recovery. This laboratory work has demonstrated that spatial memory plays the primary role in cache recovery by nutcrackers. Balda (1980b) was the first to study cache recovery by nutcrackers in the laboratory. He captured a single Eurasian nutcracker and tested it in an indoor aviary with a dirt floor. He found that the bird would cache and recover pine seeds readily under these conditions. During recovery sessions, the bird probed the soil very accurately, at levels far above chance, after retention intervals of 15–30 days. This behavior continued even after Balda removed the seeds from the room and raked the soil during the retention interval. This demonstrated that the accurate digging behavior was not dependent upon any cues emanating directly from the pine seeds.

Vander Wall (1982) studied caching and recovery of pine seeds by Clark's nutcrackers in an outdoor, dirt-floored aviary. He also found very accurate cache recovery. He extended Balda's findings in two important ways. First, when two different nutcrackers cached and recovered seeds in the aviary at different times (with all seeds remaining in place throughout the experiment), each bird recovered its own seeds almost exclusively. This finding also indicates that direct cues from the seeds are not responsible for accurate cache recovery. Second, Vander Wall found that when he moved landmarks in the aviary, such as logs and rocks, accurate cache recovery was disrupted. This suggests that spatial memory may be responsible for accurate cache recovery.

One remaining non-mnemonic explanation for accurate cache recovery might be site preferences; that is, if each bird preferred certain places, and dug in those places during both caching and recovery, accurate cache recovery, independent of direct cues, would result. If the preferences were idiosyncratic and based upon landmarks, then Vander Wall's (1982) findings could be explained without invoking memory. Therefore, Kamil and Balda (1985) developed a technique that allowed them to control where caches could be placed. They used a room that had a plywood floor with 180 sand-filled holes. Each hole could be capped with a wooden plug during any session. The nutcrackers were allowed to cache in the room with only a few of the holes available. Ten days later, they were allowed to recover their seeds. During recovery sessions, all 180 holes were open, and seeds were present only in locations where the bird being tested had cached them. The nutcrackers recovered their caches at levels much higher than would be expected by chance. These results show that nutcrackers can find their seeds even when their cache site selection is severely restricted by the experimenters, ruling out explanations in terms of site preferences.

The data from these three studies (Balda, 1980a; Kamil & Balda, 1985; Vander Wall, 1982) demonstrate that nutcrackers use spatial memory to find their cached pine seeds. When this finding is combined with the extreme specialization and dependence of the nutcracker on cached food, an important comparative question arises: have the particular natural history and adaptations of the nutcrackers produced a particularly good spatial memory system in these species? Nutcrackers possess several morphological characteristics that are particularly well suited to the harvesting and caching of pine seeds. These include a sublingual pouch that allows them to carry up to 80 pine seeds from the harvesting area to the caching area, and an unusually long, strong beak used for extracting seeds from pine cones (Bock, Balda, & Vander Wall, 1973). Do they also possess a psychological characteristic particularly well suited to recovering cached food, a highly developed spatial memory system?

The best way to answer this question would be to compare nutcrackers with closely related species that are less dependent on cached food. Fortunately, there are species in the same family as the nutcrackers, the corvid family, that are less dependent on cached food. The pinyon jay (*Gymnorhinus cyanocephalus*) also lives at high elevations, but tends to cache somewhat less food than nutcrackers do, probably about 20,000 pine seeds per year, or 70–90 percent of its diet (Balda, 1987). The scrub jay (*Aphelocoma coerulescens*) lives at lower elevations, and caches much less than the other two species, probably no more than 6,000 seeds, less than 60 percent of its diet. While the nutcrackers and the pinyon jay regularly experience times of the year when the only food available is cached food, this is not the case with the scrub jay (Balda, 1980a).

Balda and Kamil (in press) have tested cache recovery in these three species using the plywood floor technique described above. Each species was tested with 90 holes open following two kinds of caching sessions: during one condition, 90 holes in the room were available for caching (condition 90). During the other condition, only 15 holes were available for caching (condition 15). Significant differences between the species were found. Scrub jays performed worse than either pinyon jays or nutcrackers (Figure 9). Following unrestricted caching (condition 90), the pinyon jays performed at extremely high levels, but following restricted caching (condition 15), their performance was equivalent to that of the Clark's nutcrackers. This appeared to be due to an unexpected difference between the species in the use of space during caching. When allowed to place their caches in any hole, the pinyon jays placed their caches very close together, in a tight cluster. The other two species spread their caches throughout the room. This clustering of caches probably made the recovery task easier following unrestricted caching for the pinyon jays by allowing them to restrict their search to a small portion of the room.

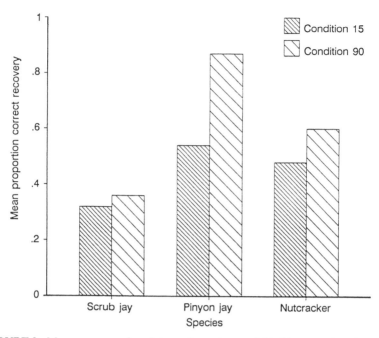

FIGURE 9. Mean accuracy of scrub jays, pinyon jays, and Clark's nutcrackers during the recovery of the first four caches after two caching conditions. During Condition 15 (narrow stripes), only 15 holes were available for caching, whereas 90 holes were available during Condition 90 (wide stripes).

Overall, these results support the hypothesis that differences in cache recovery are correlated with differences in ecology and natural history. The two species most dependent upon cached food performed most accurately. These results need to be pursued further to determine how general these differences are across different conditions, such as longer retention intervals. Although these results are consistent with a hypothesis of species differences in spatial memory, they must be interpreted very cautiously. Differences in behavior during caching may have affected the nature of the task as a memory test. For example, pinyon jays and scrub jays were more likely than nutcrackers to make repeated visits to cache sites during caching sessions. Repeated responses to a sample during matching to sample improves accuracy after a retention interval (Sacks, Kamil, & Mack, 1972). If repeat visits to cache sites have similar effects, then extra visits to cache sites would have improved the performance of the scrub and pinyon jays.

In order to test species differences in spatial memory more precisely, laboratory procedures that allow greater control over behavior must be used. Balda and Kamil (1988b) have found that nutcrackers perform very well in an open field analogue of the radial arm maze. This might provide one paradigm for comparative tests. Olson (1989) has used an operant spatial memory task and has found that nutcrackers perform better than scrub jays. If these various tests produce consistent species differences correlated with natural history, the usefulness of the comparative method based upon adaptation will be demonstrated (see Kamil, 1988, for further discussion of this issue). Furthermore, similar experiments are under way with caching and noncaching species in the parid family (chickadees and titmice), which will provide an independent test of the hypothesis that species differences in memory are associated with differences in dependence upon stored food.

CONCLUSIONS

The research we have reviewed in this chapter addresses a fundamental question for contemporary comparative psychology. Traditionally, questions about the function and about the mechanisms of behavior have been treated as separate issues. For example, it has often been argued that natural selection only operates upon outcomes, not upon mechanisms or processes (Lehrman, 1970; Shettleworth, 1983). However, some mechanisms may produce better outcomes than others under specific circumstances. If this is the case, different mechanisms will have important functional considerations.

The research on patch depletion provides an excellent example of this interaction between mechanism and outcome. In this situation, the better outcomes are those that maximize foraging efficiency. The different mechanisms are the different rules of thumb. Our results show that as patch characteristics vary, the relative efficiency of different rules changes, and so does the behavior of the jays. When the ROBL becomes the more informative cue for patch departure, the jays use it more, as would be expected from functional considerations. This kind of result demonstrates that there is often some relationship between biological function and mechanism. (If this were not true, morphologists would not be evolutionists.)

We believe that the relationships between function and mechanism will prove to be complex. In order to understand these relationships, we must study behavioral mechanisms in contexts within which the functional consequences of different behaviors are known. This approach characterizes many of the chapters in this book. In this chapter, we have emphasized this approach in the study of learning and memory. Patch depletion research is one example of how interesting questions about decision mechanisms can be generated by functional considerations. The research on cache recovery is an example of how functional considerations can be used to generate novel predictions of differences among closely related species. This natural history approach to species differences in learning and memory may revitalize the comparative study of learning and memory in animals.

SUMMARY

The most important problems that comparative psychologists confront in their research are the selection of species and the design of experimental procedures. In this chapter, we discuss how natural history and ecology can be used to solve these problems. We concentrate upon the study of foraging behavior, an increasingly important topic of research spanning ethology, ecology, and psychology. In our first example, we demonstrate how natural history and ecological theory can be used to design a laboratory simulation of a naturally occurring problem. We describe a series of experiments which used operant procedures to study the decision-making processes of blue jays confronted with depleting food patches. Our emphasis was on determining the rules blue jays use to decide when to abandon a depleting patch. The results show that the birds use multiple sources of information, not a simple rule based on a single parameter. We then turn to a second example in which natural history and ecology are used to select species for comparative study. In this case, the basic experimental question is how food-storing birds such as nutcrackers and jays locate their cached food. The results of the first comparative studies suggest that there are important differences in spatial memory among closely related species that differ in the degree to which they depend upon cached food in nature. These examples demonstrate the utility of studying behavioral systems in which the consequences and functions of the behavior are known.

CHAPTER 2

NATURAL LEARNING IN LABORATORY PARADIGMS

William Timberlake

Since the beginnings of the comparative study of learning, there has been conflict between two approaches: an ecological approach concerned with functional examples of learning in natural settings, and a laboratory approach focused on the mechanisms controlling learning in artificial settings. The study of learning in natural settings began with observations of systematic changes in natural behavior that were attributed to humanlike intentions. For example, Digby (1664, p. 323) attributed nest building in songbirds to the discomfort-reducing effects that the birds obtained by ordering the straw in the appropriate way. Erasmus Darwin (1794, Vol. 1, p. 137) argued that "many of the actions of young animals . . . appear to have been acquired . . . by the repeated efforts of our muscles under the conduct of our sensations or desires." Charles Darwin (1871/1936) and Romanes (1883) reported numerous anecdotes purported to show evolutionary progress by animals toward humanlike learning, emotions, and morality. With few exceptions (e.g., Lubbock, 1890; Spalding, 1875) the analysis of learning was guided only by argument toward the presumed causal mechanisms of association, reason, pleasure, and pain.

The laboratory study of learning developed at the turn of the 20th century in self-conscious contrast to the anecdotal approach of the 19th century. With this approach, pioneered in part by Morgan (1896) and given clear expression by Thorndike (1898), researchers emphasized experimental control and analysis. Learned and instinctual behavior were carefully distinguished by using standardized procedures and controls, and by testing animals using artificial stimuli and environments that bore little apparent relation to the organism's daily life (Galef, 1988; Johnston, 1985; Timberlake, 1983b).

Conflict between the study of natural learning and the study of laboratory learning persisted throughout much of the 20th century. Laboratory researchers, such as Pavlov and the psychologists Skinner (1938) and Hull (1943), emphasized the importance of controlled experimental environments and the power of laboratory conditioning procedures. While many early researchers studied learning and problem solving in a variety of circumstances and species (e.g., Maier & Schneirla, 1935), the laboratory study of learning increasingly focused on a small set of experimental preparations, such as alley running and lever pressing in rats and key pecking in pigeons.

In contrast, ethologists such as Lorenz (1969) and Tinbergen (1951), and biologists such as Brower (1969) examined a variety of types of learning that occur as part of an organism's functional behavior. Thus, Lorenz studied imprinting as part of the process by which ducklings identify and remain close to their mothers, and, when older, mate with the appropriate species; Tinbergen examined landmark learning in wasps, which occurs in the context of provisioning their unborn young with appropriate prey; and Brower studied how blue jays learn to avoid emetic prey, such as monarch butterflies that feed on milkweed plants.

Despite the differences in the ecological and laboratory approaches, the last 20 years have seen increased efforts toward integration. Researchers interested in functional learning problems, such as song acquisition or foraging, have begun to use the power of more controlled circumstances and manipulations to better describe these phenomena and to analyze their causal mechanisms. For example, at least partially artificial circumstances have been used in the study of spatial memory in foraging, homing, and migrating birds (Emlen, 1970; Kamil & Balda, 1985; Keeton, 1981; Sherry, 1987; Shettleworth & Krebs, 1982), song learning in perching birds (King & West, 1984; Marler & Peters, 1982), and the control of pecking in gull chicks (Hailman, 1967).

The 1970s produced a flurry of laboratory research on constraints and predispositions affecting learning which showed that neither stimuli, responses, nor species are interchangeable (e.g., Bolles, 1970; Hinde & Stevenson-Hinde, 1973; Rozin & Kalat, 1971; Seligman, 1970; Shettleworth, 1972). The prime example of this research is that on taste aversion learning, an effect of obvious ecological importance which was discovered using laboratory techniques that established its long time-frame of action and the differential associability between novel tastes or smells and internal malaise (e.g., Garcia, McGowan, & Green, 1972).

Subsequently, other ecological problems have been simulated using laboratory preparations. For example, Pietrewicz and Kamil (1979) used slides of moths photographed in natural settings to investigate the ability of foraging blue jays to profit from past experience. Collier (1983) and his coworkers studied foraging using schedules of lever pressing for food (cf. Fantino & Abarca, 1985; Killeen, Smith, & Hanson, 1981). Other research examined time horizons in foraging (e.g., Timberlake, Gawley, & Lucas, 1987), social transmission of diet information in rats (Galef, this volume), and the contribution of Pavlovian conditioning to territorial defense in fish (Hollis, this volume).

FACTORS DETERRING
THE INTEGRATED STUDY OF LEARNING

On the basis of the studies cited above, it could be argued that the split between the study of learning in field and laboratory has healed. Contemporary biologically oriented investigators do respect and use the power of laboratory techniques to answer ecological questions, and laboratory investigators have come to realize the relevance of particular species, stimuli, and responses to the mechanisms they study. However, for several reasons, a broad integration of ecological and laboratory approaches has been slow to develop.

On the one hand, biologically oriented researchers are often uncertain about the ecological validity of typical laboratory research. To begin with, it is often difficult to fit particular examples of ecological learning into standard laboratory paradigms and principles: Is song learning in birds an example of Pavlovian or operant conditioning? What is the reinforcer? What is learned? What control treatments are appropriate? In addition, there is no model that provides a framework for integrating examples of ecological learning and relating them to the paradigms and principles of laboratory learning (see also Shettleworth, 1983).

Even when an example of ecological learning is successfully simulated in the laboratory, some biologically oriented researchers still express concern about the artificial circumstances. For example, Lockard (1971) noted that ". . . since animals match their environments but mismatch the laboratory, severe distortions of behavior are common," and Johnston (1981) has argued that ". . . in searching for an alternative to . . . general process theory, it seems counterproductive to employ the methods that have been sanctioned by that theory." Additionally, some researchers object to the amount of "acting" that is required by laboratory simulations. For example, why should rats pressing levers for food treat the left lever as the travel lever, the middle lever as the search lever, and the right lever as the handling lever?

Doubt has also been expressed about the ecological reality of typical laboratory species, especially the albino rat. Laboratory rats are considered by many biologists to be artificial, genetically invariant animals with few behavioral remnants of their wild heritage. Psychologists have contributed to fears of "plastic" research animals by emphasizing the malleability of laboratory subjects and the irrelevance of particular species to the general principles studied.

On the other hand, laboratory researchers are no less uneasy about the overwhelming diversity of learning phenomena in ecological settings, where data are not as precise and replicable, and there is little attempt to separate learning and nonlearning effects. Concern that the effort directed at particular ecological problems is wasted on "botanizing" helped to blunt analysis of the ecological basis of apparent constraints and predispositions in learning. Instead, researchers have emphasized ways in which the generality of learning principles still holds (Beecher, 1988b; Logue, 1979; Revusky, 1977).

THE BEHAVIOR SYSTEM APPROACH

In short, despite the increased activity and interest of the last 20 years, the integration of the study of natural and laboratory learning remains largely a patchwork of interesting experimental stories. Too often, biologically oriented researchers remain puzzled over how to fit their work into the principles of laboratory learning and gain access to the power of laboratory techniques, and laboratory researchers remain frustrated by or uninterested in the ecological and evolutionary concerns of field-related work. A common conceptual framework that encompasses both laboratory and field research is necessary for developing an integrated approach to the study of learning. Such a framework must be concrete enough to make contact with the potential ecological relevance of specific response topographies, but abstract enough to deal with laboratory paradigms and principles. In this section, I propose such a framework, which is related to the hierarchical behavior system model of Tinbergen (1951).

The appetitive structure of behavior systems

The behavior system approach is based on the realization that any animal brings to an environment a set of functional systems of behavior, that is, hierarchical structures of control and processing that are related to particular functions (Scott, 1958). These functions include feeding (Timberlake, 1983b), reproduction (Baerends & Drent, 1982), defense (Bolles, 1970; Bolles & Fanselow, 1980), and body care (Fentress, 1983).

Figure 1 is a schematic of the feeding system of the rat drawn from a number of sources. The figure represents a behavior system as a hierarchy of four levels of control: system, subsystem, mode, and perceptual–motor module. These levels of organization are functional concepts that indicate characteristic combinations of determinants and classes of outcome, rather than specific neural mechanisms or locations. Together, these four control levels select and coordinate individual responses (action patterns). The overall conception obviously owes a debt to Tinbergen's hierarchical model (1951), but the behavior system approach emphasizes the flexibility and incompleteness of the components and the multiple relations between levels (Gallistel, 1980), and it includes a level of motivational substates controlling specific appetitive, handling, and consummatory behaviors.

The *system* level accounts for the tendency of behavior to be organized around important functions. *Subsystem* refers to a coherent subset of stimulus sensitivities and response components for meeting the needs of a particular system. For example, a predatory subsystem would involve sensitivity to moving stimuli and increased likelihood of chase and capture responses, whereas a browsing subsystem would not.

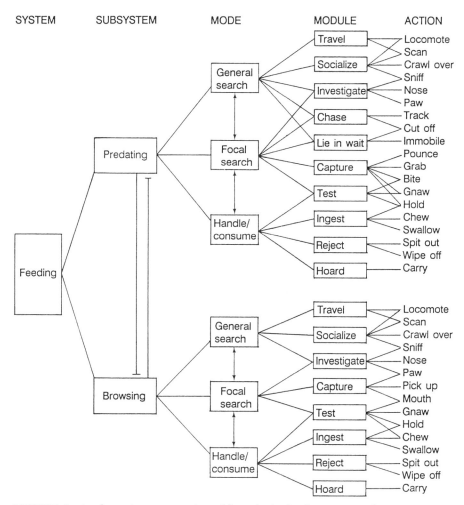

FIGURE 1. A schematic representation of hypothesized subsystems, modes, perceptual–motor modules, and action patterns included in the feeding system of the rat. (From Timberlake & Lucas, in press.)

Modes are motivational substates related to the sequential and temporal organization of action patterns from general appetitive patterns to specific consummatory responses (Craig, 1918). For example, a feeding sequence typically begins in a general search mode, characterized by attention to novelty and a search for cues that predict the location of food. When cues highly predictive of food occur, the animal switches to a focal search mode, in which action patterns are more focused and related to the immediate procurement of food. When food is present, the animal enters a handling/consuming mode, in which action patterns are focused on dealing directly with the food item. As the certainty of obtaining food declines, the animal first reenters the focal search mode (area-restricted search), then a more general search mode, then either repeats the cycle or stops foraging. Fanselow and Lester (1987) have presented a similar sequential analysis for escaping and avoiding aversive stimuli.

The level of *perceptual–motor modules* reflects the importance of predispositions to respond to particular stimuli with particular response components (see Hogan, 1988). The stimulus sensitivities can be treated as sensory filters that gate or sharpen particular stimulus dimensions or configurations (Baerends & Kruijt, 1973). The motor organization in a module results from motor "programs" or rules for their assembly related to particular stimuli and other motor programs.

A sequential–hierarchical approach to learning

From a behavior-system viewpoint, the most important quality of learning is that it occurs within this functional appetitive structure. The complexity of this structure shows why it is often difficult to conceptualize natural learning, such as homing or song learning, using laboratory paradigms and principles. Learning did not evolve in paradigms, but as small changes in a functioning system that allowed closer tracking of the environment (e.g., Mayr, 1974; Nottebohm, 1972). The appetitive structure of a system provides the raw materials for learning; it is a substrate that is integrated, linked, and differentiated by its fit with the environment. Thus, learning can be remarkably varied and complex, and can include changes in integration, differentiation, tuning, instigation, elicitation, and linkage within and across entities and levels in a system.

This view of learning—that it is a result of the combination of appetitive structure and environment—not only clarifies the complexities of ecological learning, it also provides the basis for an ecological analysis of laboratory learning. Learning in the laboratory, no less than in the field, is a product of the combination of appetitive structure and environment. Pavlovian and operant conditioning, like song learning, occur because of the contact of the environmental circumstances with the appetitive structure of the organism. The goal of this chapter is to clarify some of the nature of this contact.

SOME ECOLOGICAL CONSIDERATIONS REGARDING LABORATORY LEARNING

Before beginning an ecological analysis of laboratory learning, it might be wise to consider the objection to it raised earlier: What of the argument that the artificiality of laboratory environments and species ultimately rules out the integration of laboratory and ecological approaches?

The first point to be made is that artificiality per se does not prevent the answering of ecological questions. Much of the strength of ethology has been its mix of the artificial and the natural. Tinbergen's classic work on the releasers of stickleback courtship and of food begging in nestling thrushes was done in partially artificial circumstances using artificial stimuli (Tinbergen 1951; Tinbergen & Perdeck, 1950). Lorenz (1950, pp. 235–236) argued strongly for making use of artificial circumstances in identifying the elements of and the control of a species-typical system of action.

A second point concerns the value of research with laboratory animals. Comparative psychologists have accumulated considerable data over the past 25 years which demonstrate that even the much-maligned laboratory rat shows complex natural behaviors given the appropriate stimulus conditions (Blanchard & Blanchard, this volume; Boice, 1977; Dewsbury, 1987; Galef, this volume). It appears that laboratory domestication, like many changes in selection environments, initially alters response and stimulus thresholds, rather than eliminating old behavioral potentials or introducing new ones. Laboratory rats are less aggressive and more timid, mature earlier, and are more fecund than wild rats are, but they still behave like rats if we know how to question them.

For example, as a graduate student, I observed that gerbils scent-marked in laboratory settings, but that rats did not. I attributed the difference to the absence of a specialized scent gland in rats and the likelihood that any urine marking had been bred out through domestication. In retrospect, my speculation reflected nothing more than a lack of knowledge about the stimuli controlling marking. If low objects or edges are provided, both male and female laboratory rats are transformed into prolific urine markers (e.g., Brown, 1975; Hopp & Timberlake, 1983; Peden & Timberlake, 1988). Further, if rats are provided with a small, burrowlike space opening into a larger field, both sexes will flank-mark the entrance to the burrow on their way back from the field.

Finally, the claim that the laboratory environment is arbitrary and artificial, though not without foundation, fails to appreciate the critical dependence of laboratory researchers on the careful "tuning" of their apparatus and procedures to the particular species being studied (see Breland & Breland, 1966, p. 69). Tuning here refers to the iterative process of modifying the environment, the stimuli, and the procedures to produce more robust, coherent, and efficient responding. Tuning, though not part of most conceptual analyses, is the means by which common experimental questions can be asked of animals as dissimilar as chimpanzees, bees, and marine mollusks. A classic example of tuning is Skinner's development of an operant response for hungry rats. After trying several responses, he settled on the manipulation of a small protruding lever placed near the food magazine. The form of lever contact was controlled by installing screening above the lever to reduce rearing contacts and by increasing the lever size to prevent gnawing and tugging (Skinner, 1938).

Despite the overwhelming laboratory concern with avoiding "instinctive behavior" in studying learning (Johnston, 1985), careful tuning can produce responding that is neither arbitrary nor artificial. One can view the course of laboratory learning work as a struggle between the emphasis of the arbitrary and artificial aspects of the learning situation and the amelioration of their effects by using tuning to increase contact with the underlying appetitive structure.

Two conclusions follow: The first is that typical laboratory learning procedures developed by good experimenters contain elements of natural learning. The second is that it should be possible to produce and analyze aspects of particular examples of natural learning in the laboratory. A key to both conclusions is the ability of the researcher to recognize and produce elements of natural learning. This ability requires an appreciation of the topography and function of natural responses, which can best be acquired by experience with the same or similar species in both natural and artificial environments (Lorenz, 1950; Miller, 1977), and by analyses of ecological "tasks" contained in natural environments (Johnston, 1981; Kamil & Yoerg, 1982).

TOWARD AN ECOLOGICAL ANALYSIS OF LABORATORY LEARNING

The remainder of this chapter deals with the integration of ecological and laboratory learning in two ways: it describes how laboratory paradigms can be used to explore the appetitive structure of underlying behavior systems, and how the familiar results of laboratory learning are caused by a combination of experimental procedures and environment with that same appetitive structure. The experiments cited primarily use rats and pigeons, and thus show that appetitive structure is no respecter of domesticity. Also, the experiments cited are largely restricted to the work of myself and my colleagues because my familiarity with it allows for the most efficient use of space. I have organized the examples by procedure: simple cue exposure, timed response-independent reward, cued response-independent reward, and response-dependent reward.

Simple exposure: Maze learning in rats

In his justification for use of the maze, Small (1900) argued that passage learning is probably part of the psychobiological character of the rat. A reasonable implication of this argument is that maze learning and performance should occur in the absence of reward. Early work on latent learning (e.g., Blodgett, 1929) demonstrated that rats learned mazes by exposure, but concluded that such learning was latent, that is, it was expressed only when food was provided in the goal box. However, from an ecological point of view, local reward should not be necessary for improvement in maze running; rats that traverse familiar environments with increasing efficiency should do better when food or predators are introduced than do rats that simply acquire a latent map of the situation.

In fact, there are many studies showing that rats and other rodents increase their maze-running efficiency over trials in the absence of a food reward (Timberlake, 1983a). A striking example was provided by Brant and Kavanau (1964), who studied the behavior of several *Peromyscus* species in an environment containing three complex mazes with an average shortest path of 96 feet. Each maze began and ended in a central nest area containing food, water, and a running wheel. Though the mice were not required to enter or complete the mazes, they showed dramatic drops in the time taken to complete the maze within four self-administered trials. Research by Battig and Schlatter (1979) shows similar improvements in the efficiency of rats and mice patrolling complex mazes in the absence of any food reward.

If rats learn and perform in mazes without a food reward, it must be because of processes and mechanisms that fit the animal with such an environment. I attempted to define some of the stimulus sensitivities, response components, and motivational processes underlying maze running by examining the determinants of unrewarded straight-alley running (Timberlake, 1983a). The results showed that straight-alley running without food reward is a robust phenomenon determined by several major factors.

When the animal is first placed in the apparatus, it displays fear and engages in cautious exploration. These behaviors diminish over repeated trials, and eventually, the animal, after brief initial exploration, begins to move rapidly (some at a gallop) down the length of the alley. Stimuli such as bright lights, loud sounds, short alleys, sudden movements, novel odors, and immediate removal from the goal box tend to slow the transition from cautious behavior to running, whereas more trials per day, extensive exposure to the alley, administration of tranquilizers, interesting stimuli at the end of the runway, the presence of a long uninterrupted path, handling by the experimenter just before release from the start box, and the installation of two walls enclosing the alley facilitate improved alley running. In general, performance in alley running is a product of the fit between the rat's exploratory searching responses and stimulus sensitivities and the physical structure of the apparatus. Though the addition of a reward slightly facilitated alley running, it did not appear to alter the basic mechanisms of control.

Given that straight-alley running is based on mechanisms that do not require local reward for their operation, it should follow that performance in more complex mazes may be similarly determined without recourse to local reward. We have already mentioned the ability of *Peromyscus* to negotiate complex mazes. Similar results have been obtained using the most popular current maze apparatus, the radial arm maze. In this maze, animals are placed on a center platform with eight arms radiating out in different directions, each containing food. The rat, after a relatively small number of trials, comes to perform nearly perfectly in obtaining all eight food items without traversing any arms twice. Researchers have attributed this performance to a win–shift foraging strategy: when a rat obtains food in one location, it then shifts to one visited less recently (Olton, Handelman, & Walker, 1981).

However, consider that the efficient traversal of the radial maze may represent the expression of an evolved foraging tendency that does not depend on the presence of a local food reward. Since there is considerable evidence that rats alternate choices of two arms in a T maze whether they are rewarded or not (Dember & Earl, 1957), why would they not follow the same tendency in an eight-arm maze as well? If this surmise is true, animals that receive no food in the eight-arm maze should show efficient choices similar to those made by rats receiving food. Timberlake and White (1989) have shown this to be the case in an experiment in which food-deprived, unrewarded rats in a radial arm maze chose novel arms significantly above chance, and only slightly less efficiently than rewarded animals. The novel choices of undeprived rats were not significantly different from chance.

In short, though maze running was a key instrumental response in the development of general, context-free theories of learning, the present results indicate that this paradigm was not adequately understood (Timberlake, 1983a). Specifically, maze learning was treated as though it is assembled from unorganized responses through associations based on reward. Instead, it appears to be based on a set of organized search routines that are evoked and guided by particular stimulus circumstances.

Timed response-independent presentation of food

From the viewpoint of the behavior system approach, the periodic presentation of food provides a powerful technique for organizing (i.e., entraining) modules and modes related to the feeding structure of an organism. The absence of a response requirement means that the behavior of the animal is a product only of the fit of its own appetitive structure to the location and timing of the food and the surrounding environment. I will discuss two procedural variants, one in which food is simply presented periodically, and the other in which the presence of food is predicted by presentation of a specific environmental conditioned stimulus (CS).

Superstition. The superstition procedure (Skinner, 1948) is a classic example of timed food presentation. In the original procedure, Skinner presented grain to hungry pigeons once every 15 seconds. He reported that the pigeons rapidly acquired individually characteristic patterns of behavior that included turning, pendulum motions of the head and neck, thrusting the head into an upper corner, and stepping and hopping. He attributed such behavior to the repeated accidental juxtaposition of the food and a particular response—each time a pairing occurred, the probability of the response increased, thereby increasing the probability that accidental pairings would recur.

However, Staddon and Simmelhag (1971), Innis, Simmelhag-Grant, and Staddon (1983), and Timberlake and Lucas (1985), using similar procedures, reported that their pigeons produced common terminal behavior (responses just before the delivery of food): pecking in the case of Staddon and Simmelhag, and wall-directed stepping and pacing for Innis et al. and Timberlake and Lucas. Timberlake and Lucas ruled out significant control of wall-directed behavior by accidental contingencies by shaping an increased probability of turning or pecking under a fixed-interval (FI) schedule. Though this should have increased the likelihood of accidental pairings of turning and pecking with food, these responses rapidly decreased and wall-related behavior increased when the response contingency was removed (Figure 2).

Further experiments have shown that stepping, pacing, and bumping do not emerge unless there is a wall in proximity to where food is delivered. If no wall is nearby, the pigeons circle the source of food in a bent-over posture, swipe-pecking periodically at the floor, an obvious foraging response. After considering a variety of potential functions for wall-directed behavior, we began to recognize in it components of the food-begging behavior that emerges in squabs at about 10

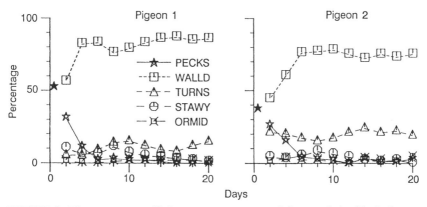

FIGURE 2. The percentage of behavior categories recorded across 2-day blocks for two pigeons when grain was presented at 15-second intervals (FT 15 seconds). The solid stars on the left of each graph indicate the percentage occurrence of pecking that was trained prior to the beginning of the response-independent FT 15-second schedule. PECKS = beak contacts with wall or floor; WALLD = behavior directed to the wall nearest to or containing the hopper; TURNS = turning of the body at least a quarter of a circle; STAWY = standing away (remaining nearly motionless in an upright posture) near, but facing away from, the hopper; ORMID = active waiting while oriented toward the middle of the chamber. (Adapted from Timberlake & Lucas, 1985.)

days of age. Adult pigeons regurgitate crop milk for their young, and must be stimulated to do so by begging as the young get older (Mondloch & Timberlake, 1988). Begging behaviors include bumping with the breast, side-to-side stepping, and head movements directed at the parent's head. These movements largely stop at fledging for males, but in females they recur in adults as elements of courtship feeding. Thus, Skinner's pigeons' superstitious behavior may represent natural food-begging responses directed toward a large vertical stimulus associated with food (perhaps a surrogate parent or mate).

We tested the food-begging hypothesis in two subsequent experiments. In the first experiment, conducted with Marceline Brown, I compared the responses of male and female pigeons. If wall-directed behavior is related to food begging, we expected to find more of it in females than in males, because adult females beg much more than males. Males, on the other hand, should show more responses related to active foraging, such as pecking and walking away. Four out of six of the males developed extensive pecking of the feeder wall (approximately the same proportion as reported in previous superstition studies using male subjects—e.g., Reberg, Innis, Mann, & Eizenga, 1978; Staddon & Simmelhag, 1971). None of the females pecked the wall; instead, they engaged in the familiar wall-directed behavior.

In the second experiment, conducted with Sharon Reilly, I attempted to provide a comparative context for the above work. If wall-directed behavior in pigeons is related to food begging, then another species with the same sort of feeding strategy should show similar responses to the periodic presentation of food. We tested this supposition using ring doves, a smaller species of the same genus as pigeons that uses the same unique crop-milk feeding system. When ring doves were placed in the same experimental chamber that was used for the pigeons, their behavior also consisted of bumping and stepping along the wall around the hopper. We were able to support further the food-begging hypothesis by observing examples of bumping, pressing, and stepping in front of parents by young doves 14–15 days of age.

Adjunctive behavior (polydipsia). The procedure for studying adjunctive behavior is similar to the superstitious behavior paradigm, but the focus is on behavior following rather than preceding food, and the delivery interval is usually longer. The prototypical adjunctive behavior is drinking, which usually occurs excessively and follows rather than precedes periodic food delivery. Though the excessive nature of adjunctive behavior has always been a puzzle, some recent success has been achieved by viewing it as part of a natural food-getting sequence in much the same way as we looked at superstitious behavior above (Lucas, Timberlake, & Gawley, 1988).

Lucas et al. placed four rats in a 24-hour baseline environment with free access to a variety of incentives including food and water. The rats were then exposed to fixed minimum spacings of 16, 32, 64, 128, 256, and 512 seconds between the delivery of 94-milligram food pellets. Each spacing condition lasted for a minimum of 12 days. As reported by others (Cohen, Looney, Campagnoni, & Lawler, 1985; Staddon, 1977), the rats anticipated the delivery of food with the focal search behaviors of nosing and pawing around and in the food tray.

As shown in Figure 3, rats on the average follow food delivery with a series of time-locked activities related to post-food, area-restricted search near and in the food tray ("activity" and "waiting by food"). Following post-food search, rats rear and drink, then engage in a combination of locomotor activity, chewing, wheel running, and returning to the nest. Both rearing and drinking (the most consistent adjunctive behaviors) appear to be transition behaviors occurring between post-food focal search and more general search or withdrawal. Following rearing and drinking, the animal either withdraws momentarily to the nest or engages in more general locomotor behavior ("activity" and "wheel running").

Lucas et al. argued that this sequence of behaviors was related to a foraging bout in which the rat showed general and focal search responses prior to food delivery and area-restricted search following food delivery. Because the animals were housed continuously in the test environment, we were able to establish baseline foraging cycles (meals) by giving unconstrained access to food and water.

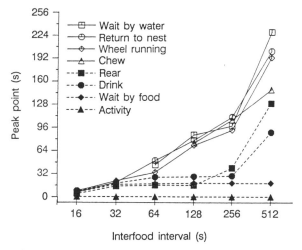

FIGURE 3. The mean time of maximum responding (in seconds after food delivery) over four rats for the distributions of responses under different fixed interfood intervals (FT schedules). Note that the responses of activity, waiting by food, and, to a lesser extent, drinking and rearing, peak at the same time across most of the range of interfood intervals. The time of the peak of the remaining responses increased as a direct function of the interfood interval. (From Lucas, Timberlake, & Gawley, 1988.)

Comparison of the behavior following termination of a normal meal with that following a single pellet revealed striking similarities at moderate and long inter-pellet intervals. The conditional probability of drinking following a normal meal and following individual pellets showed highly similar distributions under the longer interpellet intervals. In other words, with respect to the pattern of drinking following food, it appears that rats treat each pellet as though it were the end of a meal.

Cued response-independent delivery of food: Autoshaping

The autoshaping paradigm is a particularly useful procedure for investigating natural learning in the laboratory because it allows manipulation of the charac-teristics of a predictive stimulus (CS) without requiring the performance of any particular response. Thus, it preserves the opportunity for an animal to reveal its own response organization (see also Hollis, 1982) while allowing the experi-menter to manipulate important characteristics of the stimulus situation.

The first autoshaping study came from an attempt to automate the shaping of pigeons to peck keys for food. Brown and Jenkins (1968) showed that pigeons will begin pecking a lighted key that predicts food. This is readily explained by appetitive structure in that the pigeon, a visually guided feeder, is presented with a relatively discrete visual target associated with food temporally, spatially, and in type of illumination. A simpler explanation of these data can be offered by stimulus substitution, in which components of the unconditioned response (in this case, pecking) come to be controlled by the predictive stimulus. Many other examples, though, require the complexity of the appetitive structure to account for the results.

Rats as conditioned stimuli. Rats have many attractive qualities for other rats, which may approach, sniff, groom, crawl over, box, and attack them. How, then, should rats be treated as predictors of food? The stimulus substitution model predicts they will be treated as food items, or perhaps ignored. The behavior system view (Timberlake, 1983b; Timberlake & Grant, 1975) notes that rats are social feeders, following each other to food as adults, and learning as pups to eat what adults eat. On this basis, we predicted that rats would approach and contact other rats that predicted food at a significantly higher level than they would approach a rat never paired with food, a rat randomly paired with food, or a rat-sized block of wood predicting food. Figure 4 shows that rats predicting food produced extensive and complex social interaction, different in both amount and relative probability of the components from the baseline of social interaction.

Further work summarized by Timberlake (1983b) supports the predictions that weanling rats should not be good predictors of food for adults (weanlings are still learning to distinguish food from nonfood), that food reward should produce a different form of social interaction than water (water and food are different,

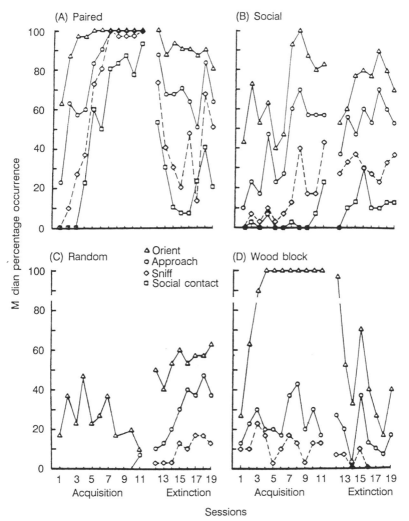

FIGURE 4. The median percentage of trials with orienting, approaching, sniffing, and social contact responses to a stimulus by four groups of rats. In the paired group (A) the stimulus was a rat predicting food. In the social group (B) the stimulus was a rat presented without food. In the random group (C) the stimulus was a rat that was presented randomly with respect to food. In the wood-block group (D) the stimulus was a rat-sized wood block predicting food. (From Timberlake & Grant, 1975.)

though overlapping, systems), and that hamsters should not approach another hamster predicting food. Hamsters, unlike rats, appear to be reasonably solitary through most of their adult life. Thus, we would not expect them to have organized behavior related to following other hamsters to food. In fact, Figure 5

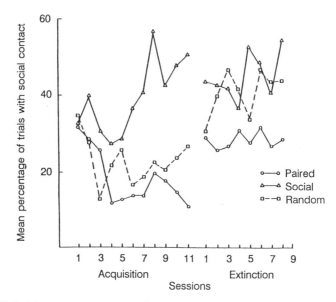

FIGURE 5. The mean percentage of trials with social contact with a stimulus male hamster by subject male hamsters during acquisition and extinction for three groups paired (the stimulus hamster predicted food); social (the stimulus hamster was presented without food); and random (the stimulus hamster and food were presented randomly). (From Timberlake, 1983b.)

shows that hamsters actually decrease their attention to another hamster when food is presented in either correlated or uncorrelated fashion.

Moving ball bearings as conditioned stimuli. Our work with ball bearings was inspired by a film of the experiments of Boakes, Poli, Lockwood, and Goodall (1978) on misbehavior in rats. Boakes and his colleagues required rats to obtain a ball bearing, transport it a short distance, and drop it down a chute in order to obtain food. Their intent was to mimic the Brelands' (1961) famous examples of training pigs and raccoons to transport and deposit tokens to obtain food.

What fascinated me in Boakes's film was the way in which the rats treated the ball bearing. They appeared completely engrossed with it, turning it, gnawing on it, releasing and retrieving it repeatedly. These responses were very much like responses we had seen rats direct at crickets. We hypothesized that these patterns were part of a predatory sequence in the rat suitable for capturing, dispatching, and eating prey. If such a sequence were based on sensitivity to moving stimuli and preorganized components of capture and handling responses, then it should be possible to evoke predatory behavior by presenting the rat with an artificial moving stimulus predicting food.

To test this idea, we rolled ball bearings (too big to swallow) past rats and followed each bearing with food. The result was the acquisition of full-blown predatory behavior toward the bearing (Timberlake, Wahl, & King, 1982). After a few days of pairing, the rats dug the bearing out of the entry hole, grabbed it and stuffed it in their mouths, ran toward the food tray, then sat and turned and gnawed the ball bearing. They then oscillated between letting the bearing roll away and retrieving it, ran after it one last time as it escaped, and buried themselves in the food tray just before the pellet came.

Figure 6 shows that the acquisition of interaction with the ball bearing was related to the temporal contiguity of the ball bearing and food rather than to its random presentation with respect to food delivery. Figure 7 supports the argu-

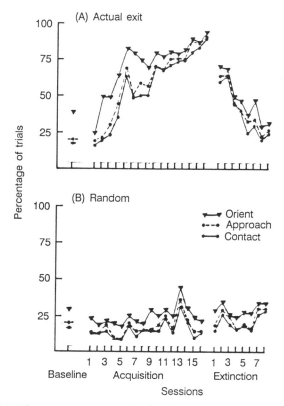

FIGURE 6. The mean percentage of trials with responses of orienting, approaching, and contact to a moving ball bearing by two groups of rats. In the actual-exit group (A), food was presented when the ball bearing exited the test chamber. In the random group (B), the ball bearing and food were presented randomly. (Adapted from Timberlake, Wahl, & King, 1982.)

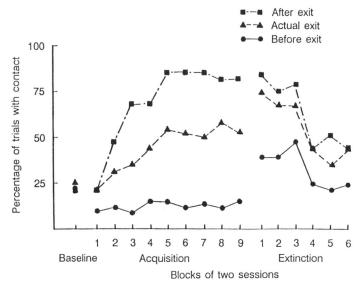

FIGURE 7. The mean percentage of trials with contact responses to a moving ball bearing by three groups of rats. In the before-exit group, food was presented 1.6 seconds after the ball bearing entered the chamber. In the actual-exit group, food was presented when the bearing actually left the chamber. In the after-exit group, food was presented 2.5 seconds after an unimpeded ball bearing would have exited the chamber (approximately 5.6 seconds after it first entered the chamber). (Adapted from Timberlake et al., 1982.)

ment that most of the bearing contact was related to search and capture of food rather than to handling and ingestion, because the tendency to contact the bearing was short-circuited in favor of going to the food tray if there were less than 2 seconds between emergence of the bearing and the delivery of food (the "before-exit" group in Figure 7).

A second test of the assumption that autoshaped behavior relates to preorganized appetitive structure compared rats' responses toward ball bearings that predicted food and those that predicted water (Timberlake, 1983c). Because predatory behaviors should be more closely related to food than to water, we hypothesized that interaction with a bearing predicting food should be longer and more complex (with an increased proportion of carrying and chewing) than interaction with a bearing predicting water. Figure 8 shows support for these hypotheses.

Given that moving ball bearings trigger field-related predatory responses, it should be possible to produce and explore field-related results in the laboratory. One test of this assumption was an attempt to replicate the dissociation between the effects of poison on ingestion and on attack observed in a variety of mammalian species (Timberlake & Melcer, 1988). For example, coyotes (Gustavson,

A subsequent manipulation indicated that the effects of poisoning generalized to the familiar food, and to a smaller extent, to the familiar bearing with a decrease in the extent of novelty. We argued that the mechanisms related to taste-aversion learning combine to produce maximum speed of effect and minimum generalization when a completely novel prey item is present. In the absence of such novel prey, poisoning may produce less rapid learning that is more readily generalized to other gustatory and exteroceptive stimuli (Timberlake & Melcer, 1988).

In sum, the response-independent delivery of food provides an unusually fertile paradigm for exploring the nature of behavior systems and natural learning. The regular presentation of small amounts of food appears to entrain a cycle of motivational modes related to foraging. The responses that occur are affected by the nature of the stimulus conditions, including both the contextual stimuli and any discrete, more predictive cues. In the case of discrete cues, as Jenkins, Barrera, Ireland, and Woodside (1978) argued, "the experimental CS–US episode mimics a naturally occurring episode for which preorganized behavior patterns exist."

Response-dependent presentation of reward: Operants

At first glance, operant responding is much less suited to eliciting the natural appetitive structure and processes of an animal than is the relatively permissive paradigm of Pavlovian conditioning. A major emphasis in operant conditioning is on the experimenter's ability to compel almost any response in the context of almost any stimulus by means of any reward. However, operant conditioning can be used to differentiate response structures within a particular module, as well as in linking different response structures and motivational states. Two classic phenomena show this latter effect quite clearly.

Misbehavior. Misbehavior is the emergence of a cohesive, motivated behavior without an appropriate response–reward contingency; in fact, misbehavior usually interferes with the effects of a response contingency that is present. In the two most often-cited examples (Breland & Breland, 1961), pigs and raccoons were successfully trained with food rewards to pick up tokens, transport them, and deposit them in a container, but when the number of tokens required was increased, cohesive interfering responses began to occur. The raccoon, instead of releasing the tokens, ". . . spent seconds, even minutes rubbing them together . . . and dipping them into the container." The pig, ". . . instead of carrying the dollar and depositing it simply and cleanly, . . . would repeatedly drop it, root it, drop it again, root it along the way, pick it up, toss it up in the air, drop it . . . and so on." As Breland and Breland remarked, "These egregious failures came as a rather considerable shock to us . . . the animal simply did not do what it had been conditioned to do."

From a behavior system view, the successful training of an operant response produced pairings between stimuli that resembled naturally occurring food cues and food. These pairings evoked response components ordinarily related to food cues (Gardner & Gardner, 1988). Thus, the token used by the raccoon apparently fit stimulus filters related to crustacean washing, whereas the token used by the pig fit stimuli that are rooted. In short, misbehavior occurs because operant contingencies promote pairings between stimuli and rewards, thereby engaging naturally occurring components and sequences of appetitive behavior.

The contribution of appetitive structure to misbehavior in operant conditioning was tested more extensively by Timberlake and Washburne (1989). We related the tendency of seven rodent species to prey on fast-moving arthropods to their tendencies in the laboratory to kill crickets and contact moving ball bearings to receive food. Based on their stomach contents and observed diet items, these species ranged from highly carnivorous (*Onychomys leucogaster*) through omnivorous (*Peromyscus californicus, P. maniculatus, P. leucopus*), to more herbivorous (*Meriones unguiculatus, Acomys cahirinus, Sigmodon hispidus*). As shown in Table 1, this ordering significantly predicted the average latency to eat the cricket, the average percentage of trials with contact of the bearing, and the average percentage of contact trials using the mouth.

Table 1 also shows that there were striking similarities in the ways each species preyed on the cricket and interacted with the ball bearing. For example, *P. californicus* showed lunge bites with paws outstretched as well as boxing of the prey with both paws with both the bearing and the cricket.

Predispositions and constraints in learning. In the behavior system view, predispositions and constraints are not causal entities, but are descriptions of the fit between the appetitive structure of the animal and a particular environment and contingency schedule. A predisposition occurs when the animal/environment fit mimics that of the selection environment; a constraint occurs when the fit conflicts. A predisposition can be changed to a constraint by changing the situation. For example, asking a *Peromyscus* to contact a moving bearing predicting food will produce a predisposition effect; requiring the same rodent not to contact a moving bearing predicting food will produce a constraint effect.

SUMMARY

The primary purpose of this chapter is to begin the integration of ecological and laboratory approaches by establishing a common behavior system framework underlying both types of learning. The major argument in this integration is that all learning is dependent upon the fit between the appetitive structure of relevant behavior systems and the stimulus circumstances of the environment. This view

TABLE 1. Characteristic Responses to the Cricket and to the Ball Bearing for Seven Rodent Species

Rodent species	Similarities	Differences
Onychomys leucogaster	Direct and unhesitant approach to prey. Paw adjustments if prey is not cleanly taken. Animal sits up to chew prey held in paws.	Bearing is often picked up in mouth first; cricket is picked up in mouth only if immobile.
Peromyscus californicus	Direct and unhesitant approach to prey. Repeated lunge-bites with paws outstretched. Boxing (stabbing the prey with both paws). Paws used to rotate prey between chewing bouts with mouth alone, animal in sitting position.	Cricket carried about in mouth more than bearing.
P. maniculatus and P. leucopus	Slow approach to prey with hesitations and recoils. During approach, body is extended, eyes squinted, nose wrinkled, and ears pulled back. Prey is pounced on with both paws, pinned, and bitten. Animal sits up to chew prey held in paws.	Pounce–bite sequence repeated less frequently with bearing.
Meriones unguiculatus	Unhurried, often not direct, but unhesitant approach. Prey is sniffed and held in place with paw.	Rarely sits and chews bearing.
Acomys cahirinus	Unhurried and not always direct approach. Runs beside prey and bites at it.	Rarely sits and chews bearing.
Sigmodon hispidus	Fails to move in presence of prey.	Every animal contacted the bearing at least once. No animal ever contacted the cricket.

Note. From Timberlake and Washburne, 1989.

can account for the diversity and complexity of natural learning and the general principles of laboratory learning, as well as its puzzling phenomena such as superstition, misbehavior, polydipsia, and predispositions and constraints.

Within the appetitive structure view, the paradigms of laboratory learning can be used as tools to explore how learning relates to the stimulus sensitivities, response components, and hierarchical and sequential control states making up a behavior system. For example, periodic presentation of a reward entrains an appetitive structure while allowing relatively free expression of the underlying elements. Manipulation of CS characteristics can be added to engage specific perceptual–motor modules. The techniques of operant conditioning can be used to explore, differentiate, and link modules and motivational states.

The application of the behavior system approach to the study of natural learning in the laboratory requires knowledge of the subject's behavior and ecology and an ability to establish and tune laboratory circumstances to engage elements of the underlying appetitive structure. To a biologically oriented researcher, attempting to tune a laboratory setting may seem like trying to draw a picture in the dark, but it can have impressive results. The fact that the three major instrumental responses of laboratory learning (maze running, lever pressing, and key pecking) can be produced reliably by simple pairings or stimulus exposure speaks well of the ability of experimenters to produce a good fit between the animal and the environment. However, the fact that most researchers have not explored this fit experimentally, nor have even appeared to recognize the ecological significance of these responses, shows that tuning alone is inadequate to drive the analysis of learning.

An important remaining issue is how to treat the mechanistic and quantitative models of modern laboratory learning research. I find overstated Kuo's comment (1967, p. 7), that "if many learning theorists have apparently succeeded in their mathematical predictions, that can be explained by the fact that they have ignored the great complexity and variability of behavior." But the point is well taken that all learning involves more complexity than is currently accounted for by these models. To clarify the nature of laboratory and natural learning, as well as the relations between them, an account of the subject's appetitive structure is essential.

CHAPTER 3

AN ADAPTATIONIST PERSPECTIVE ON SOCIAL LEARNING, SOCIAL FEEDING, AND SOCIAL FORAGING IN NORWAY RATS

Bennett G. Galef, Jr.

For 20 years, my coworkers and I have been engaged in the study of social learning in animals. During most of that time, those working in my laboratory have been analyzing several ways in which social interactions among Norway rats (*Rattus norvegicus*) can affect their selection of both foods and foraging sites.

There are a number of reasons to believe that social learning is important to young rats struggling to compose a safe, yet balanced, diet. First, we have identified four ways in which social interaction among rats can influence their food choices (see Galef, 1976, 1986a for reviews), and Gemberling (1984) has described a fifth. Such redundancy in itself suggests that information about what and where others are eating can be of considerable use to rats. Second, as we shall see below, there is direct evidence that, even in the laboratory, social interactions can be crucial to the survival of young rats as they make the potentially perilous transition from nutritional dependence on their mother's milk to independent foraging and feeding.

This chapter reviews data collected in my laboratory since 1983. It is more explicitly Darwinian in its approach than is usually the case in discussions of behavior acquisition by animals. First, in a brief introduction, I discuss my view of the relationship between the study of social learning in animals and what Lewontin and Gould have referred to, albeit unsympathetically, as the "adaptationist program" (Gould & Lewontin, 1979; Lewontin, 1978). In a second, longer section, I describe in some detail recently completed laboratory analyses of one type of social learning: olfactory communication of information about foods among Norway rats. Last, I discuss the possible implications of our laboratory findings for understanding the ways in which Norway rats may find food and avoid poisons in their natural habitat. Thus, in this chapter, analytic laboratory studies of the causes of behavior are sandwiched between an adaptationist introduction and adaptationist extrapolations to more evolutionarily relevant situations. This organization reflects the way I think about my laboratory research.

SOCIAL LEARNING FROM AN ADAPTATIONIST PERSPECTIVE

In a characteristically elegant passage, Ernst Mayr (1973, p. 651) described two rather different types of "genetic program" (I prefer to think of them as two types of "developmental program") which are translated into phenotypic characteristics during ontogeny:

We can ask what differences exist between genetic programs responsible for behaviors formerly called innate and those regarded as experientially acquired. A genetic program that does not allow appreciable modifications during the process of translation into the phenotype I call a *closed program*—closed because nothing can be inserted in it through experience. Such closed programs are widespread among the so-called lower animals. A genetic program that allows for additional input during the lifespan of its owner I call an *open program*.

I will use Mayr's dichotomy between open and closed programs as a starting point to discuss the extent to which one might expect an adaptive "fit" between the phenotype of an organism and the demands of the particular environment in which it lives.

Closed developmental programs.

By definition, the ontogeny of a behavioral phenotype that develops from the transcription of a closed developmental program is unaffected by the vagaries of the environment in which it matures. Although there are circumstances in which a closed program would be more fit than any open program that could produce similar behavior, the inability of closed programs to produce different phenotypes, each appropriate to a particular environment, constrains the perfection of design (Williams, 1966, p. 12) of phenotypic characteristics that result from translation of closed programs.

As Williams has indicated, "Favorable selection of a gene is inevitable if [that gene] has favorable mean effects compared to available alternatives of the moment" (1966, p. 27). Genes contributing to closed programs have been selected for their favorable mean effects on survival and reproduction. Consequently, the phenotypic features produced by transcription of closed developmental programs, unmodified by experience, can be adaptive only with respect to the mean properties of the range of environments in which the members of a species have evolved. Hence, closed programs cannot produce phenotypes that are matched to each of the range of conditions that contributes to the mean environment, and the fit between an individual and its environment that results from transcription of a closed program is likely to be relatively crude.

Open developmental programs.

Open developmental programs, which are sensitive to experience in their translation from genotype to phenotype, provide a way in which individual phenotypes can, in principle, achieve a greater degree of accommodation to the idiosyncrasies of the particular locales in which they mature than can phenotypes produced by transcription of closed programs. Although open programs might sometimes respond to environments experienced during ontogeny by producing phenotypes less, rather than more, able to cope with the demands of that environment, open developmental programs, like closed programs, are products of natural selection: those open programs that respond to environments by producing poorly adapted phenotypes will be selected against; those that respond by producing well-adapted phenotypes will be favorably selected. The result, in many circumstances, should be an increase in the frequency of open programs able to respond adaptively to the environments in which individuals mature.

Individual and social learning.

Although there are exceptions (e.g., Marler & Tamura, 1964; West, King, & Harrocks, 1983), most investigators of the role of experience in the modification of phenotypes during ontogeny have studied interactions between a developing organism and its physical environment, since the physical environment in which an open program is translated into a phenotype contains many useful cues as to the developmental end points appropriate to that environment. However, the physical features of an environment are not the only useful sources of information available to an open program about the path its translation to phenotype should follow.

The behaviors of adults that interact with a developing individual are, not infrequently, valuable indicators of behavioral end points towards which development should proceed. Adults with whom a developing individual interacts have phenotypes adequate for survival in the particular environment in which the interactions occur. If open programs could incorporate the behavior of those adults into the phenotype of the developing individual, production of a phenotype matched to the idiosyncratic demands of the environment would be all but assured. Open developmental programs that accepted behavior of adult conspecifics as inputs could, in effect, provide a nongenetic means for the transmission of acquired, adaptive phenotypic characteristics either between or within generations.

That it might be useful in theory for naive individuals to incorporate into their own phenotypes behavioral features exhibited by conspecifics does not, of course, prove that naive individuals actually can or do use the behavior of knowledgeable others to guide their own development. Determining whether individuals make use of conspecifics as guides in development, and, if so, describing the processes by which the behavior of conspecifics can bias the translation of open programs towards particular phenotypic end points, are empirical, rather than theoretical, enterprises.

Accordingly, for 20 years, my coworkers and I have been using the development of diet choice by rats as a model system to explore the ways in which developing individuals can incorporate the behavior of others into their own behavioral phenotypes. In the next section, I review recent findings from that research program.

RATTUS NORVEGICUS: A SOCIAL, CENTRAL-PLACE FORAGING SPECIES

Many behavioral ecologists have suggested that in environments where the distribution of foods is unpredictable and patchy, social animals foraging from a central place (for example, birds foraging from a roost) could exchange useful information at the central place concerning the availability of foods in the larger environment (Bertram, 1978; DeGroot, 1980; Erwin, 1977; Waltz, 1982; Ward & Zahavi, 1973). For example, an unsuccessful forager might spot a successful forager at an aggregation site, then follow the successful individual when it left on its next foraging trip.

Although the use of aggregation sites as information centers was originally proposed to explain the evolution of bird roosts (Ward & Zahavi), aggregations other than roosts could serve this function, and organisms other than birds could benefit from their use. For example, it has long been known that the hives of honeybees act as information centers where returning foragers provide nestmates with both olfactory information (Wenner, 1971) and visual (dance) information (von Frisch, 1967) that directs nestmates to the patchy, ephemeral sources of nectar and pollen on which honeybees feed.

Outside the laboratory, Norway rats are social central-place foragers. Each rat is a member of a colony that inhabits a burrow. When foraging, colony members disperse from the burrow, feed, and then return to the burrow (Calhoun, 1962; Telle, 1966). Thus, the burrows of Norway rats, like the roosts of some species of birds, could, in principle, function as information centers, and Norway rats are an appropriate species to use in laboratory experiments examining ways in which social interactions may facilitate food finding by members of social central-place foraging species.

The basic experiment

The laboratory studies described below were intended to simulate natural situations in which a foraging rat eats a food at some distance from its burrow, returns to its burrow, and then interacts with a burrowmate. Our initial purpose was to discover whether, as a result of such interaction, a rat could acquire information concerning the food another rat had eaten and, if so, whether it would make use of this information when it had to select a food to eat.

The subjects were housed in same-sex pairs, each pair in a cage divided in two by a screen partition. To simplify exposition, I refer below to the "successful forager" in each pair as the "demonstrator," and to the other member of the pair as the "observer." The basic experiment, illustrated in Figure 1, was carried out in five steps. In Step 1, a demonstrator and an observer with unlimited access to Purina Laboratory Rodent Chow and water were housed together for a 2-day period of familiarization with their enclosure and with each other. In Step 2, the demonstrator and the observer were placed on opposite sides of the cage and separated by the screen partition, and the demonstrator was deprived of food for 24 hours to ensure that it ate when given the opportunity to do so. In Step 3, the Rodent Chow was removed from the observer's side of the cage to prepare the observer for testing. The demonstrator was moved to a cage in a separate room and, for 30 minutes, was allowed to eat one of two different diets: a cinnamon-

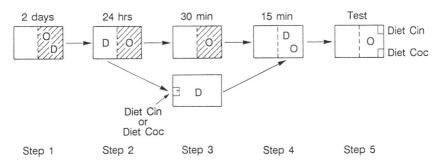

FIGURE 1. Schematic diagram of the procedure of the basic experiment. O = observer; D = demonstrator; hatching indicates maintenance diet present in cage. (After Galef & Wigmore, 1983.)

flavored diet (Diet Cin) or a cocoa-flavored diet (Diet Coc). In Step 4, immediately after the demonstrator finished eating, it was placed with the observer, and the two rats were allowed to interact freely for 15 minutes. Finally, in Step 5, the demonstrator was removed from the experiment, and for 60 hours, the observer was offered an opportunity to eat from either of two weighed food cups, one containing Diet Cin and the other containing Diet Coc.

Figure 2 shows the mean percentage of Diet Coc eaten by observers whose demonstrators had eaten either Diet Coc or Diet Cin during the experiment. As can be seen in Figure 2, (1) those observers whose demonstrators ate Diet Coc ate a much greater percentage of Diet Coc than did those observers whose demonstrators ate Diet Cin, and (2) the effects of the diet eaten by demonstrators on the diet preference of their respective observers were still apparent 48–60 hours after the interaction between the two rats had occurred. The results of this first experiment show: (1) that an observer rat can extract information from its demonstrator that is sufficient to identify the diet the demonstrator has previously eaten, and (2) that this socially acquired information is sufficient to bias observers' subsequent selection of diets.

Variations on a theme. We have performed different versions of this basic experiment many times, using a variety of different diets (Galef, in press; Galef,

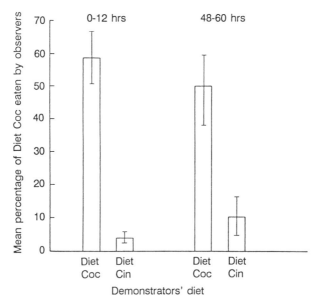

FIGURE 2. Mean amount of cocoa-flavored diet (Diet Coc) ingested, as a percentage of total amount of food eaten, by observers whose demonstrators ate either Diet Coc or cinnamon-flavored diet (Diet Cin). (From Galef & Wigmore, 1983.)

Kennett, & Wigmore, 1984; Galef & Wigmore, 1983), with both hungry and replete observers, with both male and female demonstrator–observer pairs, and with both wild and domesticated Norway rats. We have also performed versions of the experiment with demonstrator–observer pairs that were familiar with one another beforehand, and with pairs that never met each other prior to the interaction described in Step 4 of the basic experiment. We have repeated the basic experiment with old demonstrators and observers and young ones (Galef, Kennett, & Wigmore, 1984). In every case, we have seen robust enhancement of the preferences of observers for their respective demonstrators' diets. Similarly, Posadas-Andrews and Roper (1983) and Strupp and Levitsky (1984), using rather different laboratory situations, have repeatedly observed demonstrator influence on later diet selection by observers. Apparently, demonstrator rats will influence their observers' diet preferences under a broad range of conditions.

Duration of effects. Although the effects of exposure to a demonstrator fed a certain diet on its observer's subsequent food choice can be substantial, one might expect such effects to be transitory. Long-lasting learned preferences for foods have proven to be difficult to induce in mammals other than humans (Capretta & Rawls, 1974; Rozin, 1984; Rozin, Gruss, & Berk, 1979; Warren & Pfaffmann, 1959). However, in recent experiments, we have found that by the simple expedient of exposing rats to demonstrators that had eaten a diet, rather than to the diet itself, it is possible to induce preferences of indefinite duration for both palatable and unpalatable foods (Galef, in press). In these experiments, observers interacted for 30 minutes once every 2 or 3 days with demonstrators that were fed one of two roughly equipalatable diets (Diet Cin or Diet Coc) and were then allowed to choose between Diet Cin and Diet Coc for 23 hours per day. As Figure 3 shows, the observers exhibited preferences for their respective demonstrators' diets that were maintained for weeks. Similarly, observers briefly exposed on several occasions to demonstrators that had been fed an inherently unpalatable cayenne pepper–flavored diet exhibited a substantially enhanced preference for that diet (Galef, in press). In sum, socially induced enhancement of food preferences occurs under a broad range of conditions, is of substantial magnitude, can last for considerable periods of time, and can mitigate effects of other major determinants of diet selection, such as palatability (Galef, 1986b; Galef, in press).

THE NATURE OF MESSAGES PASSING FROM DEMONSTRATORS TO OBSERVERS

Implication of olfactory signals

One obvious question arising from the results described above is, How does an observer rat acquire information from a demonstrator that allows it to identify the diet its demonstrator has eaten? We have developed several converging lines of

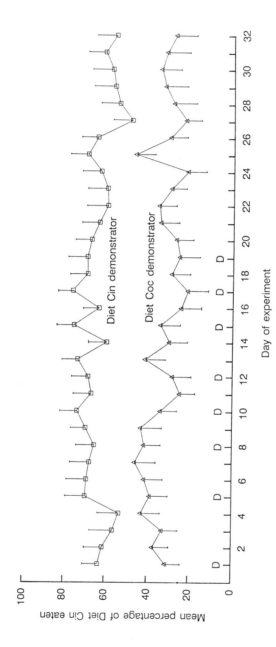

FIGURE 3. Mean amount of Diet Cin eaten daily by observers interacting with demonstrators fed either Diet Cin or Diet Coc, as a percentage of the total amount of food ingested. D = 30-minute exposure to a demonstrator. Flags = ± 1 SEM. (From Galef, in press.)

evidence, each consistent with the hypothesis that olfactory cues passing from demonstrator to observer suffice to allow observers to identify their respective demonstrators' diets.

To examine the mode of communication of information from demonstrator to observer, we had to gain some control over their interaction. We performed three experiments using a procedure similar to that illustrated in Figure 1, but with one important modification: during the part of the experiment in which the demonstrator and observer interact after the demonstrator has eaten (Step 4) they were held on opposite sides of the screen partition. As can be seen in Figure 4, the observers nevertheless developed a preference for their respective demonstrators' diets. However, as can also be seen in Figure 4, when the screen barrier separating demonstrator and observer was replaced by a Plexiglas barrier, the

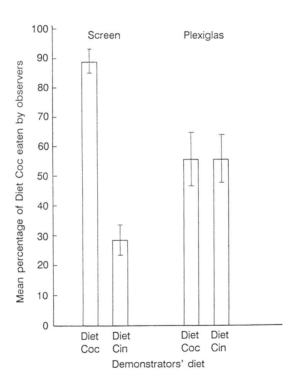

FIGURE 4. Mean amount of Diet Coc ingested, as a percentage of the total amount of food eaten by observers whose demonstrators ate Diet Coc or Diet Cin. Left: Observer and demonstrator separated by a screen barrier during interaction. Right: Observer and demonstrator separated by a Plexiglas partition during interaction. (From Galef & Wigmore, 1983.)

influence of demonstrators on the later diet preference of their respective observers was completely abolished (Galef & Wigmore, 1983). Thus, it was concluded that some sort of nonvisual contact between demonstrator and observer is necessary for successful communication to occur.

We conducted another experiment in which each demonstrator, after eating either Diet Cin or Diet Coc, was anesthetized and placed 2 centimeters from and facing the screen partition dividing the cage, with its observer on the other side of the screen. During the subsequent preference test (Figure 5), observers still exhibited a robust preference for their respective demonstrators' diets (Galef & Wigmore, 1983). Clearly, the signal passing from demonstrator to observer did not require physical contact between them.

On the other hand, as one would expect if olfactory cues play an important role in information transfer between demonstrator and observer, observers rendered anosmic by passing zinc sulfate solution through their nares (Alberts & Galef, 1971) failed to exhibit a preference for their demonstrators' diets (Galef & Wigmore, 1983). Control rats, whose nasal passages had been rinsed with saline solution, continued to exhibit a preference for their demonstrators' diets (Figure 6).

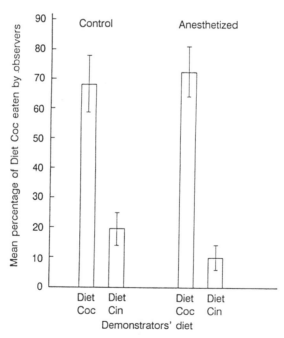

FIGURE 5. Mean amount of Diet Coc eaten by observers as a percentage of the total amount of food ingested. Left: Observers interacting with intact demonstrators. Right: Observers interacting with anesthetized demonstrators.(From Galef & Wigmore, 1983.)

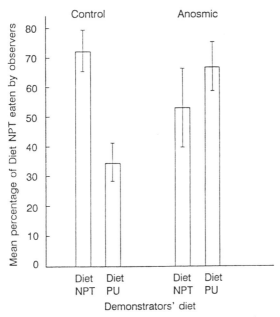

FIGURE 6. Mean amount of normal protein test diet (Diet NPT) ingested, as a percentage of total amount of food eaten, by observers whose demonstrators ate either Diet NPT or Diet Pu (Purina Laboratory Rodent Chow). Left: Observers' nasal cavities rinsed with saline. Right: Observers' nasal cavities rinsed with $ZnSO_4$, i.e., anosmic observers. (From Galef and Wigmore, 1983.)

Last, but not least, we found that humans can use olfactory cues emitted by a recently fed rat to determine which diet a rat has recently eaten. A human observer presented with a dozen rats in random order, half previously fed Diet Coc and half previously fed Diet Cin, could, by sniffing their breath, tell with better than 85 percent accuracy which rat had eaten which diet (Galef & Wigmore, 1983). The above results are all consistent with the view that olfactory cues passing from demonstrator to observer play an important role in communication between them.

CAUSES OF DEMONSTRATOR INFLUENCE ON OBSERVER DIET PREFERENCE

The simple familiarity hypothesis

One simple explanation of the influence of demonstrator rats on their respective observers' diet choices derives from the observation that rats are often somewhat hesitant to ingest an unfamiliar food (Barnett, 1958b; Galef, 1970). During interaction with a demonstrator rat that has eaten an unfamiliar food, an observer rat is exposed to olfactory cues associated with the food, and should, subsequently, be at least slightly familiar with it. Consequently, an observer rat that has interacted with a demonstrator fed an unfamiliar food should eat that food in preference to an equipalatable, but totally unfamiliar, diet. Demonstrator influence on observer diet preference could thus be explained as the result of a simple increase in the familiarity of observers with the odor of diets fed to their respective demonstrators.

We have carried out a number of experiments designed to test the adequacy of explanations of demonstrator influence on observer diet preference in terms of demonstrator-induced diet familiarity of the sort described above (Galef, in press; Galef, Kennett, & Stein, 1985; Galef & Stein, 1985). In every case, the results of our studies have been contrary to the most straightforward predictions made on the basis of the simple familiarity hypothesis.

For example, I recently completed a study (Galef, in press) in which individual rats were given access to bowls containing either Diet Cin or Diet Coc for 30 minutes per day for 5 consecutive days (Days 1–5 in Figure 7). For the remaining $23^1/2$ hours of each day, each subject was offered a choice between Diet Cin and Diet Coc. As Figure 7 shows, five 30-minute periods of simple exposure to either Diet Cin or Diet Coc had no effect on subjects' diet preferences. Next, following two days on which all subjects were simply offered the choice of Diets Cin and Coc (Days 6 and 7 of the experiment), each subject was exposed to a demonstrator that had eaten either Diet Cin or Diet Coc. On each of the final three days of the experiment (Days 8, 9, and 10), each subject that had previously been exposed to Diet Cin for 30 minutes per day was allowed to interact for 30 minutes per day with a demonstrator that had just eaten Diet Coc. Conversely, each subject that had been exposed to Diet Coc was allowed to interact for 30 minutes per day with a demonstrator that had eaten Diet Cin. All subjects continued to be tested for their preferences between Diets Cin and Coc for the remaining $23^1/2$ hours of each day. As can be seen in Figure 7, interaction with a demonstrator that had eaten a diet profoundly affected the food preferences of subjects, even after they had been eating both diets offered in the preference test for 7 days. Clearly, simple exposure to a diet and exposure to conspecifics that have eaten a diet can have very different effects on diet preference.

The contextual hypothesis

An obvious alternative to the "simple familiarity hypothesis" is the hypothesis that observers' exposure to diet-related cues within a context provided by the presence of a demonstrator is necessary if brief olfactory exposure to diet-related cues is to alter an observer's subsequent diet preference. It is this "contextual hypothesis" that has been guiding our recent research.

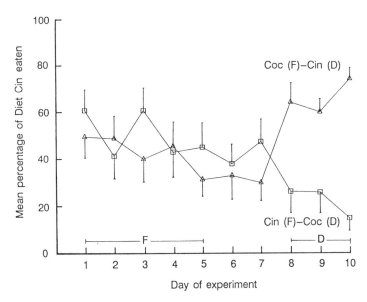

FIGURE 7. Mean amount of Diet Cin eaten daily by subjects during the 23½-hour period of choice as a percentage of total amount of food they ate each day during the choice test. Cin F–Coc D = Subjects first exposed to Diet Cin, then allowed to interact with a demonstrator fed Diet Coc. Coc F–Cin D = Subjects first exposed to Diet Coc, then allowed to interact with a demonstrator fed Diet Cin. F = 30-minute daily exposure to food. D = 30-minute daily exposure to a demonstrator. Flags = ± 1 SEM. (From Galef, in press.)

Let us assume, for the sake of argument, that I am correct in suggesting that the effects of demonstrator rats on the subsequent food preferences of observers are the result of the observers experiencing the smell of the diet within an olfactory context provided by the presence of the demonstrator. If so, then analysis of the olfactory message passing from demonstrator to observer can be treated as two separate questions: (1) What are the sources of the diet-related cues emitted by a demonstrator that permit an observer to identify its demonstrator's diet? (2) What are the contextual cues, also emitted by a demonstrator, that act in concert with the diet-related cues to alter an observer's subsequent diet preferences?

We have found (Galef & Stein, 1985) that both particles of food clinging to the fur and vibrissae of a rat and olfactory cues escaping from the digestive system of a rat are sufficient to permit observers to identify a food their respective demonstrators have eaten (Galef, Kennett, & Stein, 1985; Galef & Stein, 1985). We have been able to exploit the first of these findings to investigate both the source and the chemistry of the contextual cues that cause observers to prefer a diet.

To look more closely at the contextual cues involved in demonstrator influence on observer diet preference, we again changed our experimental procedure slightly. The new procedure was similar to the basic experiment described above, but differed both in the way demonstrators were made to emit diet-related cues and in the treatment of demonstrators and observers during the period of their interaction. Rather than feeding the demonstrators, as is done in Step 3 of the basic procedure, we anesthetized them and dusted them with either Diet Cin or Diet Coc, and, instead of permitting demonstrator and observer to interact freely, as during Step 4 of the basic experiment, each anesthetized demonstrator was placed in the screen tube of the apparatus depicted in Figure 8. The observer was then introduced into the bucket-shaped portion of the apparatus, left there for 30 minutes, then moved back to its home cage for testing.

We allowed observers to interact in the apparatus illustrated in Figure 8 with demonstrators treated in four ways. Observers in the *powdered-face group* interacted with anesthetized demonstrators whose faces had been rolled in either Diet Cin or Diet Coc. Observers in the *dead powdered-face group* interacted with demonstrators that had been sacrificed by anesthetic overdose and had then had their faces rolled in either Diet Cin or Diet Coc. Observers in the *powdered-rear group* interacted with anesthetized demonstrators whose rear ends had been powdered with either Diet Cin or Diet Coc and that were then introduced into the screen tube with their rear ends inside the bucket and their heads outside of it. Last, observers in the *surrogate group* interacted with a rat-sized, cotton batting–stuffed length of tubular gauze, one end of which had been rolled in either Diet Cin or Diet Coc, and which was then placed in the screen tube.

FIGURE 8. Apparatus used to investigate contextual olfactory cues. (From Galef & Stein, 1985.)

Figure 9 presents a measure of the degree of influence of the various sorts of demonstrators on their respective observers' subsequent diet preferences during testing. The greater the Coc-demonstrator:Cin-demonstrator ratio of a group in Figure 9, the greater the influence of demonstrators' diets on their observers' subsequent diet preferences (see Galef & Stein, 1985, for a detailed explanation of the calculation of Coc-demonstrator:Cin-demonstrator ratios).

To summarize the results of a series of statistical analyses presented in detail elsewhere (Galef & Stein, 1985), we found that observers in the powdered-face group preferred to eat the diet applied to the faces of their respective demonstrators, while observers in the surrogate group exhibited no tendency to select the diet with which their "demonstrators" had been powdered. The diet choices of observers in both the dead powdered-face and powdered-rear groups were significantly less affected by their demonstrators than were the diet choices of observers in the powdered-face group, and were significantly more affected by their demon-

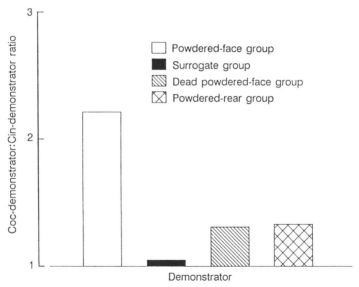

FIGURE 9. Diet Coc demonstrator:Diet Cin demonstrator ratios of groups of observers interacting with demonstrators and surrogates in the apparatus illustrated in Figure 8. Demonstrators were: powdered-face group = anesthetized rats with faces rolled in Diet Cin or Diet Coc; dead powdered-face group = dead rats with faces rolled in Diet Cin or Diet Coc; powdered-rear group = anesthetized rats with rear ends powdered with Diet Cin or Diet Coc and introduced into the screen tube with rear ends inside the bucket; surrogate group = rat-sized, cotton batting–stuffed gauze rolled in Diet Cin or Diet Coc. (After Galef & Stein, 1985.)

strators than were the diet choices of observers in the surrogate group. Taken together, these findings suggest: (1) that simple exposure of an observer rat to the smell of a particular diet is not sufficient to enhance its preference for that diet, and (2) that the contextual cues emitted by demonstrator rats that produce a preference for a diet in their observers are probably emitted most strongly from the anterior end of live rats.

Identification of the contextual semiochemical

One of the more obvious differences between live, anesthetized rats, which emit contextual cues that alter their observers' diet choices, and dead rats, which do not emit very effective contextual cues, is that the live rats are breathing and the dead rats are not. Similarly, the anterior end of a demonstrator, shown to be effective as a context, emits breath, while the posterior end of a demonstrator, which is relatively ineffective as a context, does not. Therefore, it seemed reasonable to ask whether there might be substances present in rat breath that provide the contextual cues that our data suggest cause the diets eaten by conspecifics to become attractive to observer rats.

Because rats breathe only through their noses, a comparison of the chemical contents of air samples taken from the noses of rats with similar samples taken from the throats of rats should reveal those substances that are unique to rat breath. One could then test the efficacy of substances found in rat breath as contexts. Because volatile sulfur compounds have been implicated as semiochemicals (i.e., chemical signals) in several mammalian species (Albone, Blazquez, French, Long, & Perry, 1986; Bailey, Bunyan, & Page, 1980; Pedersen & Blass, 1981; Singer, Macrides, & Agosta, 1980), we focused our chemical analyses on such compounds. Using mass spectrometric and gas chromatographic techniques (described in detail in Galef, Mason, Preti, & Bean, 1988), we found two volatile sulfur compounds, carbon disulfide (CS_2) and carbonyl sulfide (COS), at concentrations of about 1 part per million, in all samples of air taken from the nasal cavities of rats. We found neither sulfur compound in samples of air taken from the throats of rats.

Of course, the presence of CS_2 and COS in rat breath is not in itself evidence that these substances are semiochemicals playing a role in social influence on diet selection in rats. Our investigations of the efficacy of COS and CS_2 in inducing preference for odors with which they are associated are still few in number, but the results we have in hand are consistent with the hypothesis that CS_2 can play a significant role in altering diet preference in rodents. Because COS is a gas at room temperature, it is a difficult substance to work with, so we have concentrated on examining the possible role of CS_2, which is a liquid, in guiding diet choice in rodents.

Bean, Galef, and Mason (1988) have reported that, in a simple choice situation, pellets of laboratory chow moistened with a dilute CS_2 solution were preferred by mice to control pellets moistened with distilled water. Mice ate more CS_2-moistened pellets than control pellets, and they entered chambers containing CS_2-moistened pellets more frequently, and spent more time in them, than they did with similar chambers containing water-moistened pellets. The finding that a dilute solution of CS_2 increases the attractiveness of a food to which it is added, though of potential practical importance (Galef & Mason, 1986), is not directly relevant to the question of whether CS_2 played a role in enhancing diet preference in our basic experiment and its variants. In the experiments described in preceding sections, exposure to a food in an appropriate social context increased preference for the food when it was subsequently presented without a social context.

As mentioned in the preceding section, observer rats that interacted with an anesthetized demonstrator whose face had been powdered with a diet subsequently exhibited a preference for that diet. Rats that interacted with a piece of cotton batting powdered with the same diet did not exhibit a preference for it. If CS_2 is a semiochemical able to provide a context within which exposure to a diet enhances subsequent preference for that diet, then observer rats interacting with a piece of cotton batting both powdered with a diet and smelling of CS_2 should exhibit a subsequent preference for the diet with which the piece of cotton batting was powdered. The experiment we conducted to examine this possibility is a bit more elaborate than necessary, but the results are exceptionally clear (Galef, Mason, Preti, & Bean, 1988). Observer rats interacted with one of the following demonstrators: anesthetized rats whose faces were powdered with either Diet Cin or Diet Coc; pieces of cotton batting powdered with either Diet Cin or Diet Coc and moistened with six drops of distilled water; or pieces of cotton batting powdered with either Diet Cin or Diet Coc and moistened with six drops of CS_2 diluted to 1 part per million in distilled water. Each observer was next fed clean samples of Diet Cin and Diet Coc, then poisoned by intraperitoneal injection of 1 percent of body weight 1 percent weight/volume lithium chloride solution (see below for a discussion of the effects of poisoning on food preference). Following a 24-hour period of recovery from toxicosis, each observer was offered a choice between Diets Cin and Coc for 23 hours.

As Figure 10 shows, we found that observers that interacted either with anesthetized demonstrators or with pieces of cotton batting moistened with CS_2 chose to eat the diet with which their demonstrators had been powdered. Observers that interacted with surrogates moistened with water were not influenced by the diet placed on their demonstrators when subsequently choosing between Diets Cin and Coc. Apparently, CS_2 can act, as does the presence of a demonstrator rat, to enhance an observer's subsequent preference for a diet (Galef, Mason, Preti & Bean, 1988). Although not conclusive, the finding that CS_2 exists in rat breath and the finding that CS_2 enhances preference for diets previ-

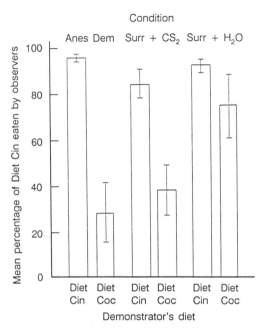

FIGURE 10. Mean amount of Diet Cin eaten, as a percentage of total amount of food ingested during testing, by observers exposed to three types of demonstrators powdered with Diet Cin or Diet Coc. Anes Dem = anaesthetized conspecific; Surr + CS_2 = cotton-batting surrogate moistened with CS_2 solution; Surr + H_2O = cotton-batting surrogate moistened with water. (From Galef, Mason, Preti, & Bean, 1988.)

ously experienced in contiguity with it surely suggest that CS_2 is a semiochemical involved in the social transmission of diet preference in rats.

RELEVANCE TO THE WORLD OUTSIDE THE LABORATORY

In this section, I use data from the laboratory to speculate about how social learning might help rats living outside the laboratory cope with the demands of their environment. Unfortunately, we know relatively little about the characteristics of the environments in which wild Norway rats live today; we know even less about the habitat in which Norway rats evolved. Consequently, the best I can do is to consider environments that appear to be reasonable ones for rats—environments with patchy, unpredictable distribution of foods, a few poisons, some nutrients in short supply, and a large number of ingestible, but non-nutritive, substances present—then speculate about how the behavioral proclivities we have demonstrated in the laboratory might help rats to thrive in such hypothetical environments. Below, I consider three ways in which socially acquired information might be used by naive individual rats to increase their feeding efficiency: first, by providing information about where to eat; second, by providing information about what to eat; and third, providing information about what not to eat.

Where to eat?

In introducing our studies on social learning about foods by rats, I mentioned the possibility that the burrow systems of rats might serve as information centers where unsuccessful rats could extract information from their more successful fellows about where to go to find food. A successfully functioning information center, as described by Ward and Zahavi (1973), requires that unsuccessful individuals be able not only to discriminate successful from unsuccessful conspecifics (otherwise it might be a misinformation center), but also to exploit successful conspecifics as sources of information about where food is to be found. In a recent study (Galef, Mischinger, & Malenfant, 1987), we found that rats that were familiar with a maze would reliably, and without special training, follow other rats through the maze to food. We also found that rats trained to follow conspecifics through a maze were more likely to follow those conspecifics that had just eaten a safe food than to follow those conspecifics that had just eaten a food known to the potential followers to be poisonous. Thus, rats in the laboratory exhibit both an eagerness to follow conspecifics to feeding sites and an ability to select conspecifics to follow on the basis of the desirability of the foods those conspecifics have been eating. If successfully foraging rats in the wild behave appropriately (i.e., eat one food at a time, return to a burrow system and interact with conspecifics in the midst of feeding bouts, and allow other rats to follow them), then unsuccessful foragers could use their successful fellows as guides to the foods that both are seeking.

If the distribution of foods in natural circumstances were appropriate, a less complex interaction among individuals might also suffice to establish an information center. Imagine that foods were available intermittently at fixed locations around a rat burrow: table scraps occasionally appeared on a compost heap, chicken scratch was sometimes to be found in a henhouse, oats appeared in a stable. Over time, individual resident rats could learn where each of these foods was sometimes to be found. However, before leaving on its first foraging trip of an evening, an individual rat would not know whether it would find food on a visit to the henhouse or to the stable. If a rat learned from its fellows that they were eating oats, it might be able to figure out where to go to find food.

We introduced our subjects into the environment depicted in Figure 11. Each of three discriminable foods was available at a different, fixed location: cheese-flavored diet (Diet Ch) in the central arm of the maze, cocoa-flavored diet (Diet Coc) in the right arm, and cinnamon-flavored diet (Diet Cin) in the left arm. Only one of the three diets was available to a subject on any given day, and

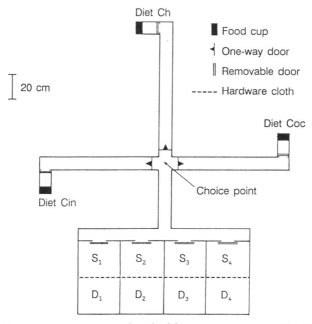

FIGURE 11. Plan of apparatus used in food location experiment. Diet Ch = cheese-flavored diet; Diet Cin = cinnamon-flavored diet; Diet Coc = cocoa-flavored diet; S = subject; D = demonstrator. (From Galef & Wigmore, 1983.)

the particular diet available to a subject on any day was selected randomly. Each subject (S_n in Figure 11) was given four trials per day in the maze using a correction procedure. On the first trial of each day, the subject had no information as to which food was available, and therefore had only one chance in three of selecting the correct arm of the maze. If it chose the correct arm, it was allowed to eat for a few minutes. If it didn't, it was locked in the arm it had chosen for a few minutes, and the trial was repeated until the subject found the food. Trials 2, 3, and 4 of each day were run in the same fashion. Each subject could, in effect, tell us when it understood this little world by exhibiting near-perfect performance in its first choices on trials 2, 3, and 4 of each day.

Once a given subject had reached the necessary criterion of near-perfect performance on trials 2, 3, and 4, we started testing that subject. On each test day, for 15 minutes prior to Trial 1 of that day, each subject was allowed to interact with a demonstrator rat (D_n in Figure 11) that had eaten the diet that was going to be available to that subject on that day. That is, if Diet Ch was going to be available to S_3 on a given day, S_3's demonstrator, D_3, was fed Diet Ch for 30 minutes, then allowed to interact with S_3 for 15 minutes prior to Trial 1 of S_3's testing.

In order to determine whether subjects were capable of using information acquired from demonstrators to enhance their foraging efficiency, we compared the probability of a correct first response on the first trial of each day of testing (when information from a demonstrator was available to subjects) with the probability of a correct first response on the first trial of each of the last days of training (when no information from a demonstrator was available to subjects). As Figure 12 shows, four of our seven subjects were able to use the information provided by their respective demonstrators to facilitate location of unpredictable foods (Galef & Wigmore, 1983). Thus, we can conclude that rats that know where to find food can use their fellows to find out what food is available and can then orient their feeding trips in the appropriate direction. Whether conditions in natural environments are often appropriate for use of this ability to enhance foraging efficiency, I do not know.

What to eat?

A classic problem in experimental psychology concerns how omnivorous mammals can select a nutritionally adequate diet from among the myriad of available substances that they might try to eat. Based on some not very convincing evi-

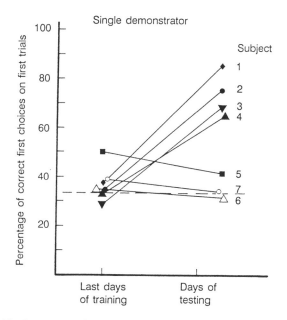

FIGURE 12. Percentage of correct first choices on first trials by subjects at the end of training and during testing in the apparatus illustrated in Figure 11. (After Galef & Wigmore, 1983.)

dence (see Galef & Beck, in press, for discussion), there seems to be a general belief that omnivores such as rats have an almost mystical ability to select foods containing needed nutrients. The fact is, however, that although rats in special situations can find a nutritionally adequate diet if one is available, the ability of rats to do so is actually quite limited (Epstein, 1967). Rats do quite poorly in choosing an adequate food if the number of foods to choose among is more than two or three, if the adequate diet is less palatable than deficient alternatives, or if relief of a deficiency state is considerably delayed after eating an adequate diet.

In a recent experiment, Matthew Beck (Beck & Galef, in press) presented individual weanling rats with a choice among four distinctively flavored diets. Three of these diets contained inadequate levels of protein (5 percent), and one diet (the least palatable of the four) had ample protein to support normal growth (20 percent). We found, as others had before us (Kon, 1931; Scott, Smith, & Verney, 1948; Scott & Quint, 1946; Tribe, 1954, 1955), that our subjects did poorly in this situation. None was able to develop a preference for the diet with adequate protein; in fact, the pups would have been well on their way to a premature demise if we had not stopped the experiment. However, weanling rats faced with the same diet selection problem while in the presence of adults that had been trained to eat the protein-rich alternative grew rapidly in the experimental situation. As can be seen in Figure 13, which shows the rate of weight gain of weanling rats with and without adult demonstrators, the learned patterns of diet selection of adults served as a useful source of information to naive juveniles.

What not to eat?

New recruits to a population, whether recent immigrants or naive juveniles, must not only select adequate foods, but must also avoid ingesting toxic foods present in the area in which they are learning to forage. A new recruit could "assume" that any living conspecifics it might encounter had not eaten a lethal quantity of any poisonous food present in their shared environment. Naive individuals could also assume that senior colony members had already learned to avoid eating any noxious nonlethal substances found in the vicinity. The same tendency to eat what others of one's social group are eating that we have found to facilitate the selection of a nutritionally adequate diet could also lower the probability of eating toxins.

Information acquired from conspecifics as to which foods they were eating could also be used in other, more sophisticated ways to facilitate poison avoidance. For example, a naive rat that ate two unfamiliar foods in rapid succession and then became ill might be well advised to act as though its illness was attributable to whichever of the two unfamiliar foods it had eaten that others of its social group were not eating. As was shown by the behavior of observers interacting with anesthetized demonstrators (see Figure 10), that is just how naive

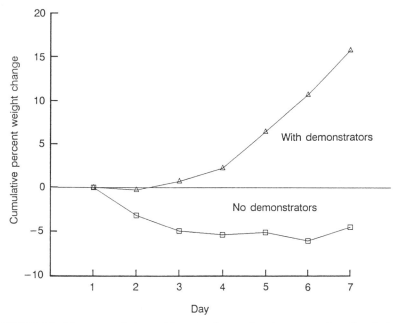

FIGURE 13. Mean cumulative weight gain of pups choosing among four diets in isolation and in the presence of trained demonstrators, as a percentage of the pup's body weight at the start of the experiment. (After Beck & Galef, in press.)

rats do behave (see also Galef, 1986b, 1986c). Naive rats that fall ill are less likely to acquire or maintain an aversion to an unfamiliar food if they have interacted with other rats that have eaten that unfamiliar food than if they have not. Thus, social learning might contribute to the development of adaptive dietary repertoires by guiding the learning of aversions. Of course, such a process would only be useful if rats encounter palatable, toxic foods in their natural habitat (Domjan & Galef, 1983), if they tend to ingest several palatable, toxic foods in rapid succession (a matter of some controversy), and if the dietary habits of others really are a reliable guide to safe and nutritious foods.

CONCLUSIONS

The results of the studies described above indicate that interactions among Norway rats can have important influences on both diet selection and foraging. In the laboratory, olfactory cues emitted by recently fed demonstrator rats permit observer rats to identify the foods that the demonstrators have eaten and cause the observers to increase their later intake of the food that their respective demonstrators ate. In the laboratory, hungry rats will follow their fellows to a feeding site. If extrapolation from our laboratory situations to natural environments is appropriate, then young rats in the wild could use information acquired from sympatric elders to help decide where to eat, what to eat, and what to avoid eating.

The development of dietary repertoires in rats results at least in part from the translation of open programs, susceptible to social inputs, into behavior. Consequently, weanling rats can cope more effectively with nutritional challenges than they could if the development of their respective dietary repertoires rested on either closed programs or open programs insensitive to social influence.

If the food choices of Norway rats were the result of closed developmental programs, one might, for example, expect all rats to prefer sweet foods to bitter ones. On average, such invariant flavor preferences would probably be adaptive throughout much of the species range, biasing rats to eat sugar-rich plants and to avoid plants containing secondary compounds. However, some areas surely contain nutritionally valuable but bitter plant material; other areas may contain palatable but toxic plants. The options of adjusting to both these situations would be forever closed to rats lacking sufficient developmental flexibility to permit experientially induced alteration of their palatability spectra. Species whose members have open programs that allow learning of aversions to toxic, palatable foods and experience-induced development of appetence for congenitally unpalatable substances can thrive in a broader range of environments than can species whose members lack this degree of flexibility in the developmental programs that determine their food preferences.

Open genetic programs for food selection that can incorporate information acquired from conspecifics, as well as information acquired by direct interaction with the physical environment, offer additional opportunities. Our data suggest that an ability to utilize the behavior of others as a source of information when selecting among behavioral alternatives may further enhance an individual's probability of survival. Rat pups unable to learn independently which of four available foods was nutritionally adequate solved the problem if permitted to interact with a conspecific eating the adequate diet.

Although the studies discussed here have focused on the role of social interaction in the development of adaptive feeding repertoires in rats, neither feeding behavior nor rats are unique in their susceptibility to influence by interaction with conspecifics. Social interaction has been found to play an important role in development of predator avoidance in both blackbirds and monkeys (Curio, Ernst, & Vieth, 1978; Cook, Mineka, Wolkenstein, & Laitsch, 1985), in the development of avian vocalizations (Marler & Tamura, 1964; Petrinovich, this volume), and in the feeding and foraging behavior both of a variety of species of birds (Palametta & Lefebvre, 1985; Mason & Reidinger, 1982) and of honeybees (von Frisch, 1967; Wenner, 1971).

It is likely that, in the future, susceptibility to social influence will be uncovered in the translation of other open programs (e.g., those supporting migration, home orientation, kin recognition, and territorial behavior) when these are investigated in appropriate species. Social interactions can provide information that markedly facilitates the acquisition of those details of behavior that match the phenotypic characteristics of individuals to the idiosyncrasies of the environment that each occupies.

SUMMARY

Laboratory studies of the development of food preferences in the Norway rat, a social, central-place foraging animal, have shown that the food choices of rats can be profoundly influenced by interaction with recently fed conspecifics. In general, rats show an enhanced preference for foods eaten by other rats. The data indicate that changes in food preference are not the result of simple exposure to a food; rather, enhanced preference for a food results from experience of the smell of a food within the context provided by the presence of a breathing conspecific. Laboratory studies also suggest that, in natural environments, socially acquired information may help naive rats to decide where to eat, what foods to eat, and what potential foods to avoid eating. Such social influences on the development of feeding and foraging patterns provide an example of an open developmental system in which social learning allows individual naive animals to match their behavior to the idiosyncratic demands of the particular environments they occupy.

CHAPTER 4

BODY SIZE, ALLOMETRY, AND COMPARATIVE PSYCHOLOGY: LOCOMOTION AND FORAGING

Del Thiessen

The common view of life is that behavioral adaptations are built slowly over generations as natural selection acts to restrain genetic and phenotypic variation (Mayr, 1982). There is another view, not necessarily in opposition to the first, which suggests that organisms acquire adaptations as the result of inherent relationships between structures and functions (self-organization; Prigogine, 1976). An example of the first view is the assumption that the complexity of cognitive functioning in higher primates results from generations of natural selection for specific neural capacities. The other possibility is that brain size and complexity are related to other factors, such as body size, and that cognitive complexity is a secondary result of these other factors.

Whichever view we take will drastically alter our thinking about comparative issues and will dictate the kinds of experiments we conduct. If we believe the adaptationist hypothesis, we will tend to seek out ecological (distal) factors that could be responsible for the evolution of behaviors. On the other hand, if we believe the self-organizational hypothesis, we will concentrate on the relations between structures and functions, and our concern will be the proximate (immediate) mechanisms controlling behavior.

Neither view need be held in isolation. Clearly there are generational effects on behavior resulting from natural selection, and there are design features of behavior that result from the interaction of physical and chemical processes. What we need, obviously, is a theoretical and practical scheme for welding the two perspectives together.

Techniques of scaling may offer a coherent methodology for addressing the problems of natural selection and self-organization (Gould, 1966). Scaling is a way of visualizing relationships between structures and functions. It can be used in broad strokes to point out general organizational features of behavior, or it can be used in delicate strokes to emphasize subtle and more distinctive variations. For example, some aspects of intelligence scale across species according to a physical dimension such as brain size or number of interconnecting neurons (Jerison, 1973). This is an example of a broad-stroke relationship between structure and function—a self-organized feature of behavior.

On the other hand, once the broad scaling is considered, there are still residual variations in brain complexity and intelligence that suggest adaptations to long-term ecological selection pressures (Domjan, 1987). These features of intelligence are the delicate strokes of scaling. Thus, the two views of life, general links between structures and functions and specific adaptations, can be cast into the same perspective.

BODY SIZE AND ALLOMETRY

In this chapter, I will emphasize the influence of body size on comparative aspects of locomotion and foraging. Body size is often a powerful but "invisible" influence on behavior. The scaling procedure that can illuminate its influence is allometric scaling, which is the relational scaling of structures and functions (Calder, 1984; Schmidt-Nielsen, 1984) A typical use of allometric scaling is to depict the relationship that exists between the body surface of animals and their body volumes. Arranging animals by length, we find that every increase in body length results in a surface area which is the square of that increase, and a volume which is the cube of that increase. In other words, for every unit of increase in body size, volume increases at a faster rate than surface area does. This simple, but remarkable, insight illustrates the invariant relationship between surface and volume, a relationship that reflects the phylogenetic and ontogenetic design features of all mammals. For us, the primary importance of knowing this relationship is that heat loss, metabolism, and behavior are associated with it.

The discovery of this relationship, a broad stroke, allows us to determine how much of an animal's performance is associated with surface:volume estimates and how much is not. The specific case, a delicate stroke, can be compared to the general expectation. Suppose we find, as is the case, that the ratio of body surface to body volume for many mammalian species is proportional to metabolism: for every decrease in the ratio there is a decrease in basal metabolic rate. Small animals will have a fast metabolism; large animals will have a slow metabolism.

Then suppose we find a deer mouse living in Alaska that has a slower metabolism than expected. It is still small in size, with a high ratio of surface to volume, and its metabolism is high, but is lower than expected. Additional observations suggest why. The mouse has a heavy layer of subcutaneous fat and long body hair, and lives in insulated nests deep underground. This deer mouse has obviously acquired adaptations to compensate for its high rate of heat loss. We know a lot more than we knew before. Beginning with allometric expressions, we can show how much of the metabolic variation among species is normally associated with surface:volume ratios, and how much is associated with specific ecological adaptations.

THE NATURE AND METHODOLOGY OF ALLOMETRY

What is allometry?

Allometry is a scaling technique that can highlight phylogenetic and ontogenetic patterns of change and that can suggest the operation of underlying processes. Allometry says, in effect, that traits often vary in a specifiable relationship to each other, so that a knowledge of the change in one trait allows for a prediction with regard to a second trait (Huxley, 1932/1972).

The equation of simple allometry illustrated in Figure 1 is, first of all, a descriptive tool that unites variations along a common dimension (Schmidt-Nielsen, 1984). An amazing number of biological features of an organism scale to body size according to the general formula:

$$y = ax^b$$

where y is the value on the ordinate (the variable of interest); a is a constant that

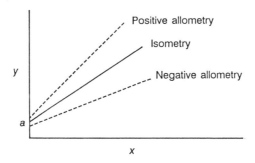

FIGURE 1. Illustrations of allometric equations. Isometry is a simple one-to-one scaling between x and y. Positive allometry indicates that y is increasing at a faster rate than x. Negative allometry indicates that y is increasing at a slower rate than x. Logarithmic transformations of the x and y axes generally result in a straight line.

fixes the intercept on the y axis; x is the value on the abscissa (the second variable of interest, and the object of regression); and b is the slope of the regression (the specific growth rates, or slope, of y and x. When the data are converted logarithmically, the formula is:

$$\log y = \log a + b(\log x)$$

When the two variables are plotted on logarithmic scales, the result is a straight line. Generally speaking, logarithmic transformations tend to diminish the differences among small numbers, thus changing an exponential growth process into a linear trend. Two important features of log transformations are that they reduce the concern for statistical outliers (deviant points), and that the slope of the log–log regression indicates proportional changes of correlated variables and is scale-independent, since it is unaffected by the unit of measurement.

An advantage as well as a drawback inherent in allometric scaling is that it assumes no preconceptions about genetic, physiological, or environmental causality—it is descriptive, not explanatory. It simply summarizes relations between two variables. Obviously, too, allometric plots provide overall regressions between variables, yet they do not necessarily describe every instance. One of the most common criticisms of body-size relationships, for example, is that the statistical description sacrifices precision in order to achieve generality (Prothero, 1986).

The use of log–log plots reduces the impact of outliers, but may, at the same time, obscure true biological variation. Also, it is difficult to overcome the linear bias of human perception using logarithmic scores. It is not immediately apparent on a log–log scale that the log values of 4.90 and 4.60 are the difference on a linear scale between about 79,000 and 40,000.

Because differences are greater between larger taxonomic groups, regression slopes tend to be higher. For example, regressions among genera are generally steeper than regressions among species (Clutton-Brock & Harvey, 1983, 1984). Thus, there are complications and limitations to the use of bivariate plots. Nevertheless, by regressing a complex variable on another, one can provide a summary of the existing relationships and can generate reasonable hypotheses about underlying causal mechanisms.

There is a limited number of interpretations that can be applied to a bivariate linear plot of two variables. Those characteristics of allometric functions which are generally of importance to researchers interested in the ontogeny and phylogeny of behavior are indicated in Figure 2. Essentially, differences can be found in (1) the slope (b) of the regression on an x–y plot (the exponent of the allometric equation), (2) the intercept (a) on the y axis, and (3) the variation (Standard Error, SE) around the regression line. The first factor illustrates the average functional relationship between variables; the second factor defines a constant of that function; and the third fixes an individual measure with regard to the general tendency.

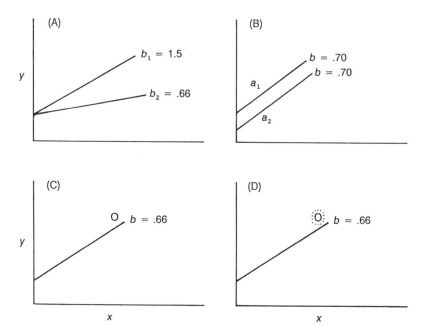

FIGURE 2. Various forms and general interpretations of allometric regressions. (A) Allometric regressions showing group differences in slope. The regression could describe differences in development or differences among populations, species, or other taxonomic groups. Points along an x:y regression indicate an equilibrium of function for those two variables. (B) Allometric regressions for groups with similar growth functions (slope), but with different y intercepts. The differences in intercepts suggest a constant (e.g., a species characteristic) that differentiates the groups. (C) Allometric regression showing a deviation (O) from the mean regression. That deviation (individual, population, species, etc.) suggests a specialization beyond the expected value. (D) Allometric regression showing a deviation (O) from the mean regression. The surrounding dots describe individual variations around the common deviation, and may suggest individual specializations or random variation. Slopes greater than 1.0 indicate positive allometry; slopes less than 1.0 indicate negative allometry.

Principle of similitude

Allometric equations are extremely valuable in detecting processes that may be coadapted, regardless of the underlying causal mechanisms. Points along a particular regression line presumably represent scaling processes that harmonize morphological, physiological and behavioral attributes (Smith, 1984). Values of parameters apparently vary in a consistent way so that the "net effect" remains the same. Thus, for example, as body surface area increases, there will be a corresponding increase in heat loss. At every increasing value of heat loss, there will be a compensating increase of heat production. The net effect is a thermal balance for every value of surface area. Organisms or parts of organisms represented on a regression line are considered to manifest fundamentally parallel processes, even though the processes are expressed at different absolute levels. This presumed parallelism has been called the *principle of similitude* (Economos, 1982; Peters, 1983). In large measure, functional relationships between similar variables are seen to occur so that an equally adapted phenotype occurs at any *x:y* value.

A number of physiological characteristics are similar, regardless of body size (McMahon & Bonner, 1983; Schmidt-Nielsen, 1984). For example, the time required for a mammal to complete 50 percent of its growth is about 2 to 3 percent of its life, regardless of species or size. Similarly, 1.5 percent of a placental mammal's life (higher primates excepted) is required for gestation, regardless of size. Functions such as the respiratory cycle and the heart cycle are nearly size-independent fractions of a lifespan. Thus, every mammal can expect to live for 3.3×10^8 breath cycles and 1.5×10^9 heartbeats. The point is that scaling is a means whereby traits are adjusted to each other so that homeostatic and other adaptive qualities persist, regardless of body size. Given these size-independent associations (dimensionless correlations), it is possible to begin to specify how traits vary with regard to each other in order to optimize functioning. It is also possible to use allometry to sift through extensive variations in structure and function and extract general comparative principles.

ALLOMETRY AND COMPARATIVE PSYCHOLOGY

Allometry is especially useful in summarizing functional correlates to body size that exist across species. As an example of what can be accomplished using these techniques, I will present data on the fundamental traits of locomotion and foraging strategies. It will become evident that allometric expressions can suggest very specific hypotheses about energy utilization and behavior. The same strategy can be applied to a wide range of behaviors, including learning, perception, and motivation.

The allometry of locomotion in homeotherms

Movement is one of the most basic attributes of animals, since it provides the means for moving toward or away from critical stimuli. Movement is also a behavior that correlates with body size and energy utilization, and is thus a prime candidate for allometric analysis.

The basic similarity among animals in the structure of striated muscle and calcified bone suggests equivalent locomotor potential for all species (Alexander, Jayes, Maloiy, & Wathuta, 1981; Hill, 1950). There are additional important commonalities. For example, in homeotherms, one liter of oxygen (STP), when used for oxidative metabolism during locomotion, is equal to approximately 20.1 kilojoules of metabolic energy, regardless of the biological system. Animals nevertheless differ in oxygen utilization and energy expenditure. Small animals expend more energy in the resting state, and expend more energy to move a gram a horizontal kilometer than do large animals; thus small animals consume more oxygen per gram of body weight (Taylor, 1977). This is due in part to the relatively large surface area of small animals and their high rate of heat loss and heat production. It is also related to stride frequency and the consequent use of energy for muscle movement.

Paradoxically, the energy cost of moving in a *vertical* direction is lower for a small animal (McMahon & Bonner, 1983). A 30-gram mouse expends eight times as much energy to move horizontally one kilometer than does a 17,500-gram chimpanzee. However, the gravitational work in lifting one gram of body weight one kilometer vertically is the same for the two animals. With similar muscular efficiency, therefore, the cost to the mouse is one-eighth that to the chimpanzee. Habitat selection, food preferences, and foraging areas will covary, depending in part upon energy and movement constraints.

The general efficiency of animal movement can be expressed in terms of power (Taylor & Heglund, 1982). The percent of efficiency is equal to the power-output:power-input ratio times 100, and is generally around 25 percent. Another way of looking at efficiency is to consider endurance time, which is the ratio of the available energy to the rate of energy use. The primary energy store is body fat, which scales as $M^{1.0}$, where M is equal to mass. The rate of use is the metabolic rate, which scales as $M^{0.75}$. The difference in the ratio between energy store and energy use is equal to $M^{0.25}$, which is one way of defining efficiency. Thus, an animal can generally translate about one quarter of its energy output into physical power. This is a critical ratio, as animals will adjust their behaviors to optimize the efficiency of energy use.

The costs can be apportioned (Fedak, Heglund, & Taylor, 1982; Heglund, Cavagna, & Taylor, 1982; Heglund, Fedak, Taylor, & Cavagna, 1982; Taylor, Heglund, & Maloiy, 1982). The cost of running is clearly a function of mass, as we have just discussed, but there is also a postural cost. Statistically, the postural cost is the difference between the *y* intercept of a metabolism–body weight regression and the resting metabolic power. Metabolic power, the efficiency of moving weight times distance, is equal to the slope times the speed plus the *y* intercept. This is equivalent to saying that the movement capacity of an animal is dependent upon the metabolic costs ascribed to resting and postural adjustments, plus the exponent of the relationship between body weight and metabolism, times the speed of movement. The *y* intercept is greater than the resting metabolic power because of the cost of vertical displacements of the center of the body mass during each stride.

Since resting and the postural adjustments are constants, the variation in metabolic power is primarily a function of speed. When Taylor (1985) looked at these relationships in detail, he found that (1) metabolic input increases as a *linear* function of speed in vertebrates, and (2) mechanical power output increases as a *negatively decreasing* function of speed; therefore, when the ratio is calculated between the two, (3) efficiency of terrestrial locomotion increases with speed. Because speed is associated with body size, the conclusion from these analyses is that rapid horizontal movement is costly for small organisms and can be obtained more readily by large organisms. These energetic relationships will bear on the distance and speed with which animals travel, and will also be the major determinants of food intake per unit of body weight.

There are qualifications to these remarks. Garland (1983) has calculated for 106 species of mammals that, although speed scales with body mass ($M^{0.17}$), the largest animals are not the fastest. The optimal weight for speed is 119 kilograms. Generally, maximal running speed is associated with the respiratory and cardiovascular competence of the particular species involved, which may not always correspond to body size.

Within closely related orders of species, there is a tendency for the relationship between speed and body weight to be zero. For example, Garland found that within the orders of Artiodactlyla, Carnivora, and Rodentia, running speed was mass-independent. This could be a statistical artifact related to the relatively large error variance among closely related species, or it could be due to the exaggerated influence of specialized traits on a reduced range of body weights. Closely related species will share similar ontogenetic programs. Among these species, therefore, allometric relationships between structures and functions are expected to remain similar. Clearly there are pronounced differences in performance characteristics among related species that will override allometric trends, depending upon variations in species-typical adjustments.

Adjusting to the costs of movement

Animals adjust to the costs of movements in various ways. A common strategy is to couple running with breathing, so that there is a constant amount of oxygen intake per stride (Bramble & Carrier, 1983). Quadrupedal mammalian species, such as jackrabbits, dogs, and horses, synchronize locomotor and respiratory cycles at a constant stride per breath in a 1:1 ratio. Humans have several phase-locked patterns (e.g., 4:1, 3:1, 2:1, 1:1, 5:2, 3:2), although the 2:1 coupling is favored. Flying birds also couple locomotion and breathing (1:1, as a general rule) in order to optimize the intake of oxygen. It is probably the case that size-dependent effects on locomotion can force an animal to assume particular patterns between breathing and movement. A more detailed study of these relationships would be valuable.

Another adjustment that occurs among mammals is a mass-specific transition from a trot to a gallop as speed increases. Speed and stride frequency at the point of transition scale according to body size (mass in kilograms) in the following way:

$$\text{Speed} = 1.53 \, M^{0.24}$$
$$\text{Stride frequency} = 4.48 \, M^{-0.14}$$

The relationship between body size and speed at transition is illustrated for several mammals in Table 1. These transition points plot as a straight line, indicating that larger animals can obtain higher speeds before moving to a gallop. The point of transition probably represents the behavioral adjustment necessary to reduce energy expenditure, and may reflect equivalent speeds in different-sized species.

Other adjustments involve morphological and behavior adaptations that are specific to ecological demands (Eisenberg, 1981). It is more difficult for small mammals to overwinter in unfavorable climates, and they cannot migrate to more favorable environments. Small homeothermic animals, in particular, may acquire hair or subcutaneous fat as insulation in order to reduce the exchange of energy with the environment. Other animals become more sedentary or sleep for relatively long periods when energy demands are intolerable. Still other small animals may rely on a densely packed and predictable source of high-energy food, thus reducing the costs of locating and processing food.

The interplay between processes affected by body weight and those affected by specialized adaptations is revealing. There are fundamental associations between body size and locomotor attributes that must be maintained if life is to continue. On the other hand, species and populations acquire a number of unique adaptations that also preserve life. Many morphological and behavioral traits appear to be secondary adaptations that provide animals a certain degree of independence

TABLE 1. Speed of Transition from a Trot to a Gallop

Animal	Body mass (kg)	Speed at trot–gallop transition (ms^{-1})
Pygmy mouse	0.0009	0.49
Mouse	0.038	0.69
Rat	0.362	1.20
Dog	1.1	1.56
Gazelle	27.3	3.38
Horse	500.0	6.78

Note. Adapted from Taylor, 1977.

from the basic energy demands associated with body size and movement. Animals tend to adjust to the allometric demands of body size in universal ways, such as with surface-related variations in metabolic rate, but, in addition, they respond to these demands with specific adaptations which provide a certain freedom from the constraints of body size. These unique adaptations may first reveal themselves as deviations from general allometric equations—deviations that might only appear striking within the comparative framework of allometric scaling. The appearance of general, as well as specific, correlations between structures and functions results from the allocation of costs and benefits for the purposes of survival and reproduction.

Home-range activities

There is a long-standing belief that the size of the home range of a species corresponds to its body size (Seton, 1909, cited in Harestad & Bunnell, 1979). Large species generally move longer distances in their search for resources. It is only within the past 25 years that this general observation has been quantified. In a classic paper, McNab (1963) demonstrated that, among mammals, the size of the home range varied as a power function of body weight, and that this relationship did not differ statistically from the relationship between body weight and basal metabolic rate (an expected exponent of approximately 0.75). This same study showed that "hunters" had larger home ranges per unit of body weight than did "croppers," suggesting that animals whose food supply is scattered and less predictable require a larger home range in order to satisfy their energy requirements. These initial observations have strongly influenced our views of animal locomotion and home-range activities. In particular, they have implicated the importance of body size and metabolic requirements in the daily activities of animals. Both general locomotion and specialized foraging strategies correlate with metabolic aspects of body size. It is also evident that the biomass of each higher trophic level must be less than the lower level, meaning that larger species will be fewer in number and will develop unique foraging strategies (Eisenberg, 1983). The findings once again point out that there are unique adaptations among species differing in food requirements.

Since these early reports, other investigators have supported the general findings of McNab for a variety of vertebrate species, including avian species and mammals with wide differences in food preferences, such as herbivores, omnivores, and carnivores (Harestad & Bunnell). The area of home range (H) can be related empirically to body mass (M) by the formulation $H = aM^b$. The size of the exponent b and whether or not it meets the criteria expected for metabolic functions are still at issue, however. It is apparent that home-range activities are regulated primarily by energy demands, and thus are related to body size and metabolic requirements. In addition, habitat conditions and unique physiological and behavioral adaptations heavily influence foraging strategies.

The allometric exponents reported by others for the relationship of H to M are generally larger than 0.75, suggesting that a simple metabolic explanation is not sufficient to account for the majority of data (Jenkins, 1981). Harestad and Bunnell, for example, found that for 55 species of mammals, H is related to body weight by a power function of 1.08. For herbivores the exponent is 1.02, for omnivores it is 0.92, and for carnivores it is 1.36. Mace and Harvey (1983) confirm that exponents in birds and small mammals are larger than expectations based on metabolic criteria (~ 0.75). These relatively high exponents suggest that among both birds and mammals, a unit of increase in body weight is associated with a greater increase in the size of the home range (Baker & Mewaldt, 1979; Schoener, 1968). Thus, the requirements for an extended home range increase at a faster rate than body weight and metabolic changes, perhaps suggesting that the larger home ranges are patchier and produce less energy per unit of body weight. This may be more of a problem for carnivores than for birds and other mammals; carnivores have larger home ranges than do noncarnivores of the same body weight.

The increases in the patchiness of the environment, and thus the necessity for extended home ranges, are apparent for increasing latitudes, for seasons of slow plant growth, and for environments with decreased precipitation (Harestad & Bunnell, 1979; Rosenzweig, 1968). Whenever the energetic yield for an environment decreases, there will be a tendency for animals to extend their home range to compensate for that loss. Obviously, animals will adjust their behaviors in order to maintain an optimal homeostatic balance. The conclusion is that the relationship between home range and body weight is simply a general approximation of the relationship between the engineering features of the organism and the probability that sufficient energy will be found to accomplish the necessary functions of survival and reproduction. What we need to be measuring, then, is not the direct association of body weight to home-range size, but the interaction between body weight, energy demands, and the environmental yield of energy. Nevertheless, the equation $H = aM^b$ accounts for about 75 to 90 percent of the variance among species, and is certainly the starting point from which to consider the more complex and unique functional requirements of organisms.

Specializations and home-range activities

Even sex differences in home-range size among carnivores and primates can be in part accounted for by variations in body size (Oxnard, 1983, 1984). Female carnivores weigh less than males by about 33 to 50 percent. Their expected home ranges, therefore, should be between 49 percent and 75 percent as large as those of males. In fact they are 52 percent as large as those of males (Harestad &

Bunnell, 1979), not materially different than what is expected on the basis of body weight. Thus, the relationship between body weight and home-range size adds some explanatory power to our search for the underlying principles of sexual dimorphism.

The specificity superimposed on allometric relations reflects species-typical behaviors and the distribution of food supplies. Milton and May (1976) measured the relationships among body weight, home-range size, and diet in 46 species of primates (Prosimians, Ceboidea, Cercopithecoidea, and Hominoidae), and found that the regression slope between body weight and home-range size was 0.79 for all species combined. This relationship accounts for approximately 62 percent of the statistical variance. In addition to this general picture, the investigators found that terrestrial primates have a larger home range than expected for their body weight. Eating of plant foliage (folivory), where resources are concentrated, is associated with small home ranges. And fruit eating (frugivory), where fruiting trees are widely dispersed, is associated with larger home ranges than expected on the basis of body size. Similar findings have been reported by Harvey and Clutton-Brock (1981) for 22 species of primates (Lemuridae, Cebidae, Cercopithecidae, Hylobatidae, and Pongidae), and several species of rodents, insectivores, and lagomorphs. Frugivores have larger home ranges in relation to their body weight than do folivores.

In both small mammals and primates, folivores have relatively smaller brains. In general, specialists, whose food supplies are spaced widely and occur unpredictably, have larger home ranges than do generalists, whose food supplies are varied and more readily available. Brain size and the cognitive capacity to deal with a heterogeneous and unpredictable environment may be associated with habitat selection and food preferences. These, in turn, are influenced by body size. The overall conclusion is that body size accounts for most of the variation in home-range size, whereas particular adaptations to cope with food abundance and distribution account for the remainder.

Finally, social interactions and social dominance hierarchies can influence home-range size in very specific ways (Jarman, 1983; Schaffer & Reed, 1972). Overlap in resource use between dominant and subordinate species invariably decreases when these species interact (Morse, 1974). Sexual selection for body size and antler size will also affect energy requirements and home-range size (Clutton-Brock, Albon, & Harvey, 1980; Manning, 1985).

Specialized adaptations, like the foraging habits discussed above, correlate with body form as well as size. Webb (1978, 1984a, 1984b), working with aquatic species, found that each fish's form corresponds to its habit of swimming. Some are specialized for cruising, some for accelerating, and some for maneuvering. Most, however, are generalists, with a combination of locomotor qualities. They all are uniquely adapted to their foraging requirements. Webb's classification of aquatic types is shown in Table 2.

TABLE 2. A Functional Classification of Aquatic Locomotor Propulsion Mechanisms

Characteristics	Optimal design features	Functions	Examples
A. Body/caudal fin periodic propulsion Cyclically repeating kinematics Relatively high power Small linear and angular accelerations	High aspect ratio lunate tail Narrow caudal peduncle Relatively stiff, streamlined anterior body Large anterior depth/mass Endothermy?	Swimming sustained for several seconds to several weeks in cruising, prolonged swimming, and sprint swimming (steady and two-phase patterns), during chases, patrolling, station holding, searching, migration, etc.	Tuna Shark Salmon
B. Body/caudal fin transient propulsion Brief noncyclic kinematics High power Linear and/or angular acceleration, usually large	Large body depth and area, especially caudally Flexible body Large muscle mass relative to body mass	Fast starts and powered turns lasting tens of milliseconds and used in prey capture, predator evasion, etc.	Pike Flounder Sculpin
C. Median and paired fin propulsion Variable kinematics involving discrete fins Low power Lower speed, low acceleration rates	Lateral insertion pectoral fins Anterior ventrolateral insertion of pelvic fins Extended anal and dorsal fins Deep, laterally flattened body	Slow swimming and precise maneuvering in searching, stalking, feeding, hiding, etc.	Bonded butterfly fish Bluegill
D. Mixed traits for variable effects	Not specialized in body form	Generalist with varied locomotor skills	

Note. Adapted from Webb, 1984a.

There appears to be a correspondence between body size, home-range size, food-retrieval behaviors, and locomotor specializations. Fish that cruise long distances tend to be large and to possess specialized body-fin characteristics, whereas fish that rely on bursts of acceleration to ambush prey, especially generalists that are highly maneuverable and remain within a small home range, are smaller and possess different body-fin characteristics. These variations in function, size, and form are to some extent analogous to variations reported in primates. In both classes of animals, body size and home-range size are correlated. Also, the patchiness of the environment and the distance of locomotion necessary to obtain food are related to speed, extent of foraging, and maneuverability. A heuristic hypothesis is that for both fish and primates, living and foraging within a small home range is associated with small size, more generalized features of locomotion, and greater maneuverability. Brain size per unit of body weight would also be expected to be smaller among species living in a smaller and more stable environment, as suggested by the mammalian studies by Harvey and Clutton-Brock (1983) and Harvey, Clutton-Brock, and Mace (1980). The convergence of functional types is well worth investigating in detail.

Specializations converge on common solutions

Comparisons such as those related to swimming extend to flying animals as well. The study of bat wings by Norberg (1981) shows a strong convergence of lifestyles with terrestrial and aquatic vertebrates. In a remarkable investigation of 130 species of bats, Norberg demonstrates how body size, wing conformation, and foraging habits interrelate. As expected, wing size varies allometrically with body weight. Wingspan, wing area, and wing loading show the following allometric equations with mass (M) for two suborders of chiropteran species, megachiropteran and microchiropteran species:

Wingspan
$$1.2 \, M^{0.36} \qquad \text{Megachiropteran}$$
$$1.3 \, M^{0.35} \qquad \text{Microchiropteran}$$
Wing area
$$0.21 \, M^{0.69} \qquad \text{Megachiropteran}$$
$$0.23 \, M^{0.69} \qquad \text{Microchiropteran}$$
Wing loading
$$47 \, M^{0.31} \qquad \text{Megachiropteran}$$
$$47 \, M^{0.42} \qquad \text{Microchiropteran}$$

These parameters are critical in determining flight capabilities, and probably explain why the suborders do not differ in their regression exponents. The species across suborders do differ in other critical ways. The wingspan squared, divided by the wing area, is called the *aspect ratio*, and is the ratio that sets the characteristics of a species' flight. A high aspect ratio refers to a relatively long wing with a small surface area. Conversely, a low aspect ratio refers to a relatively short wing with a large surface area. Higher lift (L) and lower drag (D) are associated with a high aspect ratio and with an increase in speed. Thus, species with wings that are narrow tend to have smaller surface areas and therefore higher wing loadings. The lower ratio, L:D, can only be overcome with speed. Maneuverability is correspondingly sacrificed. The associations among various characteristics in bats are indicated in Table 3.

What Table 3 shows is that a host of adaptations are associated with flight characteristics, regardless of the genetic relatedness among species. Bats with low aspect ratios are maneuverable and spend their time foraging among vegetation, skillfully picking insects off plants. Bats with high aspect ratios, on the other hand, forage in open areas, often at high altitudes. These latter bats are less maneuverable, but cover long distances in their tracking of insects in flight. Bats with intermediate aspect ratios show mixed foraging strategies and appear more generalized in their behaviors. They are also more frequent in number. Frugivorous and nectarivorous bats (those with low aspect ratios) of the suborder Megachiroptera converge in strategies and forms with frugivorous and nectarivorous bats of the suborder Microchiroptera.

Eisenberg and Wilson (1978) make the point that bats whose foraging strategies involve searching for patchy, unpredictably located, energy-rich foods, which demands spatial abilities, have relatively large brains. Nectarivores and frugivores, for example, have heavier brains (higher encephalization quotients) than expected for this group than do insectivores, a finding paralleled by Harvey et al. (1980) for small land mammals and primates (see above). Perhaps large, complex brains are necessary to solve the geometric and temporal problems associated with unpredictable, three-dimensional environments. One can expect other species that converge in foraging strategies to demonstrate similar differences in brain size and complexity.

The convergence of flight characteristics extends beyond chiropteran species and includes birds. Molossid bats of the Microchiropteran group, with high aspect ratios, converge in wing form and flight characteristics with flycatchers and swallows. These birds fly at high altitudes and speeds in their quest for food. The Nycteridae, of the Macrochiropteran group, with low aspect ratios, converge in wing form and behavior with members of the passeriform group of birds. Passerines tend to fly within vegetation at relatively low speeds and are fairly maneuverable. Thus, form and function often coexist in particular patterns regardless of genetic variations.

More striking, perhaps, is the observation that bat-wing aspect ratios and behaviors are somewhat similar to fish tail-fin aspect ratios and behaviors (see Table 2). Fish that specialize in cruising long distances have caudal fins with high aspect ratios. These fish are analogous to insectivorous bats with high wing aspect

TABLE 3. Associations Among Various Characters in Bats

Characteristic	Low aspect ratio	Average aspect ratio	High aspect ratio
Wingspan	Short or average	Mostly average	Mostly average but large variation
Wing area	Average or large	Mostly average	Mostly small
Wing loading	Low or average	Mostly average	Mostly high
Foraging habitat type	Among vegetation, not above treetop level in forest	Among vegetation and in open areas; often along vegetation edges, usually at or below treetop level in forest	In open areas, often at high altitudes
Foraging behavior	Often sallying in flycatcher style; hovering and picking insects off vegetation, etc.	Straight flight (megabats); hovering (mainly nectarivores); patrolling to and fro at various levels (insectivores)	Straight flights over large distances
Flight style	Slow and maneuverable	Slow and rather maneuverable; average; fast	Medium and fast
Hovering ability	Often good	Good in some species (nectarivores); not very good in others	None
Pinna size	Often extremely big and upright	Small or average	Often adpressed and forwardly pointing
Percentage of species (of those investigated)	12	71	17
Examples of families and species	Megadermatidae, Nycteridae, *Rhinolophus ferrum-Equinum* (Rhinolophidae), *Chrotopterus auritus* (Phyllostomidae), *Plecotus* (Vespertilionidae)	Pteropodidae, Phyllostomidae, Vespertilionidae	Molossidae, *Rhynchonycteris naso* (Emballonuridae), *Noctilio leporinus* (Noctilionidae), *Phyllostomus* (Phyllostomidae), *Nyctalus leisleri* (Vespertilionidae)

Note. Adapted from Norberg, 1981.

ratios that cruise at fast speeds high over the forest canopy in search of food. Fish that are generalists and depend upon maneuverability within dense vegetation have caudal fins with low aspect ratios. These fish are analogous to bats with low wing aspect ratios that maneuver within the dense forest canopy. Both fish and bats that use mixed foraging strategies show intermediate aspect ratios. One should be careful in making generalizations of this kind; nevertheless, it may be possible in some cases to demonstrate convergent evolution of form and function based upon similar allometric equations and similar ecological demands.

A general comment

The investigations of locomotion and home-range size among mammals, fish, and birds show the indelible influences of body size. From two-thirds to three-quarters of the variation in foraging behavior can be attributed to body size. Species-typical specializations in habits and food preferences account for one-third to one-quarter of the variation. One should not assume that these two processes are unrelated, one being allometric and the other being nonallometric. They are, in fact, closely related. Where movements are metabolically expensive, as with small species, specializations will be compatible with body size. Thus, small species should be adapted for finding, manipulating and eating localized and predictable resources, since long-range foraging would be impossible for them. It is likely that such species will rely on proximate sensory mechanisms and will have the manipulative skills necessary to deal with circumscribed environments. Large species, on the other hand, should have metabolic and behavioral adaptations, as well as sensory and consummatory traits, that are compatible with long-distance explorations of patchy and unpredictable environments. Many specializations, therefore, must be genetically fixed through natural selection to conform to body size and its associated requirements.

GENERAL USES OF ALLOMETRY IN COMPARATIVE PSYCHOLOGY

A dictionary of allometric equations

Body size is one of the primary variables that scales with physiological processes and behavior. It is also a parameter that can be measured with relative ease. Moreover, body size is often the target of natural selection (Gould, 1977). It may be possible to compile a dictionary of allometric equations based on body size that would allow for the comparison of a wide range of species and behaviors. Similarities and differences among functions would immediately be apparent. We could also see deviations from general trends.

Little has been done to compile a dictionary, certainly not one for behavior.

TABLE 4. Allometric Relations for Animal Home Range and Body Weight

Taxon	Standardized relation		
	Intercept at W = 1 kg. a (km)	Slope b	r^2
Mammals	0.154	1.06	0.60
Primates	0.010	0.78	0.44
Mammalian hunters	0.057	0.71	—
Carnivorous mammals	1.39	1.37	0.80
Hunting primates	0.21	0.83	0.66
Omnivorous mammals	0.33	0.92	0.90
Omnivorous and carnivorous mammals	0.83	1.17	0.75
Herbivorous mammals	0.032	0.998	0.74
Cropping mammals	0.014	0.69	—
Birds	1.64	1.23	—
Carnivorous birds	8.26	1.37	0.86
Herbivorous birds	0.026	0.70	0.89
Secondary consumers	0.67	1.27	0.91
Herbivores	0.047	1.03	0.87
Lizards	0.121	0.95	0.58
Primates[a]	0.068	1.23	—

Note. Adapted from Peters, 1983.
[a]Dependent variable is group home range.

Peters (1983) has made some preliminary steps in this direction. Table 4 presents allometric equations on home range for a number of different species. Home-range scales isometrically with body weight for many of the species. About 50 to 90 percent of the variance in home range can be accounted for by body weight. There are obvious deviations from the general functions. Taxonomic comparisons, using allometric expressions, classify groups in terms of functional differences and similarities. As more data are compiled, the "elements" may take on patterns that permit predictions for particular groups and ecologies.

Dimensionless analyses of structures and functions

Statistically, body size can be disassociated from two related regressions when the slopes of the two functions are equal, or can be equalized with mathematical transformation. For example, if brain size is scaled to body size with the same exponent as spinal cord size, then one can relate brain size to spinal cord size without regard to body weight. Both variables in the regression analysis must have similar relationships to body weight if weight is to be removed from the equation. These dimensionless relationships presumably express biological ratios between associated functions that must occur regardless of size. Table 5 gives several dimensionless processes.

The underlying commonalities may not be difficult to understand in some cases. For example, it makes intuitive sense that both the mass of blood and the mass of the heart must be scaled isometrically to body size; thus, it is not unexpected that the ratio between the two would be 8.3 regardless of size. Similarly, it is probably understandable in terms of energy consumption that the cardiac cycle to lifespan ratio is constant regardless of size. Many such dimensionless processes are probably at work with behaviors.

TABLE 5. Size-Independent Dimensionless Groups in Mammals

Dimensionless group	Numerical ratio for animal weighing 1 kg	Allometric mass exponent (b)
$\dfrac{\text{Tidal volume}}{\text{Breath time}}$	2.0	0.00
$\dfrac{\text{Heart stroke volume}}{\text{Pulse time}}$	2.0	0.00
$\dfrac{\text{Mass of blood}}{\text{Mass of heart}}$	8.3	0.01
$\dfrac{\text{Velocity of pulse waves in aorta}}{\text{Velocity of blood in aorta}}$	26.0	−0.05
$\dfrac{\text{Pulse wavelength in aorta}}{\text{Length of aorta}}$	8.7	−0.05
$\dfrac{\text{Time for 50\% of growth}}{\text{Lifespan in captivity}}$	0.03	0.05
$\dfrac{\text{Gestation period}}{\text{Lifespan in captivity}}$	0.015	0.05
$\dfrac{\text{Respiratory cycle}}{\text{Lifespan in captivity}}$	3.0×10^{-9}	0.06
$\dfrac{\text{Cardiac cycle}}{\text{Lifespan in captivity}}$	6.8×10^{-10}	0.05
$\dfrac{\text{Half-life of methotrexate}}{\text{Lifespan in captivity}}$	0.95×10^{-5}	0.01

Note. Adapted from McMahon & Bonner, 1983.

One important example of dimensionless analysis of behavior is an experiment conducted by Bainbridge (1958). He showed that among several different species of fish, swimming speed increased with increasing tailbeat frequency. The relationship was linear and existed for both small and large fish. However, for any given tailbeat frequency, larger fish swam faster than smaller fish. The data could be plotted as several parallel regression lines of similar slope (one regression line per species) but with different intercepts. On the other hand, if swimming speed is expressed in terms of body length, rather than as tailbeat frequency, an allometric function is derived which is independent of body size. Thus, the distance moved over time for one beat of the tail is always a constant fraction of body length. Species differences disappear using this approach. The physiological explanation may resolve down to the relationship of body size to muscle efficiency and water resistance.

This is a remarkable example of how to take an array of species-typical attributes and extract out a general principle of behavior. Three insights were necessary to achieve the generalization: (1) homologous structures and functions can be described allometrically in order to achieve uniformity of data presentation; (2) scale transformations from one to another (as from centimeters to percent of body length) can sharpen our perception of uniformities; and (3) comparative and phylogenetic generalizations are entirely possible, even for the most complex behaviors.

Experimental manipulations

Allometric functions are like correlations, in that they demonstrate relationships. They do not, however, indicate causal influences among the variables. Allometric functions can, nevertheless, suggest how variables are interrelated and co-adapted. Once the relationships have been made explicit, the variables can be experimentally manipulated for greater understanding.

For example, one can genetically select for one characteristic and predict the outcome for a second characteristic. Based on what we know about body weight and related functions, one could select populations for high and low body weights and find allometric changes in metabolic rate, home range, diet, r and K selection, and learning abilities. It is also predictable that genetic linkage between some traits would be stronger than for others. For example, the selection of animals for long limbs and fast running speed should proceed faster than selection for long body limbs and slow running speed. And in the reproductive area, the selection for sexual dimorphism in size and polygamy should occur faster than selection for sexual dimorphism in size and monogamy.

The types of predictions possible are varied, and can lead toward a better understanding of how structures and functions covary and how they are controlled. The study of allometry in the laboratory may reveal relationships among individuals, populations, and species. It can expose genetic correlations among traits and can suggest mechanisms of control. Allometry can also pinpoint specializations that depend upon ecological selection pressures. Allometry can be the brush stroke that unites diverse approaches in comparative psychology.

SUMMARY

Allometry is a scaling technique that expresses relative growth between variables. Comparative psychology can take advantage of allometry in describing relationships among structures and functions within and between taxonomic groups. The power of this technique is illustrated by scaling body size (usually weight) with variations in locomotion, foraging, and home-range activities.

Body size determines metabolic efficiency and is related to locomotor performance, foraging and home-range size. In some cases, allometric functions are similar for different traits, allowing for the effects of body size to be removed. Thus, body size scales similarly for locomotor speed and home-range size, allowing the two behaviors to be directly associated. In other cases, significant deviations from an allometric function can suggest the effect of specialized ecological selection pressures. Thus, if home-range size deviates from expected size, based on body size, it is necessary to consider other ecological influences.

Allometric scaling can illuminate species similarities. Among species of bats, birds, and fish there are similar scaling relationships between body size, wing or fin characteristics, and locomotion. These similarities demonstrate the overriding influences of structural features that determine behavior, regardless of taxonomic variations.

Comparative psychology can use allometry to classify behaviors along structural/functional dimensions. Allometry is primarily a descriptive and correlational technique, but one that can suggest the operation of phylogenetic and ontogenetic influences. It can therefore generate experimental hypotheses for examining causal relationships between structure and function.

CHAPTER 5

THE BEHAVIOR OF
THE BROWN TREE SNAKE:
A STUDY IN APPLIED
COMPARATIVE PSYCHOLOGY

David A. Chiszar

Although there are ample theoretical issues to motivate research by ethologists and comparative psychologists, there are also many practical problems that demand our attention. Applied research sometimes lacks the glamour of experiments designed to test cutting-edge theory, and all too often, applied work is avoided because of this. Yet it is possible to formulate applied problems in ways that unite practical considerations with timely theoretical ones.

An example of this is the case of the brown tree snake, *Boiga irregularis*, accidentally introduced on Guam during or shortly after World War II. In this chapter, I describe the problems created by this snake and the research designed to solve those problems. The U.S. Fish and Wildlife Service and the Guam Division of Aquatic and Wildlife Resources are coordinating this effort, and they have recruited a wide variety of scientists to study an equally wide variety of questions related to the snake. I emphasize the behavioral research projects that form just one component of the overall program, but for the sake of completeness, I also discuss other program components, as well as some of the interactions that inevitably occur as laboratory results are tested under field conditions.

Along with telling the story of the brown tree snake on Guam, this chapter also has the mission of illustrating the kinds of contributions that comparative psychology can make to conservation efforts. Its specific contributions will

101

become apparent a bit later, when I discuss concrete research projects; for the moment, however, the general point can be made that conservation research frequently requires three laboratory components. First, the causal mechanisms that underlie ecological problems must be identified (e.g., the traits responsible for the brown tree snake's colonizing ability). Second, this understanding of causal mechanisms can give rise to hypotheses regarding intervention strategies that can be tested initially and quickly under laboratory conditions (e.g., the brown tree snake's sensitivity to prey-derived chemical cues might be capitalized upon in a trapping program). Third, strategies that are successful in initial tests can be tried again under quasi-natural laboratory conditions as a final step prior to actual field tests.

These three laboratory steps require careful control of environmental conditions so that critical (i.e., causal) variables can be identified and/or manipulated. Comparative psychologists have special expertise along these lines, as well as training in the measurement and interpretation of behavior. It is not surprising, therefore, to find comparative psychologists involved in conservation efforts requiring this mix of skills. I do not mean to imply that comparative psychologists are strictly laboratory workers, with no contributions to make to field projects; nor do I wish to imply that ecologists do not possess experimental skills. Nevertheless, ecologists tend to focus more on parameters of fitness, natural history, community structure, and population dynamics than on causal mechanisms. Consequently, a team effort is required to deal with conservation issues posed by introduced species, with different specialists focusing on different aspects of the problem, and with different specialists pooling their expertise at certain crucial moments, such as field tests of laboratory-developed techniques.

THE PROBLEMS

There are two clusters of problems arising from the presence of B. *irregularis* on Guam: the snake is at least partially responsible for the extinction of several species of birds on the island, and the snake causes a substantial number of electrical outages that result in serious economic losses, as well as other significant problems when electrical outages interfere with the operation of U.S. military installations on the island.

Because Guam has been studied by ornithologists before and after World War II (Baker, 1946, 1951; Seale, 1901), we have a reasonably clear view of the effect of the introduction of the snake on the avifauna. Of the 18 native resident bird species that existed in significant numbers on Guam during the 1940s, 9 are now extinct, 6 are nearly gone, and 3 remain in low numbers; of the 8 introduced species that had established breeding populations, 5 are now uncommon or rare (Engbring & Ramsey, 1984; Engbring & Fritts, 1988; Jenkins, 1983). Forest birds have suffered the most, but all bird species have declined in numbers. Recent investigations have produced no evidence that pesticides, avian diseases, or hunting by humans are responsible for the loss of birds (Grue, 1985; Savidge, 1986), but the introduction of the snake has been clearly implicated (Fritts, 1984; Fritts & Scott, 1985; Savidge, 1986, 1987a, 1987b).

Savidge (1987a) analyzed historical records of snake sightings on Guam and showed that B. *irregularis* was first reported in south central Guam (at Naval Magazine) in the early 1950s. During the next three decades, the snake gradually invaded the rest of the island, with bird disappearances occurring in a manner that was temporally correlated with the appearance of the snake. Trapping studies have estimated the density of B. *irregularis* on Guam to be from 16 to 50 snakes per hectare (Fritts & Scott, 1985; Savidge, 1986). There are no predators that take significant numbers of B. *irregularis*; consequently, the population of these snakes on Guam (which has an area of 550,000 hectares) is enormous. Since the snake can reach up to 2.4 meters in length, the population contains individuals that can eat a very large range of prey sizes. Indeed, since most of the native bird fauna has disappeared, most birds and bird eggs now found in B. *irregularis* on Guam are chickens and caged birds (including psitticines), and their respective eggs. It is noteworthy that other Micronesian islands, including nearby Cocos, that do not harbor B. *irregularis* populations have thriving bird faunas (Engbring & Pratt, 1985). The snake has also reduced the populations of small mammals, including the Mariana fruit bat, *Pteropus mariannus*, and of lizards on Guam.

The power outages known to be caused by B. *irregularis* became so frequent that separate records were kept of them by the Naval Public Works Command. These data were analyzed by Fritts, Scott, and Savidge (1987), who calculated an average of 43.6 outages per year during the period studied (1978–1985), giving a total of 349 outages. Accordingly, this problem has been and continues to be of major economic importance (Coulehan, 1987).

The most serious concern at present derives from the fact that much of the cargo entering Micronesia passes through Guam. This raises the possibility that snakes will sooner or later stow away and be introduced elsewhere in the Pacific. Although no extralimital populations of B. *irregularis* are currently known outside of Guam, specimens have been found on Oahu (Hawaii), Wake Island, Kwajalein Atoll, and Diego Garcia Atoll (Fritts, 1987). These animals probably came from Guam in military planes or ships, and such cases increase the concern that it may be only a matter of time before the Guam disaster is repeated elsewhere (Figure 1).

STRATEGY FOR STARTING

The bad news is that we know precious little about the brown tree snake, but the good news is that we have no misconceptions that might interfere with our studies. At the moment, it is not possible to predict which aspect of the species'

FIGURE 1. This poster has been produced by the agencies listed at the bottom in cooperation with the U.S. Fish and Wildlife Service. Copies of the poster are being distributed on various Micronesian islands to alert the human populations regarding the damages that could result from colonization by *Boiga irregularis*.

repertoire will be most vulnerable to manipulations designed to control the population, so we must approach the snake with a willingness to explore all avenues—feeding behavior, locomotion, habitat preferences, reproduction, and so on. Nevertheless, we must start somewhere, and this requires us to make some guesses regarding avenues that appear most promising. My laboratory has concentrated upon feeding and locomotion, and I will describe why we began with these behaviors and what we have discovered. Before discussing this work, however, I would like to lay out a set of ideas that form an overall strategy.

Tinbergen (1963) characterized the study of behavior as involving four problems or levels of analysis: causation, ontogeny, survival value (function), and evolution. He and Lorenz (1975) also argued that descriptive work is of great value in serving as a foundation for analytical projects at each of the four levels. Since coping with the brown tree snake on Guam requires that we understand the species' behavior, it follows that we must accumulate descriptive analyses of its patterns of predation, antipredation, locomotion, habitat preferences, and reproduction, and we must eventually study these behaviors at each of Tinbergen's levels, using his 1963 paper as a framework within which to organize our inquiry as it gradually moves forward.

This chapter presents descriptive and causal analyses of selected behaviors in adult brown tree snakes, but many other questions remain to be answered. For example, it is important to figure out not only how the snake got to Guam, but also from what part of its natural range (Northern Australia, the Solomon Islands, and Papua New Guinea) the colonizers came. If we know the geographic derivation of the Guam population, we can then study the parent population to discover the ecological mechanisms that regulate its density. Although there is no guarantee that such information will be useful on Guam (or elsewhere), we will at least learn something about predatory ecology that might explain why *B. irregularis* turned out to be an effective colonizer, and we will probably gain insight into the normal functions of behaviors that, on Guam, are unusually effective. The term "ecological release" has been used as a label for situations in which an organism (or a population) is liberated from its normal constraints, such as predators, competitors, or limiting resources (Wilson, 1975). The brown tree snake on Guam presumably has experienced ecological release, but this thought will remain shallow until we understand the agent(s) from which it has been released. Clearly, functional and evolutionary questions about the behavior of *B. irregularis* are both theoretically interesting and urgent, and our knowledge of the brown tree snake will remain incomplete until we have answered these questions.[1]

The importance of looking at the brown tree snake from an ontogenetic perspective has already been implied by the statement that the snake can reach a length of 2.4 meters. This means that different age-size classes probably take different foods and occupy different microniches. Thus, a developmental orientation needs to be incorporated into our research from the outset, because controlling the snake population on Guam may very well necessitate different techniques for different age–size classes, and it would be of limited utility to generate procedures that control the large adults if these procedures have no effect

[1]Analyses of scale patterns show the snakes on Guam to be most similar to those of the Admiralty Islands of northern Papua New Guinea. Several military bases were established in these islands during World War II, and it is probable that snakes stowed away in cargo subsequently shipped to Guam (T. H. Fritts, personal communication; manuscript in preparation).

on smaller (but reproductive) individuals. These are reasonable speculations, and ontogenetic research is clearly needed to test them.

The position taken by the U.S. Fish and Wildlife Service and the Guam Division of Aquatic and Wildlife Resources is that research on all four of Tinbergen's levels must proceed in such a way that each subproject can inform the others. This underscores the point that applied research can (and should) be cast into the same exciting and psychobiologically sound framework that Tinbergen (1951, 1963) advocates as a model for the proper conduct of ethological inquiry. With some thoughtful planning, it will be possible eventually to get the whole job done and to balance the strictly applied subprojects with the theoretically exciting ones. We may even discover unexpected theoretical nuggets in the results of strictly applied experiments.

Our initial research on the brown tree snake focused on its predatory behavior, partly because such an analysis was necessary in order to understand the impact of the snake on Guam's avifauna, and partly because it was possible that an understanding of its predatory behavior might lead to techniques for controlling the snake population, such as effective baits that could improve trapping success. Later, it became clear that an analysis of the snake's locomotion was important for understanding its foraging behavior and for dealing with the problem of power outages. Accordingly, the following sections will present first our studies of predatory behavior, then our work on locomotion.

PREDATION

Stimuli that guide foraging and predatory attack

Dr. Thomas Fritts of the U.S. Fish and Wildlife Service visited our laboratory to present a colloquium about the situation in Guam and to ask us to undertake some experiments on the feeding behavior of the brown tree snake. Dr. Fritts provided some snakes, and we used more or less traditional techniques to assess the stimuli influencing their predatory behavior. There was, however, a preliminary step that I considered essential. Since B. irregularis has been reported to be nocturnal in nature, we had to show that the snakes continued to be nocturnal in the laboratory. This would establish that at least one basic aspect of natural behavior persists in captivity, and it would also direct us to study the snakes in the dark. The snakes indeed proved to be active nocturnally in the laboratory (Chiszar, Carrillo, Rand, Chiszar, & Smith, 1985), and they remained this way even when we reversed the photoperiod (Chiszar & Kandler, 1986). Our nocturnal phase was created using two 25-watt red incandescent bulbs that produced a luminance of 5.3 lux at cage level; our photophase, by using four fluorescent bulbs that provided 277.7 lux.

We next executed a series of predation experiments during the 5.3 lux scotophase. The first studies (Chiszar, Kandler, & Smith, 1988) assessed the effects of chemical and visual cues from prey on predatory attack, using the procedures of Chiszar, Taylor, Radcliffe, Smith, and O'Connell (1981). Prey (small rodents) or their odors were presented to the snakes in Petri dishes or in Plexiglas boxes. The rodents elicited immediate and repeated attacks, but the chemical cues had no effects on either attack behavior or chemosensory investigation (i.e., tongue flicking). The snakes looked at our odoriferous Petri dishes and Plexiglas boxes, determined that no prey were present, and lost interest in our stimuli. Even under very dim illumination, the snakes could see rodents quite well, and we interpreted the null effect of chemical cues to be a further consequence of the excellence of snake vision. Visual inspection of an otherwise empty container overrode any attractive effects of chemical cues, unlike the typical result for garter snakes, which will readily attack prey-derived odors presented on cotton swabs or in Plexiglas boxes (Burghardt 1967, 1969, 1970; Chiszar et al., 1981). Our finding that chemical cues did not release chemosensory investigation or predatory attack in *B. irregularis* was disappointing in its implication about the usefulness of prey-derived odors to attract brown tree snakes to traps.

It was possible, however, that a different kind of experiment would reveal that *B. irregularis* used chemical information. Instead of presenting chemical cues in transparent containers, we could simulate dark burrows or tree cavities, where quick visual inspection could not confirm the presence or absence of prey. Perhaps the snakes would resort to chemosensory investigation of such settings before abandoning them. We used heavy cardboard tubes (30.5 centimeters long and 4 centimeters in diameter) to assess this possibility, and results were remarkably different from those just described (Chiszar, Kandler, Lee, & Smith, 1988). The snakes were presented with pairs of tubes, one of which was clean and the other of which contained a small quantity of soiled rat bedding and a rat pup. Masking tape which was either clean or which had been rubbed with a rat pup was placed outside the entrance to each tube. The "baited" tube was placed on the right and left side of the pair with equal frequency. The experiment was conducted during scotophase, and a Simpson light meter registered no illumination when its probe was inserted into the cardboard tubes. Hence, we are reasonably certain that the snakes could not see the rat pups or bedding in the baited tubes. Nevertheless, the snakes entered the tubes. They began the experiment with above-chance selection of the baited tube. Furthermore, the snakes were trained to a criterion of four successive correct choices, and they required a mean of only 4.8 trials (SEM = 1.4) to reach this level of performance. Next, we administered trials in which soiled bedding, but no rat pup, was placed in the baited tube. Snake performance was unaffected by this manipulation, strongly suggesting that chemical cues, rather than other stimuli such as vibrations or ultrasonic vocalizations that might arise from a live rat pup, were guiding their choices.

Another experiment reported by Chiszar, Kandler, Lee, and Smith (1988) again provided no visual cues, but exposed brown tree snakes to chemical trails made by rubbing rat pups on lengths of masking tape. The snakes were presented with three tapes, each 150 centimeters long, mounted on wood strips that radiated from a central platform. Two tapes were clean; one contained a rodent trail. The snakes exhibited unequivocal trail-following behavior, not only by selecting the path marked with rodent chemical cues, but also by their slow, methodical movement, during which the bifid tongue was frequently touched to the substrate. Hence, B. irregularis made use of chemical information under foraging conditions that did not simultaneously contain unambiguous visual information regarding the presence or absence of prey. Furthermore, the experiments suggested that substrate-borne cues were probably the most important, and that brown tree snakes might, therefore, be vulnerable to traps baited with such stimuli. Fritts, Scott, and Smith (1988) have recently reported a field test on Guam in which traps containing chicken and quail manure were more successful in attracting B. irregularis than were unbaited (control) traps. We hypothesize that the application of nonvolatile prey-derived cues in the form of trails leading to the traps will increase trap success.

Another approach to the problem of developing an effective chemical bait involves identifying pheromones that might be released by female snakes to attract males during the reproductive season. A related possibility is that the snakes may use chemical cues to mark aggregation sites. If such cues can be shown to attract conspecifics, they might also be used to bait traps. These ideas are being studied by P. J. Weldon of Texas A&M University and M. Attenbach of the U.S. Fish and Wildlife Service.

Our foraging experiments, although motivated by practical considerations, led to a theoretically interesting situation. It appears that B. irregularis is primarily a visually guided hunter that is also quite capable of switching modalities when visual cues are ambiguous or irrelevant. In an earlier paper dealing with predation by rattlesnakes and garter snakes, I argued that natural selection has predisposed snakes to attend preferentially to stimuli most highly correlated with appropriate prey, and that such cue utilization priorities might be altered by variation in ecological conditions, as when prey types vary in abundance or when prey refugia vary in availability (Chiszar et al., 1981). Using this interpretive framework, the brown tree snake could be described as relying upon visual cues when prey are not obscured by refugia, but switching to chemical cues when searching for hidden prey. Taylor (1974, 1984) developed a quantitative measure of switching that he called "cue value," defined as the difference in the probability of successful predation before and after a specific cue or modality is used. Under laboratory conditions, this measure can be used as an alternative to traditional ways of describing perceptual and/or learning phenomena (e.g., in the above experiments, the value of switching ranged from + .30 to + .50, and this fact implies that snakes learned to use chemical cues, because the switching score would be zero if no learning occurred). Under natural conditions, the measure takes on additional importance because Taylor considers switching scores of high value to lead to Holling's (1964, 1965, 1966) type III predation responses. A lengthy discussion of this point is beyond the scope of this essay and is certainly beyond the scope of our current data, but the significance of the issue justifies a brief paragraph.

In modeling the relationship between predator and prey populations, the effect of varying prey density is a central consideration. Two quite different (but not mutually exclusive) effects are possible: the density of predators may change, and the rate of predation by individual predators may change. In population biology these are called the numerical effect and the functional response respectively. Holling and others investigated the properties of four classes of functional response curves, one of which (type III) is a sigmoid relationship between rate of predation per predator and prey density. In the 1960s, it became clear that such a relationship implied that predators focus on prey that happen to be locally abundant, and that there is a brief temporal delay between the appearance of the prey in the environment and its appearance in the predator's diet. Learning must, therefore, be involved in generating this functional response, and the term "specific search image" was first used in precisely this context (L. Tinbergen, 1960). This term has since had a history remarkable for its complexity (Curio, 1976; Dawkins, 1971; Guilford & Dawkins, 1987), and today we know that many experiential factors besides "learning to see the prey" can give rise to the ability of predators to switch to locally abundant prey (Taylor, 1984).

Three points are important here: (1) the fact that switching or behavioral plasticity in a predator can generate the type III functional response, (2) that this response has important implications for the effects of predation on the prey population, and (3) the substantial capacity of the brown tree snake to switch sensory modalities when prey type and density are constant but when prey become visually inconspicuous. If analogous switching ability is also seen when prey types and densities are manipulated, then it will be reasonable to hypothesize that *B. irregularis* has exhibited a type III functional response on Guam. This, in turn, can generate useful predictions about the fate of prey populations remaining on Guam and about the effect of manipulations designed to control the snake population. For example, we might predict that as preferred prey species are exhausted, *B. irregularis* will switch to prey that are visually inconspicuous but chemically detectable, such as skinks and rodents; we might also predict that the snakes will then become more vulnerable to chemically baited traps than is the case now when visual cues are primarily used. Clearly, I have traveled far from our database, but it is important to present a broad view of our goals as well as a sense of how control measures can be guided by theory.

Prey handling as a function of prey size

Predators that take a wide variety of prey species are especially interesting when the prey species vary considerably in size and habits. This is clearly the case for brown tree snakes, since they are known to eat amphibians, reptiles, birds and their eggs, and small mammals. The diversity of prey taken by *B. irregularis* raises an important question: Do the snakes normally rely upon an eclectic diet, or do they specialize in certain types of prey and take others opportunistically? Analysis of gut contents of museum specimens taken from the native range indicates that young *B. irregularis* eat mostly lizards, while older specimens shift to other prey (H. W. Greene, personal communication). On Papua New Guinea, rodents are the preferred food of adult brown tree snakes, but birds are usually taken by such snakes on smaller islands. Hence, the situation on Guam might be regarded as a special case of an opportunistic predator capitalizing upon a vulnerable prey supply that would ordinarily constitute a significant percentage of its energy budget. The native birds on Guam are particularly vulnerable, partly because they have not coevolved with predators and thus have few defenses against them, and partly because the canopy on Guam is simple by comparison with the canopy on New Guinea, thereby offering fewer refugia to birds and easier hunting for the snakes.

Because the prey taken by *B. irregularis* vary in so many ways, including mass, shape, and retaliatory ability, we studied the snake's prey handling techniques to learn how it manages to subdue and ingest such a diversity of foods. To investigate this, we varied meal size (in terms of percentage of snake body weight), but used only rodents as prey in order to maintain experimental control over the general shape of the prey. A live rodent was simply placed in a snake's cage, and we recorded latency to attack, latency for prey to die (defined as cessation of respiratory movements), and latency for the snake to complete swallowing. Since *B. irregularis* is known to use constriction as well as envenomation (Shine & Schwaner, 1985), we wanted to assess the extent to which constriction varied with prey mass. Therefore, we scored each predatory episode according to a three-part nominal measure: (1) no constriction, (2) partial constriction (a loop of the body was used to control the prey during killing and/or swallowing, usually by simply "pinning" it against the floor or some object, but the loop was not wrapped around the circumference of the prey), or (3) full constriction (at least one loop of the snake's body was wrapped around the prey with suffocating pressure clearly being applied by the snake). The results of this study are shown in Figures 2 and 3. Larger prey were attacked with shorter latencies, indicating that large prey were more effective releasers of predatory attack than were small prey. Not surprisingly, larger prey took longer to kill and to swallow than did smaller prey, revealing that the energetic cost of predation increased with rodent mass. Interestingly, full constriction was seen infrequently with relatively small prey items, and became increasingly frequent as prey mass increased. Full constriction was always seen with prey equal to or larger than 30 percent of the snake's body weight.

Routine husbandry for captive snakes usually involves presenting meals that are less than 10 percent of the snake's body weight. Consequently, we had rarely seen full constriction prior to this experiment, and we would have described *B. irregularis* as representing an early stage in the evolution of constriction in that it

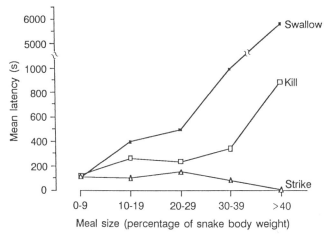

FIGURE 2. Average latencies to strike, kill, and swallow for rodent prey of varying mass (relative to snake body weight). Each measure was timed separately, i.e., latency to swallow does not include latency to kill which, in turn, does not include latency to strike. Statistical analyses revealed that large prey (≥ 30 percent of snake body weight) were struck significantly sooner than were smaller prey, and that larger prey required more time to kill and to swallow than did smaller prey. Hence, large prey were attractive to *B. irregularis*, but these prey required greater handling time.

used body loops mainly to control the prey while biting and swallowing. This view is clearly incorrect. The snake is a skilled constrictor, but it deploys this energetically expensive tactic only when dealing with formidable prey. (See Shine & Schwaner, 1985, for an evolutionary hypothesis that can explain the apparent paradox of why a species should use both venom and constriction to subdue its prey.)

The largest meal consumed during this experiment was a rat that was 60 percent of the snake's body weight. This fact probably does not seem astonishing, because snakes and some lizards are generally reported to be able to swallow very large prey, and the herpetological literature contains many accounts of remarkable swallowing accomplishments by pythons and Komodo dragons (Auffenberg, 1981; Oliver, 1958). Rarely, however, do squamates eat meals greater than 50 percent of their own body weight. Vipers exhibit the greatest degree of specialization for engulfing large prey, and a recent study (Pough & Groves, 1983) which compared vipers and nonvipers (not including specimens of any species of *Boiga*) stated that "the largest prey item successfully engulfed by a nonviper was 18.4 percent of the snake's mass. Vipers swallowed rodents as large as 36.4 percent of their own masses and failed to swallow items that were 40 and 45 percent of the snakes' masses" (p. 449). In light of this information, the 60 percent figure for *B. irregularis* should take on greater meaning.

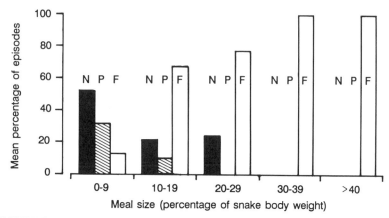

FIGURE 3. Mean percentage of feeding episodes involving no constriction (N), partial constriction (P), and full constriction (F) as a function of prey mass (relative to snake body weight). Statistical analyses confirmed the significance of the increase in the frequency of full constriction as prey size increased; with large prey, full constriction was the exclusive mode of prey handling.

A useful measure of swallowing is the number of mandibular protractions needed to swallow a meal as a function of meal size (Pough & Groves, 1983). This measure is not influenced by external disturbances that might cause a snake to stop swallowing temporarily and thereby might increase latency to swallow in an artificial manner. Disturbances simply cause mandibular protractions to cease; the total number of protractions remains the same whether or not the snake has been disturbed. Furthermore, Pough & Groves (1983) have shown that the length of the mandibles and the circumference of the head at the quadrates (and several other head characteristics) are related to this measure in a very interesting way. Vipers have much larger values on these morphological measures than do nonvipers, and consequently the two groups of snakes exhibit very different relationships between prey size and swallowing effort. Both relationships are linear, but the regression for nonvipers has a far steeper slope than the regression for vipers (see Figure 4), indicating that nonvipers exert much greater effort than do the vipers, especially as meal size increases. We gathered a comparable set of data for *B. irregularis*, and it is clear that these animals exhibited a relationship that was quite similar to that seen in vipers. In fact, the slope of the *B. irregularis* relationship was numerically shallower than that for the vipers. Comparing the slope of our *B. irregularis* data with the slope for vipers reported by Pough and Groves gave a nonsignificant difference, whereas comparing the slope for *B. irregularis* with the slope for Pough and Groves's nonvipers revealed a robust difference.

The brown tree snake is a member of the family Colubridae, which contains

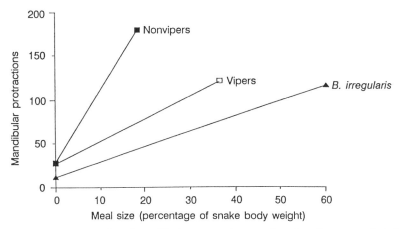

FIGURE 4. Mean number of mandibular protractions as a function of prey mass (relative to snake body weight). The data for vipers and nonvipers are from Pough and Groves (1983; this study did not include any specimens of the genus *Boiga*); that for *B. irregularis* is based on new data. The regressions are not extrapolated beyond the largest meal ingested by each group of snakes.

mostly nonvenomous species, including the common snakes that are familiar to most North American readers (e.g., garter snakes, bull snakes, king snakes, etc.). Although *B. irregularis* is venomous, it possesses rear fangs, a primitive venom delivery system, and has none of the maxillary specializations that characterize snakes of the family Viperidae. On the other hand, *B. irregularis* exhibits a phenomenon called head triangulation, in which a triangular outline of the head (from a dorsal view) can be created or enhanced by spreading the ventral tips of the quadrate bones. This behavior is seen in *B. irregularis* and in certain other colubrids when they are disturbed and respond with defensive displays.[2] The snake may simply be making itself appear larger than it really is, but the triangular shape of the head certainly takes on a viperlike appearance. Consequently, head triangulation is typically discussed under the rubric of mimicry (i.e., colubrids are mimicking vipers; Werner 1983, 1985, 1986; Werner & Frankenberg, 1982; see Pough, 1988 for a review).

Although I do not dispute the use of head triangulation during defensive maneuvers in *B. irregularis*, I suggest that this phenomenon probably also has something to do with the ability of this species to swallow very large meals and to behave more or less like vipers vis a vis mandibular protractions (Figure 4). Dr.

[2]Although *B. irregularis* clearly exaggerates the triangular outline of its head during defensive maneuvers, it should be noted that it has a triangular-shaped head even when at rest. This is especially conspicuous in young (small) snakes, but it is also visible in older (large) individuals.

Yehudah L. Werner of the Hebrew University of Jerusalem has worked extensively on the role of head triangulation during defense. In a letter of 13 June 1988, he wrote: "I find it hard to believe that triangulation primarily evolved in relation to feeding. But if the triangulators turn out to have longer quadrates, it would sound reasonable that the longer quadrates evolved for feeding, and that such snakes then had a greater probability of evolving (defensive) triangulation."

In any case, B. *irregularis* exhibits several flexibilities in predatory behavior, including the ability to switch from visual to chemical cues during foraging, the ability to use constriction to subdue large prey, and the ability to swallow large prey in an energetically efficient manner. Undoubtedly, these flexibilities have contributed to this animal's success as a colonizer and to its success in exploiting (to the point of devastation) a prey base containing species that vary greatly in size and habits.

Strike-induced chemosensory searching

Many vipers release adult rodents after envenomating them, presumably to avoid injury from the struggling prey's teeth, claws, and guard hairs. The snake then follows the chemical trail deposited by the wounded prey as it wanders away from the site of the attack. This phenomenon is called strike-induced chemosensory searching (SICS), and is characterized by an acceleration of the rate of tongue flicking from near zero prior to the strike to a high asymptotic rate thereafter. The tongue gathers molecules and transfers them to the vomeronasal organs (Gillingham & Clark, 1981; Halpern & Kubie, 1980), and SICS facilitates the location of the prey's trail as well as the snake's ability to follow it (Golan, Radcliffe, Miller, O'Connell, & Chiszar, 1982; Chiszar, Radcliffe, Scudder, & Duvall, 1983). Brown tree snakes, by contrast, typically do not release prey after the initial strike. Very small prey, such as neonatal rodents, are swallowed alive; slightly larger prey are held and envenomated; and still larger prey are constricted and envenomated.

Holding prey makes perfect sense for a snake that hunts birds, because a released bird leaves no trail and is virtually certain to be a lost meal. With rodent prey, however, the situation could be quite different, especially if the snake tries to subdue a very large (though ingestible) prey item capable of significant retaliation. Even cobras are sometimes induced to release large, struggling adult rodents (Kardong, 1982; Radcliffe, Stimac, Smith, & Chiszar, 1983; Radcliffe, Estep, Boyer, & Chiszar, 1986), and we have observed B. *irregularis* doing the same when the situation did not permit the snake to get a constriction grip on the prey. We wondered if cobras and brown tree snakes would exhibit SICS under such conditions. The answer for cobras turned out to be yes (Chiszar, Stimac, Poole, Miller, Radcliffe, & Smith, 1983; Radcliffe et al., 1986). An analogous experiment with B. *irregularis* has recently been completed, and the results are shown in Figure 5. Twelve snakes were observed for 10 minutes prior to any treatment, and the resulting data indicated that the baseline rate of tongue flicking was low. The snakes were then exposed to three conditions. In the no-strike condition, a live rodent was suspended in the snake's home cage, but was held out of its striking range, for 3 seconds. In the strike condition, a rodent was suspended in the cage, was struck, and was removed as soon as possible. Since the strike condition typically involved manipulating the snake, we added a manipulation condition, in which the snake was manipulated in the same manner, but no prey item was present. As can be seen in Figure 5, the no-strike condition and the manipulation condition produced only small elevations in the rate of tongue flicking relative to the baseline. The strike condition, however, was characterized by a conspicuously elevated and sustained rate of tongue flicking that clearly resembled the SICS effect seen in vipers (Chiszar, Andren, et al., 1982).

Many questions are raised by this finding: What is the duration of SICS in *B. irregularis* (Chiszar, Radcliffe, O'Connell, & Smith, 1982)? How frequently do these snakes release large but ingestible rodent prey following a strike (Chiszar, Stimac, Poole, Miller, Radcliffe, & Smith, 1983; Radcliffe et al., 1983; Kardong, 1986)? Does SICS characterize snake behavior in such cases (Chiszar, Stimac, Poole, Miller, Radcliffe, & Smith, 1983b)? Does SICS contribute to trail following, and does it have other functions (Chiszar, Radcliffe, Scudder, &

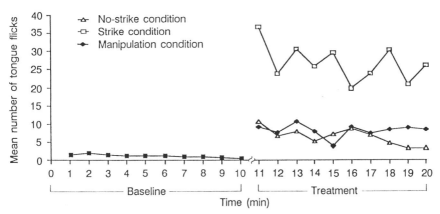

FIGURE 5. Rate of tongue flicking per minute in *B. irregularis* during a baseline period (no disturbance) and following three experimental manipulations: (1) a rodent was seen at close range (10–15 centimeters) for 3 seconds but not struck (no-strike condition), (2) a rodent was struck and then removed (strike condition), and (3) snakes were disturbed by brief handling (manipulation condition). Statistical analyses showed that rates of tongue flicking following the manipulation and no-strike treatments were not significantly higher than the rate of tongue flicking during baseline, but that the rate of tongue flicking following a strike was significantly higher than that seen in all other conditions.

Duvall, 1983; Chiszar, Stimac, Poole, Miller, Radcliffe, & Smith, 1983; Golan, Radcliffe, Miller, O'Connell, & Chiszar, 1982)? Although answers are not yet available, it nevertheless appears that Cooper (1988a, 1988b; Cooper, McDowell, & Ruffer, 1988) is correct in arguing that SICS has a phylogenetic distribution that extends well beyond the vipers that specialize in rodents and that it may be put to different uses by different taxa. In the absence of additional data at this time, we can only hypothesize that SICS in *B. irregularis* might contribute to the harrying of rodent prey when they are released following an initial strike, or that it might facilitate the capture of additional burrow inhabitants after a first one has been attacked. These and other ideas will soon be tested in brown tree snakes living in quasi-natural habitats. However these experiments turn out, it seems clear that the presence of SICS in *B. irregularis* represents yet another aspect of its predatory flexibility.

LOCOMOTION

Modes of progression

In order to deal with the problem of power outages caused by snakes on Guam, field researchers must find out how the snakes are reaching the wires and transformers. Are the snakes climbing the poles, or are they ascending the guy wires that stabilize some of the poles, or both? Fritts (personal communication) has provided convincing evidence that the snakes do not climb the poles, which have a large circumference and are made of smooth concrete, but that they do climb the guy wires, which are steel cables 1.2 centimeters in diameter. Wires on poles with guy wires have had a far higher frequency of power faults than those on poles without guy wires. Squirrel guards were installed on guy wires and on power lines in Guam, but to no avail. A disc with a radius of about 45 centimeters that stops squirrels and arboreal rats has little effect on *B. irregularis*.

Our first step in investigating this problem was simply to observe snakes of various lengths (.5–2.0 meters) moving along taut hemp ropes 1.2 centimeters in diameter (which simulated guy wires) set at various angles. We hoped to gain insight into how the snakes moved along such surfaces and how we might interfere with this movement. Five basic types of snake locomotion have been described (see Table 1), and we expected to observe mainly concertina movement on our narrow substrates. This was in fact seen when the snakes were moving up a rope inclined at 25°. However, when the snakes moved down the same rope, or along a horizontal one, a curious form of lateral undulation was seen. The entire body moved at the same relatively rapid rate (a distinguishing feature of lateral undulation), but forward propulsion clearly could not be attained by pushing against objects lying parallel and adjacent to the path of movement. Instead, the snake's body was arranged in a series of loops that clamped against

TABLE 1. Modes of Progression Seen in Snakes

Movement type	Characteristics
Lateral undulation (serpentine locomotion)	Forces are transmitted to discrete sites that are contacted by the postero-lateral surfaces of the undulant curves. Variations on this theme occur in swimming and in movement through arboreal habitats.
Slide pushing	Each backward-passing loop contacts the ground at only a single site. The loop presses down, and the resistance encountered propels the animal simultaneously along its longitudinal axis and laterally.
Concertina	The front is held in a fixed position and the trunk moves forward; the hind end is then fixed and the front moves forward to a new fixation site.
Sidewinding	A specialized form of locomotion seen in some species adapted to sandy deserts. Movement occurs at an angle to the average longitudinal plane of the body. As the anterior part of the body is lifted from its resting point, the posterior part is brought forward to this same point and tends to dig in, increasing the propulsive force.
Rectilinear	The body moves in a straight line. The belly skin bunches at a fixation point (or at several points along the body). The anterior is extended, freeing part of the bunched skin which is replaced by skin just posterior to the former fixation site. Bunching and rebunching happens in a smooth and well-coordinated manner so that the snake appears to be progressing with more-or-less constant velocity.

Note. Adapted from Gans, 1986.

alternate patches of rope. Propulsion was obtained by pushing these loops against the rope as the loops moved posteriorly along the snake's body. Gans (1986) would probably refer to this pattern of movement with the term "off-the-ground undulation," which he recognized as a special type of lateral undulation. H. M. Smith (personal communication) suggested the new term "stenegryous (narrow or tight) undulation" to emphasize that the locomotion, although undulatory, is extremely linear—more so than is typically the case for lateral undulation or off-the-ground undulation. It may be possible to justify Smith's new term and, hence, to recognize the unique nature of brown tree snake movement on narrow substrates, but such an argument would be beyond the scope of this essay, so I will not pursue the matter here. Rather, I will use the term lateral undulation, with the tacit understanding that B. irregularis exhibits a specialized form of it while moving along ropes and similar supports.

Since the snakes shifted from lateral undulation to concertina movement when moving up a rope inclined at 25°, we decided to study this shift by varying the angle of the substrate systematically between 0° (horizontal) and 90°. We used ropes and wooden dowels 3 centimeters in diameter as substrates. Some of the dowels were smooth, and some were roughened with glued-on sand and fine gravel to simulate tree bark. We placed snakes on substrates set at various angles and recorded the amount of time they spent in lateral undulation and in concertina movement. Results were expressed as the percentage of locomotion that was lateral undulation (Figure 6). On ropes, the snakes switched from lateral undulation to concertina movement as the angle of inclination increased, with 10° being the point at which at least 50 percent of progression involved concertina movement. On the smooth dowels, concertina movement was the only mode of progression seen at any angle. The surprising result came from the roughened dowels, on which lateral undulation was the exclusive mode of progression, even when the snakes moved straight up (90°). Since lateral undulation is much faster than concertina movement, this means that the brown tree snake is capable of rapid movement over rough surfaces at all angles. Consequently, these snakes would be able to execute rapid pursuit and capture tactics on natural bark, facilitating their capture of birds, as well as geckos and other arboreal vertebrates. Indeed, Gordon Rodda of the U.S. Fish and Wildlife Service (personal communication) observed a 1.5-meter snake on Guam capturing a dove that was in the process of trying to escape. The bird apparently saw the snake and took wing, but

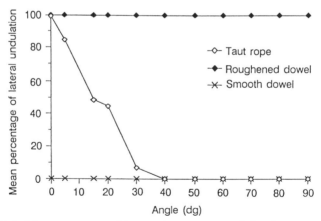

FIGURE 6. Mean percentage of locomotion up ropes and dowels set at various angles that involved lateral undulation. Since the only other form of locomotion seen in this situation was concertina movement, the mean percentage of concertina movement can be obtained by subtracting the plotted values from 100. Ropes were taut, and dowels were either smooth wood or were roughened by gluing particles of sand and small gravel to the surface.

the snake was able to move rapidly enough to close on the bird before it flew a sufficient distance to avoid the attack. It is probable the snake was not simply striking from ambush, but had to move its entire body to reach the bird. Lateral undulation makes this kind of rapid pursuit possible, and the snakes apparently capitalize upon this ability.

Our next step in this analysis will be to construct quasi-natural habitats and observe brown tree snakes in them over long periods of time. The immediate goal will be to construct a time budget showing the average percentage of a 24-hour day the snake spends at rest and the average percentage that it spends hunting. Simultaneously, we will determine the extent to which hunting involves ambush tactics and active foraging tactics, and we will characterize the modes of progression used in both categories. Eventually, these data will be converted to an energy budget, so that we will be able to specify the caloric investments involved in hunting as well as the benefit:cost ratios associated with different types of prey and different modes of progression. This information will help us not only to understand the snake's energetic economy, but also to understand the energetic basis for the snake's numerical and functional responses to changes in prey density.

Experiments with obstructions

Because the prevention of power outages caused by brown tree snakes is an immediate goal on Guam, we have conducted experiments to study the snake's responses to various obstructions that might be placed on guy wires and other substrates on which the snakes climb. Our experimental method involved mounting two obstructions at opposite ends of a dowel. The snake was placed between these obstructions, and we observed whether or not the snake escaped during a timed trial. Usually our trials were from 2.5 to 5 minutes long. We readily admit that failure to escape during such a brief trial does not necessarily indicate that the obstruction will successfully stop snakes in field tests on Guam, but we used the brief trials to expedite the screening out of obstructions that show no promise. When successful obstructions are identified in our standard laboratory tests, they will be studied again with longer trials and under more natural conditions. Obstructions that continue to be successful during this second phase of laboratory testing will be recommended for field tests on Guam.

Our initial experiments focused on discs (i.e., squirrel guards) of varying radius, and the results are shown in Figure 7. It is clear from these data that brown tree snakes can get over very large discs. Therefore, discs even larger than those we used would be needed to stop the snakes, and such obstructions are simply not practical on an island that experiences 200 mile-per-hour winds. A slight modification of this type of obstruction might, however, be workable. It is possible that a rotating disc, which would spin under the weight of a snake, thereby causing the snake to fall from the disc and thus from the wire, might be more effective in blocking the snake's movement than a stationary disc. We

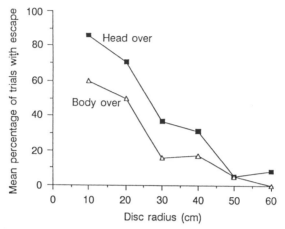

FIGURE 7. Mean percentage of trials on which escapes occurred as a function of disc radius (in centimeters). Snakes were placed on a horizontal dowel, between two discs of equal radius that were also mounted on the dowel. Two dependent variables were recorded: (1) "body over" means that the snake actually escaped; (2) "head over" means that the snake lifted its head to the top of a disc and could have, therefore, escaped. All escapes involved getting the head over a disc; there were, however, many trials on which a snake achieved the head-over posture, but "elected" not to escape. Since the snake could easily have escaped on such trials, we deem it important to regard the head-over data as indicative of potential escapes. Although both measures declined significantly as disc radius increased, it is noteworthy that even the largest discs were not unpassable.

fabricated a set of rotating discs and used them in a replication of the preceding experiment, the results of which are shown in Figure 8. These discs were more effective than the nonrotating ones in stopping brown tree snakes, but fairly large discs were still necessary. Although this approach continues to deserve attention, a pattern of snake behavior observed during the tests does not bode well for its success. Snakes usually tried to climb over the obstructions, but after falling from spinning discs several times, a few snakes developed an alternative method. These animals clamped their tails on the dowel and dropped their bodies below the disc, coming back up to the dowel behind the disc. Going under a disc is harder than going over it, because the snake's body is not supported until its head reaches the dowel behind the disc. Nevertheless, some snakes learned to do this during our brief laboratory tests with spinning discs, and it seems reasonable to expect similar learning to occur on Guam.

Brown tree snakes are attracted to dark crevices because they use them as refugia during the daylight hours. A concave (i.e., conical) device attached to a guy wire might, therefore, act as a sort of trap by luring the snake into its interior. Using the same basic method as we used in the disc experiments, we placed two

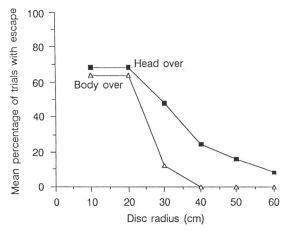

FIGURE 8. The basic procedure and the dependent variables shown here are the same as those described in Figure 7. In this experiment, however, the discs could rotate under the weight of a snake that was crawling over them; hence, "head over" no longer implies that an escape is easily possible. These discs were more effective in stopping *B. irregularis* than were the nonrotating discs (compare "body over" performance on rotating discs 40 and 50 centimeters in radius with performance on nonrotating discs of the same size in Figure 7.

cones at opposite ends of a dowel, and placed snakes between them. Each cone was 23.5 centimeters long, and the mouth of each cone was only 11 centimeters in radius. From the results shown in Figures 7 and 8, it is clear that discs of 10–20 centimeters in radius were easily scaled by the snakes. Yet the relatively small cones turned out to be a substantial obstruction. Escapes occurred on only 8 percent of our trials with the cones. The snakes usually entered the cones, moved to the rearmost part, and stayed there, with some snakes emerging from the cone only to head back the way they had come until they entered the other cone. Attraction to the small, dark interior of the cone seemed to override any tendency to go up and over the cone (see discussions of anachoresis, regular occupation of crevices or holes, in Edmunds, 1974; Jackson, 1988). These results suggest that cones should be pursued, and perhaps developed, not only as obstructions but also as traps.

DISCUSSION

The full impact of the brown tree snake on Guam has scarcely been grasped at this time. Although it is relatively easy to visualize its primary effects (e.g., the elimination of birds, bats, and geckos), we can expect numerous secondary effects to develop. For example, the removal of insectivores is bound to have some consequences on insect demographics, and the removal of pollinating birds is bound to have some effect on plant demographics. Consequently, there is still much to be learned from the careful study of Guam, and there is much to fear if the brown tree snake manages to colonize other Pacific Islands.

In the midst of the urgency that attends this problem, however, many theoretical issues of fundamental importance in ecology, ethology, and evolutionary biology have been raised. The purpose of this chapter has been to show that applied research can make contact with some of these issues, even though the research has as its primary goal the solution of a practical problem. Indeed, I think it could be argued that applied research has a responsibility to connect with basic theory whenever possible; otherwise, applied research produces little or no advance in knowledge, no matter how successful it might be in solving problems. To turn the emphasis slightly, solutions that work are phenomena worthy of explanation, and good explanations can provide at least retrospective insight into the behavior of *B. irregularis* on Guam and, perhaps, prospective readiness to respond effectively if similar events occur elsewhere in the Pacific.

I would like to end this chapter by reporting a troublesome observation made by Thomas Fritts and Gordon Rodda during a trip to Guam in May 1988. These scientists visited an area of Guam that has been denuded of birds and arboreal lizards. Would the snake population be declining in the wake of this devastation of the prey supply? It turned out that there were plenty of snakes in good condition, but the snakes were behaving in surprising ways. Of 37 snakes captured by Fritts and Rodda, 35 were foraging on the ground, presumably searching for skinks. We tend to think of arboreal snakes as highly specialized creatures that are unlikely to exhibit departures from this lifestyle. Terrestrial foraging by *B. irregularis* was, therefore, unexpected; but, in keeping with the empirical theme of this chapter, this new fact further illustrates the brown tree snakes's substantial degree of behavioral–ecological plasticity. This makes the animals all the more interesting, while the problem of controlling them becomes all the more difficult.

SUMMARY

The brown tree snake (*Boiga irregularis*) was accidentally introduced on Guam during or shortly after World War II. This nocturnal, arboreal predator has reached an alarming population density on the island, and has been implicated in a drastic decline of bird, bat, and lizard populations. In addition, the snake causes numerous power outages by crawling on electrical transmission equipment, frequently creating short circuits. There is great concern that such events could be repeated on other Pacific islands should the snakes be inadvertently established on them. The U.S. Fish and Wildlife Service and the Guam Division of Aquatic and Wildlife Resources have mounted an effort to study and control *B. irregularis* on Guam and to prevent the species from colonizing other islands.

This chapter has described research on snake predation and locomotion. By understanding these behaviors, we hope to gain insight into the colonizing ability of *B. irregularis*, and we may be able to use this information to control its movements and predatory activities. The snake appears to be a visually guided forager that switches to chemical cues when visual cues regarding the presence or absence of prey are unavailable or inconclusive. The snake takes a surprising range of prey, and uses several different techniques in capturing prey of varying sizes and defensive abilities. Experiments on locomotion likewise revealed the snake's ability to shift between various modes of progression depending upon the nature of the substrate. The present data suggest that *B. irregularis* is a very flexible creature, and this probably contributes to its colonizing success. Yet these laboratory results indicate that it appears to be vulnerable to several types of traps, so field tests of these devices on Guam are a logical next step.

PART II

Mating Behavior

The effective acquisition of food, avoidance of predators, and individual survival are necessary, but not sufficient, for the survival of genetic lines; reproduction is also critical. Because effective reproduction is so critical in natural selection, it is not surprising that many studies in comparative psychology have been concerned with reproductive behavior. The four chapters in this section deal with different aspects of mating behavior in deer mice, spiders, ground squirrels, and fish—a comparative potpourri.

First, I present a summary and overview of a long-term, integrated research program on the copulatory behavior of deer mice (Chapter 6). The program is used to illustrate some basic principles that are widely accepted as regulating the evolution of behavior: (1) that natural selection appears to work primarily at the level of the individual; (2) that those individuals that are most successful at surviving and reproducing will leave the most offspring, and hence, the most copies of their genes; and (3) that behavioral patterns affected by those genes will thus increase over successive generations.

After a description of the basic behavioral patterns of deer mouse copulation and some of the factors that affect it, I explore some of the factors that lead to differential reproductive success in deer mice. The very initiation of pregnancy in the female depends on the pattern and amount of stimulation derived from copulation with a male, because this stimulation initiates a set of neuroendocrine responses that are essential for pregnancy to occur. Because females often mate with more than one male during an estrous period, the conditions favoring sperm competition obtain. Male strategies will thus be favored if they somehow ensure that it is their sperm, rather than the sperm of another male, that fertilize the ova. Patterns of sperm competition are affected by genetic strain, the timing of mating, the relative number of ejaculations by different males, and other factors. If a second male mates soon after a first, he can disrupt the transport to the uterus of the sperm from the first ejaculation. Females exposed to more than one male around the time of mating or to strange males after mating display a blockage of pregnancies. Because male capacity to produce ejaculates is limited, they are faced with a problem of prudent allocation of their ejaculates. Deer mice appear to be less selective than many other species when interacting with conspecifics in situations involving mate choice and kin discrimination. Finally, many of the phenomena that have been demonstrated in small-cage situations appear to be generalizable when tested in more naturalistic settings. The data are generally consistent with the view that natural selection works at the level of the individual, and illustrate the complexity of the interactions of animals in relation to differential reproductive success.

Christenson (Chapter 7) is concerned with processes that are quite similar to those treated in the previous chapter. However, he works with a very different animal—the orb-weaving spider, Nephila clavipes. On the basis of his original field studies, Christenson provides a general summary of the natural history of these spiders, focusing on their reproductive strategies. The key to the social structure of these spiders lies in the web. Early in life, webs facilitate the survival and development of spiderlings. During adulthood, females use their webs for predation, but males abandon their webs to search for females; the differentiation of male and female reproductive strategies is apparent. Christenson considers the various options that might be open to males and females and their possible consequences for reproductive success and fitness. Males compete among themselves for the hub position on the female's web, with larger males winning out over smaller males. Thus, it appears adaptive for the smaller males to leave and seek better conditions.

Many characteristics of reproductive interaction in this species differ from the mammalian model. There appears to be a first-male advantage in sperm competition. Both males and females appear to display little active mate choice, a finding quite different from those for other species. Also, males release all of their sperm with the first newly molted female with which they mate, again differing from the prominent mammalian pattern. This sperm depletion does not prevent the males from remating, however. Females mating with depleted males receive no sperm, so the reproductive cost of this characteristic is significant.

After mating, males may leave or may remain with the female. Christenson considers various costs and benefits of each alternative. In general, the spider behavioral patterns appear quite adaptive in the natural habitat, but there are enough incongruities between theory and data to leave many interesting questions to be answered in further research and theory development.

Schwagmeyer's work (Chapter 8) is another study of reproductive strategies as examined under field conditions. Hers is a comparative analysis of reproductive strategies in ground-dwelling squirrels, with an emphasis on the thirteen-lined ground squirrel. The focus of the chapter is on male–male competition and the different ways in which this competition can lead to reproductive success. Animals adopt different mating systems, and different mating systems are apparent in the ground squirrels. These, in turn, reflect the densities and spatial distribution of males and females. Schwagmeyer contrasts three major mating systems. In female defense polygyny, males compete for reproductive success by maintaining harems of females and defending them against other males. In male dominance polygyny, males compete with each other for dominance status, and privileged access to females is presumed to accrue to dominant males. In scramble competition polygyny, there is less overt competition among males, and locating females and mating with them effectively is all-important.

Schwagmeyer is especially interested in the ways in which different male strategies are effective in different mating systems. Overt conflict between males seems quite important in many dominance and female defense systems but of little importance with scramble competition. Where there is scramble competition polygyny, by contrast, male mate locating ability is critical and dominance is of minimal impact. Sperm competition occurs in some species and represents yet another mode of male–male competition for reproductive success.

Schwagmeyer's chapter is a nice study of the contrasting mating systems of different species in different habitats and of the kinds of competition that are effective in those mating systems. Her work also illustrates the joint and supplemental benefits of field and laboratory work, as her observations of mating systems under natural conditions are enriched by her analysis under controlled laboratory conditions of such questions as the mode of sperm competition.

The species and conditions discussed in this work are very different from those in the previous two chapters. The first-male mating advantage of thirteen-lined ground squirrels is mediated by a mechanism very different from that in Christenson's spiders or my own deer mice, and male size and dominance are less important than in either of those species. In each case, however, we see the same principles of male–male competition working in different species and under different conditions to yield differential reproductive success for those males that are most effective in adapting to the prevailing conditions.

Hollis' chapter (Chapter 9), like Timberlake's, deals with learning, and might thus have been placed in a separate section on learning. In a more fundamental way, however, the chapter deals with male–male competition and success in attracting mates. Although the processes emphasized by Hollis differ somewhat from those emphasized in the other chapters in this section, the end is the same, as it is the role of behavior in promoting success in male–male competition and reproduction that is considered. Thus, a major characteristic of Hollis's approach is that learning is viewed not as a faculty that is separate from the life history of the organism, but rather as an integrated part of its adaptation.

The fundamental notion in Hollis's chapter is that Pavlovian (or "classical") conditioning can be viewed not only in relation to the processes underlying it, but in terms of its effects in promoting the reproductive fitness of the organism showing conditioning. In her work on blue gouramis, she focuses on male–male competition as it is displayed in both territoriality and male–female courtship. However, as Hollis treats territoriality essentially as a mating tactic, the "bottom line" concerns reproductive success. Hollis's view is that Pavlovian conditioning prepares an animal to deal more effectively with significant recurring stimuli in its environment. If animals can respond to stimuli that regularly and predictably precede significant events, they may be better prepared to deal with these events when they occur. Hollis shows that males do better in territorial disputes when they have undergone Pavlovian conditioning. Conversely, if a conditional stimulus is reliably associated with the absence of an intruder, this is learned as well, and Hollis points out how this phenomenon could also be adaptive in the field. Similarly, males conditioned with the presentation of females as the unconditional stimulus respond more effectively in courtship with females: their initial aggressive responses may be inhibited and courtship may proceed more quickly. It appears to be adaptive for females to mate with such males.

These results can be viewed both functionally and in relation to proximate causation. Hollis points to implications of these findings for both general process learning theory and for work on the possible endocrinological bases of some of the effects observed. Functionally, these fish breed in a system of resource defense polygyny that is analogous to the systems described by Schwagmeyer for some species of ground squirrels. Learning thus can be viewed as subject to sexual selection and as having evolved to support other aspects of overall mating strategies of males and females in different species.

DEER MICE AS A CASE STUDY IN THE OPERATION OF NATURAL SELECTION VIA DIFFERENTIAL REPRODUCTIVE SUCCESS

Donald A. Dewsbury

Contemporary versions of Darwin's theory of evolution by natural selection provide a powerful means of organizing and synthesizing the mass of diverse information in biology and comparative psychology. They also provide guides for selecting meaningful questions in empirical research. Such research serves to improve our understanding of the origins of behavior and feeds back to sharpen the theoretical structure from which it emerges. After a period of rapid theoretical advances in the 1970s, the 1980s have seen the development of integrated research programs designed to test and refine our understanding of natural selection. I shall describe one such program, in which deer mice have been the subjects.

SOME PRINCIPLES OF NATURAL SELECTION

Although theorizing about natural selection can become quite sophisticated and quantitative, the basic underlying principles are quite straightforward (see Dawkins, 1976). Animals in populations differ with respect to both genotype (the genes they carry) and phenotype (their measurable characteristics, including behavior). Genes, together with many other influences, affect phenotypes. Alternative alleles at the same locus produce animals that behave differently when they develop in the range of environments typically encountered by the species. Some of these phenotypes are more successful at surviving and reproducing in particular environments than are others. Copies of the genes borne by the more successful individuals become relatively more common in future generations, as do the behavioral patterns affected by those genes. The relative contribution of a particular genotype to future gene pools is its *genetic fitness*.

Natural selection generally acts at the level of the differential reproductive success of individual organisms (see Williams, 1966). Individuals rarely, if ever, sacrifice themselves for the good of the group or species. Rather, individuals have been selected to behave in ways that maximize their own levels of genetic fitness. Thus, when a genetically unrelated male and female of a species come together to reproduce, each cooperates with the partner only as long as it is in its own genetic interests.

The differential reproductive success of individual animals lies at the heart of natural selection—and of my research program. At the ultimate level of analysis, all behavior should, in the long run, be selected to lead to maximal genetic fitness. The challenge to the empirical researcher is to determine proximally how behavior affects reproductive success. In so doing, the traditional distinction between studies of ultimate causation (evolution and adaptive function) and proximate causation (immediate causation and development) (see Tinbergen, 1963) becomes narrowed.

Individual reproduction is not the only way in which to ensure the presence of copies of one's genes in future gene pools. Because one shares genes with close relatives, aiding their quest for reproductive success can help ensure representation of copies of one's genes as long as the costs are not too high (see Hamilton, 1964). This aspect of natural selection, working through close relatives, is known as *kin selection*. The total genetic fitness of an individual, including that component due to increases in the fitness of close relatives caused by the individual, is known as *inclusive fitness*.

The goal of this research program has been to study the ways in which these rather basic principles may apply to deer mice. Although the data generally appear consistent with the view that selection works at the level of the individual, they do not constitute a critical test of that view. I begin by describing deer mice and their basic copulatory patterns. I then proceed to explore the ways in which behavior appears to promote the differential reproductive success of individual animals.

DEER MICE

Deer mice, *Peromyscus maniculatus*, are classified as members of the superfamily Muroidea of the order Rodentia in the class Mammalia. The muroid rodents, which include such species as Norway rats, golden hamsters, and house mice, are excellent species for laboratory study (Dewsbury, 1974, 1984c). The diverse range of species adapted to different lifestyles in nature provides rich comparative material. Many species adapt well to the laboratory and can thus be studied under controlled conditions. Deer mice in particular are a diverse and widespread species, with subspecies living throughout much of North America. By studying a native species, we hope to be able to relate our laboratory research observations to those made under natural conditions.

In nature, deer mice tend to live alone, with relatively little overlap of the home ranges of same-sex individuals (e.g., Wolff, Freeberg, & Dueser, 1983). Males and females appear unlikely to form stable pair bonds (Dewsbury, 1981b), although they can cohabit if humans provide nest boxes (e.g., Howard, 1949). Most often, deer mice appear relatively asocial when not mating. The existence of sexual dimorphism, with males being somewhat larger than females (Dewsbury, Baumgardner, Evans, & Webster, 1980), suggests that males may compete for females. Females ovulate spontaneously, and have an estrous cycle averaging about 4–6 days (Clark, 1936). They go into estrus immediately postpartum, becoming receptive the evening after they deliver a litter (Jameson, 1953).

COPULATORY BEHAVIOR IN DEER MICE

Basic patterns

According to the classification scheme of Dewsbury (1972), deer mice display copulatory pattern 13 (no lock, no intravaginal thrusting, multiple intromissions prerequisite to ejaculation, and multiple ejaculations (Clemens, 1969; Dewsbury, 1979a). This pattern is common in rodents (Dewsbury, 1975a).

In a typical laboratory test, a receptive female deer mouse is introduced into the home cage of a male. The female may be in one of three modes of estrus: cycling estrus, which can be detected by monitoring estrous cycles with vaginal smears; postpartum estrus, which occurs several hours after the birth of a litter; or hormone-induced estrus, induced by sequential injections of an estrogen and a progestin. When mounted by the male, a receptive female adopts a posture of lordosis.

There are three primary classes of events in the copulatory behavior of deer mice: mounts (without vaginal penetration), intromissions (with vaginal insertion and no sperm transfer), and ejaculations (with insertion and sperm transfer). These events are mutually exclusive and are organized in "series," each of which begins with an intromission, ends with an ejaculation, and is separated from other series by a postejaculatory refractory period (see Figure 1). Deer mice typically complete about four series in a copulatory episode. After a number of organized series, males sometimes display a pattern of "long intromissions," which resemble ejaculations but appear to entail no sperm transfer and lack the

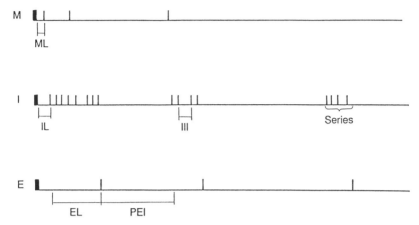

FIGURE 1. Diagrammatic representation of the copulatory pattern of deer mice and laboratory rats and the standard measures used in their study. The period shown is about 30 minutes. The events represented on the three time lines by vertical bars are mounts (M), intromissions (I), and ejaculations (E). ML = mount latency; IL = intromission latency; EL = ejaculation latency; III = interintromission interval; PEI = postejaculatory interval. (From Dewsbury, 1975b.)

temporal patterning of organized series (Dewsbury, 1979a). The following measures are generally taken:

Mount latency (ML): time from the start of a test until the first mount or intromission

Intromission latency (IL): time from the start of a test until the first intromission

Ejaculation latency (EL): time from the first intromission of a series until ejaculation

Intromission frequency (IF): the number of intromissions in a series

Mount frequency (MF): the number of mounts in a series

Mean interintromission interval (MIII): the mean interval separating the intromissions within a series

Postejaculatory interval (PEI): the time from ejaculation until the next intromission

Correlational and factor analytic methods have been used to determine the relatedness of these different measures (Dewsbury, 1979d).

There are orderly changes in behavior across series; these appear due to changes in both males and females, with the males exerting the greater effect (Dewsbury, 1979b). This is revealed both by changing male and female partners between series and by calculating test–retest correlations when changing partners between successive tests. Familiar male–female pairs are more likely to mate than unfamiliar animals, but familiarity does not affect the parameters of copulatory behavior once copulation is initiated (Dewsbury, 1979b).

Stability

Copulatory patterns in deer mice are remarkably stereotyped and stable. In an experiment in which male deer mice were mated with female cactus mice (*P. eremicus*), a different species that uses intravaginal thrusting, the copulatory pattern remained typical of male deer mice (Dewsbury, 1979b). In another study, newborn male deer mice were cross-fostered to and raised by female house mice (*Mus musculus*). When tested as adults, these deer mice copulated in their own species-typical pattern (Dewsbury, 1979a).

Because deer mice are so widely distributed, it is possible to compare the patterns of different subspecies; animals from subspecies in Michigan, New Mexico, and California show essentially the same copulatory pattern (Clemens, 1969; Dewsbury, 1979a). Even when copulating in larger social groups, the basic copulatory pattern is the same as that shown by male–female pairs (Dewsbury, 1979b, 1981d, 1985a). Copulatory patterns thus appear quite species-typical.

Some influences on copulatory behavior

Although the qualitative characteristics of deer mouse copulatory patterns appear quite stable, quantitative changes occur in response to changing conditions. For example, the mode of estrus (cycling, postpartum, or hormone-induced) affects the parameters of copulatory behavior (Dewsbury, 1979b). Male deer mice are slower to initiate mating and display fewer ejaculatory series with females in hormone-induced estrus than with females in cycling or postpartum estrus. In another study, the parameters of the copulatory behavior of deer mice mating in standard laboratory cages were compared to those of deer mice mating in a seminatural enclosure built on a 4 × 8 foot (1.2 × 2.4 meter) base. The male and female took longer to initiate copulatory activity in the enclosures, but other measures of copulatory behavior were unaffected (Sawrey & Dewsbury, 1981).

When males are permitted to remain together in seminatural enclosures, they form dominance relationships (see below). If the dominant and subordinate males are later tested for copulatory behavior, subordinate males tend to ejaculate after fewer intromissions (Dewsbury, 1988c). This may be adaptive in that the subordinate male may thus be able to complete a series before a dominant male can interfere.

PREGNANCY INITIATION

In studying the adaptive significance of behavior, one searches for the consequences of different behavioral patterns that are important for survival and reproduction. Experimental designs, therefore, are the reverse of those in most of psychology: behavior becomes the independent rather than the dependent variable. The search is for consequences, rather than immediate causes, of behavior.

Female reproductive physiology

An important function of male rodent copulatory behavior is its stimulative effect on female reproductive physiology. Females of species such as laboratory rats and deer mice have short estrous cycles. Ova are shed every cycle, whether or not the animals mate. However, in contrast to some species, the uterus of a female rat or mouse is not prepared for the implantation of fertilized ova unless she mates or receives comparable vaginal stimulation. If she does not mate, the lining of the uterine wall does not proliferate; the female can thus return to estrus quickly. Because copulatory stimulation eventually leads to the secretion of the hormone progesterone, one may say that the female has become "progestational." This male behavior–female response system is an ideal one for studying the consequences of male copulatory behavior; here is an important consequence in the female of the male's behavior.

Pregnancy initiation in laboratory rats has been studied extensively by Adler (e.g., Adler, 1969). Most young, virgin female rats in cycling estrus become progestational after just a single ejaculatory series. The multiple intromissions that precede ejaculation are critical. If a male mates for several intromissions with a nonexperimental female before the experimental mating, he delivers only a few intromissions to the experimental female before he ejaculates. A female receiving a small number of intromissions is unlikely to become progestational and pregnant, even though she receives the same number of sperm as a female receiving a full complement of intromissions.

Pregnancy initiation in deer mice

In our first study of pregnancy initiation in deer mice, young females were allowed to mate for one ejaculatory series, two ejaculations, or to sexual satiety (about four ejaculations) (Dewsbury, 1979c). Only 42 percent of the females delivered litters after mating for one series; 92 percent of the females became pregnant in the other two conditions. Thus, unlike rats, young female deer mice in cycling estrus require more than one series to reach maximal probabilities of pregnancy.

Additional studies were conducted to determine the range of variation in female stimulus requirements for pregnancy initiation. Older females that had delivered at least seven litters had much higher stimulus requirements; only 50 percent became pregnant after two ejaculations. By contrast, when young females mated for just one series in postpartum estrus, rather than cycling estrus, most became pregnant. Females thus have lower thresholds for pregnancy initiation in postpartum estrus (Dewsbury, 1979c). The stimulus requirements of pregnancy form a dynamic system, changing with prevailing conditions, rather than a static species-typical system (Dewsbury, 1978b). Changing thresholds may be a proximate expression of the ultimate advantages to a female of making a reproductive commitment at various life stages. However, no detailed analysis of how this might work has been attempted.

In an additional set of experiments, it was possible to trigger the progestational response in females with stimulation from an artificial "penis," the blunt end of a small artist's paint brush. (Dewsbury, 1979c). There were orderly relationships between the amount and pattern of stimulation and the probability of a progestational response in the females.

Once the mechanisms necessary for pregnancy are initiated, litters are delivered 23–24 days later. Females mating in postpartum estrus, while nursing young, have a longer gestation period than females mating in cycling estrus.

SPERM COMPETITION

It is known that in the field, female deer mice often mate with more than one male during a single estrous period (Birdsall & Nash, 1973). Thus, it is of critical importance for a male not only that his mate become pregnant, but that she bear his offspring.

The phenomenon of sperm competition

The term *sperm competition* is used when the sperm from more than one male are in a female's reproductive tract at a given time (Parker, 1970a). As Parker noted, one would expect mechanisms to evolve in individual males that would somehow neutralize the effects of ejaculates delivered to a female before that male mates and that would prevent subsequent matings after that male mates.

A basic paradigm can be used in controlled studies of sperm competition. The first task is to search for order effects. Females are mated sequentially to two different males, with each male mating for the same number of ejaculations. A genetic paternity marker, such as coat color, is needed so that the paternity of the offspring can be determined. The order of mating by the different males is counterbalanced. The dependent variable is the number of pups sired by each male. When such studies are done with different species, different results are obtained (Dewsbury, 1984d). First-male advantages, last-male advantages, and no order effects have been reported for different species.

Sperm competition in deer mice

This basic paradigm of sperm competition studies was used with deer mice bearing genes for different coat colors: wild type, brown recessive, wide-band agouti, and blonde (Dewsbury & Baumgardner, 1981). Each male was allowed to attain two ejaculations, with several minutes allowed between the first male's last ejaculation and introduction of the second male. No significant order effects were found. Thus, when other factors are controlled, it appears not to matter whether a male mates first or last. The combination of blonde and wild-type animals was chosen for further study because they were the most nearly equal with respect to the *differential fertilizing capacity* of their ejaculates (the ability of males to gain representation in litters when factors such as the order and timing of matings are controlled).

By varying the basic design of this experiment, one can begin to explore the dynamic structure of the system and thus the constraints under which males work in maximizing fitness levels. The rules of the game are established in the female's reproductive tract; male behavior must be adapted to work within these rules. Varying the relative number of ejaculations by two males reveals that the male that gets more ejaculations sires more offspring (see Figure 2). Thus, a male that delivers multiple ejaculations to a multiply mating female is likely to sire more offspring than a male delivering only one or two ejaculations; Dickinson (1986) terms this "sperm loading."

One can also vary the delay between matings by two males. Delays of up to 2 hours appear to have little effect on sperm competition in deer mice (Dewsbury & Baumgardner, 1981). With longer delays, the interaction is more complicated (Dewsbury, 1988e). There appears to be a peak time of fertilizability near the end of the dark phase of the light–dark cycle. If a 4-hour delay is imposed early in the dark phase, it benefits the last male. However, the same delay late in the dark phase benefits the first male, the one mating nearest to the time of peak fertilizability.

Almost all studies have been done with females in cycling estrus. The same general pattern of sperm competition, with no order effect, also is found with females in postpartum estrus (Dewsbury, 1988e). However, delays between males appear to have less effect on postpartum females.

One problem that develops in studies of this sort is that the marker genes, or genes linked to them, may have secondary effects. For example, males of one genotype may generally prevail in gaining social dominance, a confounding factor if the relationship between dominance and differential reproduction is under study. We have therefore worked with variation in blood proteins, determined by electrophoresis, to find a marker gene for studies of sperm competition. We have chosen two alleles at the transferrin locus, one of which causes the blood proteins to migrate relatively fast on a starch gel, the other relatively slowly. There are few reliable differences in differential fertilizing capacity or behavior between "slow" and "fast" males. As with coat color, there is no order effect when the basic paradigm is used (Dewsbury, 1985d).

At the time of ejaculation, males deliver not only sperm, but also secretions of the reproductive accessory glands that coagulate to form a solid plug in the

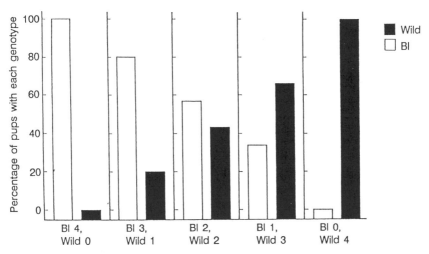

FIGURE 2. Litter composition of deer mice as a function of the number of ejaculations attained by two males. In each case, a blonde female mated for four ejaculations. When the two males mated, the blonde male (Bl) mated first and the wild-type male (Wild) mated second. The number of ejaculations attained by each male is shown at the base. Litter composition reflects the relative number of ejaculations by the two males. (From Dewsbury, 1984d.)

female's reproductive tract (Hartung & Dewsbury, 1978). It has been hypothesized that such plugs may benefit males in sperm competition situations by preventing, or reducing the effectiveness of, subsequent copulations by other males. They appear to do so in some species, but not in deer mice. In one study, we removed the plug of the first male before the second male mated, and compared the sperm competition effects with a control condition in which the plug was unmanipulated. There was no significant effect on litter composition (Dewsbury, 1988f). In practice, the plugs may not remain in place long, as the multiple intromissions appear effective in removing them (Dewsbury, 1981c).

In all of these studies, it has been the experimenter that controlled male access to females—surely an unnatural situation. The principles established with controlled access, as in the studies just discussed, apply well to more complex situations when two males have simultaneous access to a female (Dewsbury, 1984c, 1985a). Some additional complexities will be discussed below.

BLOCKS AND DISRUPTIONS OF EJACULATES AND PREGNANCIES

The complex interplay of male–male, female–female, and male–female interactions can be quite varied and subtle, as can its effects on the maintenance and blockage of pregnancies and the disruption of ejaculates.

Pregnancy maintenance and blockage

In some species, such as montane voles, the female is less likely to maintain a pregnancy if she is housed alone than if she is housed with or near the male with which she mated (Berger & Negus, 1982). There appears to be no such effect in deer mice (Bronson & Eleftheriou, 1963; Dewsbury, 1989a, 1989b). However, if several days after a female mates, the male with which she mated is replaced by a strange male, she generally fails to carry her pregnancy to term. This pregnancy block is called the Bruce effect (see Marchlewska-Koj, 1983) and has been demonstrated in deer mice (Bronson & Eleftheriou). A very weak effect may occur even later in pregnancy, after the fertilized ova have already implanted in the uterine wall (Kenney, Evans, & Dewsbury, 1977).

Another related pregnancy block has been found in deer mice. This was first apparent in the sperm competition studies described above (Dewsbury & Baumgardner, 1981). Females that had received two ejaculations from each of two males had a lower probability of pregnancy than those that received comparable stimulation from just one male. We then studied this phenomenon of pericopulatory pregnancy blockage more systematically. In a first experiment (Dewsbury, 1982d), females were more likely to deliver a litter if they mated with one male for three ejaculations than if they mated for the same number with two males, with or without a delay imposed. In subsequent experiments, females that mated with one male for three ejaculations, and that were then exposed to a strange male or the bedding of a strange male for 2 hours, were less likely to deliver a litter. As is the case with the original Bruce effect, however, nursing females display no such pregnancy blockage, presumably as a result of elevated prolactin levels (Dewsbury, 1985c).

Ejaculate disruption

Male–male competition can extend to the disruption of each other's ejaculates. Female rats require a period of quiescence, with no vaginal stimulation, for about 5 minutes after an ejaculation if sperm are to be transported into the uterus and pregnancy is to be successful. Because of the normal postejaculatory interval, males rarely disrupt the pregnancies they initiate. However, if another male delivers intromissions soon after the first male ejaculates, the number of sperm in the uterus is decreased, and the probability of pregnancy is reduced (Adler & Zoloth, 1970).

A similar effect was found in deer mice (Dewsbury, 1985a). In a study in which two males had simultaneous access to one female, we were more successful in predicting the composition of litters resulting from multiple-male mating if we eliminated from consideration those ejaculations that were followed within a minute or less by intromissions. This phenomenon was explored in more detail by Dewsbury, Shapiro, and Taylor (1987). When a second male delivered non-ejaculatory intromissions soon after an ejaculation, there were fewer sperm in the uterus than if a delay was imposed before the second male mated. However, in contrast to the results of the correlational analysis, no functional consequences of the reduced sperm numbers could be detected in parametric experimental studies of pregnancy initiation or sperm competition.

MALE CAPACITY

Following Darwin (1871), the processes by which males and females gain differential access to mating partners are termed *sexual selection*. This is generally treated as a subcategory of natural selection. The emphasis in research on sexual selection in polygamous species has been on male–male competition and female choice. It is believed that, because females of most species make a greater parental investment than males, they should be more selective of mates, and because sperm are not very costly to produce, males should mate less discriminately with many mates (Trivers, 1972). The general view is that male capacity for mating is virtually unlimited; a male "can never get enough copulations with as many different females as possible: the word excess has no meaning for a male" (Dawkins, 1976, p. 176).

In fact, at least among muroid rodents, male capacity is quite limited. After about four complete ejaculatory series, male deer mice generally slow their rate of copulation to the point that they can be regarded as sexually satiated (Dewsbury, 1979a). Recovery can be slow. When tested the day after a satiety test, males achieved a mean of less than two ejaculations. This level continues if males are tested daily (Dewsbury, 1983). Other measures of copulatory behavior, such as those shown in Figure 1, are also affected. This satiation is not absolute. Some resumption of copulatory behavior can be achieved in "satiated" males if a novel female is introduced (Clemens, 1969). This is called the "Coolidge effect" (see Dewsbury, 1981a).

The number of sperm deposited decreases in successive ejaculations within an episode (Figure 3), further revealing the limitations on male capacity (Dewsbury & Sawrey, 1984). A series of studies was completed to search for functional correlates of these decreased sperm numbers; none were found. Males that were partially depleted, having just mated with other females, were studied in tests of pregnancy initiation and sperm competition, but no effects of depletion were revealed in either situation (Dewsbury & Sawrey, 1984). Even when males were permitted to mate for one hour with each of three females, no effects were found in those males that continued to ejaculate (Dewsbury, 1988d). It appears that, unlike laboratory rats and golden hamsters, male deer mice stop ejaculating before the contents of the ejaculates become so minimal as to be of significantly reduced potency. In the sense of Halliday and Houston (1978), males may be

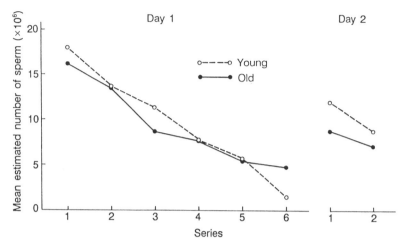

FIGURE 3. Estimated sperm counts ($\times 10^6$) over successive series and days for young (97–219 days of age) and old (325–623 days of age) males. (From Dewsbury & Sawrey, 1984.)

"honest salesmen" with respect to the delivery of ejaculates. It may be more beneficial to the male, in the long run, to avoid excessive depletion so that the recovery to levels of maximum potency is not delayed.

These and other data force us to alter our view of males, even of polygamous species. Male capacity to produce and deliver ejaculates, the true functional unit of reproductive capacity, is limited. Selection may not favor males that mate indiscriminately with as many females as possible, but rather, those that allocate their limited resources prudently (Dewsbury, 1982c).

SOCIAL DISCRIMINATION

In recent years, animals have been found to make finer social discriminations than had previously been thought likely. Researchers have looked for these capacities because theories suggested their existence. For example, individuals in at least some species should be able to discriminate kin from nonkin; doing so should help maximize inclusive fitness. Some potential mates should be of greater potential benefit to fitness than others. They might be better at accruing and defending resources, such as a territory or food; they might be more fecund; or they might possess genes that are either better adapted to the local environment or are a better complement to those of the individual. Because of these possibilities, we would expect mate choice to occur (see Bateson, 1983). As mentioned above, the general view is that females should be more discriminating than males (Trivers, 1972).

Estrus choice in deer mice

We planned a series of studies on the social discriminations made by deer mice, especially those related to mate choice. We began with what we expected to be easy: the discrimination by males of estrous (sexually receptive) from diestrous (sexually unreceptive) females (Dewsbury, Ferguson, Hodges, & Taylor, 1986; Dewsbury, unpublished data). Because rodents often use olfactory cues, it is common to present two odors to an animal and search for a preference (see Vandenbergh, 1983). First, we tried clean versus soiled bedding. Males and females both spent more time on the side of a cage lined with bedding soiled by a male or female conspecific than on clean bedding, suggesting that the olfactory apparatus was sensitive to conspecific odors. However, when we used bedding from estrous versus diestrous females, males showed no preference. Various combinations were tried: the nature and amount of the males' sexual and social experience were varied; the duration of soiling was varied; bedding was presented on the floor of the cage or in small test jars. Some males were given a choice between being near anesthetized estrous and diestrous females; others were given a choice between conscious females placed behind hardware-cloth barriers and males could choose to associate with them. We found no reliable evidence that males could discriminate estrous and diestrous females, or that they preferred estrous versus diestrous females. We did find that males preferred the odors of females to those of males. Even this preference, however, was displayed only when the odors were fairly intense (with bedding soiled for 6 to 9 days) or when the males had experience in a seminatural enclosure.

Preferences for kin

The predictions for tests of kin preference outside of the mating context are straightforward: animals should be selected to discriminate kin and nonkin, and should respond more positively to kin than to nonkin. Such preferences have been found in various species (e.g., Hepper, 1986). However, in three experiments with young deer mice, we found no such preferences (Dewsbury, 1989b).

Predictions are more difficult in the mating context. Countering considerations of kin selection are the potential deleterious effects of inbreeding. No clear predictions can be made (Dewsbury, 1988b). In one study, we paired either siblings or nonsiblings in breeding cages. Nonsibling pairs produced significantly more litters than did sibling pairs, suggesting some incest avoidance (Dewsbury, 1982a).

In a later study, females were tested for proximity to either a brother or a strange, unrelated male in four 15-minute tests, two when in estrus and two when in diestrus (Dewsbury, 1989a). In the first test in estrus, females preferred the sibling male; this was the only preference displayed. Our first attempt to replicate this preference effect was a failure. However, we were then able to repeat the result, but only in females that grew up with their sisters. It appears that familiarity with a sibling is necessary for the display of the sibling preference, even if the stimulus sibling is not the familiar one. At first, these results were surprising, because such preferences should lead to inbreeding. However, inbreeding by deer mice has been observed in the field (Howard, 1949). Further, these data are part of a wave of similar data suggesting that inbreeding may be less deleterious than previously thought (e.g., Bulger & Hamilton, 1988; Dewsbury, 1988b).

In studies in a seminatural enclosure, we found no differential direction of behavior toward kin when two brothers or two unrelated males were introduced (Dewsbury, 1988c) or when two male–female pairs were introduced (Dewsbury, 1989a).

We have tested for other social discriminations, including preferences for dominant versus subordinate males and for slow versus fast transferrin phenotypes; all have failed. Deer mice appear either not to make fine social discriminations or not to have strong preferences. The relative sensitivity of different species in making social discriminations appears related to the mating system they show in the field. Monogamous prairie voles are the most discriminating species with which we have worked (Dewsbury, 1988a). Although there is reason to expect finely tuned social preferences (and they are displayed in some species), we cannot assume such preferences to be universal. Deer mice provide a case in point.

COMPLEX SOCIAL SITUATIONS

Although in most of the research discussed thus far we have studied just one male–female pair at a time, more complex groupings have been discussed at various junctures. It is in such situations that the generality of and interactions among phenomena studied in isolation become apparent.

A potentially important determinant of reproductive success is *social dominance*. We define dominance solely as a stable asymmetry or predictability in the outcome of aggressive encounters. Thus, whether or not there is a priority of access to resources, such as mating partners, is an empirical question (Dewsbury, 1982b). Operationally, a male is treated as dominant to another male when he chases the other male at least twice as often as he is chased, provided that the dominant male shows at least 10 chases. It is generally believed that as a result of high dominance status, dominant males mate more than subordinates and, as a result of this, sire more offspring. However, in few studies have all three necessary links in this logical chain been demonstrated (Dewsbury, 1982b).

Our first studies were done in small test cages without a genetic marker; tests were conducted in a manner identical to those with a single male–female pair, except that two males and one female were present (Dewsbury, 1979b). The level of aggression in this situation varies with conditions. If the test occurs in one male's home cage, appreciable aggression occurs. In general, the dominant male achieves a disproportionate number of the copulations (see Figure 4A). However, if the two males are familiarized with each other by housing them together in a clean cage for 3 days, aggression is greatly reduced, and it is more likely that both males will mate (Dewsbury, 1979b, 1985a).

Next, we added the genetic marker by studying triads composed of a blonde male and female and a wild-type male in small cages. Again, dominant males achieved significantly more copulations than subordinate males. However, there

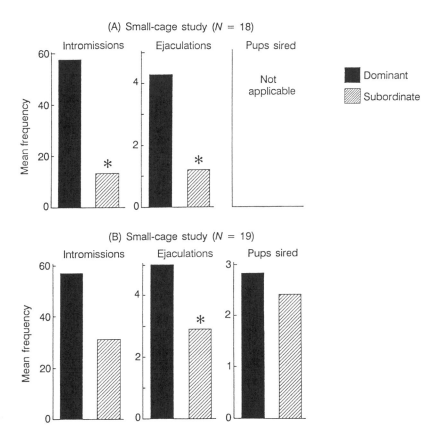

FIGURE 4. Results of two studies of dominance in deer mice tested in small cages containing two males and one female. The mean frequency of intromissions, ejaculations, and pups sired are shown for the dominant and subordinate males. In the first study (A), genetic markers were not used, and litter composition was not determined. In the second study (B), genetic markers allowed for the determination of the number of pups sired by each male. An asterisk indicates statistical significance.

was no significant reproductive advantage with respect to the number of pups actually sired (Figure 4B) (Dewsbury, 1981d).

Subsequent work on these problems has been done with seminatural enclosures, which have the advantage of being more like the deer mouse's natural habitat than small cages are. Each enclosure was constructed on a 4 × 8 foot (1.2 × 2.4 meters) plywood base and had three plywood walls, a Plexiglas front, and a hardware-cloth cover. Rocks, branches, food, water, and bedding were provided. Two males and two females were placed in each enclosure. Rather than lasting for a few hours, these tests generally lasted 5 days, and behavior was sampled according to a predetermined schedule (Dewsbury, 1981d). In the first studies, two blonde females were used with one blonde and one wild-type male.

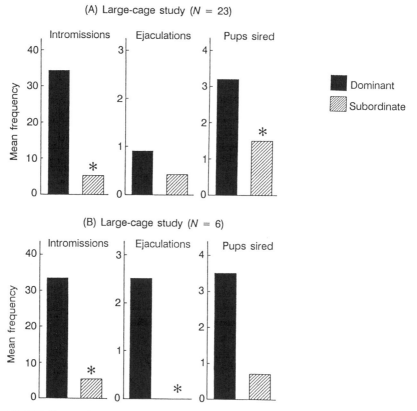

FIGURE 5. Results of two studies of dominance in deer mice tested in seminatural enclosures over 5 days (A) and over 12 days (B), with two males and two females present. The mean frequency of intromissions, ejaculations, and pups sired are shown for the dominant and subordinate males. An asterisk indicates statistical significance.

The dominant male copulated more than the subordinate male did and sired more offspring (Figure 5A). In an additional study, tests were run for 12 days, with substantially the same result (Figure 5B). In the seminatural enclosures, the amount of overt fighting was greatly reduced, as the subordinate male had much more room and more objects to help him avoid the dominant male.

The level of aggression in the enclosures is affected by several factors. Kinship per se has little effect. Placing pairs of brothers or unrelated males in the enclosure makes little difference. However, as with the small cages, familiarization has a considerable effect. If two males grow up caged together, whether or not they are brothers, the amount of aggression between them in the enclosure is greatly reduced (Dewsbury, 1988c). Placing two male–female sibling pairs in the enclosure produces little effect on male–female behavior; siblings are not treated differentially (Dewsbury, 1989a). Finally, the presence of females per se has a great effect on the level of aggression; there is little aggression if two unfamiliar males are placed in the enclosure with no females present (Dewsbury, 1984a).

If there is a selective advantage to dominance, one would expect it to be heritable. An important question is whether the son of a dominant male would be dominant to the son of a subordinate male. As deer mice generally do not disperse over great distances, such interactions are likely to occur in nature. Twenty-eight pairs of males were tested for dominance in a seminatural enclosure using our standard procedures. Then, after removal from the enclosure, the two males were mated to females that were sisters of each other but were unrelated to the males. The males were with the receptive females for one afternoon, pregnancy was initiated, and the males had no contact with their pups. When the pups matured, one male was selected from each litter, so as to minimize differences in body mass, and the sons were tested under the same conditions as their fathers. The paradigm was a variant of the standard genetic selection procedure. If the son of the dominant male was dominant, the procedure was repeated for successive generations. The sons of dominant males were generally dominant to the sons of subordinate males, even though they had never been in contact with their fathers. They displayed more chases, attacks, and displacements than the sons of subordinates did (see Figure 6). The differences were not due to differences in body mass. These data show that genetic differences are one factor among many influencing the dominance relationship.

A final study was designed to integrate many of the phenomena previously studied separately (Dewsbury, 1984a). One male was placed alone in the seminatural enclosure for 2 days. A second male was then introduced, and the two remained together for 5 days. The male with priority of residence gained an advantage with respect to chasing. Females were introduced into the enclosure only on two successive afternoons, so that we could obtain a complete sample of all copulations that occurred. The dominant male again copulated more than the subordinate male did. Sperm competition functioned in a manner similar to that

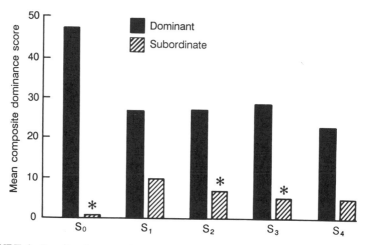

FIGURE 6. Results of an experiment on genetic selection for dominance in deer mice. The dependent variable is the mean composite dominance score (the total number of chases, attacks, and displacements) for each male. The values for the S_0 animals are for the original dominant and subordinate males in the base population. Remaining values are for the four subsequent generations, in which scores for the sons of dominant and subordinate males are compared. An asterisk indicates statistical significance.

in the controlled tests in small cages. Limitations on male capacity were apparent, as males both copulated less and were less aggressive on the second afternoon with females than on the first. Thus, the phenomena studied in small cages appear to be quite similar when examined in the seminatural enclosures, which provide a kind of "halfway house" between the small test cage and the field.

PARENTAL BEHAVIOR

The reproductive cycle is completed when young are born and are cared for by their parents. Although male deer mice are unlikely to reside with females and their litters in the field, they display appreciable amounts of paternal behavior when housed with them in small cages (Hartung & Dewsbury, 1979). In our study, both males and females sat on the nest, licked pups, and manipulated nesting material. Only females retrieved pups, however. In general, levels of paternal behavior were somewhat lower in deer mice than in other species studied. Although male deer mice have the capacity to display paternal behavior, one must be cautious in extrapolating from results of tests in small cages to behavior in the field.

CONCLUSIONS

I have described an integrated research program on the reproductive behavior of deer mice and its consequences for differential reproductive success. Its goals have been to reach a comprehensive understanding of the characteristics and constraints in the system and to relate these to important principles concerning the operation of natural selection. The key notions are that natural selection generally works at the level of the individual, and that the reproductive behavior of individual deer mice should be explicable as the outcome of individual animals acting in ways that should maximize levels of inclusive fitness.

Taken as a whole, the data seem to fit the principles quite well. The behavior of a male when alone with a female appears selected to maximize the chances that the female will become pregnant and carry her litter to term. When in the presence of other males, however, males compete for matings with females, as reflected both in the dominance interactions they display when in the presence of females and in sperm competition. Males chase each other and disrupt each other's ejaculates.

Other results appear more problematical. For example, male capacity appears more limited than previously thought. This has implications for understanding the need for prudent allocation of ejaculates and male choice. Deer mice appear much less discriminating in their social interactions than do other species of rodents. There is a need to determine more completely why some species appear quite precise in making such social discriminations, whereas others do not. It is surprising that young deer mice, in which kin selection should be the dominating factor, do not display kin-related preferences, whereas adult, estrous females do. Further, as the focus of much work has been on the avoidance of inbreeding, it is surprising that estrous females should associate selectively with their brothers. If we are to understand these phenomena fully, some revisions are necessary either in the theory or in the way in which the theory is applied to this system under study. With comprehensive, long-term research programs, we can gain an understanding of the complex processes related to differential reproductive success sufficient to test and refine important theoretical notions.

SUMMARY

This chapter includes a presentation of some contemporary views of the operation of natural selection and a description of a research program designed to explore the operation of these principles. Deer mice are found throughout much of North America, where they generally live in individual home ranges. Their copulatory pattern is quite stereotyped, with no lock, no intravaginal thrusting, multiple intromissions prerequisite to ejaculation, and multiple ejaculations in an episode. One consequence of male-derived copulatory stimulation is the initiation of a set of neuroendocrine responses in the female that make implantation and pregnancy possible. When more than one male mates with a female, as occurs in the field, there are typically no advantages to the first or last male to mate. Rather, the male delivering the most ejaculations sires the most young. If one male mates soon after another, he can disrupt the first male's ejaculate. Females mating with more than one male display a reduced probability of pregnancy. Male capacity is limited; this has implications for male choice. Deer mice display fewer fine social discriminations than other rodent species. In general, dominant males appear to copulate more and sire more offspring than subordinates do. The phenomena found in controlled tests in small cages apply well when tested in seminatural enclosures. Both males and females provide parental care when in small cages. These and related results relate to contemporary views of the operation of natural selection and the ways in which behavior is adapted to increase the reproductive success of individuals. Such research leads to a refinement of our understanding of both the theoretical principles we generate and the animals we study.

CHAPTER 7

NATURAL SELECTION AND REPRODUCTION: A STUDY OF THE GOLDEN ORB-WEAVING SPIDER

Terry E. Christenson

My principal interest is the evolution of reproductive behavior in the spider *Nephila clavipes*. In this chapter, I focus on the reproductive consequences of phenotypic (in this case, behavioral) variation, a cornerstone in the idea of evolution by natural selection. It is generally believed that the more commonly occurring behaviors or strategies in a population are maintained through the action of natural selection, and that selection operates at the level of the individual (Williams, 1966). To demonstrate that natural selection so operates, it is necessary, in part, to document differential reproductive success between individuals that display different strategies. In order to examine reproduction in N. *clavipes* from this theoretical perspective, I describe the natural history of reproduction for the species, assess the reproductive success of individuals showing different reproductive strategies, and determine whether certain reproductive strategies result in higher reproductive payoffs.

The description of the natural history of N. *clavipes* begins with courtship and mating. Then the reproductive consequences of the copulatory act are assessed. For two reasons, this assessment requires more than just counting copulations, although such frequency data are obviously important. First, it is possible that a male has no sperm to release to the female. Although sperm, in relation to eggs, are generally considered inexpensive and readily supplied (Trivers, 1972), the production of sperm or ejaculate might be limited in some species (Dewsbury, 1982c, this volume). Therefore, sperm transfer during copulation and sperm depletion are described. Second, males that mate with a given female may differ in the number of eggs they fertilize (Parker, 1970a). Austad (1984), in a pivotal review of spider reproduction, indicated that in the few species investigated, the first male has the advantage. So the first-male advantage in N. *clavipes* is quantified, and possible underlying mechanisms are examined.

The natural history continues with an examination of factors that might influence male access to females and likelihood of mating: male movement to the female's web, male defense of sexually immature females, duration of male residency on the female's web, the alternatives available to smaller males that are unsuccessful at overt aggressive competition, and mate choice. Postcopulatory behaviors, including male guarding of the female and female abandonment of the web, are described, and their effects on reproductive success are discussed. Many mated females move to open areas along the forest edge and build their webs in aggregations. The effects of such habitation on reproduction are briefly noted. The natural history is completed with a description of oviposition, egg hatching, and survival rates of the young.

Next a model of N. *clavipes* reproduction, consisting of critical aspects of the natural history, is outlined to determine whether certain common strategies shown by the majority result in relatively high reproductive benefits for the individual. The following fundamental issues concerning reproduction are addressed: (1) Female receptivity—what do female N. *clavipes* gain by being ready (and willing) to mate with more than one male? (2) Alternative strategies—since the most important decision the adult male has to make is whether to remain with a given female or to search for another, do small male N. *clavipes* who are unsuccessful at overt competition on a female's web opt for the most advantageous alternative available to them? (3) Apportionment of sperm—what do N. *clavipes* males gain by investing all of their available sperm with one newly molted female? The behavior of N. *clavipes* is then discussed in terms of natural selection.

THE SPECIES

The golden orb-weaving spider, Nephila *clavipes* (Figure 1), is a New World species described by Linnaeus in 1767 and last taxonomically revised by Levi (1980). Nephila is a practical choice for behavioral study because matings are easily observed and individuals are abundant, large, easily marked for individual recognition, relatively site tenacious, and readily maintained under controlled field conditions.

In our subtropical study site, there is one generation of N. *clavipes* per year. In the spring, spiderlings emerge from the egg sac and construct a communal

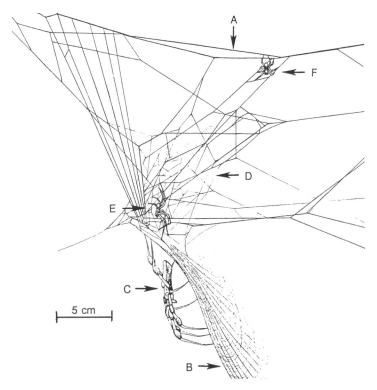

FIGURE 1. Side view of male and female *Nephila clavipes* on the female's orb web. A = support strands; B = viscid spiral; C = female (facing downward) at hub of viscid spiral; D = barrier strands; E = hub male; F = peripheral male. (From Christenson & Goist, 1979).

web, in which predatory behaviors are very limited. Within a week or two, the spiderlings disperse and construct individual orb webs consisting of radial strands and a surrounding viscid spiral in which prey are ensnared. Sexual maturation occurs within 3 or 4 months. Early in the summer, males mature to adulthood and shift from a sedentary, predatory existence to one spent searching for mates. Adult males are small (an average of about 8 millimeters cephalothorax–abdomen length) in comparison to the females (21 millimeters average at the final molt). During the mating season, there are about 2.5 adult males per adult female. Females mate just after they mature to adulthood, and also during adulthood, particularly when feeding. About 6 weeks after reaching sexual maturity, females at our study site construct one egg sac (rarely more), and provide no care for the young thereafter. Spiderlings emerge from the egg sac the following spring, and the cycle continues.

METHODS

Observations of N. *clavipes* were made at the F. Edward Hebert Center of Tulane University, situated about 20 kilometers south of New Orleans, Louisiana. The study site is a bottomland hardwood forest (see Christenson & Wenzl, 1980, for a more detailed description). Most of the observations reported in this chapter were gathered on females and males inhabiting a wooded portion of the study site in which females are generally solitary. (Connected web situations are discussed later).

The data were gathered systematically in the field, in much the spirit described by Schneirla (1950). Transect lines were checked weekly for 2 years to determine sex ratio, growth rates, and seasonal changes in microhabitat preferences. A census population of marked, unrestrained individuals was maintained during six mating seasons; more than 1000 males and 600 females were observed. Census data gathered each morning included: identification of animals on tagged webs, observations of behavior, and evidence of molting, oviposition, and male movement to other webs. Finally, hour-long detailed observations (serial records) were made on unrestrained and restrained animals.

Manipulative experiments have been facilitated by placing subjects in field boxes situated in the forest (Figure 2). By gathering penultimate instar females (those in the last immature stage prior to sexual maturation, just before the final

FIGURE 2. Field boxes placed in typical hardwood bottomland forest at our Louisiana study site.

molt) and having them mature in our boxes, we are assured that the females tested in our studies are virgin at the onset of the experiment. By collecting males that have just constructed sperm webs, we are assured they are virgin. While in the boxes, the spiders are subjected to normal climatic conditions; the females build normal webs and the males demonstrate normal defensive and mating behavior. With this method, we can control the females' access to mates, keep subjects from abandoning the web, and be sure of the maternity and paternity of a particular egg sac.

COPULATORY BEHAVIOR

Newly molted females

Female *N. clavipes* mate repeatedly during a 2-day period just after their final molt, and they also mate later in adulthood, primarily when feeding (Christenson, Brown, Wenzl, Hill, & Goist, 1985). Let us first consider mating that occurs just after the female's final molt. Males construct sperm webs (about 5 × 5 millimeters) on their last orb web on which sperm are placed and quickly picked up with the pedipalps (copulatory organs) (Myers & Christenson, 1988). Sperm induction to the pedipalp is efficient; examination of the sperm webs of several males revealed no remaining sperm. Thus, males that arrive on a female's web already have sperm in their pedipalps.

Males appear to require some stimulation in order to commence mating. Some males present at the female's final molt appear "excited," often moving onto and drumming their pedipalps against her exoskeleton. If placed onto females' webs about 12 hours after the females have completed the final molt, most males showed no interest in mating, at least for the few hours they were observed (Goist, 1982; Brown, 1985). It is possible that these males miss a volatile pheromone that is present at the final molt.

Males show virtually no courtship vibrations as they approach the female. They do not bind the female's legs with silk, as is noted in *N. maculata* (Robinson & Robinson, 1973). The male moves down onto the female's ventrum, drumming his pedipalps against her upper abdomen and the region where intromission occurs (Figure 3). The pedipalp (Figure 4A) consists of four important parts: the sperm storage duct, the conductor (a styluslike projection which enters the female), the embolus (the tube in the conductor through which the sperm move), and the hematodochal bulb (an inflatable sac at the base of the conductor). The conductor is thrust forward into the female's epigastric furrow (Figure 4B), sometimes inserted and sometimes withdrawn and thrust forward again. A copulation is scored when the hematodochal bulb rhythmically contracts.

Copulatory behavior is vigorous. Sixteen pairs of males and females were observed for 1-hour serial records on the morning the female's exoskeleton was

FIGURE 3. Male and female *Nephila clavipes* in the mating position.

noted. Pairs averaged 14 copulations, and 28 minutes in copula, per hour (Christenson et al., 1985). Census data reveal that 84 percent of newly molted females were observed mating the day of their final molt. Of the remaining females, 13 percent were with a male, but no mating was observed, and 3 percent were not with a male. It is difficult to turn the male off once he has begun mating, so matings frequently continue into a second day. We removed six unrestrained males that were mating with newly molted females and placed each of them with a penultimate instar female of comparable size. The males continued to attempt to copulate, even when the females oriented to, plucked at, and attempted to capture them. Five males were killed within an hour.

Older adult females

Now let us consider copulations with an adult female that is at least 4 or 5 days past the final molt. This is the time when the female usually leaves her web and relocates, so second males usually are not found with an adult female until after this time. Females that have mated at the final molt will mate again, usually when they are feeding (Christenson et al., 1985), although there is a tendency for virgin adult females to mate when they are not "occupied" with a prey item (Brown, 1985). The male demonstrates several often vigorous vibratory responses when approaching the female (Cohn & Christenson, 1987). Some responses,

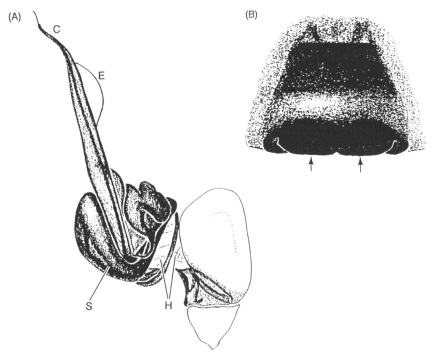

FIGURE 4. (A) Male *Nephila clavipes* pedipalp, or copulatory organ. S = sperm storage duct; C = conductor; E = embolus; H = hematodochal bulb. (B) Ventral view of female *Nephila clavipes* epigynum or sclerotized plate which contains sperm uptake tracts and spermathecae (just under the surface). Arrows point to areas in the epigastric furrow where the pedipalp conductors are thrust. (Adapted from Levi, 1980.)

such as strand plucking and probing with the forelegs, occur most frequently prior to the male's approach to the prey item. Only body jerking, a vigorous shaking of the body in which the forelegs lift off the web, occurs specifically prior to mating behavior. As noted by Robinson and Robinson (1980), courtship behavior in *N. clavipes* is limited in comparison to that of other orb-weaving species. We have noted no obvious relationship between male courtship vigor and likelihood of mating, but this should be verified through photographic analysis.

Once the male has moved onto the female's ventrum, insertion of the conductor occurs with some difficulty. Insertion is brief, and the contractions of the hematodochal bulb are so intermittent that they are difficult to count accurately. The intermittent nature of hematodochal bulb contractions (copulations) does not appear to be due to overt female action, because older females remain largely unresponsive.

REPRODUCTIVE CONSEQUENCES OF COPULATION

Sperm transfer and sperm depletion

The pedipalps of virgin N. *clavipes* males contain an average of 520,000 sperm (Cohn, 1988). In all males examined thus far, all of the sperm in the pedipalps are released within 3 hours after the onset of mating with a newly molted female, despite that fact that males continue to mate, intermittently, for 2 days. About 62 percent of the male's sperm are found in the female's spermathecae (sperm storage sacs) when they are checked about 5 days after the initiation of mating (Cohn, 1988). Males that mate with a newly molted female have no sperm left with which to inseminate another female. When placed with two additional sex-ually receptive, newly molted virgins, depleted males did not construct sperm webs and did not replenish their pedipalps with sperm. The additional females were made available over a 7-week period, longer than the longevity of unre-strained census males. Twenty percent of the sperm-depleted males mated with a second female, but examination of these females revealed that no sperm were present (Christenson, 1989). Therefore, copulation does not necessarily result in the transfer of sperm. As a consequence of sperm depletion, about 10 percent of unrestrained males sampled in hub positions in midseason had palps which contained no sperm.

The proximate factors that limit the number of batches of sperm available to the male are unknown, but there are at least three possibilities: that spermatoge-nesis has ended and no more sperm are available, that the ejaculate is costly and is not replaced (Dewsbury, 1982c), and that damage to the embolus from pro-longed copulation precludes the induction of sperm to the pedipalps. It is com-monly thought that broken emboli preclude further mating (e.g., Foelix, 1982). However, Breene and Sweet (1985) have shown that black widow males are capable of inseminating a second female even when the embolus is damaged. The cost-of-ejaculate hypothesis appears attractive: Lopez (1987) notes that male spider sexual activities decline after mating because of degeneration of "glands responsible for associated secretory processes." However, the nature and time course of such changes await histological definition.

In contrast to copulations at the final molt, Cohn (1988) has found that males that mate with older virgin adults over a 4-day period (Days 11–15 post–final molt) release about 66 percent of their sperm. On the average, only about 21 percent of the released sperm (14 percent of the male's total) is found in the female's spermathecae. This is, however, enough to fertilize her clutch of eggs. We do not know exactly how many of a second male's sperm are released after copulation with an already mated adult female, or how many of the released sperm will eventually be found in the spermathecae. The upper limits are 62 percent and 21 percent, respectively. To determine actual numbers, we are tag-ging sperm with tritiated thymidine, using autoradiographic techniques developed with Gary Dohanich. By examining the spermathecae of females mated to control males and then to males with radioactively tagged sperm, we should be able to assess the number of each male's sperm that are taken up by the female.

Male advantage at fertilization and putative mechanisms

Because spider females often mate with more than one male, male priority patterns for egg fertilization could affect the reproductive consequences of copulation. In the four spider species examined thus far, the first male to mate has the advantage in fertilizing the eggs: these include the jumping spider, *Phidippus johnsoni* (Jackson, 1980); the bowl and doily spider, *Frontinella pyramitela* (Austad, 1982); the golden orb-weaving spider, *N. clavipes* (Christenson & Cohn, 1988; Vollrath, 1980a); and the Sierra dome spider, *Linyphia litigiosa* (Paul Watson, personal communication).

We quantified the number of eggs the first male fertilizes in *N. clavipes* by presenting males sterile by X-ray irradiation (as described in Christenson, Schlosser, Cohn, & Myers, 1987) and intact males in a counterbalanced fashion to females and assessing egg hatching rates, as done by Parker (1970a) and Austad (1982). Let us say, for example, that one female receives an intact male and then a sterile male, and another female receives a sterile male and then an intact male. If the hatching rate of the first female's egg sac is high and the hatching rate of the second female's sac is low, we would consider this evidence for a first-male advantage. We introduced the first male at the time of the final molt because at least 84 percent of our unrestrained census females mate then for the first time. To simulate the typical case in which a newly molted female mates with one male and then mates again with other males as an older adult, a second male was added on Day 4 or Day 18 post–final molt, and was allowed to remain with the female for a week. We found that the first male fertilized about 82 percent of the female's eggs, with the remainder being fertilized by the second male. Fertilization rates were not significantly affected by the week in which the second male was added.

The structure of the female reproductive system appears to underlie the second-male advantage noted in many insect species (Drummond, 1984). Many insect females have a common sperm uptake and fertilization duct, so when fertilization occurs (often weeks after mating), the last sperm taken in are likely to be the first released; thus, they would be the first to contact the eggs. Austad (1984) suggested that the anatomical structure of female entelegyne spiders (those with separate sperm intake and fertilization ducts) also might facilitate the serial ordering of sperm. It is possible that the first sperm taken up are arranged in such a way as to be the first out during sperm release at oviposition. This is perhaps most likely to occur when sperm can be spatially segregated, as in species with spermathecae consisting of several compartments.

Nephila clavipes females have separate intake and fertilization ducts, but serial arrangement of sperm does not appear to account for the first-male advantage in this species. Preliminary histology of the reproductive anatomy of mated females, which I conducted with Brent Opell, reveals that the spermathecum is essentially a hollow ball (Figure 5), a shape that should facilitate sperm mixing, a possibility that Austad has noted. Mixing of different males' sperm is suggested in two other studies. Examination of the pedipalps of males in our advantage pattern study indicated that 62 percent of the sperm of the first male to mate with a given female (at her final molt) were found in her spermathecae. Cohn's (1988) analysis of matings with virgin adults on Days 14–17 post–final molt showed that 14 percent of the male's sperm were taken up by the female. Taken together, these studies indicate that about 82 percent of the sperm in the female's spermathecae come from the first male and 18 percent come from the second male. These numbers are similar to the percentage of eggs fertilized by the first and second males in our advantage pattern study. Thus, it appears that the males' sperm mix, and that sperm from each male have about an equal probability of fertilizing an egg. I should note, however, that because prolonged copulation by the first male after transfer of sperm appears to reduce the number of eggs the second male fertilizes (as will be discussed in more detail below), it is possible that fewer of the second male's sperm are actually stored. This could mean that the second male fertilizes about 18 percent of the eggs when his sperm account for less than 18 percent of the total sperm in the spermathecae. Histological and autoradiographic analyses should determine whether the second male's sperm, once in the spermathecae, have an advantage at fertilization.

What inhibits the second male from releasing all of his sperm, and why are so few of his released sperm taken up into the spermathecae? The possibilities include hardening of the female sperm uptake tract, plugs, and sperm maturation. The first-male advantage pattern in N. clavipes appears to be, in part, a byproduct of female maturation and subsequent sclerotization (hardening) of the female reproductive tract. Female tissues are relatively soft during the period of initial sexual receptivity, just after the final molt. As noted earlier, at this time males can easily insert the conductor, and within 3 hours of intermittent copulation, release all of their sperm (Brown, 1985; Christenson & Cohn, 1988). In contrast, males mating with older adult virgin females with sclerotized tissues, have difficulty inserting the conductor and, as already noted, subsequent copulations result in the release and uptake of only a relatively small proportion of the male's sperm (Cohn, 1988). Stimulation from prolonged male copulation just after the female's final molt may influence the sclerotization process. Linden Higgins (personal communication) has noted that stimulation (of unknown character) from male copulation facilitates changes in the external features of the sperm uptake duct and the size of the spermathecae. Unmated adult females were sclerotized to a lesser degree than females that had mated at the time of the final molt.

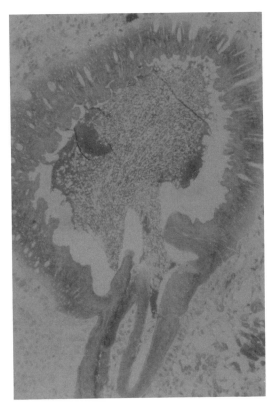

FIGURE 5. Photomicrograph of a *Nephila clavipes* spermathecum (400×). Coiled sperm are visible in the central mass. Note the two downward-pointing projections of sperm and supportive tissue. The right projection is pointing into the sperm uptake duct and the left into the beginning of the fertilization duct.

Certain of the data from our male advantage pattern study are consistent with such changes in the female sperm uptake system. By manipulating the copulatory time of first males mating with newly molted females, we influenced the percentage of eggs the second males fertilized. We observed 11 females molting, so we knew exactly when their mating began. They were allowed to mate for only 3 hours, enough time to allow release of all of the first male's sperm. A second male was added on during Days 4–11. Under these conditions, the second male fertilized 36 percent of the eggs, as compared to 18 percent if the first male had mated for the usual 48 hours. The increase in the fertilization rate of the second male could be due to increased sperm release and uptake. However, it is also possible that fewer of the first male's sperm were taken up into the spermathecae if prolonged mating facilitates sperm transport to the spermathecae. Histological examination is required to test these possibilities.

The formation of postcopulatory plugs could also influence the uptake of the second male's sperm. Such plugs occur in a variety of invertebrate and vertebrate species (Dewsbury, 1984c; Parker, 1984b) and it has been suggested that they may occur in spiders (Austad, 1984; Jackson, 1980). It would seem advantageous for the male to produce such plugs if this precludes the uptake of a second male's sperm. There is ample evidence of material lodging in the sperm uptake tracts of female spiders. Wiehle (1961) has noted broken emboli in the spermathecae of N. *madagascariensis*, although there has been no demonstration that such emboli can restrict uptake of subsequent sperm.

As Thornhill (1984) has pointed out, phenomena interpreted in terms of male benefit are subject to possible alternative explanations. In this case, plugs could be formed by the female. The female has the potential problem of sperm leakage, perhaps explaining why about 40 percent of the male's released sperm are not accounted for inside the newly molted female's spermathecae (Cohn, 1988). In N. *clavipes*, Brent Opell and I have found muscle tissue impinging at a narrowing of the fertilization duct, which would serve to keep sperm from leaking out at that end. However, no such muscle is found along the intake duct, so a plug might serve to restrict leakage at that end. We have found amorphous material in the sperm uptake tract of mated N. *clavipes*, but further histology on mated and unmated females and males is needed to clarify whether plugs occur, and if so, which sex produces them.

I have suggested that inactivity of sperm might underlie the first-male advantage in N. *clavipes* (Christenson, 1984). Spider sperm are coiled in a protein sheath at the time of induction into the male's pedipalp, and thus are immotile (Sharma & Gupta, 1956). If the second male's sperm were still coiled at the time of oviposition, the first male would have the advantage. However, Brown (1985) found that if mating occurs within a week prior to oviposition, the sperm become motile more quickly. In fact, we now know the sperm are motile within a day. The ability of rapid sperm capacitation has obvious reproductive consequences for both sexes.

MALE ACCESS TO FEMALES AND THE LIKELIHOOD OF MATING

Male movement to female webs

When his pedipalp receptacles contain sperm, the male leaves his web in search of mates. Males move mostly at night, and not necessarily to the nearest female. The likelihood of moving successfully is limited; only about 55 percent of the marked census males that disappear from one female's web are found with another female. Male size influences the likelihood of a successful move. Vollrath (1980a) noted that tropical N. *clavipes* males of medium size (by leg measurement) moved more successfully than larger or smaller males. Our subtropical census data reveal a similar pattern. Fifty percent (157) of our census males between 8 and 8.5 millimeters in cephalothorax–abdomen length moved from one female's web to another at least once, compared with 37 percent (14) in the 6–6.5-millimeter size range and 33 percent (26) in the 10–10.5-millimeter size range (Christenson, unpublished data).

The rate of successful moves is low in part because, unlike some other orb-weavers (Olive, 1982; Tietjen & Rovner, 1982), female N. *clavipes* appear not to produce an airborne pheromone which attracts males to their webs from a distance (Vollrath, 1980a). Males have not been attracted to the outside of our field boxes, which over the years have contained hundreds of molting and sexually receptive females.

Male defense of juvenile females

All males that arrive on a female's web with no other males present move quickly to what we call the hub position, in the barrier strands just above and opposite the female (see Figure 1). This is an area in which the female is not likely to respond to or catch prey. Now consider the situation in which a male arrives and another male is already present. Austad (1984) suggested that if the first male spider has the advantage in fertilizing the female's eggs, then males might be expected to defend a penultimate instar female that is approaching initial sexual receptivity. This is the case in a number of species (Robinson & Robinson, 1980), including N. *clavipes*. When a second male is placed on a female's web with a male already present, the resident male vibrates and leaves the hub area to move about the barrier strands (Goist, 1982). Males interact by probing each other with extended forelegs, chasing, and less frequently, fighting and biting. Two or three encounters are usually sufficient to establish the outcome (Goist, 1982); the larger male wins in about 90 percent of the cases (Christenson & Goist, 1979; Vollrath, 1980a). Intermale interactions are rarely fatal, although leg loss does occur (Goist, 1982). As Riechert (1982) suggests, communication seems more important than physical coercion in determining the outcome. The winner assumes the hub position, and the loser, or peripheral male, is relegated to the barrier or peripheral strands. Hub males mate to the total exclusion of the peripheral males in almost every case (Christenson & Goist, 1979; Vollrath, 1980a). Defense does not insure, however, that a male will mate—the female may abandon the web prior to mating, the male may be displaced by larger males, or the female may have already mated by the time the male arrives. Only 20 percent of our marked census hub males were observed to mate with a newly molted female. Some caution should be employed when interpreting male defensive behavior as defense of the female. Males occasionally move onto an abandoned web, or remain on a web after the female has departed, and defend the web from introduced males (Cohn, Balding, & Christenson, 1988).

Duration of male residency

If the first male to mate with a female has an advantage at fertilization, males that respond in ways that increase the likelihood of being the first mate would benefit reproductively. Is, for example, the duration of male residency on a female's web related to her proximity to sexual maturity? Census data reveal that hub males with smaller juvenile females (fifth or sixth instar) remain with them for an average of 3 days, while those with penultimate instar juveniles (approaching sexual receptivity) remain for about 5 days, no matter what the size of the female. However, in this case, male preference and female aggressiveness are confounded. Smaller juvenile females are quite aggressive toward males (Hill & Christenson, 1988). They pluck the web strands with their forelegs, as they do in predatory encounters, and chase the male (Christenson et al., 1985). The same problem holds true for males' slightly longer duration of residency with juvenile females than with adult females. Male preference is confounded with the possibility that repeated copulation (which occurs with the already mated female) regulates the timing of web abandonment. Choice experiments in which male spiders have equal access to females of different ages and reproductive histories are difficult to conduct because females generally are intolerant of one another.

Females of some orb-weaving species advertise their reproductive status once the male is on the web. Male *Frontinella pyramitela* first pseudocopulate (with no sperm) with a female, and then are more likely to build a sperm web and transfer sperm to the pedipalps if the female is virgin (Robert Suter, personal communication). In *Linyphia litigiosa*, a species in which the sexes are of about equal size, the juvenile female moves into the upper strands of her web, away from the hub area, when a male comes onto the web (P. Watson, personal communication). As her final molt approaches, the female moves under a domelike sheet. This movement and her subsequent behavior give the males present cues concerning impending sexual receptivity. As a consequence, male competition increases, and presumably the female benefits by mating with the most competitively successful male. In contrast, male *N. clavipes* attempt to mate even if the female is not virgin, and *N. clavipes* females do not change position when a male enters the web, perhaps because of the extreme dimorphism in size. However, the observation that older virgin adult females mate quickly, even when not feeding, suggests some means of communication of sexual readiness to the male. Contact sex pheromones are present on the female and silk in a number of orb-weavers (Lopez, 1987; Tietjen & Rovner, 1982), a possibility that needs to be explored in *N. clavipes*.

Alternatives available to the small male

Peripheral males on a female's web have the alternative of staying or leaving. If they remain, it is possible that the larger resident male will leave or die. However, as already noted, it is unlikely that peripheral males will mate with the female when a larger hub male is present. Sneaking has been noted (Christenson & Goist, 1979), however, this occurred only once and has not been noted by us since. If the peripheral male leaves the web and searches for another, he might find a receptive female with no male or a smaller male present on her web. The vast majority opt for searching (Christenson & Goist, 1979); they remain for an average of 2 days on a web, while hub males remain for an average of about 5 days. Of 457 marked peripheral census males, only 78 remained for longer than 2 days. Six (7.7 percent) of those that remained mated with the female. Of those that left within 2 days and were found on another female's web, 6.9 percent mated with a newly molted female (Christenson, unpublished data). The reproductive implications of staying or leaving will be assessed later in this chapter.

Mate choice

Given that males invest all the sperm they have with a newly molted female, males that exercise some choice of mate might be more reproductively successful than those that do not. However, N. *clavipes* males that mate with newly molted females do not appear to vary their copulatory time in relation to mate size (Vollrath, 1980a). Our studies indicate that males deplete their sperm stores no matter what the size of the newly molted female. Males release relatively few sperm when they mate with older adult females. Could this be attributed to male choice, with the male releasing fewer sperm in smaller females or females with sperm already stored? I do think not so, because males do not release more sperm to larger females and fewer sperm to smaller females (Cohn, 1988), and because there is evidence, already discussed, suggesting that female aging is a principal regulator of the uptake of sperm.

There are few well-documented cases of female choice in spiders; for example, female *Pisaura mirabilis* mate preferentially with males offering a nuptial food item (Austad & Thornhill, 1986). Female N. *clavipes* appear to show no choice, at least at the overt behavioral level. Newly molted females do not vary their copulatory time in relation to mate size (Vollrath, 1980a). Our observations also indicate that mating continues intermittently over 2 days, well beyond the time needed to transfer sperm, regardless of mate size. While gathering census data, we have observed very small males and males with only three legs mating with females. In addition, we have placed small and large males with eight or four legs with females that were about to molt. After molting, most pairs were observed to mate, and almost all of the mated females' spermathecae contained sperm. Nine of the 14 four-legged males were eaten by the females, compared to none of the eight-legged males; however, all instances occurred after mating.

Females probably have little to gain by mating preferentially with larger males. Body weight appears more under the control of food availability and ecological conditions than of genetics (Vollrath, 1980, 1987), although it is possible that genetics could influence web site selection and thus indirectly affect body size. Vollrath (1987) also notes that it is relative male size that determines mating success; that is, whether the male is the largest on the web. Larger does not necessarily mean better. Perhaps this explains, at least in part, why females do not advertise their reproductive status over a distance, a response which might increase the likelihood of mating with the largest male possible.

Under some conditions, female cannibalism of the male might be an expression of mate choice. Female spiders are commonly thought to devour their mates; however, the frequency of such cannibalism is actually quite low (Jackson, 1979). In 6 years of census data gathered on over 1000 marked males, we have noted only 30 instances of cannibalism, 8 of which involved adult females (Christenson et al., 1985). Of these, 6 occurred within 4 days after the final molt. At this time, the female appears very sensitive to the frequent approaches of the male. She may brush the male away from her abdomen, and eventually some males are bitten and devoured. It has been suggested that males sacrifice themselves as a food item for the mate. I agree with Vollrath (1980b) that this is unlikely. First, the male is small in relation to the female, so his food value is insignificant, especially since the unrestrained female does not lay her clutch of eggs until about 6 weeks after the final molt. Second, the male always attempts to move away from the female when not actually mating. Just after the female molts, the male will chew a hole in the hub just opposite the female to facilitate movement onto and away from her ventrum (see Figure 3).

It is possible that mate choice occurs after mating. Eberhard (1985) has suggested that variation in pedipalp morphology might influence the likelihood or extent of sperm uptake and storage. We have found no reliably measured variation in complexity of pedipalp structure, even using image analysis. However, Cohn (1988) explored the possibility that males with larger copulatory organs differentially stimulate the female and thus transfer or have taken up more of their sperm. He suggested that if this occurred in N. clavipes it would happen with older adult females because males routinely release all of their sperm when mating with a newly molted female. He mated males to older virgin adult females and then correlated various measures of pedipalp size with the percent of sperm available that the male transferred to the female. Larger males transferred more sperm; however, larger males also contained more sperm. Cohn concludes that pedipalp size by itself does not appear to relate to differential uptake of male sperm. Although our studies have thus far revealed no evidence of mate choice by the female (or male), we cannot rule out at this time the possibility of cryptic choice, particularly in postcopulatory utilization of sperm.

POSTCOPULATORY BEHAVIOR

After mating, male orb-weavers can either continue to defend the female or search for another mate. Males with a first-male advantage might not be expected to defend a female after mating, and they probably don't in species in which sperm are available to the male for subsequent inseminations. However, most male N. *clavipes*, which do not have sperm for additional inseminations, will remain with a newly molted female after mating. For 4 days after the female's final molt, the male will defend his mate against male intruders with about the same intensity as do males with penultimate instar females (Cohn, Balding, & Christenson, 1988). Although we have not added males after this time, most unrestrained census males continue to defend as long as the female remains on the web.

What benefits could the male derive by prolonged defense of a mate? Postcopulatory defense, at least within a few days of the female's final molt, might keep second males from introducing sperm if the female's reproductive tissues have not completely hardened. This possibility has been difficult to test. We have introduced second males within 2 days after the female's final molt, after the female has mated. However, as noted earlier, males that are not present at the time of the final molt are unlikely to mate with the female. Mating is seen several days later, after the female has commenced web repair and feeding. As Austad (1984) has suggested, postcopulatory guarding does not preclude mating by other males. Within 4 or 5 days after the final molt, about 80 percent of all mated N. *clavipes* females have abandoned their webs (Cohn, Balding, & Christenson, 1988). Males rarely move with the female, so when she establishes another web, other males are likely to be present.

We had once suggested that male postcopulatory defense might result in increased food intake, since the hub male occasionally feeds on prey captured by the female (Christenson & Goist, 1979). It is not surprising that giving isolated males prey items killed by a female increases their longevity (Cohn & Christenson, 1987). However, such feeding would potentially benefit those males who have not mated with a female at the final molt. In summary, the reproductive implications of postcopulatory guarding have not been clearly assessed but it is possible they are limited.

What benefits could the female gain by abandoning the web a few days after mating? The cost to the female must be great, as the moving animal is at risk. It is unlikely that the female abandons the male in order to find new mates; female N. *clavipes* have enough sperm from mating with one male to inseminate three clutches of eggs (Wenzl, 1980), more than are laid under unrestrained conditions. The reproductive implications of web abandonment by the female are deserving of further study.

Behavior on connected webs

The data presented to this point were generated from observations on unconnected female webs. However, intraspecific comparative study reveals variation in behavioral strategy related to ecological factors. Later in the mating season, many already-mated females build their individually constructed webs in aggregations in open areas where prey availability is relatively high (Brown et al., 1985). Farr (1976) and Rypstra (1985) also have noted aggregations of *Nephila* where prey availability is high. The costs and benefits to females of inhabiting such aggregations are not clear. Presumably, greater prey intake would facilitate rapid development of many large eggs, but females displace one another from webs, so there are costs.

Observations I made with Elizabeth Hill and Susan Brown indicate that under these conditions, male N. *clavipes* tend to mate and change webs often. As a consequence, males mate briefly with a relatively large number of females. The reduced degree of male defense could be due to several factors. First, the large number of males that are found on web aggregations might make web defense more difficult. Defensibility does, in part, determine the nature of competitive strategy employed (Emlen & Oring, 1977). Second, males may modify their defensive responses in relation to the value of the resource, because most females in aggregations in our population are adults, at least 84 percent of which have already mated at the final molt. Third, the males may be exhibiting risk-sensitive strategies, as noted in other spider species for foraging (Uetz, 1988) and mating (Rubenstein, 1987). When aggregated and solitary females are available, it is possible that some N. *clavipes* males might be acting in a risk-aversive manner by fathering few of the young of a particular female but by mating with several females. We are currently assessing the reproductive consequences of mating in aggregations through the use of radioactively tagged sperm.

OVIPOSITION, EGG HATCHING, AND SURVIVAL OF YOUNG

During the fall, usually after most males have died, females oviposit. Only 6 percent of our marked census females observed at the final molt were also observed to produce an egg sac; 91 percent of these females produced only one sac. The former figure is of course an underestimate of the actual number ovipositing, since some marked females leave the immediate study area.

To construct an egg sac, the female lays a mat of silk on the underside of two or three leaves, binding them together in the shape of an inverted basket (Christenson & Wenzl, 1980). Eggs are released onto the silk mat, and the female immediately wraps silk around the egg mass. She then moves from the egg sac along the connecting branch, flips around the branch, and moves back to the egg sac, laying silk the whole time. After an hour or two of such repeated movements, the egg sac is securely tied to the branch. Naturally occurring variation in sac structure results in variation in the survival of the young. Most egg sacs are attached to a branch as described above. However, a few are formed in the web; they fall to the ground and the eggs fail to hatch.

We assessed the functions of the egg sac's various components by manipulating the silk covering, the leaf canopy, and the sac's location on the tree before and after egg hatching (Christenson & Wenzl, 1980). The effects on the survival of spiderlings were profound: the choice of twig tip microhabitat, silk covering, and leaf canopy were all important for the successful hatching of the eggs. Secure attachment of the sac to the adjoining branch was essential at all times, since egg sacs that fell or were placed on the ground failed because of moisture and rotting, being preyed upon, or premature emergence. Only attachment to the branch was essential to the survival of the second instar spiderlings, the stage of development reached after the first molt, about 1 week after hatching. At this time, spiderlings are capable of producing silk, and thus of repairing and maintaining the sac. The spiderlings overwinter as second instars in the egg sac for 6 to 7 months, about half of their lifespan. Only about 50 percent of the egg sacs laid produce second instar spiderlings in the spring.

Egg sacs contained an average of 400 eggs, but those laid early in the season (August) contained more and heavier eggs than the relatively few laid in November (Christenson, Wenzl, & Legum, 1979), perhaps because the early females matured at a larger size. Spiderling weight might relate to survival through the long overwintering period, but our pilot data are only suggestive. In productive sacs, about 90 percent of the eggs would hatch. Eggs hatched in about 85 percent of the sacs laid early in the season compared to about 15 percent of those laid late in the season. This is probably due to egg infertility because of the relatively small number of males available to females that mature sexually late in the season. Maturation of males and females is synchronized so that most mature and mate in July. However, each year a few females mature sexually after the males have died. This phenomenon deserves further study.

RELATIVE ADVANTAGES OF
Nephila REPRODUCTIVE STRATEGIES

Figure 6 outlines the five aspects of natural history that are critical in evaluating the reproductive consequences of behavioral strategies of orb-weaving spiders. (I will not deal here with seasonal variation in body size and female tendency to build webs in aggregations.) Female sexual receptivity and male apportionment

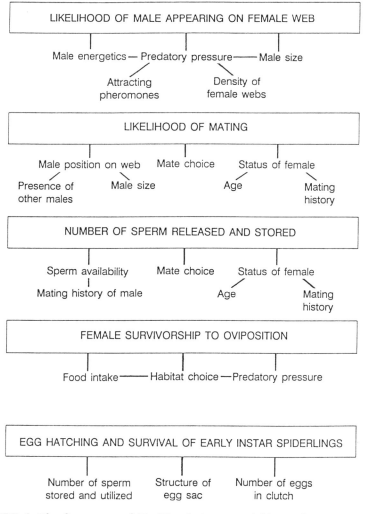

FIGURE 6. The five aspects of *Nephila clavipes* natural history that are critical to determining reproductive payoffs. Below each box are the factors that contribute to the numerical determination of each critical aspect.

of sperm will be treated hypothetically because I have noted no variation in these strategies under field conditions, and so no field data are available as to payoffs of various alternatives. As will be noted, further field and histological data are needed, so the following should be considered as preliminary attempts to assess the consequences of various reproductive strategies. For brevity's sake, payoffs for male strategies are figured in terms of eggs fertilized rather than spiderlings fathered.

The pattern of female sexual receptivity

Do female N. *clavipes* benefit from being able to mate with more than one male? As Austad (1984) has suggested, a high energy expenditure would be needed to keep persistent males from mating. He noted that when copulations occur during feeding, trying to keep the male from mating might inhibit effective feeding. I would add that the potential for multiple mating enhances the likelihood of receiving sperm. About 3 percent of our census females did not mate at the final molt because no male was present, and the pedipalps of about 10 percent of unrestrained hub males sampled midseason did not contain sperm. The likelihood of a male arriving at a female's web without sperm is less than 10 percent (estimated here at 5 percent, since the 10 percent figure undoubtedly includes males that were sperm-depleted because they had mated with the female on whose web they were collected.)

The likelihood that a female will receive sperm when mating only just after the final molt is estimated as follows: .97 (probability a male is present) × .95 (probability the male has sperm) = .922. The likelihood of mating as an adult female is conservatively estimated at 80 percent, based on 1-hour observations of unrestrained adults after prey were added (Christenson et al., 1985). The likelihood of receiving sperm when mating only as an older adult is estimated as follows: .9 (probability male present) × .8 (probability of mating) × .95 (probability male has sperm) = .684. So the chance of a female's being fertilized if she is more or less continuously receptive is estimated as follows: [.922 + (.078, the probability of not receiving sperm from first mating × .684)] = .975, which is greater than that if she is receptive only just after the final molt.

Alternatives for peripheral males

Do small male N. *clavipes* that are unsuccessful at overt competition on a female's web opt for the most advantageous alternative available to them? Peripheral males can remain on the web, and perhaps the hub male will die or leave and the peripheral male can assume hub status. Or the peripheral male can search for another female.

What is the payoff for staying on a web as a peripheral male? There is a 50 percent chance (at midseason) that the female is juvenile (or an older adult). The probability of a peripheral male mating with a newly molted female is .077 (this figure comes from census data, so it includes the possibility of male displacement and female abandonment of the web), and the probability of his mating with an older adult we estimate at .6 from observations of feeding adults (Christenson et al., 1985). The .6 estimate is lower than the .8 estimate (above) of the female mating, because at least three or four males will visit the female during her adult lifetime. A male mating with a newly molted female fertilizes 82 percent of her eggs (400 eggs in an average clutch). A male mating with an older adult female can fertilize up to 18 percent of the eggs, assuming she has already mated at the final molt, which is true of at least 84 percent of females, and assuming that she mates with no other males afterwards. To determine whether the latter assumption is justified, we need to determine how many males the unrestrained female mates with, and whether there is a maximum number of sperm (or volume of seminal fluid) the spermathecae can hold. Here, we estimate that the second male fertilizes 18 percent of the female's eggs. Because females appear not to advertise their reproductive status over a distance, males are equally likely to land on a juvenile's or an adult female's web. Therefore, both possibilities are included in the following calculations. The average payoff for a male that remains on a female's web is estimated as follows: [.5 (probability female is juvenile) × .077 (probability of mating if and when the juvenile female molts) × .82 (percentage of eggs fertilized) × 400 (eggs)] + [.5 (probability female is older adult) × .6 (probability of mating) × .18 (percentage of eggs fertilized) × 400 (eggs)] = 34.2 eggs fertilized.

Now consider the payoff for the peripheral male that leaves and searches. The chance of reaching another female is estimated as follows: .65 (census data indicate the probability of successfully moving as .55, an underestimate because some males undoubtedly move up in the canopy or out of the study area) and the chance the female is juvenile (or an older adult) is .5 (a figure which actually varies with the season). The probability of mating with a newly molted female is .069 (from census data), and with an adult .60 (estimate). Thus, the average payoff for leaving is: [.65 (probability of successful move) × .5 (probability female is juvenile) × .069 (probability of mating if juvenile female molts) × .82 (percentage of eggs fertilized) × 400 (eggs)] + [.65 (probability of successful move) × .5 (probability female is older adult) × .6 (probability of mating) × .18 (percentage of eggs fertilized) × 400 (eggs)] = 21.4 eggs fertilized. It appears that the better peripheral male response would be to remain on the web occupied by a larger male, because the risk of moving is high and the likelihood of mating with the female once on her web is low. However, as noted earlier, peripheral males leave rather than remain.

It would be premature to conclude that peripheral males are acting in a manner that leads to payoffs lower than those that are feasible. There are important data that need to be gathered. First, peripheral males might be monitoring social conditions on the web which could influence the decision to stay or leave. Therefore, comparisons are needed between situations in which peripheral males stay and those in which they leave. Second, census data need to be gathered in the upper canopy. Third, more detailed data concerning adult female matings are needed. Estimates had to be made at critical points in the calculations: For example, what is the likelihood that a male will mate with an adult female? How many adult females does a wandering male inseminate? Is there a maximum number of sperm that can be held in the female's spermathecae? We are examining these questions through the use of radioactively tagged sperm.

Male apportionment of sperm

What benefits do males gain by investing all of their available sperm with one newly molted female? Consider that the first male that mates with a newly molted female releases all of his sperm (1000 sperm, for the purposes of our calculations), 62 percent (620) of which end up in the female's spermathecae. As indicated by our study, a male that mates with a virgin adult female releases 66 percent of his sperm, of which 21 percent (140) end up in the female's spermathecae. There is a problem with using the latter figure in that, as noted earlier, it is not known how many sperm the male releases when copulating with an already mated female. Post–sperm transfer copulation of a prolonged nature by the first male might inhibit the release and uptake of the second male's sperm. For the purposes of this calculation, I assume that this is not the case. Therefore, in this example, a total of 760 (620 + 140) sperm is available to the female. Assuming that sperm of the males mix within the spermathecae and have equal probability of fertilizing the eggs (as discussed earlier in this chapter), the payoff for sperm depletion with the newly molted female is the fertilization of 81.6 percent of her eggs, about what we found in the male advantage pattern study.

Now let us consider a hypothetical apportionment strategy in which the males invest 50 percent of their sperm with the first female and 50 percent with a second female. I choose 50 percent because males can inseminate all of a female's eggs by releasing just over half of their sperm (Cohn, 1988), and males are not likely to visit more than a few females. Under an apportionment strategy, the estimate of how many of each male's sperm are taken up into the spermathecae is tricky. I assume that by releasing only 50 percent of the sperm, the first male to mate with the female would lose some of the first-male advantage. This assumption comes from the observation that the percentage of eggs the second male fertilizes increases (from 18 percent to 36 percent) when the mating time of the first male is decreased from the usual 48 hours to 3 hours. This increase in fertilization rate could be due to an increase in the number of sperm the second male releases and has taken up, or to a decrease in the number of first male's sperm that are taken up. Estimates of the sperm taken up by both males would depend upon which of the these two possibilities is applied to the calculations; therefore, separate calculations will be performed.

First, if the number of the second male's sperm released and taken up is increased, the first male to mate would release 500 sperm (half of the arbitrary figure of 1000), and would transfer 310 to the female. The second male to mate would release 50 percent of his sperm, of which 42 percent (about 210) would end up in the female. The 42 percent figure is derived by simply doubling 21 percent, since the percentage of eggs the second male fertilizes (21 percent) is doubled when the first male's mating time is decreased. When apportioning his sperm, the first male to mate would fertilize about 59.6 percent (310 of 520) of the first female's eggs. The payoff for mating with a second female is estimated as follows: [.65 (probability of successful move) × .5 (probability female is juvenile) × .077 (probability of mating) × .596 (percentage of eggs fertilized)] + [.65 (probability of successful move) × .5 (probability female is older adult) × .6 (probability of mating) × .404 (percentage of eggs fertilized)] = 9.4 percent of eggs fertilized. The total payoff for mating with both females would be fertilization of 69 percent (59.6 percent + 9.4 percent) of the eggs the two females laid.

Now consider the second possibility, that the second male increases the percentage of eggs he fertilizes not because more of his sperm are released and taken up, but because reduced first-male copulatory time reduces the number of the first male's sperm that are taken up. The first male would release 500 sperm (half of 1000) of which 44 percent (220) are taken up. This figure is arrived at somewhat arbitrarily by subtracting the 18 percent increase in second-male fertilization rate when first-male copulatory time is reduced from the 62 percent that are released when copulatory time is not reduced. The second male would release 50 percent of his sperm (500), of which 21 percent (105) would be taken up. The payoff for mating with the first female is estimated at 67.7 percent (220 of 325) of eggs fertilized. The payoff for mating with the second female is estimated as follows: [.65 (probability of successful move) × .5 (probability female is juvenile) × .077 (probability of mating) × .677 (percentage of eggs fertilized)] + [.65 (probability of successful move) × .5 (probability female is older adult) × .6 (probability of mating) × .323 (percentage of eggs fertilized)] = 8.0 percent of eggs fertilized. The total payoff for apportionment would be fertilization of 75.7 percent (67.7 percent + 8.0 percent) of the total eggs. In either scenario, it appears that investment of all of a male's sperm in a newly molted female results in a higher payoff (81.6 percent) than apportioning sperm. However, as noted, key census data need to be refined, and histological analyses need to be completed.

SUMMARY AND CONCLUSIONS

Field observation and experimentation were used in this study to explore the reproductive behavior of the golden orb-weaving spider, *Nephila clavipes*. Females determine the nature of strategies observed. Their stationary, solitary nature facilitates intermale competition because the female's web is a defensible unit. The outcome of such competition is size-dependent. The costs to the male of moving from web to web, in part due to the female's failure to advertise her presence over a distance, make it worthwhile for the male to remain with a female. This, plus the restricted probability of mating with another female if the male should move successfully make it worthwhile to invest all available sperm with one newly molted female. The first-male advantage pattern appears to be, in part, a byproduct of female maturation, which the male influences by continuing to copulate long after the sperm are released.

The reproductive strategies addressed in this chapter are interpreted in terms of natural selection. Hailman (1982) points out that in order to demonstrate natural selection, five separate issues need to be addressed: specification of the unit of selection, existence of phenotypic variance among units, transmission of phenotypic differences to successive generations, differential change with time in numbers of individuals with differing phenotypes, and reproductive or survival rates due to phenotypic variation among units. I assume that selection operates at the level of the individual, describe variation where it occurs, and assume that transmission of phenotypic variation is genetic. I have made no attempt to define the local population ecologically or genetically. Therefore, the work presented here is not a rigorous test of natural selection, but an examination of subparts of the overall problem, in particular, the reproductive implications of behavioral variation.

It is interesting to note which reproductive phenomena vary and which do not. Differences among individuals were noted in the duration of hub male residency on the female's web, the peripheral male's staying or leaving, the duration of postcopulatory guarding, and various features of egg sac construction. The variance in male activities can be ascribed in large part to the actions of the female and to male size.

Where phenotypic variation does occur in N. *clavipes* reproduction, the evidence (existing at this time) is mixed regarding whether the most commonly employed strategies result in relatively high possible payoffs. High payoffs are noted with increased duration of male residency on the female's web and with appropriate female responses during formation of the egg sac. There are, however, questions concerning the reproductive implications of male defense of the female after mating and the female's leaving her web after the final molt. Further, there is the finding that the majority of peripheral males leave the female's web when the higher payoff (at this time) appears to occur with staying on the web. However, as noted throughout this chapter, more detailed field and histological data are needed before one could conclude that any particular behavior or strategy leads to a reproductive payoff lower than what is feasible.

No phenotypic variance was noted in male drive to be in the hub position, in males' release of all their sperm with a newly molted female, in there being no female advertisement of reproductive condition over a long distance, or in there being no evidence of mate choice by males or females, at least at the time of copulation. These strategies appear to lead to high reproductive payoffs. Why is there variation in some strategies and none in others? Varying social conditions is one answer. I think the central (and invariant) phenomenon for male N. *clavipes* is a motivation to be near the hub, but how remaining at the hub is accomplished entails taking into account, for example, the number and size of competitors and female responsiveness. Therefore, there is variance in duration of stay on the web and in which alternative the small male opts for.

Two possible explanations for a lack of variance are that selective pressure has resulted in reduced genotypic and thus phenotypic variation, and second, that there was no variation in the strategy at the time of species inception. It will be difficult to test these alternatives, but any attempt to do so should include a comparative method that utilizes the phyletic history of the species and relevant sister groups. As Coddington (1988) suggests, perhaps the best way approach to evolutionary phenomena is through a wedding of ecological (as in this chapter) and cladistic (phylogenetic) approaches. This would provide a broad comparative framework from which to explore behavioral variation and the role natural selection plays in the evolution of strategies employed by a species.

CHAPTER 8

GROUND SQUIRREL REPRODUCTIVE BEHAVIOR AND MATING COMPETITION: A COMPARATIVE PERSPECTIVE

P. L. Schwagmeyer

The reproductive behaviors of animals offer a host of fascinating and worthy research topics. From an evolutionary standpoint, reproduction clearly is one of the critical moments of truth: genes more successful at promoting reproduction by the bodies that carry them tend to spread. On the behavioral level, of course, we cannot study genes directly; we can only study the activities of bodies, but this exercise can help clarify the diverse factors that affect differential reproductive success. The reproductive game can differ greatly for males versus females, young versus old, strong versus weak, and so on. It can also hinge on external conditions, such as habitat, conspecific density, predator traffic, and food dispersion.

As a graduate student, I began investigating a topic quite different from the present one: alarm calling and kinship-related behavior in thirteen-lined ground squirrels. I was a bit demoralized to find that field hours I spent watching marked individuals often yielded no data on social interaction whatsoever. The dramatic changes that occurred during the brief mating season thus were inescapably conspicuous: a 2-week social flurry occurred in which animals actually came into contact with each other on a predictable basis. Males chased each other about, pursued females, and harassed copulating pairs. In my naiveté, I thought that the overall level of male–male aggression during the mating season seemed extraordinarily high. As it turns out, neither the frequency nor severity of male aggression during that period is especially high, compared with that of some of the more social members of the genus. With growing opportunities for comparison among the related species (as field study results trickle in), we can now contemplate the diversity among these squirrels and try to understand it. That is, we can generate and test various hypotheses for why males of species A are prone to fight viciously over mating opportunities whereas males of species B adopt a more pacifistic style. From a bit of descriptive natural history, we can even begin making testable predictions about male behavior in unstudied species.

All of this, in turn, reflects back on and is enmeshed within the larger theoretical framework of sexual selection. Insights gained from work on crickets, dungflies, toads, and hyenas should, in principle, be applicable to ground squirrels, and vice versa. Each of these study systems offers unique combinations of advantages and disadvantages that allow piecemeal research progress on many fronts, but all can be coordinated into a more general picture through reference to underlying evolutionary principles.

Regardless of the animal under investigation, field research on reproductive behavior and sexual selection has traditionally included simple classification of the observed mating system as one of its preliminary tasks. This classification system (although not without difficulties, as will be illustrated) provides a shorthand description of whether monogamy or polygyny or polyandry seems to prevail, and, in the case of polygynous systems, of the methods used by males to obtain mates. In effect, it makes comparative work on the ecological and evolutionary determinants of mating systems possible.

I review below the array of ground squirrel polygynous mating systems, briefly describing the characteristic features of each. Next, I consider the phenotypic correlates of male mating success under the different forms of polygyny. If there has been a runner-up for the title of most popular topic within field research on reproductive behavior, it surely has been the study of which phenotypic traits of males are associated with obtaining many matings. These should vary according to the mating system, so male morphological or behavioral traits favored by sexual selection may also be expected to vary. Finally, I examine interspecific differences in particular aspects of reproductive behavior, with discussion of their potential sources.

INTERSPECIFIC DIVERSITY IN THE MATING SYSTEMS OF GROUND-DWELLING SCIURIDS

Before focusing on diversity among the North American ground-dwelling sciurids (marmots, prairie dogs, and ground squirrels), it seems appropriate to mention a few of their shared characteristics. First, they are generally quite cooperative and appealing subjects for field studies of behavior (Figure 1): unlike most rodents, they are diurnal, they are large enough to observe at a distance

FIGURE 1. Female "V" (*Spermophilus tridecemlineatus*) with a portion of her recently weaned litter. (Photo by D. W. Mock.)

(they can carry a 5-centimeter-high identifying number or letter dyed into their fur that can be recognized easily at a convenient distance), and they are usually easy to trap without harming them (being irresistibly drawn to peanut butter). Many of the species studied thus far live in relatively open habitats, so maintaining visual contact with individuals is feasible. Most of the temperate North American species hibernate, and have a single mating season each year that commences shortly after spring emergence (Michener, 1984) and lasts for 2 to 3 weeks (Dobson, 1984). Breeding is thus relatively synchronous. The trend seems to be that each female is sexually receptive for only a few hours (e.g., Hanken & Sherman, 1981; Hoogland & Foltz, 1982; Schwagmeyer & Parker, 1987).

Now for the diversity. At the outset, it should be noted that the past decade of empirical research has yielded evidence for considerable *intra* specific variation in animal mating systems—rather than being species-specific features, the methods individuals use to acquire mates may be observably different in different populations, or may change substantially across time within a population. Sciurid examples of the labile nature of mating systems include hoary marmots

(*Marmota caligata*) and Richardson's ground squirrel (*Spermophilus richardsonii*). Some *M. caligata* populations are polygynous (Barash, 1981), whereas others are monogamous (Holmes, 1984); populations of *S. richardsonii* vary in the prevalence of male territoriality (Davis & Murie, 1985). The following characterization of species as having a distinct mating system, then, is simply a shorthand way of saying that, in the particular population(s) scrutinized thus far, certain aspects of the reproductive behavior of individuals conformed to some author's definition of that system.

Female/harem defense polygyny

Depending on whose definitional framework is followed, and whether one prefers to lump or split, three to seven forms of polygyny can be applied to ground-dwelling sciurids (Table 1). The most commonly reported pattern is one in which sexually active males defend areas in which females reside (see also reviews by Armitage, 1986; Dobson, 1984). In many cases, the territorial defense is reinforced by direct defense of the resident females against intruding males (e.g., *S. variegatus*: Johnson, 1981; *S. beecheyi*: Dobson, 1983; *S. parryii*: McLean, 1983; *Cynomys ludovicianus*: Grady & Hoogland, 1986). An assortment of labels has been applied to this method of mate acquisition: male territoriality, female defense polygyny, resource defense polygyny, harem defense polygyny, and male defense polygyny (Table 1; see also Dobson, 1984). It seems doubtful that these various terms actually reflect real differences in male reproductive behavior within this group, and this has tempted some authors to lump them into a single system (Armitage, 1986; Dobson, 1984). Armitage has argued persuasively against the use of "resource defense polygyny" as a label for this pattern, on the grounds that it differs radically from resource defense polygyny as practiced by birds (the distinction being that, unlike birds, male sciurids do not defend resources that will attract females, but instead defend areas already occupied by females). This leaves "female defense" or "harem defense" as the remaining terms available within what seems to have become the most standard classification of polygynous systems (Emlen & Oring, 1977).

   Whatever it is called, one of the distinguishing characteristics of this mating system is that male dominance is site-related during the breeding season (Dobson, 1984); that is, males tend to win aggressive disputes with competitors when those occur within their own home areas, and to lose when they take place elsewhere. Each male's domain may be quite small: territory sizes for *S. richardsonii*, for example, range from 0.16 to 0.57 hectares (Davis & Murie, 1985), and the average for territorial *S. columbianus* males is only 0.1 hectares (Murie & Harris, 1978). Other distinctive behaviors that have been described as components of territorial defense include scent marking (*S. columbianus*: Harris & Murie, 1982; Murie & Harris, 1978), routine patrolling (*Marmota caligata*: Ar-

TABLE 1. Variation in Ground Squirrel Mating Systems

Latin name	Common name	Form of polygyny	Reference
Cynomys ludovicianus	black-tailed prairie dog	harem defense	Hoogland & Foltz, 1982
Marmota flaviventris	yellow-bellied marmot	female defense	Armitage, 1986
Marmota caligata	hoary marmot	territoriality[a]	Barash, 1981
Spermophilus beecheyi	California ground squirrel	male defense	Dobson, 1983, 1984
Spermophilus beldingi	Belding's ground squirrel	male dominance	Sherman & Morton, 1984
Spermophilus columbianus	Columbian ground squirrel	territoriality[a]	Murie & Harris, 1978
Spermophilus parryii	arctic ground squirrel	territoriality[a]	McLean, 1983
Spermophilus richardsonii	Richardson's ground squirrel	male defense	Davis & Murie, 1985
Spermophilus tridecemlineatus	thirteen-lined ground squirrel	scramble competition	Schwagmeyer & Woontner, 1986
Spermophilus variegatus	rock squirrel	resource defense	Johnson, 1981

[a]Author indicates male territorial behavior during the mating season, but does not designate a specific form of polygyny.

mitage, 1974), and parallel running along adjacent boundaries (S. parryii: Carl, 1971; McLean, 1983).

Few estimates of the seasonal mating success of males practicing female/harem defense have been published so far, but those that have suggest that the number of mates per male is probably quite restricted. In yellow-bellied marmots, harem size averages 2.27 adult females (Armitage, 1986); in black-tailed prairie dogs, males are reported to copulate with an average of 3.7 females per year (Hoogland & Foltz, 1982).

Male dominance polygyny

The site-specific dominance and site-specific defense that typify female/harem defense polygyny seem to be absent in several species of *Spermophilus*. In *S. armatus* (Balph, 1984), *S. tereticaudus* (Dunford, 1977), and *S. beldingi* (Sherman & Morton, 1984), males apparently do not defend geographic positions throughout a mating season, although elements of territoriality are observable on a shorter time scale in S. *armatus* and S. *beldingi*. The S. *beldingi* mating system has been described as both "male dominance polygyny" and as a "resource-based lek": males aggregate near females' hibernacula, and females are reported to solicit matings with dominant males (Sherman & Morton, 1984). While highly successful males may mate with up to seven females per breeding season, the majority of males apparently fail to copulate (Sherman, 1980).

Scramble competition polygyny

Male thirteen-lined ground squirrels (S. *tridecemlineatus*) also do not defend discrete areas during the mating season. This species represents yet another mating system, namely, "scramble competition polygyny." Males search extensively for mating opportunities, covering a mean of 4.7 hectares during two weeks of breeding (Schwagmeyer, 1988). The number of mates acquired per male averaged five or six per season (derived from focal-male sampling data presented in Schwagmeyer, 1988), although this surely varies across years with changes in female density.

In sum, the tribe Marmotini (ground-dwelling sciurids) exhibits considerable diversity in its polygynous mating systems, even when the farrago of terminology is trimmed sharply. The underlying evolutionary causes for these differences can be explored by examining the ecological characteristics of each species.

Ecological correlates of mating system diversity

Dobson (1984) recently evaluated several hypotheses about variation in ground squirrel polygyny. His results indicated that male territoriality during the mating season tends to occur in species with relatively low adult densities, while high-density species lean toward nonterritorial forms of polygyny. Dobson's proposed general explanation for this finding was that the economic defensibility of territories (and of the females residing within them) declines with increases either in male density (Emlen & Oring, 1977) or in the density of females requiring defense.

The outlier in Dobson's results was the thirteen-lined ground squirrel, which is nonterritorial and lives at densities far lower than those of several of the territorial species. The lack of territorial defense in S. *tridecemlineatus* is, again, perhaps best explained in terms of economic defensibility. Whereas its overall population densities fall within the range of those reported for a territorial congener, S. *parryii* (Dobson, 1984), a more critical factor, female spatial dispersion, differs between the two species. Female S. *parryii* tend to live in clusters near major burrow systems (McLean, 1982), which should facilitate male territorial defense (Armitage, 1986). Thirteen-lined females, by contrast, tend not to cluster. Ordinarily, it probably would be impossible for a male thirteen-lined ground squirrel to control access to several females simultaneously. As in insects (Alcock, 1980; Smith & Alcock, 1980; Thornhill & Alcock, 1983), scramble competition polygyny in the ground-dwelling sciurids seems to be favored when females are spatially dispersed.

The relative importance of various forms of intrasexual competition across mating systems

After decades of automatically equating male–male competition with physical combat, the contemporary trend has been toward a much more expansive view of the ways in which males compete. This greater open-mindedness has led to a spate of astonishing discoveries, including the fact that damselfly penises have hooks for scooping out other males' ejaculate (Waage, 1979), that male bower-birds steal especially attractive decorations from the courtship bowers of their competitors (Borgia & Gore, 1986), that male scorpionflies sometimes impersonate females so as to filch nuptial gifts (Thornhill, 1979), and so on. Clearly, fighting is not the only means of competing.

Male ground squirrels also have diverse channels through which they affect each other's reproductive success. Overt aggression is, of course, one of these: it accompanies territory maintenance in some species (e.g., Armitage, 1974; Dobson, 1983; Murie & Harris, 1978), and is used to establish mating priority in others (Sherman & Morton, 1984). Sexual interference also occurs (Grady & Hoogland, 1986; Schwagmeyer & Brown, 1983; Schwagmeyer & Parker, 1987), though its reproductive consequences have not yet been established. Males of some species engage in competitive mate searching (Schwagmeyer & Woontner, 1986); infanticide also has been documented (McLean, 1983). Finally, in some cases males face sperm competition, a phenomenon that can transform otherwise equivalent copulations by two males into vastly different numbers of offspring sired by each (see Dewsbury, 1984d, this volume). With the exception of infanticide, these forms of intrasexual competition can be partitioned into two precopulatory modes, overt conflict and competitive mate searching, and one postcopulatory mode, sperm competition.

Most schemes for classifying mating systems recognize either implicitly or explicitly that the significance of specific forms of male–male competition will differ according to the type of polygyny practiced. Clear-cut predictions regarding the relative impact of both overt conflict and competitive mate searching across mating systems are already firmly established in the literature. Emlen and Oring (1977), for instance, define "female (or harem) defense polygyny" as the direct control of access to females by males, and indicate that such control probably will require aggressive exclusion of other males. The importance of overt conflict to male reproduction also is evident in their description of "male dominance polygyny," wherein males are chosen by females primarily on the basis of their dominance status. Thus, victory in territorial disputes or in combat over estrous females is expected to have a major influence on male mating success under male dominance or female defense polygyny (see also Trivers, 1972). In contrast, "scramble competition polygyny" features mate searching rather than combat as the chief mode of precopulatory competition (by definition: Alcock, 1980; Thornhill & Alcock, 1983; Wells, 1977); skill in competitive mate searching presumably is less relevant in female defense polygyny or male dominance polygyny.

The predictions are not so clear cut with respect to how sperm competition ought to vary in importance across polygynous systems. The general consensus is that it will be less of a factor in breeding systems where a single male is guaranteed exclusive access to a group of females than in contexts where males are unable to monopolize females (Harvey & Harcourt, 1984). A major problem exists in attempts to refine this principle into specific predictions of sperm competition's role across more narrowly defined polygynous systems, as is clearly illustrated by the harem-polygynous ground squirrels. In *Marmota flaviventris* (Schwartz & Armitage, 1980) and *Cynomys ludovicianus* (Foltz & Hoogland, 1981; Hoogland & Foltz, 1982), males appear to have exclusive or virtually exclusive access to the females residing within their territories. On the other hand, extensive male trafficking between territories has been noted during the mating season in *S. columbianus* (Murie & Harris, 1978) and *S. parryii* (McLean, 1983), and copulations by subordinate, nonterritorial males have been observed in *S. richardsonii* (Davis, 1982; Davis & Murie, 1985). Given this range in de facto monopolization of sexual access to females, the only safe conclusion about sperm competition's relative importance in this mating system leads us full circle back to our general expectation: it can be considered trivial only to the extent that female defense is impermeable or effectively so. Basically, the ecological and demographic parameters that shape a population's mating system are not perfectly matched with those that determine the degree to which sexually active females can or will be monopolized.

Factors affecting the relative importance of sperm competition and species variation in the incidence of sperm competition will be treated further in the next section. First, the information available on the significance of overt conflict and competitive mate searching across ground squirrel mating systems will be reviewed. Two lines of evidence are used in assessing the significance of overt conflict and competitive mate searching across ground squirrel mating systems: (1) whether male performance in each category of competition is related positively to mating success in field populations, and (2) whether the male attributes that are expected to confer an advantage in the competition are relatively exaggerated.

PHENOTYPIC CORRELATES OF MALE MATING SUCCESS AND THE COMPARATIVE STUDY OF SEXUALLY SELECTED TRAITS

The role of overt conflict ability

Traditionally, research on which males win in mating competition has focused overwhelmingly on determining whether males dominant in aggressive interactions are favored. Several factors have no doubt contrived to establish the pursuit of dominance/reproductive success data as especially appealing to students of mammalian sexual selection. First of all, perspectives on how mating competition operates have been historically intertwined with theoretical views on the evolution of sexual dimorphism; Darwin's theory of sexual selection was, after all, an attempt to explain how secondary sexual characteristics arose (1871, vol. 1). The most obvious of such features among mammals are horns, antlers, and the large body size of males, that is, attributes that were reasonably inferred as being advantageous during aggressive disputes over mating opportunities. When coupled with Darwin's conviction that combat was the predominant mode of intrasexual competition operating among mammals (1871, vol. 2), a widely held expectation followed, namely that polygynous mammals would show strong positive correlations between both male body size and dominance and between dominance and mating success. A less intellectually laudable, but no less compelling, reason for the bias toward such studies is that dominance often is the most readily measured or estimated characteristic that *might* correlate with mating success (but see Dewsbury, 1982b, for discussion of possible pitfalls in measuring dominance). Further speculations regarding mammalian researchers' obsession with this variable will be left to the reader.

For mammals generally, though, the relationship between male dominance and reproductive success remains poorly understood (Dewsbury, 1982b). This applies to the ground-dwelling sciurids as well, with at least part of the problem stemming from the difficulties in estimating male reproductive success. Male ability to win in aggressive contests has been reported to confer significant mating advantages in the male dominance polygyny system of S. beldingi (Sherman, 1976). (In addition, males, but not females, of this species routinely do not become reproductively mature until they are two years old; this sexual bimaturism has been interpreted as reflecting the importance of overt conflict ability to male reproductive success: Bushberg & Holmes, 1985). Among S. columbianus, subordinate, nonterritorial males have not been observed to participate in breeding (Murie & Harris, 1984), although the majority appear to be reproductively mature (Murie & Harris, 1978).

By contrast, dominance seems generally to be an unreliable predictor of male mating success in the scramble competition polygyny system of thirteen-lined ground squirrels. Nonsignificant positive correlations between the percentage of conflicts won by males and copulatory success occurred at a Michigan site in two breeding seasons (Schwagmeyer & Brown, 1983). In an Oklahoma population, neither the percentage of conflicts won by males when searching for mates (data from two mating seasons) nor the percentage won when contesting access to estrous females (data from three mating seasons) was significantly associated with mating success (Schwagmeyer & Woontner, 1986). Thus, there do seem to be interspecific differences within the group in the relative importance of overt conflict ability for male mating success, but additional data will be necessary to determine whether these differences are consistent with the trends predicted by the mating system(s) typically practiced by the species.

Selection for large males

Further work also is needed before a related issue—whether male body size and mating success covary predictably—can be addressed adequately. For three species of *Spermophilus* (*beldingi*: Sherman, 1976; *tereticaudus*: Dunford, 1977; *tridecemlineatus*: Schwagmeyer & Brown, 1983; Schwagmeyer & Woontner, 1986), data are available on how a male's weight influences his ability to dominate competitors. Not surprisingly, all indicate an advantage for larger males. One might expect, then, that (1) when overt conflict ability serves as a consistently strong predictor of mating success, there should be a positive correlation between weight and mating success, and, conversely, (2) when male dominance is relatively unimportant as a determinant of mating success, there should not.

Amazingly, this argument has two data points in its favor. With regard to prediction (1), in the combat-oriented *S. beldingi*, heavier males seem to have an advantage in mating (Sherman, 1976). With respect to prediction (2), male weight and mating success appear not to be reliably associated in *S. tridecemlineatus* (cf. Schwagmeyer & Brown, 1983; Schwagmeyer & Woontner, 1986). The results for *S. tridecemlineatus* were based on male mating success scores that included every focal female with which each male copulated. However, a more subtle channel exists through which dominance or large size could affect male reproductive success: large males may be superior in securing matings that are particularly effective in fertilization. This is plausible, because in local competition over individual estrous females, there is a tendency for the first male that locates and copulates with a female to be heavier than the second male, the second to be heavier than the third, etc. (Schwagmeyer & Parker, 1987). In addition, paternity analyses suggest that only the first two males to mate with a female are likely to sire any offspring (Foltz & Schwagmeyer, 1989). But even when sperm competition effects are incorporated into estimates of male mating success, no large-male advantage emerges on a population-wide basis. With mating success scores modified to exclude third and fourth males, the relationship between mean weight during the mating season and success in mating was nonsignificant (1983: $r = 0.05$, $p > .10$, $N = 14$ males; 1984: $r = -0.24$, $p > .10$, $N = 11$ males).

Nevertheless, the predicted *lack* of a relationship between male body size and mating success when dominance fails to confer an advantage is based on overly simplistic assumptions. Specifically, it assumes that large male size is good for nothing other than overt conflict. Clearly, in some species large size could be advantageous in alternative forms of intrasexual competition: big males may be capable of searching farther or faster, big males may be preferred by females, big males may metabolize feistier sperm, and so on.

Several authors recently have reexamined the question of whether species differences in male size-related advantages in sexual selection can be expected to explain interspecific variation in sexual size dimorphism. One of the important (but frequently neglected) take-home messages is that sexual selection for large male size need not be accompanied by sexual size dimorphism, depending on how size influences the reproductive success of females and on how variable female reproductive success is relative to male reproductive success (Clutton-Brock, 1983). Size dimorphism is the norm among adult ground squirrels, with male body mass averaging 1.25 times that of females (see review by Armitage, 1981). There is considerable diversity (range = 1.01 to 1.82) among species, and the sources of it deserve further examination. Armitage has suggested that the sexual dimorphism of ground squirrels is probably affected by sex-specific requirements for nutrient stores used during spring breeding. He notes that the degree of size dimorphism is likely to be limited, even when sexual selection favors large males, if it is accompanied by a large-female advantage in surviving hibernation and breeding successfully upon emergence. The application of new techniques for measuring the daily energetic expenditures of free-living sciurids (see Kenagy's 1987 work on *S. saturatus*) should be highly useful in future attempts to identify the origins of interspecific variation in size dimorphism.

Effects of mate location ability

By far the majority of research on male mate-searching behavior has concerned insects (reviews by Parker, 1978a, 1978b; Thornhill & Alcock, 1983), although this activity is likely to be common among many of the solitary or asocial mammalian species. Certainly the males of many such species are known to expand their home ranges and visit multiple females during a breeding season, and the extent to which their reproductive success hinges on mate location ability has probably been underestimated. Mate location ability may also contribute in a subsidiary fashion to male reproductive success in more social mammals. In *M. caligata*, for example, territorial males seem to use mate searching as a means to supplement the reproductive opportunities available to them within the areas they defend (Barash, 1981). Similarly, both *S. parryii* and *S. columbianus* males have been noted to seek mating opportunities outside of their own territories (Murie & McLean, 1980).

Among the sciurids generally, extensive movements by males during the mating season have been documented most frequently for tree squirrels, namely *Sciurus carolinensis* (up to 600 meters of linear travel: Thompson, 1977) and *S. aberti* (whose home ranges expand to about 20 hectares: Farentinos, 1972). Females of these species tend to be spatially dispersed, and while differential ability to locate those in estrus no doubt underlies some of the variation in male mating success, its strength as a predictor may be diluted by the effects of overt conflict. Males often track and/or begin aggregating around a female several days prior to onset of estrus, so that on the day when she actually is receptive, she is attended by a small swarm of males (Farentinos, 1972; Thompson, 1977). The direct competition among the males then acts to reduce the correspondence between the number of females a male finds and the number of mates he obtains. The opportunity for overt conflict to affect male mating success in these species may be related to the relative asynchrony of estrus (Elliott, 1978; Schwagmeyer, 1988). (Note that tree squirrels, in general, tend to breed less synchronously than ground squirrels: cf. Dobson, 1984; Heaney, 1984.) Additional data from species in which females are spatially scattered would be useful in testing this hypothesis.

For a male thirteen-lined ground squirrel, the number of mates acquired is often exactly equivalent to the number of estrous females he finds; variation in the number of receptive females located by males accounts for some 62 to 91 percent of the variation in male mating success, depending on the season (Schwagmeyer & Woontner, 1986). The correspondence between male success in finding estrous females and mating success is chiefly an outgrowth of two factors: (1) female willingness to mate with multiple males and (2) the rarity with which males are excluded from copulation by overt conflict over access to an estrous female.

Selection for mobile, perceptive males

The thirteen-lined ground squirrel mating system thus places an exceptionally high premium on male mate location abilities. Three phenotypic features have been hypothesized as favored under these circumstances: mobility (Alcock, 1979; Lloyd, 1979; Trivers, 1972; Wells, 1977), perceptiveness (Alcock, 1979; Lloyd, 1979) and spatial ability (Gaulin & FitzGerald, 1986).

To examine the contribution of mobility, over 300 hours of focal male observational data were collected across 2 years. The basic protocol for this research consisted of collecting focal male data on 8–11 individuals per season, with each individual sampled repeatedly from 2–3 weeks prior to onset of the mating season through 2 weeks or so after termination of breeding. In the second year of the study, focal male success in locating and mating with estrous females was also estimated independently through observational sampling of the sexual activity of females residing throughout the area that the males were searching (Schwagmeyer, 1988).

The results revealed male mobility to be a significant correlate of success in finding and mating with estrous females. Males that obtained an above-average number of mates tended to cover about twice as much area during the breeding season as their less successful competitors, and they expanded their ranges across successive samples (i.e., explored new areas) significantly more than did males with below-average mating success. Furthermore, the basic correlation between how extensively males searched during the breeding season and the number of mates they acquired also held when matings that were unlikely to have resulted in fertilization (i.e., by the third and fourth males to mate, above) were eliminated from mating success scores.

Male mobility, then, does seem to confer an advantage in competitive mate searching, but the data on male behavior also revealed that other factors probably play important roles as well. In other words, there remain large holes in our understanding of the features that distinguish "good" searching from "mediocre" searching. One such hole can be viewed by considering *how* it is that increased mobility is advantageous to males. Searching males encountered other males and females at approximately equivalent rates—about one of each per 1.5 hours of searching. Once the breeding season began, the females could be of three types: those that would not be receptive for another 1–12 days or so (whereupon the male usually left after about 10 minutes), those that had already mated (whereupon the males left after about 3 minutes), and those that were in estrus (the male stayed around for a while).

Intuitively, it would seem that increased mobility should be advantageous to the degree that it exposes males to a greater number of potential mates. Yet no relationship was evident between male mating success and their rate of contacting proestrous females. In fact, hourly averages of the number of proestrous females encountered per area covered by each male were negatively related to mating success (Schwagmeyer, 1988), which suggests that the brief visits males pay to females that have not yet mated are less valuable than exploring more area. These somewhat paradoxical results may be interpretable only when finer-grained data on male search behavior are available. Specifically, it would be interesting to know if males with the highest rates of encountering proestrous females simply engaged in redundant contact with a small pool of prospective mates. Currently the frequency of repeat visits to a female cannot be estimated reliably; to measure it accurately would require continuous observation of each focal male every day throughout the breeding season.

Questions such as whether males would be better off repeatedly visiting a few females or contacting a greater number of females less frequently are basically questions concerning search efficiency, wherein the effects of male perceptiveness (Alcock, 1979; Lloyd, 1979) and spatial memory (Gaulin & FitzGerald, 1986) may play their hypothesized roles. Progress in assessing the contributions of male perceptual and memory capacities to success in competitive mate searching clearly will require not only more detailed field data on search behavior, but also experimental studies of those processes.

Certainly the capacity and accuracy of male spatial memory are likely to influence the extent to which searching can deviate from random exploration of yet another section of land. Field tests of male ability to remember the locations of individual females should be quite feasible, using some of the techniques employed in research on the spatial memory of caching birds (e.g., Sherry, Krebs, & Cowie, 1981, wherein visitation to cache sites is monitored after removal of the cached seeds). Determining what constitutes efficient mate searching also necessitates knowing something about how accurately males can predict the onset of estrus (i.e., whether they are able to discriminate between females that will become receptive 3 days later as opposed to the next morning). If a male can remember the location of a particular female, for example, plus information that she will not be in estrus today, then *ceteris paribus*, he probably should explore an alternative area to check the female residing there.

The role of sperm competition

Parker (1970a) identified two broad categories of sperm competition adaptations: (1) those that prevent rival males from copulating with or successfully inseminating a female with which a male has mated, and (2) those that increase a male's fertilization chances when mating with a previously mated female. Selection for these two types operates in what Parker termed an "evolutionary balance," such that selection for type (2) adaptations declines with the increased effectiveness of type (1) adaptations, and vice versa. (Imagine, for example, a situation in which the first male to mate with a female always sires 100 percent of her offspring. In that circumstance, there would be no advantage gained from male attempts to court or pursue previously mated females.) The incidence of sperm competition thus is likely to be highest when males are only moderately effective at preventing other males from copulating with their mates, as discussed previously for female defense polygyny species, or when male interests (i.e., overall fertilization rate) are best served by foregoing investment in sperm competition avoidance mechanisms.

Theoretically, a variety of factors should influence the value to a male of investing in sperm competition avoidance mechanisms. These include: (1) the costs of obtaining alternative females as mates (if they are low, his option of expending time and energy in protecting a current mate from further inseminations suffers in comparison: Dewsbury, 1982c; Parker, 1970a); (2) the current mate's opportunities for remating prior to fertilization (as determined both by the rate at which receptive females are located by males as well as the temporal relationship between female receptivity and fertilization: Parker, 1970a); and (3), as above, the effectiveness of the time/energy investment in preventing subsequent rematings (Parker, 1970a). In addition, optimal sperm competition avoidance investment is contingent on the magnitude of the fertilization advantage to be derived from it, which can be influenced by mating order effects (see Dewsbury, this volume), male constraints on ejaculate production (Dewsbury, 1982c), and assorted other variables that shape the relationship between specific levels of investment and number of ova fertilized. The effects of several of these factors on male investment will be illustrated below in a discussion of one particular sperm competition avoidance mechanism, postcopulatory guarding.

Although data are still lacking for most North American sciurids, those currently available show variation among species in the prevalence of sperm competition in that the frequency of multiple mating by females differs markedly. At one extreme, females of some species exhibit no indication of multiple mating, as revealed either by behavioral observations of estrous females (Table 2) or

TABLE 2. Incidence of Multiple Mating by Females in Some North American Sciurids

Species	Multiple mating reported?	Mean number of mates per female	Range	Reference
Sciurus carolinensis	no	1	—	Horwich, 1972 Thompson, 1977
Sciurus aberti	yes	4	2–6	Farentinos, 1980
Cynomys ludovicianus	yes	1.49	1–3+	Hoogland & Foltz, 1982
Marmota flaviventris	no[a]	1	—	Schwartz & Armitage, 1980
Spermophilus beldingi	yes	1977: 2.7 1978: 3.3	1–5	Hanken & Sherman, 1981
Spermophilus tridecemlineatus	yes	1978: 1.8 1979: 1.0 1983: 2.2 1984: 2.9 1984: 2.1	1–4	Schwagmeyer & Woontner, 1985
Spermophilus richardsonii	yes	—	—	Michener, 1983a

[a]Based on electrophoretic evidence and habitat barriers to potential intruding males.

by electrophoretic paternity analyses (M. *flaviventris*: Schwartz & Armitage, 1980). On the other hand, S. *aberti* females copulate with an average of four different males per estrous period (Farentinos, 1980). The results summarized in Table 2 further reveal within-species variation in the potential for sperm competition; in both S. *beldingi* and S. *tridecemlineatus*, the average number of mates per female appears to fluctuate seasonally.

The source(s) of the variability in levels of sperm competition have not yet been explored, but three extreme possibilities are that: (1) males of different species and populations differ in their investment in sperm competition avoidance mechanisms (e.g., in postcopulatory guarding); (2) sperm competition avoidance mechanisms are advantageous in all cases, but their effectiveness varies among species and populations; or (3) the avoidance mechanisms are uniformly disadvantageous, but females differ in the opportunities they have for remating.

Seasonal fluctuations in the incidence of sperm competition among thirteen-lined ground squirrels (Table 2) appear to be influenced by (3), differential remating opportunities available to females. As mentioned previously, most S. *tridecemlineatus* females copulate with any and all males that find and attempt to mate with them during estrus. The number of males locating each estrous female differs between breeding seasons, however, and so the average number of mates per female differs accordingly. Notably, in years when females are most plentiful, the mean number of males with which each copulates can drop to one (Schwagmeyer & Woontner, 1985); sperm competition in those seasons therefore has minimal impact on male reproductive success.

Selection for sperm competition avoidance mechanisms

Sperm competition among male mammals recently has been invoked as an influence on a growing list of male morphological and behavioral features. These include testis size (Harvey & Harcourt, 1984; Kenagy & Trombulak, 1986), copulatory plugs (Martan & Shepherd, 1976; Voss, 1979), patterns of ejaculation and copulatory behavior (Dewsbury, 1981c, 1984d; Lanier, Estep, & Dewsbury, 1979), male selectivity in mating (Dewsbury, 1982c), and the presence or absence of postcopulatory guarding (Schwagmeyer & Parker, 1987). Full-fledged comparative analyses of sciurid variation in such sperm competition adaptations have yet to be conducted, however, mainly because the outcome of sperm competition is still unknown for most species. The need for further information on sperm competition is reiterated in the next section's treatment of how specific elements of male reproductive behavior vary among sciurids.

COMPARATIVE ANALYSES OF PARTICULAR ASPECTS OF REPRODUCTIVE BEHAVIOR

Postcopulatory guarding

After the first thirteen-lined ground squirrel male to locate an estrous female begins copulating with her, he typically spends an additional 1.5 hours with her, accumulating some 18 minutes total time spent in copulation. He then leaves to resume searching for other mates. In his absence, the female remains sexually attractive for an additional 3 hours or so, and usually copulates with at least one more male (Schwagmeyer & Parker, 1987). A hypothetical first male that remained with and guarded the female for those 3 hours or more should, at the very least, be able to postpone or interfere with the copulatory attempts of any later-arriving males. He might even be able to prevent subsequent matings altogether. The fact that such guarding is never observed suggests that it is less profitable than the alternative of resuming the search.

The ESS (Evolutionarily Stable Strategy: see Maynard Smith, 1982; Parker, 1984a) approach is ideally suited to this type of problem, and was used to compare the payoffs available from each of the two general options. Details of the model are presented elsewhere (Schwagmeyer & Parker, 1987); what follows is a brief synopsis, with some elaboration of the roles played by several of the factors discussed above. The estimated payoff for a nonguarding male had two components. First, the male was credited with the proportion of a litter he would gain from his current mate, weighted according to the probability that she would remate after his departure. Note that if females virtually never remated, the guarding and nonguarding options would yield equal payoffs at this point. However, nonguarding males have a second payoff component, namely, their credit for the proportion of an extra litter they might sire by finding a second estrous female when they resume searching. This "extra" litter portion of the payoff was weighted by the average time it takes searching males to locate an estrous female; the longer the time necessary to find an alternative mate, the smaller the gain from the nonguarding strategy. As before, it also was discounted by the probability that the second female mated with other males.

For the guarding alternative, the payoff excludes any gain from "extra" search effort; the hypothetical guarding first male would benefit only to the extent that he was able to avoid sperm competition. The results of the model indicated nonguarding to be the more profitable strategy if (1) guarding is more costly than searching and/or is likely to be very ineffective, or (2) there exists a first-male advantage in sperm competition.

While the first hypothesis is difficult to test empirically (simply because males never attempt to guard after copulating, so neither the costs nor effectiveness of guarding attempts can be measured), the second hypothesis was tested by using electrophoretic paternity analyses of litters born to females of known mating history. Those results (Foltz & Schwagmeyer, 1989) indicate the existence of a first-male advantage in thirteen-lined ground squirrel sperm competition. Specifically, under field conditions, the first male to mate sires an average of 75 percent of the offspring in a litter. When the payoffs from the ESS model are recalculated using that value as the estimate of the proportion of the litter sired by first males, the comparisons show nonguarding to be distinctly advantageous over guarding, even if guarding against a single intruder were to be completely effective.

The model for thirteen-lined ground squirrels (see also Parker, 1974) specifies that the guarding alternative becomes more attractive as an option if either the search costs involved in finding alternative mates or the gain in the proportion of offspring sired by guarding (as opposed to nonguarding) males increases. Given this, the sciurid species most prone to postcopulatory guarding should be those in which estrous females are relatively difficult to find or gain access to (such that the costs involved in acquiring alternative mates are high for males) and/or those that have a last-male advantage in sperm competition (thereby exaggerating the discrepancy between the proportion of offspring sired by a first male that guards versus one that does not). In addition, there must be some chance that unguarded females will mate with additional males should their first partner leave; the search costs mentioned above should not be *so* high that females would be unlikely to mate again if they were not guarded.

Males of several sciurid species have been known to guard their mates (e.g., *M. caligata*: Barash, 1981; *Spermophilus beecheyi*: Dobson, 1983; *Sciurus carolinensis*: Horwich, 1972; Thompson, 1977; *Sciurus aberti*: Farentinos, 1980; *C. ludovicianus*: Grady & Hoogland, 1986), although in some of these cases it is not clear whether the guarding activity extends into the postcopulatory stage. Nevertheless, unambiguous descriptions of postcopulatory guarding are available for *S. carolinensis* and *S. aberti*; the authors specify that males continue to attend females for several hours after copulating with them. In both species, females breed relatively asynchronously and live at low population densities, indicating that search costs may be high for males. Furthermore, the fact that multiple males are in pursuit of an estrous female while she is guarded (and often succeed in copulating with her in *S. aberti*: Table 2) suggests that females would be likely to remate if they were *not* guarded. Whether the outcome of sperm competition in these species also would favor postcopulatory guarding is unknown.

Escalated aggression

Males of some ground squirrel species are conspicuously prone to engage in escalated contests during the mating season, and their battle scars at the end of a season testify to their pugnacity. In *Spermophilus richardsonii*, for example, 100 percent of the males were found to have incurred wounds or scars during the mating season (Michener, 1983b); in S. *variegatus*, 77 percent were wounded (Johnson, 1981). Mating season skirmishes among male S. *beldingi* have been cited as a significant source of mortality (Sherman & Morton, 1984).

By contrast, escalated aggression is rare among male thirteen-lined ground squirrels, the majority of which pass through mating seasons without acquiring any evident wounds or scars. In part, this may stem from the fact that males are sometimes able to mate without encountering any competitors (Schwagmeyer & Woontner, 1985; 1986); thus the mere opportunity for escalated aggression is relatively low. Yet conflicts over access to estrous females do occur, but have never been observed to produce visible wounding of the participants (Schwagmeyer & Woontner, 1986). These disputes usually are settled in favor of whichever male was first to find the female: that individual has priority in copulating, and mating by the later-arriving male is deferred until the first male departs (the "queuing" convention: Schwagmeyer & Parker, 1987).

Why do later-arriving males tolerate this situation, rather than aggressively challenging the earlier male? As noted previously, comparisons of the features of the first, second, and third males to arrive indicate that, for one thing, later males often are outweighed by earlier males, and therefore are likely to be trounced in aggressive interactions. Perhaps more importantly, later males are slower in locating the female as she moves around: even if a later male were to win an aggressive challenge, his ability to profit from that victory (in terms of access to the female) is doubtful (Schwagmeyer & Parker, 1987).

Information on the value to males of winning escalated contests in the more combative ground squirrels would be quite interesting. ESS models of contest behavior (adapted from game theory; see reviews by Maynard Smith, 1982; Parker, 1984a) suggest that prolonged or vicious fighting should be especially likely to occur in circumstances where the value of winning the contest is much higher than the time, energy, and risk of injury involved in fighting. Males' risk of sustaining serious injury in conflicts over estrous females has been well documented, but little has been published on the consequences of victory, specifically, the regularity with which it leads to copulation and fertilization.

Potpourri

Numerous other features of sciurid reproductive behavior differ interspecifically, and remain open to future comparative analyses. For example, males of some species appear to advertise that they have copulated with a female by emitting a specific postcopulatory vocalization (C. *ludovicianus*: Grady & Hoogland, 1986; S. *beldingi*: Leger, Berney-Key, & Sherman, 1984); others do not (S. *tridecemlineatus*). The function of the postcopulatory calls is unknown. Leger et al.

suggested that calling may allow individuals to reestablish their dominance status as they resume competition for access to estrous females; an alternative suggestion was that the calls may signal mating prowess to females, thereby attracting future mates. Still other hypotheses, including the possibility that the calls dissuade competing males (see Parker, 1984b) have been considered for *C. ludovicianus*, with no definitive resolution (Grady & Hoogland, 1986).

Ground squirrels also differ in their inclinations to mate below versus above ground, with copulation in burrows being more common (e.g., *C. ludovicianus*: Hoogland, 1981; *S. columbianus* and *S. parryii*: Murie & McLean, 1980; *S. beecheyi*: Owings, Borchert, & Virginia, 1977; *S. richardsonii*: Davis, 1982; *S. armatus*: Balph & Stokes, 1963). At least two species, however, routinely mate above ground (*S. beldingi*: Hanken & Sherman, 1981; *S. tridecemlineatus*: Schwagmeyer & Brown, 1983). One proposed advantage of mating covertly is that it reduces the risk of predation (Elliott, 1978; Davis, 1982). It also has been suggested to function in avoiding disruption and possible takeovers by rival males (Davis, 1982).

The habit of mating in burrows poses obvious problems for comparative analyses of other facets of reproductive behavior. Information on whether pairs

TABLE 3. Field Data on Copulation or Mount Durations for Various North American Sciurids

Species	Range in duration	Reference
Sciurus aberti	47–72 s	Farentinos, 1972
Sciurus carolinensis	15–30 s	Horwich, 1972
Tamiasciurus douglasii	4–8 min 1–25 min	Smith, 1968 Koford, 1982
Tamias striatus	1–2 min	Elliott, 1978
Cynomys ludovicianus	2–16.5 min[a]	Hoogland, 1981 Hoogland & Foltz, 1982
Spermophilus beldingi	8–12 min	Leger, Berney-Key, & Sherman, 1984
Spermophilus richardsonii	3–4 min	Davis, 1982
Spermophilus tridecemlineatus	1–17 min[a]	Schwagmeyer & Brown, 1983

[a]Minimum value used in operationally defining "copulation."

copulate repeatedly, the average interval between copulations, the frequency of sexual interference, and, in species whose females mate multiply, the average delay between copulations with rival males, is notably lacking for most of the ground squirrels. A few data exist on sciurid copulation duration, however (Table 3), and these are quite provocative. Comparison of the species' values is clearly subject to bias from investigator differences in operationally defining "copulation" (in many of these species, neither intromission nor ejaculation are detectable under field conditions). In *S. tridecemlineatus*, for example, copulations have been defined operationally as mounts that last more than one minute (Schwagmeyer & Brown, 1983); in *C. ludovicianus*, copulations are inferred, in part, from a pair's co-occupation of a burrow for at least 2 minutes (Hoogland & Foltz, 1982). Furthermore, simple durations of copulations may be a misleading measure if pairs copulate repeatedly in some taxa and not in others. Nevertheless, the species differences are tantalizing, and merit future analyses of how copulation duration affects sperm competition (Dewsbury, 1981c, 1984d; Parker 1970b, 1984b) and pregnancy initiation (Dewsbury, 1981c, 1982c). Information on the former is, needless to say, lacking for most sciurids. A similar situation exists for pregnancy initiation requirements: in most cases, even anecdotal reports of the minimum values are lacking. An exception is Denniston's (1957) finding that a single copulation of 2.5 minutes duration resulted in pregnancy of an *S. richardsonii* female under captive conditions.

SUMMARY

When classified by the predominant methods used by males to acquire mates, the ground-dwelling sciurids show three basic forms of polygyny: female (harem) defense polygyny, male dominance polygyny, and scramble competition polygyny. The mere fact that male solutions to the mate acquisition problem are similar in some species but radically different in others demands explanation. Comparative analyses suggest that the form of polygyny prevailing in any given population depends on male and female densities plus the extent to which females are spatially clustered. Data on additional species, especially those representing the extremes of these factors, would be useful for testing the hypotheses, as would experimental manipulations of the critical variables. Indeed, the topic seems ideally suited for such a mix of comparison and experimentation.

Because specific polygyny types reflect different male strategies for obtaining mates, the impact of two dimensions of intrasexual competition—overt conflict and competitive mate searching—is expected to vary in a predictable fashion. In certain male dominance and female defense systems, male combat ability does, in fact, appear to be favored. By contrast, male dominance seems to have minimal effects on mating success under scramble competition polygyny; instead, success in competitive mate searching plays a major role. At present, interspecific comparisons of these facets of male reproductive competition, and of the phenotypic traits promoting success in each, can be made only on a qualitative and preliminary level. There is ample room for new input.

A third major category of intrasexual competition, sperm competition, occurs unevenly across the North American sciurids. Females of some species routinely mate with more than one male during a single estrous period, females of other species typically do not. Again, the diversity exposed by the comparative data naturally prompts questions regarding its underlying sources. In this case, we currently are at the stage where we can generate a series of possible explanations for interspecific differences in levels of sperm competition, but cannot yet test them. Future investigations of the effects of sperm competition on male fertilization success should prove useful in doing so. Such studies also would be valuable in elucidating species differences in a suite of reproductive behaviors, including male postcopulatory guarding, use of escalated aggression, postcopulatory vocalizations, and copulation duration.

CHAPTER 9

THE ROLE OF PAVLOVIAN CONDITIONING IN TERRITORIAL AGGRESSION AND REPRODUCTION

Karen L. Hollis

It is pretty evident that under natural conditions the normal animal must respond not only to stimuli which themselves bring immediate benefit or harm, but also to other [events] which in themselves only *signal* the approach of these stimuli; though it is not the sight and sound of the beast of prey which is in itself harmful . . . but its teeth and claws (Pavlov, 1927, p. 14).

The ability of animals to discern signals predicting the occurrence of biologically important events and to react to those signals with an anticipatory response was, to Pavlov, the palpable manifestation of *tselesoobraznost*, or "purposiveness" (Babkin, 1949; Pavlov, 1927). Whether the anticipatory response (the conditional response, or CR) was an overt motor reaction, such as the avoidance response to which Pavlov refers in the above quotation, or an internal response, such as salivation, Pavlov believed that an animal's CR was "directed towards the preservation of its existence" (Pavlov, 1927, p. 8). Today, we would say instead that CRs are *adaptive*, meaning that the performance of an anticipatory response increases an animal's reproductive success, preserving copies of its genes rather than its existence per se. Nevertheless, this translation into neo-Darwinian terminology still reflects very well Pavlov's own conception of *tselesoobraznost*. In-

197

deed, Pavlov's functional explanation of food CRs, an example of anticipatory responding that Pavlov employed frequently to illustrate *tselesoobraznost*, predates much modern thinking (Hearst & Jenkins, 1974; Hollis, 1982). According to Pavlov, signals for food elicit signal-directed approach behavior that, in turn, enables animals to locate edible substances. Simultaneously, conditioned anticipatory alimentary secretions make that food easier to digest (Pavlov, 1941).

Despite the inseparable connection between causal and functional themes in Pavlov's own writings, his successors concentrated on the causal mechanisms of CR performance. Pavlov's own hypotheses concerning *tselesoobraznost* were virtually ignored. For example, Pavlov's suggestion that anticipatory alimentary responses actually improved digestion was not confirmed experimentally until some 30 years later (Bykov, 1959). Similarly, experimental investigations of the adaptive value of skeletal CRs, such as the approach-to-food signals mentioned above, have begun to be investigated only in the last 10 years.

Several historical forces conspired to suppress experimental consideration of adaptive value. Undoubtedly, the simplest was the success of the behaviorist tradition within psychology, a school of thought that was very much attracted to Pavlov's methodology (Watson, 1925), but was philosophically more wedded to proximal questions than to functional ones (Boring, 1957; Terrace, 1984). In the years following Watson's founding of behaviorism, many animal learning psychologists speculated about the adaptive value of behavior. However, functional questions became worthy of real consideration only when researchers were forced to confront numerous examples of biological constraints on animals' learning abilities (Hinde & Stevenson-Hinde, 1973; Shettleworth, 1972).

Another contributing factor to the recent legitimization of functionalist thinking has been the enviable success of neo-Darwinian evolutionary analyses in the field of behavioral ecology. Pioneered by Tinbergen's (1951) use of creative yet simple experiments, behavioral ecology has helped to provide the experimental methodology for investigations of biological function. Thus, while a burgeoning constraints-on-learning literature might be said to have provided animal learning psychologists with the impetus to explore functional questions, the field of behavioral ecology contributed the techniques to do so.

Today, although most studies of animal learning still tend toward causal analyses, investigations in which an attempt is made to integrate causal and functional approaches to learned behavior are becoming increasingly common (e.g., Fanselow & Lester, 1988; Staddon, 1983; Timberlake, 1983b). While the causal approach has revolutionized our thinking about the underlying mechanisms of Pavlovian conditioning (Rescorla, 1988), the functional approach often is credited with having the potential to reconcile animal learning theory with studies of natural behavior (Beecher, 1988b; Bolles, 1988). Indeed, the integration of functional and causal approaches to learning has helped to create a new direction of study within behavioral ecology, namely operant simulations of optimal foraging (see Stephens & Krebs, 1987, for a review). In addition, integrative analyses have helped researchers to discover many new questions for investigation within traditional psychological paradigms (see, for example, Blanchard & Blanchard; Galef; Kamil & Clements, this volume).

The purpose of this chapter is to detail some recent experimental studies in which my coworkers and I have attempted to integrate causal and functional approaches to the study of Pavlovian-conditioned behavior. A major goal of these studies has been to test the hypothesis that the biological function of the CR is to prepare animals for important events (Hollis, 1982). That is, we have attempted to test experimentally Pavlov's conception of *tselesoobraznost*. In addition, because the experimental focus has been the conditional aggressive and reproductive behavior of a territorial fish, the blue gourami (*Trichogaster trichopterus*), another more specific goal of this research has been to illustrate the potential importance of Pavlovian conditioning to the behavioral ecology of a territorial species. Although our research is still in the earliest stages of development, I hope to show how an integrative approach has enabled us to raise new questions in several fields of study, including animal learning psychology, neuroendocrinology, and behavioral ecology, as well as to discover what may be an adaptive specialization of learned behavior. I hope, too, to convince the reader that, when translated into neo-Darwinian terms, Pavlov's conception of *tselesoobraznost* has considerable validity.

TERRITORIAL BEHAVIOR

The blue gourami, *T. trichopterus*, is one of several closely related fishes that inhabit shallow pools and weedy streams in southeast Asia and Africa. Territorial behavior in this species is triggered by the arrival of seasonal monsoon rains.[1] Males migrate to the lowlands when they become flooded and begin to establish territories. As in many other territorial animals, male blue gouramis arrive on the breeding grounds well in advance of females. Once there, males choose a suitable location for nesting and aggressively defend their territory against all intruders, especially conspecific males.

In blue gouramis, the initial response to an intruder, called a frontal display, is a rapid approach to the would-be rival with all fins erect. If the intruder does not respond to this threat by assuming the submissive posture or fleeing the territory, a fight ensues. Fighting consists of tailbeating, a rapid motion of the tail fin that forces water against the sensory nerve endings of an opponent's lateral line organ, and biting. With this escalation of aggression, the contest becomes a battle for possession of the territory. Tailbeating and biting, both of which are

---

[1]Details concerning the natural history of *T. trichopterus* have been taken from Forselius (1957), Miller (1964), and Picciolo (1964). Descriptions of reproductive and agonistic behavior are based primarily on these studies but also on my and my coworkers' own observations.

capable of seriously injuring an opponent, continue until one participant adopts the submissive posture. The loser is then chased from the territory.

In addition to defending his territory, each blue gourami male also builds a nest fabricated from tiny air bubbles. Usually this nest is completed before females arrive on the breeding grounds. To construct his nest, a male repeatedly goes to the surface, takes a gulp of air, mixes it in his mouth with a special mucous secretion, and ejects this frothy melange just below the water's surface, usually near the center of his territory. As a result of many such trips, a mass of foam collects at the surface. However, because the foam tends to evaporate and disperse, a male must attend to his nest throughout the day, replenishing and recollecting his supply of bubbles. Between periods of intensive nest construction, he actively patrols the boundaries of his territory, protecting his investment against rivals.

The vigor of males' territorial defense reflects the importance of territory ownership to successful reproduction. Females rarely mate with males without territories. Consequently, any strategy that enhanced a male's ability to defend his territory would be favored, albeit indirectly, by natural selection.

Pavlovian conditioning of territorial aggression

The conditional aggressive response, in which a male approaches, and reacts aggressively to, a signal predicting the appearance of a rival, was demonstrated first in *Betta splendens* by Thompson & Sturm (1965; but see also Adler & Hogan, 1963). Thompson (1966) suggested that the Pavlovian conditioning procedure probably mimics naturally occurring situations in which rivals unavoidably announce their imminent invasion of a territory by the visual, chemical, or mechanical changes in the environment that their presence creates. I have elaborated on this functional speculation of Thompson's in a theoretical paper in which I hypothesize that the conditional aggressive response, like all other CRs, enables animals to optimize their interactions with subsequent unconditional stimuli (Hollis, 1982). In the case of conditional aggressive behavior, an anticipatory response to signals of impending rivals enhances a male's territorial defense by making him better prepared to do battle.

This functional hypothesis of conditional aggressive behavior has been supported in several experiments with blue gouramis (Hollis, 1984a). In these experiments, males were paired on the basis of similar body size and level of aggression. Pair members were placed on opposite sides of a divided 20-gallon aquarium. One member of each pair received a Pavlovian conditioning treatment in which each of 15 daily presentations of a 10-second light (the conditional stimulus, or CS) was followed by a 15-second presentation of a rival fish (the unconditional stimulus, or US). The other pair member received a control treatment. Pair members did not see or interact with one another at all during training. Separate training of each fish was accomplished by temporarily removing its partner and substituting one of several extra males. By lifting the opaque divider that separated the two fish, the subject could view the rival US. A second, clear barrier prevented the subject and the rival from physically contacting one another during US presentation.

In our first experiment, the control treatment was an explicitly unpaired procedure in which 15 daily presentations of the 10-second light CS were followed, an average of 4 hours later, by 15 presentations of the rival US. In our second experiment, control fish received only rival presentations and were never exposed to the light CS (this is referred to below as the "aggression-only" treatment).

Following 24 days of training, pair members confronted one another for the very first time in a test encounter. For the Pavlovian-conditioned fish, as well as for the explicitly unpaired control fish, this first confrontation was preceded by the presentation of the light CS used in training. For the aggression-only control fish, the test encounter was unsignaled.

Figures 1 and 2 illustrate the main findings of these studies, namely the superiority of Pavlovian-conditioned males in the defense of their territories, regardless of whether their rivals in the encounter had received the explicitly unpaired control treatment (Figure 1) or the aggression-only control treatment (Figure 2) during training. In the test encounters, the Pavlovian-conditioned males all rapidly approached the light CS in the frontal display threat posture,

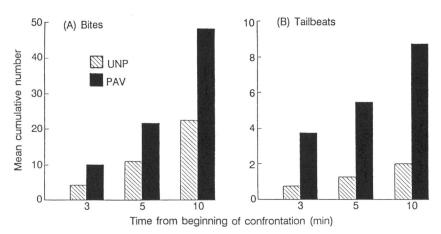

FIGURE 1. Mean cumulative number of bites (A) and mean cumulative number of tailbeats (B) in the first 3 minutes, 5 minutes, and 10 minutes of the test confrontation between males receiving the Pavlovian (PAV) conditioning treatment and males receiving the explicitly unpaired (UNP) control treatment. (From Hollis, 1984a.)

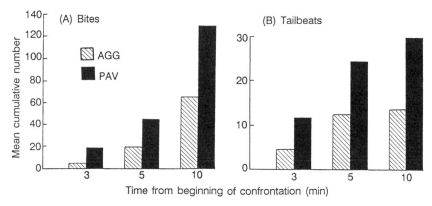

FIGURE 2. Mean cumulative number of bites (A) and mean cumulative number of tailbeats (B) in the first 3 minutes, 5 minutes, and 10 minutes of the test confrontation between males receiving the Pavlovian (PAV) conditioning treatment and males receiving the aggression-only (AGG) control treatment. (From Hollis, 1984a.)

and thus were able to confront their rivals at the territory boundary with fins already erect. In the subsequent battles for territory ownership, the Pavlovian-conditioned males were able to deliver significantly more bites and tailbeats than their rivals. Indeed, even in the closest contest between two males, one in which the control fish had received the aggression-only treatment during training, the Pavlovian-conditioned male nonetheless was able to deliver 18 percent more bites and 23 percent more tailbeats than its rival.

Learned inhibition of territorial defense

Although all of the Pavlovian-conditioned males displayed a similar aggressive advantage during the test encounters, the overall level of aggression was very different in the two studies. As a comparison of Figures 1 and 2 will reveal, the total number of bites and tailbeats was far lower in the encounters between Pavlovian-conditioned and explicitly unpaired control fish than it was in the contests between Pavlovian-conditioned and aggression-only males. This differential level of aggression in the two studies led my coworkers and I (Hollis, Martin, Cadieux, & Colbert, 1984) to question whether males receiving the explicitly unpaired control treatment might have suffered a disadvantage not shared by males receiving the aggression-only control treatment.

For explicitly unpaired males, presentations of the light CS in training predicted a period of time when rival US presentations would never occur. Consequently, these males may have learned to relax their territorial defense during light presentations. That is, for explicitly unpaired males, presentation of the light CS might have become what animal learning psychologists call a *conditioned inhibitor* (or CS−), a signal that predicts the absence of the US and results in the inhibition of behavior normally elicited in Pavlovian-conditioned males by the CS (or CS+).

We speculated that if a light CS could function as a conditioned inhibitor of aggression for males receiving the explicitly unpaired control treatment, then these males would be expected to lose territorial contests with Pavlovian-conditioned males rather quickly. A quick defeat would mean that explicitly unpaired males would receive less aggressive treatment from Pavlovian-conditioned rivals than would males that did not succumb so quickly. Because aggression-only males would not suffer from conditioned inhibition of their aggressive behavior, contests between Pavlovian-conditioned and aggression-only males would be expected to involve more aggression than contests between Pavlovian-conditioned and explicitly unpaired males, as was observed in the previous study.

We tested the hypothesis that a CS− for territorial invasion can inhibit aggressive behavior by using a Pavlovian discrimination procedure in which both members of a pair received two daily training sessions. In one of the two sessions, we used an excitatory conditioning procedure in which each of five presentations of a colored light CS+ was paired with a rival US. In the other daily session, we used an inhibitory conditioning procedure in which five presentations of a different colored light (the CS−) never were followed by presentations of a rival US. Such discrimination training has been used before with many different species and with many different CRs and results in a characteristic pattern of performance such as that illustrated in Figure 3. During the 30 days of daily excitatory and inhibitory conditioning sessions, responses to the CS+ (here, the frontal display) increased steadily, while responses to the CS− increased at first, then leveled off, and eventually began to drop out altogether. This differential pattern of responding to the two CSs (the CS+ and CS−) indicates that the males were able to discriminate presentations of the CS+ from the CS−.

To determine whether the CS− served as a conditioned inhibitor of aggression, we tested pairs of males that had been trained with the CS+ and CS− in encounters preceded by different stimuli. Five such test groups were formed: in one type of test group, both pair members received the CS+ prior to the test encounter (CS+/CS+); in a second, both pair members received the CS− (CS−/CS−); in a third, one male received the CS+ while its partner received the CS− (CS+/CS−); in a fourth, both pair members received neither the CS+ nor the CS− (NS/NS); and, in the fifth type of test, one male that had received a different type of prior training, namely daily presentations of only the rival US, received neither the CS+ nor the CS− in the test encounter, while its rival received a CS− (US-only/CS−).

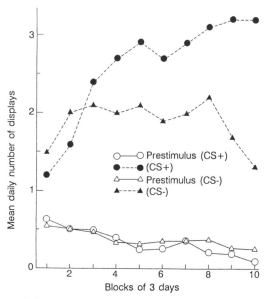

FIGURE 3. Mean daily number of frontal displays performed by males during the prestimulus periods (10 seconds before CS+ or CS− presentation) and during the presentations of the CS+ and the CS−. (From Hollis, Martin, Cadieux, & Colbert, 1984.)

Based on the functional hypothesis that the aggressive CR enables males to defend their territories more effectively than when the CR is absent (Hollis, 1982, 1984a, 1984b) and combined with the suggestion that a CS− can act as a conditioned inhibitor of territorial aggression, we made two predictions concerning the outcomes of different types of test encounters. The first prediction was that two rivals receiving the same type of pretest stimulus should engage in similar levels of aggressive behavior; only in the CS+/CS− and the US-only/CS− pairs did we expect to see a difference between males in the frequency of aggressive behavior. Second, we predicted that the overall level of aggression should be significantly higher in the CS+/CS+ group and significantly lower in the CS−/CS− group than in the NS/NS control group.

The results of the test encounters confirmed both of our predictions. Figure 4 shows the difference between male rivals in the frequency of bites (A) and tailbeats (B) during the territorial defense test. As the data in Figure 4 suggest, males receiving different types of pretest stimuli performed differently in the encounter. Males receiving the CS+, as well as US-only males that had received no pretest stimulus, delivered more bites and tailbeats than did males receiving the CS−. In addition, as Figure 5 shows, the number of bites and tailbeats was significantly higher in the CS+/CS+ group than it was in the NS/NS group;

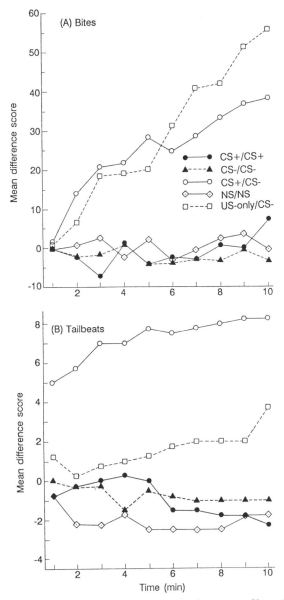

FIGURE 4. Mean difference between partners in the frequency of bites (A) and tailbeats (B) at 1-minute intervals during the first 10 minutes of the territorial defense test. CS+/CS+ = both pair members received the CS+ prior to the test encounter. CS−/CS− = both pair members received the CS−. CS+/CS− = one male received the CS+ while its partner received the CS−. NS/NS = both pair members received neither the CS+ nor the CS−. US-only/CS− = one male that had received US-only presentations during training received neither the CS+ nor the CS− in the test encounter while its partner received a CS−. (From Hollis, Martin, Cadieux, & Colbert, 1984.)

205

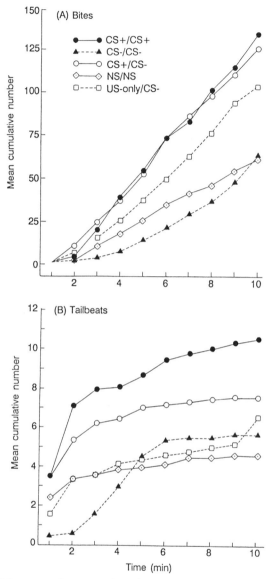

FIGURE 5. Mean cumulative number of bites (A) and mean cumulative number of tailbeats (B) at 1-minute intervals during the first 10 minutes of the territorial defense test. CS+/CS+ = both pair members received the CS+ prior to the test encounter. CS−/CS− = both pair members received the CS−. CS+/CS− = one male received the CS+ while its partner received the CS−. NS/NS = both pair members received neither the CS+ nor the CS−. US-only/CS− = one male that had received US-only presentations during training received neither the CS+ nor the CS− in the test encounter while its rival received a CS−. (From Hollis, Martin, Cadieux, & Colbert, 1984.)

CS−/CS− males, on the other hand, not only were slow to initiate aggressive behavior but also performed significantly fewer bites and tailbeats than did males in the NS/NS group. The inferior aggressive performance of males receiving a CS− prior to the test is all the more dramatic given their highly aggressive response to CS+ presentations during training. Clearly then, learned signals, whether warning of an impending attack or predicting a period of time free from threat, are capable of controlling the aggressive behavior of territorial males.

What might be the adaptive value to a territory owner of a signal predicting the absence of territorial invasion? One possibility is that a CS− inhibits aggressive behavior at a time in which territory ownership is unlikely to be threatened, thus decreasing energetically costly territorial defense activity and allowing the male to engage in other, equally important, activities. For example, during the early part of the breeding cycle in which males are contesting territory ownership, a territory holder frequently interrupts his nest building to patrol his territorial boundaries (Forselius, 1957). If a signal were to predict the absence of rivals for a certain period of time, the male would be able to forego patrolling and attend to his nest instead.

In the wild, temporal cues that might, for example, signal the absence of a territorial rival during a particular time of day could function as conditioned inhibitors. Some evidence that animals are able to make such temporal discriminations has been found in gulls that travel to certain locations only at certain times of the day to coincide with food availability (Niebuhr & McFarland, 1983; see Hollis et al., 1984, for a discussion of this example).

Other possible examples of naturalistic CS−'s might be geographical landmarks or spatial cues. Called *contextual stimuli* in the animal learning literature, spatial cues have been shown to exert control over a variety of learned behavioral patterns (Balsam & Tomie, 1984). For example, spatial cues, either alone or in combination with visual landmarks, were used by territorial male *Betta splendens* to locate sites where they had had several encounters with a rival male (Bronstein, 1986). Males not only spent a disproportionate amount of time patrolling the sites of previous aggressive encounters (with mirror images) but, in several instances, they exhibited "keep out" displays. Whether those same male subjects simultaneously neglected areas where aggressive encounters did not occur remains to be investigated. However, several studies with other vertebrate species suggest that this possibility is highly likely. Just as animals will approach a CS+ for an appetitive US (e.g., food) they will actively avoid a CS− for that same US (Hearst & Franklin, 1977).

Such signal-elicited approach and avoidance behavior has obvious adaptive value, enabling animals to increase the efficiency with which they locate objects or events of biological significance. If, for example, a territorial male fish could neglect areas where encounters were unlikely to occur, such as locations where geographical barriers prevent a rival's entry, while anticipating a rival's entry at sites of frequent intrusion, he could substantially increase the efficiency of his territorial defense.

Causal and functional analyses of conditioned inhibition

Above, I have suggested several ways in which a CS− that predicts the absence of rivals might modify the behavior of a territorial male. The functional interpretation of the CS− that I have described assumes that a CS− predicts the absence of one particular event. However, not all causal explanations of conditioned inhibition are consistent with this view. For example, Dickinson (1980) has suggested that animals do not encode specific properties of the omitted event. Rather, animals encode only that "something aversive" or "something attractive" will be omitted. According to other animal learning theorists, however, the CS− does predict the absence of a specific US (Konorski, 1948; Rescorla, 1979). Experiments that have attempted to resolve this issue of predictive specificity have produced mixed results (e.g., Kruse, Overmier, Konz, & Rokke, 1983; Nieto, 1984; Pearce, Montgomery, & Dickinson, 1981; see Mackintosh, 1983, for a review).

An ecological approach to the question of predictive specificity would suggest that for inhibitory learning to be advantageous, the animal's representation of a CS− should contain highly specific information concerning the omitted event. For example, many events are attractive, they can occur simultaneously, and each one may require a different response. A male that learned only that something attractive was not available in a certain location might avoid not only a poor foraging area but also an area in which a mate could be found. Far better for the male to avoid the area only when he is searching for food. Generally, then, we might predict, from a functional vantage point, that a CS− should be represented in memory as specifically as is a CS+ (see Mackintosh, 1983, for a review). Regardless of the theoretical outcome, further investigations of the functional question of *why* conditioned inhibition occurs will help to address the causal question of *how* a CS− inhibits behavior.

Proximate mechanisms of territorial aggression

An important issue that we have thus far overlooked is the proximate means by which learned signals are able to effect increases or decreases in aggressive behavior. How does a CS+ enable a male to deliver more bites and tailbeats in an encounter with a rival? Similarly, what behavior change occurs during CS− presentation that prevents an otherwise highly aggressive male from defending his territory? At the behavioral level, several alternatives are possible. During presentation of the CS+, territorial males rapidly approach the signal (and site of intrusion) in a frontal display threat posture. This posture in itself might frighten a rival into early capitulation if the frontal display were a sign of strength or of superior fighting ability. This explanation of the aggressive advantage exhibited by Pavlovian-conditioned males does not require any underlying change in aggressive motivation per se. Alternatively, a CS+ or CS− might alter the level of male aggressiveness by, for example, increasing or decreasing aggressive motivation or changing the threshold for aggressive behavior.

The results of recent neuroendocrine studies are consistent with the latter hypothesis. Although a full discussion of the neuroendocrine control of aggressive behavior is beyond the scope of the present chapter, below I describe a few of these studies to demonstrate how an understanding of the proximate mechanisms of territorial aggression complements behavioral analyses of Pavlovian conditioning. A caveat is in order, however. Because neuroendocrine studies of male aggression have relied upon subject species that are phylogenetically unrelated to blue gouramis, the implications of neuroendocrinological findings for the present analysis of conditional aggressive behavior are necessarily speculative. Proximate analyses of male aggression are described below only to demonstrate the way in which those studies might be used to drive further behavioral research.

Studies with mice (Bronson, 1973), rats (Militzer & Reinhard, 1982), and fish (Hannes, Franck, & Liemann, 1984) provide converging evidence of similar patterns of change in neuroendocrine function following aggressive interactions. Males that lose aggressive contests to more dominant individuals suffer from what may be called an aggressive stress syndrome. Compared to the winners of an aggressive encounter, losers have higher levels of circulating corticoids, or stress hormones (Bronson, 1973; Hannes et al., 1984). Losers' adrenal glands, which secrete the corticoid hormones, become enlarged, and finally, defeated males lose body weight, which is in part attributable to a decrease in the weight of several organs, including the heart, spleen, and testes (Militzer & Reinhard, 1982). Males that are successful in aggressive contests, on the other hand, show higher levels of androgen concentrations and lower levels of corticoid release than do their unsuccessful opponents (Hannes et al., 1984).

Behavioral studies of territorial male aggression have produced similarly consistent results. Significant and relatively permanent changes in the aggressive behavior of males are produced by the experience of winning or losing an aggressive encounter, an effect that is dependent upon male androgens (see van de Poll, Smeets, van Oyen, & van der Zwan, 1982, for a review). Put simply, winners become winners and losers remain losers.

One implication of neuroendocrinological findings for the present analysis of conditional aggressive behavior is that signaling of an aggressive encounter may provide a territorial male with an aggressive advantage that persists long after that signaled contest. Experiments with swordtail fish (Xiphophorus helleri) have demonstrated that the androgen levels of winners remain elevated for as long as 14 days after a single contest (Hannes et al., 1984). If such elevations in androgen increase a male's likelihood of defeating a rival, an inference to which the neuroendocrine research points strongly, then we might predict that Pavlovian signaling of an aggressive contest would be doubly advantageous. Not only would signaling increase the likelihood that a male would win that particular encounter, but if he were successful, he might then be hormonally predisposed to win subsequent encounters as well, whether or not the latter encounters were signaled. Behavioral and neuroendocrinological experiments with blue gouramis are being planned to test this potential long-term effect of winning a signaled encounter on subsequent unsignaled contests.

Pavlovian conditioning may contribute even more directly to a territorial male's tendency to remain a winner or a loser. Aggressive interactions undoubtedly are replete with environmental stimuli that, on subsequent occasions, could serve as potential CSs. In the wild, these cues might be contextual stimuli, such as the physical landmarks of another male's territory, or they might be visual and chemical characteristics of particular rivals. Might such stimuli, if paired with a previous victory, elicit an anticipatory release of androgen that in turn would produce an increase in a male's aggressive behavior and a corresponding increase in his likelihood of winning the contest? Similarly, might CSs that are paired with a previous defeat elicit an anticipatory release of stress hormones that in turn would produce the characteristic submissive behavior of losers?

Studies that attempted to answer questions such as these would help to elucidate the role of learning in territorial aggression, specifically the way in which Pavlovian conditioning might contribute to a male's tendency to remain a winner or a loser. In addition, however, such studies would provide a deeper understanding of the findings of the Pavlovian conditioning experiments discussed earlier in this chapter, namely that Pavlovian-conditioned males have an aggressive advantage in signaled encounters.

REPRODUCTIVE BEHAVIOR

Thus far, I have discussed the territorial strategy of male blue gouramis as if territoriality were only an adjunct to their reproductive behavior. However, male territoriality in blue gouramis, as well as in many other species, is a mating tactic. Males control access to an area in which some limited resource that is valuable to females (such as food or nest sites) is concentrated. Thus, males are able to attract several females to their territory and to mate with each of them (Krebs & Davies, 1987). Because territoriality can evolve only when a defended resource is both relatively scarce and economically defensible (Davies & Houston, 1984), the study of territorial behavior has revealed some striking commonalities in the ecological and behavioral profiles of divergent species in which territoriality occurs. For example, commonalities in the reproductive and parental behavior of many species of freshwater fish are the result of common selection pressures imposed by the scarcity of good nesting sites in freshwater habitats.

Fresh waters, such as lakes and streams, pose difficult ecological obstacles to reproduction. Unlike the oceans, which provide a uniform environment, smaller freshwater habitats are affected greatly by the earth and air that surround them. The temperature and chemical composition of lakes and streams, for example, fluctuate both spatially and temporally (Baylis, 1981). Because such fluctuations are often detrimental to zygotic development, some microhabitats are better suited to reproduction than others. If the number of breeding individuals exceeds the number of good sites, then competition results. Territoriality in many freshwater fish is, thus, a strategy to secure an optimum environment for the development of offspring. Further, because protein-rich eggs are an important food resource for many aquatic predators, continuous egg guarding has tended to evolve in many teleost (bony) fishes (Baylis, 1981; Blumer, 1979; Ridley, 1978). Sticklebacks, bluegill sunfish, and our study species, blue gouramis, are a few examples of fish that guard their eggs. However, more interesting than the occurrence of nest guarding per se is the observation that in each of these species, as well as in many other freshwater teleosts, males do all of the guarding.

The reason that males are favored by evolution for the parental role is not completely understood. One explanation is that because males' energy stores are not depleted by egg production, they are more able than females to assume constant guarding, and they can do so more aggressively than can females (Maynard Smith, 1977). According to this explanation, a male's reproductive fitness is increased if he takes over the role of egg guarding rather than leaving the parental responsibility to the female. Another explanation is that guarding eggs may not require much more effort than guarding a territory, and the presence of eggs may make a male's territory more attractive to additional females. Thus, guarding eggs may increase a male's chances of obtaining multiple mates (Gross & Sargent, 1985). Given that uniparental male care in freshwater teleosts is nearly always accompanied by male territoriality and polygyny, it seems reasonable to conclude that both of these functional explanations of male parenting have some validity.

Uniparental male care in freshwater teleosts, in turn, has had evolutionary consequences for females, adding an interesting twist to our ecological story that bears greatly on the discussion of learning adaptations to follow. Because females are relieved of all parental responsibilities by their mates, they are able to replenish their supply of eggs and donate a second clutch to another male. Male parental care permits females to be polyandrous. This mating system, a combination of male polygyny and female polyandry, is called *polygynandry*.

The role of learning in reproductive strategies: Intrasexual selection

Whenever individuals attempt to reproduce with more than one mate, which is true of both sexes in polygynandrous species, they must compete with others of their own sex for access to available mates. Competition within a sex results in *intrasexual selection* for adaptations that increase an individual's chances of competing successfully (Halliday, 1978; Trivers, 1972; Wilson, 1975). Dominance behavior among males is one example that is common to many polygynous species, including blue gouramis.

Domjan and I (Domjan & Hollis, 1988) have proposed that learning capacities, which we assume to have been subject to the same intrasexual selection pressures as other behavioral and morphological features, should have evolved to support and parallel an individual's reproductive weaponry. The ability of territorial males to defeat rivals via the conditional aggressive response discussed earlier is one potential example. But male territoriality, we suggest, might be subserved by several other learning processes as well.

If territorial males were predisposed to react to all intruders with a ready aggressive response, habituation and sensitization mechanisms could restrict the use of this energetically costly, and potentially injurious, response to occasions of serious threats to the territory. For example, habituation processes could attenuate the aggressive response of territory owners toward long-standing neighbors or toward members of other species that do not threaten a defended resource. On the other hand, sensitized increases in aggressive behavior could protect the territory if it suddenly became especially vulnerable to attack.

These suggestions correspond closely to observations of the convict cichlid (*Cichlasoma nigrofasciatum*) made by Peeke and Peeke (1973, 1982). Transitions between stages in the parental cycle, from eggs to larvae to free-swimming fry, were marked by abrupt (sensitized) increases in aggressiveness between conspecific neighbors. Within a particular stage of the cycle, however, aggression waned with continued exposure to the same individuals. Similar findings have been obtained with white-crowned sparrows (Petrinovich & Patterson, 1979). Both the pattern of the aggressive response and its habituation were influenced by the breeding condition of the female.

Another way in which male territoriality might be controlled through learning is suggested by a recent experiment with blue gouramis. Cadieux, Colbert, and I placed male–female partners on opposite sides of divided aquaria and exposed them to one another visually each day, using one of two procedures (Hollis, Cadieux, & Colbert, 1989). In one procedure, each male–female pair received Pavlovian conditioning training, in which a red light (the CS) was presented to both the male and the female fish simultaneously, and was followed 10 seconds later by a 15-second exposure to one another (the US). Each Pavlovian-conditioned pair received 10 daily pairings of CS and US. In the other explicitly unpaired procedure, each male–female pair received 10 presentations of the light CS followed, 6 hours later, by 10 US presentations. After 12 days of training, each fish was allowed to interact with its partner in a test encounter. Three test groups were formed: for the explicitly unpaired treatment pairs, and for half of the Pavlovian-conditioned pairs, the encounter was signaled by the same light CS used in training; for the remaining Pavlovian-conditioned pairs, the encounter was not signaled.

Although the test encounter was conducted with partners that had seen one another daily over the 12-day training period, and although the three groups of females behaved identically in the test, the effects of signaling on male behavior were profound, as the data in Figure 6A illustrate. Whereas explicitly unpaired males responded very aggressively to their partners, delivering significantly more bites than did both of the remaining test groups, Pavlovian-conditioned males that received the signal prior to interacting with their female partners (PAV-light) rarely, if ever, exhibited this aggressive behavior. Instead, the PAV-light males spent much of their time in the courtship appeasement posture, a behavior pattern in which the male leads the female to his nest and which is an essential prelude to mating. Courtship appeasement was never observed in any fish for which the encounter was not signaled.

Our results suggest that signals accompanying a female's appearance in the territory could play an important role in the reproduction of territorial species, namely by permitting highly aggressive males to suspend temporarily their prepotent aggressive reaction to a female "intruder" without compromising territorial defense. The conditional courtship response also could serve to mitigate some of

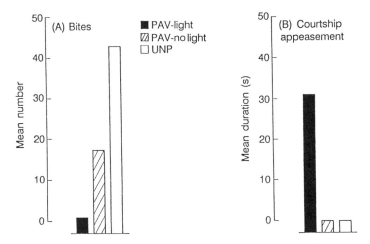

FIGURE 6. Mean number of bites (A) and mean duration of the courtship appeasement posture (B) performed by males in the test encounter between males and females. PAV–light = males receiving a signaled presentation of the female in the test encounter following Pavlovian conditioning training. PAV–no light = males receiving an unsignaled presentation of the female in the test encounter following Pavlovian conditioning training. UNP = males receiving the CS prior to the test encounter following training in which the CS never was paired with the female. (From Hollis, Cadieux, & Colbert, 1989.)

the costs, especially the high metabolic costs, associated with territorial aggression. Another benefit of signaling, as the data in Figure 6B suggest, is that males might be able to engage in courtship behavior with signaled females more quickly than with females that are not signaled. It is possible that this outcome of signaling has direct consequences for male reproductive success, namely by increasing a male's chances of securing a mate.

Pavlovian conditioning of courtship and reproductive behavior has been demonstrated in several other animals, including rats (Graham & Desjardins, 1980; Zamble, Hadad, Mitchell, & Cutmore, 1985), Japanese quail (Domjan, Lyons, North, & Bruell, 1986; Farris, 1964, 1967), and pigeons (Rackham, 1971, cited in Moore, 1973); moreover, in sticklebacks (Sevenster, 1973) and mice (Dizinno, Whitney, & Nyby, 1978; Nyby, Whitney, Schmitz, & Dizinno, 1978), the involvement of classical conditioning processes in reproductive behavior seems highly likely (see Domjan & Hollis, 1988, for a review). However, despite what might seem to be a potential for commonality of CR function across such divergent species, another caveat is in order. Although we may discover that many different animals exhibit conditional courtship responses, we also must recognize that these responses probably subserve specific functions in divergent animals.

For example, the results of studies investigating the proximate mechanisms of CR production in rats suggest that one specific function of male courtship responses may be to facilitate sperm competition. Hart (1983) observed that signals predicting the appearance of a female elicit a conditional neuroendocrine response that, in turn, causes large amounts of testosterone to be secreted into the male's bloodstream (Graham & Desjardins, 1980). This anticipatory hormonal release may be responsible for the decrease in ejaculatory latency achieved by male rats when access to females is signaled (Zamble et al., 1985). Because testosterone is known to enhance males' penile reflexes, which are essential to the deposition and dislodging of mating plugs in rats, Hart hypothesized that *conditional* testosterone release should also enhance males' penile reflexes. Conditional testosterone release would increase the ability of a male to dislodge an opponent's plug while simultaneously enabling him to deposit his own plug as tightly as possible. Taken together with our findings, these studies suggest that anticipatory Pavlovian CRs, which perhaps increase an animal's ability to secure a mate, might augment the competitive abilities of polygynous males in rather specific ways.

Intersexual selection of Pavlovian conditional responses

Intersexual selection, often called female choice, occurs when members of one sex, usually females, select mates on the basis of some attribute. This choosiness imposes selection pressures that favor individuals possessing the preferred attribute (Partridge & Halliday, 1984). In the context of our present discussion, we might ask whether Pavlovian conditional courtship responses, which are of obvious benefit to males engaged in intrasexual competition, also might be advantageous to females, and thus might have been subject to intersexual selection pressures as well. In blue gouramis, at least, the answer would seem to be yes.

Several features of male territoriality can conflict with a female's reproductive success. One of these is the risk of injury that male territorial aggression poses to a female (Daly, 1978). Another potential cost to a female is that a male's initial hostility to her requires that she wait until his aggression subsides, or that she seek a less aggressive mate elsewhere (e.g., Forselius, 1957; Tinbergen, 1960). Each of these factors could reduce a female's reproductive success, and both could be attenuated if a male were to anticipate a female's arrival via Pavlovian conditioning.

In blue gouramis, for example, the costs of male territoriality to a female can be high. A female can be injured seriously by a male in the early part of courtship (Forselius, 1957), and delays in releasing eggs to her chosen mate restrict the number of clutches that a given female can produce. Finally, gravid females would seem to be more vulnerable to predators than females that are not so obviously laden. Although in many species a lengthy period of courtship or copulation (and, perhaps, aggression) is required by females to assess male quality (e.g., Loher & Rence, 1978; Oglesby, Lanier, & Dewsbury, 1981), this type of assessment is characteristic of species in which a female makes a much larger investment in the offspring than does a male and therefore must be more discriminating. In many polyandrous species like the blue gourami, however, a female can afford to take greater risks in choosing a mate, and the accelerated courtship of a male exhibiting conditional courtship behavior should be as beneficial to the female as it is to the male.

If male conditional courtship behavior does indeed benefit polyandrous females, then we might predict that, given a choice of males, females should prefer those that exhibit this CR over those that do not. The results of an experiment now under way, although too preliminary to be conclusive, tend, so far, to support this hypothesis (Hollis & Roberts, 1989). A female whose appearance was signaled simultaneously to two unfamiliar males, one previously trained in a Pavlovian conditioning procedure, the other previously trained in an explicitly unpaired control procedure, spent significantly more time with the Pavlovian-conditioned male than with the control male in a 15-minute test encounter (see Figure 7).

Of course, additional control groups will be required to evaluate properly this preference of blue gourami females for Pavlovian-conditioned males. However, should we find that females do indeed prefer these males, then the possibility exists that Pavlovian conditional courtship behavior in blue gouramis evolved in response to intersexual, as well as intrasexual, selection pressures.

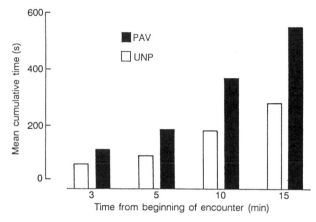

FIGURE 7. Mean cumulative time in seconds that females spent closer than 7 centimeters to each of two types of males in the first 3, 5, 10, and 15 minutes of the test encounter. PAV = males that had received the Pavlovian conditioning treatment during training. UNP = males that had received the explicitly unpaired control treatment during training.

Pavlovian conditional responses: Adaptive specializations in learned behavior

A corollary of Domjan's and my (Domjan & Hollis, 1988) proposal that learning capacities should be subject to sexual selection is our prediction that differences in learning capacities should parallel differences in mating strategies. That is, not only do we predict differences in learning capacities between species, but also we predict differences between the sexes of the same species whenever males and females employ dissimilar tactics. For example, because the reproductive tactics of polyandrous female blue gouramis are very different from those of females that are not polyandrous, comparative studies should reveal predictable differences in females' responses to anticipatory courtship behavior. A comparison of courtship behavior in blue gouramis and in Japanese quail is consistent with this latter prediction.

Domjan and Hall (1986) describe large differences between male and female Japanese quail in what they call social proximity behavior. That is, whereas males remain in proximity to females—behavior that has been characterized by Farris (1964) as the "relentless pursuit" of females by males—females seem to be indifferent to males. Not surprisingly, an approach response to stimuli predicting the appearance of females can be conditioned very rapidly in male Japanese quail (Domjan et al., 1986; see also Farris, 1967). Although Domjan and his colleagues have not attempted to condition this approach behavior in female quail, the female's apparent indifference to being near males suggests that a female approach CR is highly unlikely. Rather, in species like Japanese quail, a female might be more likely to adopt an anticipatory posture that enabled her better to evade males whose quality she has not yet had time to assess.

A very different pattern of behavior is exhibited by female blue gouramis than by female Japanese quail. In the study by Cadieux, Colbert, and I, discussed earlier, we observed that female blue gouramis, like males, rapidly learn to approach the light CS and exhibit anticipatory conditional courtship behavior, namely the frontal display. This display, adopted by territorial males when confronting a rival, also is exhibited by both males and females when encountering one another. In the latter situation, it would seem to be more like a conspecific greeting; however, whether these two uses of the display are differentiated by blue gouramis, or whether they are controlled by different mechanisms, is unknown. Figure 8 illustrates the acquisition of this conditional display by male and female partners.[2]

[2]As Figure 8 clearly suggests, PAV-no light females performed significantly fewer displays than PAV-light females and both groups of PAV males; this is undoubtedly a sampling error in that all PAV groups received the same Pavlovian treatment procedure during the training period. Statistical analyses revealed that the remaining PAV groups did not differ from one another.

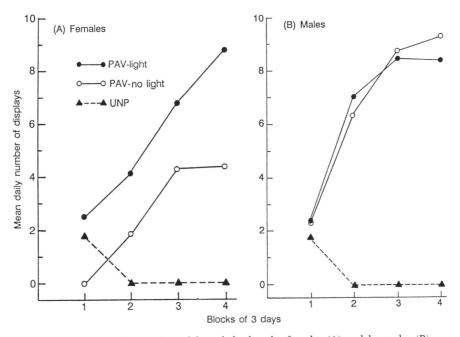

FIGURE 8. Mean daily number of frontal displays by females (A) and by males (B) elicited by the red light CS over 12 days of training. PAV–light and PAV–no light = fish receiving the Pavlovian conditioning treatment during training (but different treatments during the subsequent test confrontation). UNP = fish receiving unpaired presentations of CS and mate. (From Hollis, Cadieux, & Colbert, 1989.)

The ardor of blue gourami females versus the indifference of Japanese quail females is consistent with these species' mating strategies. Polyandrous blue gourami females, like polygynous blue gourami males, must compete with other members of their sex for access to a partner. In Japanese quail, only the polygynous males compete for access to mates (Farris, 1964).

Although a comparison of such divergent species as fish and birds might seem insufficiently circumspect, this comparison is intended to show the types of predictions that one might make regarding the learning capacities of males and females across different species. Notwithstanding this disclaimer, the application of neo-Darwinian theory to reproductive behavior has revealed striking commonalities across species with similar reproductive tactics (e.g., Emlen & Oring, 1977; Orians, 1969; Trivers, 1972; see Vehrencamp & Bradbury, 1984, for a review). In species from insects to mammals, similar selection pressures have tended to produce similar reproductive strategies. Pavlovian conditional courtship responses would be expected to have been subject to these same selection pressures and, therefore, should represent yet another example of cross-species commonalities.

SUMMARY

In this chapter, I have attempted to describe the role that Pavlovian conditioning might play in the agonistic and reproductive behavior of a territorial species, *T. trichopterus*. Work in my laboratory suggests that signaling of an aggressive encounter enables Pavlovian-conditioned males to deliver significantly more bites and tailbeats than males for which an encounter is not signaled. Because maintaining a territory is essential to reproduction in this species, an anticipatory response to Pavlovian CS+'s is likely to increase a male's reproductive success by enhancing his territorial defense. Just as CS+'s can control aggressive behavior, so, too, can events that signal a period of time free from territorial threat. These CS−'s might enable males to relax their territorial defense at times when an intrusion is unlikely to occur or in places where rivals are unlikely to appear. Together, CS+'s and CS−'s could make a male's territorial defense more efficient. Conditional courtship responses, observed in both male and female blue gouramis, may be one reproductive strategy for competing with members of the same sex to secure a mate. In addition to the role that these intrasexual selection pressures may have exerted on Pavlovian courtship responses, some preliminary work suggests that courtship CRs may have been subject to intersexual selection pressures as well. That is, females prefer males that exhibit conditional courtship behavior.

Because the reproductive strategies of blue gouramis are similar to the reproductive strategies of other polygynous males and polyandrous females, the role of Pavlovian conditioning that I describe for the blue gourami is likely to be found in other species, too. Thus, in some sense, this research might be characterized, not unkindly, as a functionalist approach to General Process Theory.

Finally, I also have attempted to demonstrate the importance of an integrative approach to the understanding of Pavlovian conditional responding. Many of the anticipatory digestive responses that Pavlov studied are controlled by proximate (neuroendocrine) mechanisms that were unknown in Pavlov's time. Although a large body of literature today is devoted to neuroendocrine control of behavior, still little is known about the role that learned signals play in hunger, or in aggression and reproduction. Attempts to link the findings of neuroendocrinologists with the rich literatures of animal learning theory and behavioral ecology have been enormously fruitful. Not only has this integrative approach revealed new questions for both proximate and functional analyses of Pavlovian conditioning, but it has also provided strong support for the adaptiveness, or *tselesoobraznost*, of Pavlovian CRs in the territorial and aggressive behavior of blue gouramis.

PART III

Parental Behavior and Development

The typical consequences of mating behavior are the production of young and, in many species, parental care. Parental care can play a key role in the survival and development of the young. The chapters in this section are concerned with the control of parental behavior and with the effects of parental behavior and other influences on the development of behavior in the young. As one progresses through the four chapters in this section, the emphasis shifts progressively from parents to young.

Snowdon (Chapter 10) deals with the relationships among mating system, parental care, and development, and provides an excellent transition from the previous section of this book. Like other authors in the book, Snowdon believes that a complete explanation of behavior requires attention to the full program proposed by Tinbergen: observation and description followed by analysis of function, phylogeny, development, and immediate causation. His study of monogamy and parental behavior in marmosets and tamarins follows this general design.

Snowdon sees monogamy in these primates occurring not in relation to male paternal certainty, as is argued by some theorists, but rather primarily in response to the female's need for assistance in rearing the young. Snowdon points out that male interest in young is quite common among many species of primates. What is critical is that the female be willing to relinquish care of the young to the male so that he can display paternal behavior. Thus, the female exercises a considerable degree of control over the occurrence of paternal behavior in the male. Siblings in these species stay with the parents and also aid in the rearing of the young. Snowdon believes this is because, by doing so, the older siblings perfect skills that will later be useful in rearing their own young, and that in some cases the siblings stay with their parents because territories appropriate for breeding may be unavailable to them. These are functional explanations, not to be confused with those relating to immediate causation. Snowdon also emphasizes the need for accurate information on the endocrine profiles of these animals as they change over time in order to pinpoint the occurrence of ovulation and to determine the gestation period accurately. Ovulation is concealed in this species, and males and females display more sexual activity than would be expected in a monogamous species.

Snowdon concludes his chapter by considering paternal care in humans in relation to the same economic considerations used with nonhuman primates. He argues that it is in societies in which females cannot rear young successfully without assistance that paternal behavior appears most prevalent. It is especially significant that Snowdon works with an endangered species, because information on the conditions needed for successful reproduction can be important in facilitating captive breeding programs so that endangered animals may someday be reintroduced into their natural habitat.

Silver (Chapter 11) is primarily concerned with the proximate causation of behavior, which she addresses in her studies of the temporal organization of parental behavior in ring doves. The problem of the temporal organization of behavior is a general one, and is relevant to many kinds of behavior. However, the problem is compounded when studying animals in a social situation, rather than individually. Silver emphasizes the physiological mechanisms associated with the circadian control of parental behavior, discussing the role of the suprachiasmatic nucleus (SCN), retino-hypothalamic tract, and pineal gland in the control of periodicity.

The problem of how to analyze the temporal patterning of parental behavior in ring doves is placed in a broad context. Silver first elaborates some principles concerning the control of rhythmical cycles developed in individual mammals, and then shows how to apply similar methods to the more complex situation of incubation in a pair of birds. Males and female ring doves differ in that males generally sit on eggs for a block of time in the middle of the day, whereas females sit the rest of the time. The proximate control mechanisms of males and females differ too; males seem to use an interval timer to control the duration of sitting, but females seem to initiate sitting according to an internal clock. These sex differences appear to be hormonally based. The story of the delineation of these relationships exhibits the effective use of multiple approaches, including the design of effective test apparatus, manipulation of hormones, and alteration of the photic schedule, in answering a single, important question.

The remainder of the chapter is concerned with a search for the anatomical locus of the clock. In mammals, the SCN is the primary locus. Because the homologue of the SCN in birds is not clear, it is difficult to be sure where the effective control originates. The systematic exploration of the effects of different loci is still in progress. As with many problems in comparative psychology, the solution to this one is not yet clear. However, it appears likely that a solution will come soon; motivated scientists have the techniques with which to address the question effectively.

Moore (Chapter 12) deals with the development of sexual behavior, and this is another chapter that serves to bridge this section and the previous one. The first part of the chapter is comparative: Moore delineates the great range of patterns and influences on the development of sexual behavior in diverse species. Environmental factors that affect the rate of maturation, sex, and sexual differentiation are described. The plasticity and flexibility characteristic of alternative patterns of behavioral organization are elaborated. The length of the developmental period is related to life history strategies.

Moore uses the descriptive terms *cascades* and *webs* to describe behavioral development. The term *cascade* is used to refer to the considerable ramifications that can stem from even some relatively modest events early in the lives of organisms. The term *web* is used to delineate the complex network of interconnecting events at any time in an organism's development. These principles are illustrated with a treatment of information concerning the effects of hormones early in life on sexual development. Moore's research on the role of maternal licking in development provides a beautiful example of the ways in which cascades and webs act in behavioral development.

The parents are not the only significant individuals in developing animals' lives. Porter (Chapter 13) adds another dimension to the problem of the development of behavior by emphasizing the relationships among siblings in litters. The chapter begins with a discussion of the effects of the presence of siblings on development. Spiny mice reared with siblings tend to huddle more and to be more effective in food competition situations than animals reared alone; socially reared pups thus appear to be more socially competent than those reared in isolation. Porter then elaborates on this finding by showing that the kind of sibling with which an animal interacts makes a difference in development. Both the age and the species of the littermate can affect the development of spiny mouse pups. The presence of littermates can be of special benefit to animals with various kinds of deficits. Porter explores the effects of littermates on pups rendered anosmic by infusions of zinc sulfate. Anosmic pups reared with siblings are more likely to survive and are better able to locate food in a test situation than are anosmic pups reared alone.

Porter then turns to the selective nature of sibling interactions. In much of his earlier work, he has shown that spiny mice associate preferentially with their littermates as opposed to other animals. Although this preference is based on familiarity during rearing, rather than on some genetic marker, nevertheless, in the normal environment of spiny mice, it may reflect the action of kin selection. One persistent problem in the literature on the discrimination and recognition of kin has concerned the adaptive value of such behavior. Porter shows that in some test situations, littermates are especially effective at exploiting a test situation with limited food availability and share food more effectively.

The developmental picture is thus broadened, as we must consider not only the interactions between parents and the young, but the interactions of siblings among themselves and their implications for development.

CHAPTER 10

MECHANISMS MAINTAINING

MONOGAMY IN MONKEYS

Charles T. Snowdon

Late in the afternoon, the mother began to enter labor, showing clear signs of contractions. Early in the evening, the delivery began. The father grasped the first infant as it emerged from the birth canal and proceeded to assist the mother in the delivery. He cleaned the membranes from the newborn infant and returned to assist his mate in the delivery of the second infant. Both parents then cleaned the twins, and the mother nursed them briefly.

During the next several months, the mother held the twins only during nursing. The rest of the time the infants were carried and cared for by their father and by their older brothers and sisters. The older siblings appeared to compete with each other for the privilege of carrying the new babies. The mother spent most of her time working to provide food for herself and her infants. As the time of weaning approached, the father distracted the twins by calling to them and offering them pieces of solid food.

. This description of a home birth and communal infant care is not an idealized view of a liberated human family, but is a routine description of family life in a small South American monkey, the cotton-top tamarin (*Saguinus oedipus*). This behavior is not limited to this particular species; it is found throughout all species within the family Callitrichidae, the marmosets and tamarins. The extensive involvement by fathers and by older siblings in infant care is unusual among mammals (although not among birds), and among human beings such paternal involvement in infant care has, in the past, appeared to be equally rare. Why do marmosets and tamarins behave this way while so few other mammals do?

Tinbergen (1951) proposed four questions of study for any phenomenon of animal behavior such as paternal care of infants: causation, ontogeny, function, and phylogeny. I consider each of these questions to be of equal importance in the study of behavior. To have a complete understanding of behavior one must understand the mechanisms of causation: what neurological, hormonal, and behavioral events induce a given behavior to occur at a given time. One must understand the development of the behavior within the life span of the individual exhibiting the behavior, and one also must understand the phylogenetic origins of the behavior. Finally, one must know the adaptive function that the behavior serves for the animal.

In the early years, ethologists divided their attention relatively equally among Tinbergen's four levels. However, since the publication of *Sociobiology* (Wilson, 1975), a large number of zoologically trained animal behaviorists have focused attention on questions of function and phylogeny, ignoring for the most part questions of causation and ontogeny. The study of causation and ontogeny historically has been one of the strengths of comparative psychology, although many comparative psychologists have also been concerned with issues of phylogeny and function. The collective contributions to this volume illustrate how the traditional involvement of psychologists with causation and ontogeny can be integrated successfully with concerns of phylogeny and function.

In this chapter, I use the communal infant rearing of cotton-top tamarins as a case study of how comparative psychologists can make use of Tinbergen's four levels in the analysis of a phenomenon. While I think that an integrated study of infant care in cotton-top tamarins is of interest in its own right, the study of this behavior is also important in two practical areas. First, cotton-top tamarins are seriously endangered, and the species has been listed in the Red Data Book of the International Union for the Conservation of Nature since 1973. The species is endemic to Colombia, and recent surveys in Colombia indicate that destruction of its forest habitat is continuing. Information about the mechanisms of successful infant rearing has great practical importance in captive breeding programs to preserve the species, and is necessary for making intelligent decisions about the management of these animals in protected reserves in the wild. Second, there is considerable interest in the new role of human fathers in infant care (Lamb, 1987). Understanding how and why males become involved in parental care in cotton-top tamarins may provide practical suggestions for increasing human fathers' involvement in infant care.

There are two categories of paternal behavior: substitutive or direct paternal care, which consists of activities that the female normally performs, such as carrying infants, feeding them, and so on, and complementary or indirect paternal care, which consists of activities in which females rarely engage, such as defending territory or defending the infants from attack (Kleiman & Malcolm, 1981; Snowdon & Suomi, 1982). Because substitutive or direct paternal care is relatively rare, I focus on direct paternal care in this chapter. I argue that direct paternal care is a possible outcome of a monogamous breeding system, and I analyze several characteristics of monogamy with respect to the cotton-top tamarin and related species. Then I present an integration of various aspects of monogamy as they affect paternal care, showing how each of Tinbergen's four questions is of value to our understanding of paternal care. Finally, I develop some generalizations from the data on cotton-top tamarins to aspects of human paternal care.

THE ISSUE OF MONOGAMY

The first step in understanding why cotton-top tamarin males care for infants is to find some commonality among all species where males show extensive infant care. The most obvious commonality among the birds and the primates displaying extensive paternal care is a monogamous breeding system. Although most monogamous primates display some degree of paternal care, the expression of paternal care is quite variable, ranging from involvement from the earliest days after birth in some marmosets and tamarins, to paternal involvement after the first three or four weeks of birth in other marmosets and tamarins, to involvement in infant care only after weaning in siamangs (Chivers, 1972), to almost total neglect of infants in DeBrazza's monkey (*Cercopithecus neglectus*) (A. Gautier-Hion, personal communication). Thus, monogamy per se does not assure paternal care, but there is a high correlation between monogamy and paternal care.

Various authors have characterized the nature of monogamy. Dewsbury (1988a) provided three criteria that have been used in defining monogamy: (1) there must be mating only between one male and one female; (2) there must be joint parental care of infants; and (3) there must be an exclusive or preferential association between the mating male and female. Kleiman (1977) examined the characteristics exhibited by monogamous mammals, and her list of characteristics can be summarized in five main points: (1) Monogamous mammals show intrasexual aggression against conspecific intruders. (This is the equivalent of the mating exclusivity point made by Dewsbury). (2) There is little sexual dimorphism; males and females have little difference in size or coloration. This is quite different from the birds, in which plumage dimorphisms are common. (3) There is infrequent sociosexual behavior, and few, if any, signs of ovulation. That is, there is little solicitation of sexual behavior and relatively little social contact between the reproductive pair. (4) There is a delayed sexual maturation in offspring, with only the adult pair breeding. (5) There is extensive paternal care, and older siblings also help with infant care. (This is equivalent to Dewsbury's point about joint parental care of infants.) Dewsbury (1981b) has used these characteristics and some additional ones to predict the occurrence of monogamy or polygyny in 42 species of muroid rodents.

In order to understand the potential significance of monogamy for the expression of paternal care, we must examine some theoretical issues relating to the expression of paternal care. Trivers (1972) described a concept of parental investment: "any investment by the parent in an individual offspring that increases the offspring's chance of survival (and hence reproductive success) at the cost of the parent's ability to invest in other offspring." Part of this cost is the production of gametes, but in mammals these costs are inconsequential compared to the mother's investment in her infant during pregnancy and lactation. Since female mammals invest disproportionately in their offspring compared to males, and since female mammals are always certain of their relatedness to their infants, while a male mammal can never be absolutely certain of his paternity, it follows that once a pregnancy is established, it should be to the male's advantage to desert the female and attempt to inseminate other females. This scenario leads to the evolution of polygyny as the most adaptive strategy for males. Thus, for theoretical reasons, monogamy can be viewed as a bizarre mating strategy from a male's perspective; for the same reasons, male care of infants can also be viewed as a bizarre behavior. Given paternal uncertainty and the advantage of inseminating additional females, a male that stayed with a mate through pregnancy and assisted in parental care would presumably be reducing his own reproductive success.

Under what conditions might one expect paternal care to be adaptive? If the pair-bond were well established and long-lasting, and if there were mechanisms to maintain the exclusivity of the pair-bond, then the male would no longer have the problem of paternal uncertainty. If a male could be relatively certain of his paternity, then it might be to his advantage to assist in the care of offspring. However, paternal certainty is not a sufficient condition for paternal care. Snowdon and Suomi (1982) reviewed paternal care in primates with a variety of mating systems. While there was a general trend for monogamous males to show paternal care, this care was not expressed in all monogamous species, nor was it expressed at the same infant developmental stage in all species. In harem-maintaining species, in which a male has exclusive access to several females and controls their movements with tight discipline, and thus should have complete paternal certainty, there is virtually no evidence of male care of infants (Hall, 1965; Kummer, 1967, 1968).

A second condition that could lead to paternal care is concealed ovulation. The female might use concealed ovulation as a counterstrategy to prevent a male from deserting before infants are born (Burley, 1979). If a male is never certain when a female is ovulating, then he must stay around her long enough to ensure that a conception has occurred. Thus, the female is tricking the male into staying with her against his own better interests. However, at some point in pregnancy, the female's body shape changes, providing cues that conception has taken place, and Trivers's theory predicts that it would still be to a male's advantage to desert at this point. It is difficult to see how a concealed ovulation strategy would be sufficient to explain paternal care.

A third condition that could lead to monogamy and paternal care of infants is the economics of infant care. In polygynous or promiscuous breeding systems, all of the postnatal infant care must be provided by the mother. The father is either unknown or, as in a harem-maintaining social structure, he has too many females and infants to provide much help to any one of them. However, if the resources in the environment were limiting in such a way that a female could not provide food and infant care by herself, then monogamy and subsequent paternal care of infants would be highly adaptive. If the help of a male is necessary for the successful postnatal rearing of his offspring, then a monogamous relationship and extensive parental care is the most adaptive behavior for the male (e.g., Lancaster, 1985; Snowdon & Suomi, 1982). Under these conditions, neither monogamy nor paternal care of infants need be viewed as bizarre. I argue that the female's need for extensive help from other animals in rearing infants is the ultimate cause of the appearance of paternal care in marmosets and tamarins.

A BRIEF NATURAL HISTORY

Marmosets and tamarins are found throughout South America, ranging from Panama to Bolivia and Uruguay. They are small arboreal monkeys with adult weights ranging from about 90–100 grams for the pygmy marmoset (*Cebuella pygmaea*) to over 700 grams for the golden lion tamarin (*Leontopithecus rosalia*). In almost all species, twinning is the rule (with triplets found frequently in captive colonies of the common marmoset, *Callithrix jacchus*: Box & Hubrecht, 1987). In captivity and at some field sites, the female can produce two sets of twins each year, while at other sites, a female typically produces a single set of twins each year. In every field study and every captive colony known, there is only a single reproductive female in a group, no matter how large the group's size; thus, polygyny can be definitely eliminated from consideration as a breeding system. Recent field reports on the saddle-back tamarin (*Saguinus fuscicollis* ssp.) by Goldizen and her colleagues (Goldizen, 1987; Terborgh & Goldizen, 1985) have shown a facultative polyandry for this species. In groups without any prior offspring, two males have been observed to mate with a female and to share in the care of the infants that result. However, in groups of saddle-back tamarins with older offspring available as helpers, monogamy appears to be the rule.

All of the species appear to be highly territorial and to have a variety of calls, aggressive displays, and scent-marking behavior that they use in territorial defense (Dawson, 1979; McConnell & Snowdon, 1986; Neyman, 1977). When new groups are formed in captivity, deaths can occur as animals fight with each other for breeding status (de la Ossa, Moreno, & Segura, 1988). In both field and captive studies, fathers and older offspring have been observed to care for infants, although the exact timing and extent of this care varies between individuals within a species and between species. At present, little is known about dispersal patterns in the wild, although Neyman (1977) reports that young male and female cotton-top tamarins were equally likely to disperse. McGrew and McLuckie (1986), in a clever laboratory analogue of dispersal, found subadult cotton-top tamarin females were more likely to leave their home cage and to use a complex system of air-conditioning ducting to explore other parts of the tamarin colony than were subadult males.

The animals eat a variety of insects and fruits, and in the marmosets, gum exudates from trees are an important food resource. Territories appear to be constructed to include significant fruit and gum-producing trees. There appear to be three classes of predators on marmosets and tamarins: raptors, snakes, and mustelids (Bartecki & Heymann, 1987; Dawson, 1979; Heymann, 1987; Neyman, 1977). The major activities of marmosets and tamarins in the field relate to obtaining food, caring for infants, and avoiding predation.

In my laboratory, my colleagues and I have attempted to simulate the natural environment of cotton-top tamarins as much as possible. Our captive environments are quite large, ranging between 3 and 12 cubic meters. The enclosures are filled with a complex array of branches and ropes to simulate the arboreal environment. The enclosures are large and complex enough to house a mated pair and several sets of offspring together. The basic diet is a commercial marmoset chow, but we supplement this with a wide variety of fruits, vegetables, and protein sources, including yogurt, insects, chicken, and hamburger. Different foods are presented at different times throughout the day. All food and water is located at least 1 meter above the floor. All of our observations and experimentation occur in the home cage, so that we rarely need to capture and handle animals. (See Snowdon, Savage, & McConnell, 1985, for more details).

CHARACTERISTICS OF MONOGAMY IN MARMOSETS AND TAMARINS

With this theoretical and natural historical background, let us now look at each of Kleiman's (1977) characteristics of monogamy with respect to marmosets and tamarins.

Intrasexual aggression and exclusivity of mating

Monogamous monkeys are generally less tolerant of intruders than are polygynous monkeys. Mendoza and Mason (1986) studied the responses of monogamous titi monkeys (*Callicebus moloch*) and polygynous squirrel monkeys (*Saimiri sciureus*) to conspecific intruders. The titi monkeys displayed increased levels of intrasexual aggression in response to intruders, and male titi monkeys displayed elevated cortisol levels in the presence of male intruders. In contrast, squirrel monkeys showed few aggressive responses to intruders, and both sexes showed reduced cortisol levels in response to female intruders.

Several studies on marmosets and tamarins indicate that intrasexual aggression occurs, but the details of the manifestation of this aggression vary between species. Studies on common marmosets (Sutcliffe & Poole, 1978, 1984) and on saddle-back tamarins (Epple, 1977; Epple & Alveario, 1985; Epple, Alveario, & Katz, 1982) showed that both sexes displayed high levels of aggressive behavior toward intruders of the same sex. However, French and Snowdon (1981) found a sexual dimorphism in the cotton-top tamarin's response to intruders. Females responded to intruders of both sexes with increased levels of scent marking, but showed no direct threat or aggression responses to either male or female intruders. Males, on the other hand, showed no scent marking and showed little response to female intruders, but they displayed high levels of threat and attack behavior toward male intruders. Only males behaved aggressively toward same-sex intruders in our captive study. (I will discuss later how females can maintain sexual exclusivity without being aggressive toward intruding females.)

Recently, French and Inglett (1989) repeated this study with golden lion tamarins. Surprisingly, they found results exactly opposite to those found in cotton-top tamarins. Golden lion tamarin females displayed high levels of aggression toward female intruders, but males showed no attack behavior toward intruders, and showed only slight increases in levels of agonistic behavior in the presence of male intruders. The intensity of female aggression was increased with the presence of helpers in the group.

There are some demonstrations that the social context affects the degree of aggression displayed. Evans (1983) tested common marmosets with same-sex and opposite-sex intruders either with their mates present or separated from their mates. In the presence of their mates, both males and females showed high levels of aggressive behavior toward the opposite sex. However in the absence of their mates, females were indifferent to novel males, while males actively solicited contact and sexual interactions from novel females.

Anzelberger (1985) studied the same species in three conditions: animals isolated from their families, animals that could see their families through a one-way glass, and animals in the presence of their families. Males showed higher levels of sexual display when alone or out of sight of their families. However, the response also varied according to the dominance status. Males showed more sexual activity toward subordinate females, and subordinate females showed greater sexual responsiveness to males. Dominant females showed more aggressive responses than sexual responses toward both dominant and subordinate males, and they showed the highest levels of aggression when alone or in the presence of their families.

Many marmosets and tamarins display some degree of intrasexual aggression toward intruders, although there are some interesting cases where one sex displays aggression and the other does not. Social context clearly influences the display of sexual or aggressive behavior toward opposite-sex intruders. Males react sexually to novel females when their mate is absent, but aggressively when their mate is present.

Lack of sexual dimorphism

In general, there is little sexual dimorphism in marmosets and tamarins, especially when they are compared with polygynous primate species. Male Hamadryas baboons (*Papio hamadryas*) and gorillas (*Gorilla gorilla*) weigh almost twice as much as females, and male red howler monkeys (*Alouatta seniculus*) weigh 40 percent more than females (Alexander, Hoogland, Howard, Noonan, & Sherman, 1979). In contrast, gibbons, marmosets, and tamarins show no sex differences in body weight, body length, and other physical measures. In pygmy marmosets, the degree of monomorphism is so great that the female's large labia and clitoris are very difficult to discriminate from the penis and scrotal sac of the male. French (1982) found no sex differences in weight or in various physical measurements of cotton-top tamarins, but he did find a significant difference in the scent gland area. French and Cleveland (1984) have shown that scent-marking behavior is dimorphic in cotton-top tamarins, being found almost exclusively in adult females. In other species, such as the saddleback tamarin, there is no dimorphism in scent gland size nor in scent-marking behavior (Epple, 1986).

If the notion of sexual dimorphism is expanded to include behavioral dimorphism, then there are several differences between male and female tamarins. In the cotton-top tamarin, there are sex differences in addition to the scent-marking rate and gland size already noted. Both Cleveland and Snowdon (1984) and Tardif, Carson, and Gangaware (1986) have found that males are more involved in infant carrying than females are. In contrast, Tardif et al. found no sex differences in infant-carrying behavior in the common marmoset. McConnell and Snowdon (1986) simulated territorial encounters between groups of cotton-top tamarins by opening doors between adjacent colony rooms. There were differences in the roles played by males and females in territory defense. Some types of vocalizations were given more frequently by females and others by males.

In comparison with polygynous species, there is a lack of sexual dimorphism in marmosets and tamarins. Nonetheless, there are some interesting morphological and behavioral sex differences in some callitrichid species.

Infrequent sociosexual behavior and few signs of ovulation

In cotton-top tamarins, as in most other species of callitrichids studied to date, there are few, if any, signs of ovulation observable in the female's physical appearance or behavior. In 1981, when we first began studying reproductive behavior in cotton-top tamarins, Jeffrey French observed that a peak of sexual activity, involving attempted copulations, female scent marking, and male interest in scent marks, appeared to be occurring at the time of conception. French observed pairs of tamarins each day until parturition occurred, then counted backwards the 140 days of the presumed gestation period. It was at this point that the increased sexual behavior and scent marking occurred. However, before publishing the exciting news that females did communicate their ovulatory state to their mates, we decided it would be wise to develop a technique for assaying the ovarian state of the female.

Serum assays require repeated captures and blood drawings, and can be used only for short time periods in small primates because they cause rapid depletion of red blood cells. Therefore, we decided to develop a urinary assay. The first assays were for estrone and estradiol, two forms of estrogen (French, Abbott, Scheffler, Robinson, & Goy, 1983). Once the assay had been validated, French returned to look for changes in the behavior of female and male tamarins that would indicate ovulation. This time there was no correlation between the peak of estrogen concentration and any behavioral measure: no peak in female scent marking, in male interest in female scents, in the proportion of time that the pair spent in contact, in the rates of approaches toward each other, or in the rates of grooming correlated with the estrogen peak observed (French, 1982).

Why were the pilot data so promising and the subsequent data so unpromising? What produced the peak of sexual activity that French originally observed? There are two answers. First, in gathering the urinary data, we were still handling the females each day to capture them and place them in a metabolism cage, and it was possible that the stress of capture and confinement interfered with the behavioral expression of receptivity. To get around this problem, we have developed a new technique of urine collection where animals are unrestrained. We make use of the fact that most primates, including ourselves, urinate upon waking in the morning. We have trained monkeys to approach us for food treats after they wake up, and we simply hold a container underneath them and wait until they urinate. With this technique we can obtain behavioral observations that are uncontaminated by the technique of hormone collection (Ziegler, Bridson, Snowdon, & Eman, 1987; Ziegler, Savage, Scheffler, & Snowdon, 1987).

The second problem is that estrogen peaks alone are not adequate to determine when ovulation occurs. We have recently developed a technique to measure luteinizing hormone (LH)/chorionic gonadotropin (Ziegler, Bridson, Snowdon, & Eman, 1987), and we found that the LH peak occurred before the estrogen peak. We consider LH to be a more accurate marker of ovulation than estrogen, since recent metabolic studies using radio-labeled markers in cotton-top tamarins indicates that the excretion of estrone, the major estrogen, is delayed for two days or more after injection (Ziegler, Sholl, Scheffler, Haggerty, & Lasley, 1989). In subsequent behavioral observations using our more precise determination of when ovulation is occurring, we have still failed to find any behavioral correlate with ovulation (Savage, Ziegler, & Snowdon, 1988) confirming French's original observations and a report by Brand and Martin (1983).

Using LH as the marker for ovulation, we have found that the gestation time of cotton-top tamarins is significantly longer than previously expected—183 days, as compared with our original guess of 140 days. Brand and Martin had indicated that cotton-top tamarin gestation lengths might be as long as 166–170 days, based on inferences from limited pair testing. Thus, when French made his original observations of increased sexual behavior and scent marking, he was observing females that had already been pregnant for six weeks. This finding implies a continuous receptivity on the part of females. Recent work by Stribley, French, and Inglett (1987) confirms concealed ovulation and continuous receptivity for the golden lion tamarin as well.

One serious problem with the concealed ovulation hypothesis is that it is best supported by negative results. The fact that we have not been able to observe differences in behavior or in responsiveness to scent marking does not mean that no signals exist, only that we might not yet have been clever enough to detect them. Since the development of our urinary hormonal assays, we now routinely monitor all of the breeding females in our colony, and we find that, about 80 percent of the time, females conceive on the first postpartum ovulation. Thus, it is rare that an ovulation occurs without a conception. There must be some communication between mates in order to achieve this high conception rate.

A series of studies on common marmosets by Dixson and his colleagues shows that some subtle cues can be observed to correlate with the female's ovulatory state. Kendrick and Dixson (1983) found an increase in tongue-flicking behavior (used as a copulation invitation) during the periovulatory period. Males responded to females with tongue flicks, and males were more successful in achieving intromissions and ejaculations in interactions that the female initiated with tongue flicking. In parallel with our results on cotton-top tamarins, Kendrick and Dixson found no changes in grooming, scent marking, or olfactory investigation over the cycle. Kendrick and Dixson (1985) found that injections of estradiol at preovulatory levels induced tongue flicking and reduced the number of mounts refused by ovariectomized females. Dixson and Lunn (1987) made detailed videotape observations on eight groups of marmosets immediately after parturition and simultaneously recorded their hormonal data. They found that mounts began within a median of 4 days after parturition, although the LH peak did not occur until a mean of 13 days postpartum. Mounts and copulations continued at high levels after the female was pregnant.

Although there might be some subtle cues that can communicate ovarian status to a male, the existence of continuous receptivity suggests another mechanism that could account for the high conception success in cotton-top tamarins. If mates copulated frequently, at least once a day, then conception could occur with high probability even if the females were not communicating their ovarian state to their mates. However, a high rate of sexual activity in monogamous monkeys is counter to the predictions by Kleiman (1977) that monogamous pairs should show little sociosexual interaction. How can we resolve this contradiction?

I think the impression that monogamous mammals have a low rate of socio-sexual interaction is due to temporal differences in the distribution of sexual behavior between monogamous and polygynous species. In many polygynous species, there is relatively little daily contact between males and females, and females appear to have developed very vivid signals to indicate their sexual status. For example, chacma baboons (*Papio ursinus*) have extraordinary genital swellings that reach peak size at the time of ovulation. Bielert (1982) has shown that males are quite stimulated by these swellings and will increase their rate of interaction with females showing sexual swellings. When baboons mate, there is a intense period of mating activity between a female and a sequence of consorts over a week-long period. From data presented in Hall and DeVore (1965) on females observed continuously throughout the receptive period, it is possible to estimate the copulatory rate. In four females for whom extensive data are presented the rate of copulation was 74.3 ± 35.2 per female per estrous cycle. This copulatory activity occurred over 3 to 12 days. Kummer (1968) reported a rate of 43.9 mounts per female in the one month each year when Hamadryas baboon females were receptive. However, after conception, there is no subsequent sexual interaction until the female has delivered an infant and nursed it through weaning (Hall & Devore, 1965; Kummer, 1968). Gestation length in baboons is approximately 5.5 months, and infants are weaned at 11–15 months of age. Thus, after a burst of copulatory activity during a brief receptive period, a female baboon is unlikely to mate again for 18–24 months.

In time-limited pair tests with cotton-top tamarins, Brand and Martin (1983) found high rates of mounting and copulation, and they suggested that mating activities are important in pair-bond formation. We have observed the rates of mating behavior in newly formed and well-established pairs of cotton-top tamarins that were living together all of the time (Savage et al., 1988). We have found copulation rates of once per hour during daylight in newly formed pairs, and slightly more than once per day in well-established pairs. Thus, cotton-top tamarins, and, I suspect, most other marmosets and tamarins, have a very active sex life. If we were to sample baboons on a day of maximum receptivity, they would show high rates of sexual activity compared with tamarins, but if we were to summarize the total number of copulations over a year, marmosets and tamarins would have much greater levels of sexual interaction, since they are continuously receptive throughout their reproductive cycles.

Delay of sexual maturation

As noted above, no field or captive studies have ever reported more than a single reproductive female in a group of marmosets and tamarins. Either there is a delay in sexual maturation, or females disperse from their groups as soon as they reach puberty. In captivity, maturing females cannot disperse voluntarily, and many studies have found that females living in a family group do not reach sexual maturity, while younger females who have been removed and paired with a mate are reproducing. Thus, there appears to be some means by which a reproductive female can delay sexual maturity in the other females in her group.

Using our urinary hormonal assay techniques, we have monitored a large

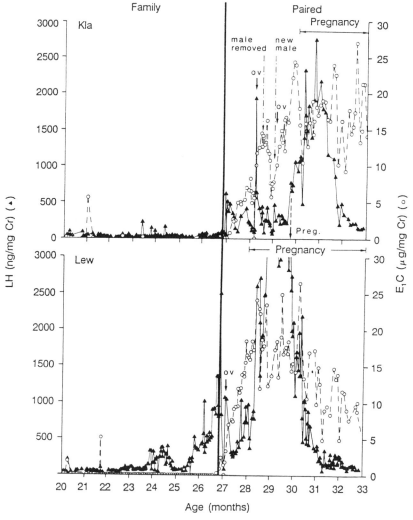

FIGURE 1. Hormonal data for twin sisters monitored while they were in a family group and after they were paired with a mate in a new environment. Although the levels of luteinizing hormone for Lew increased before pairing, estrogen levels were not detectable. Lew ovulated and conceived 8 days after pairing. Kla conceived on her second ovulation. LH = luteinizing hormone; E_1C = estrone conjugate; Cr = creatinine; ov = ovulation. (From Ziegler, Savage, Scheffler, & Snowdon, 1987.)

number of subordinate females living with a reproductive female. In no case has there been evidence of normal ovulation while females were living in the same group as a reproductive female (French, Abbott, & Snowdon, 1984; Ziegler, Savage, Scheffler, & Snowdon, 1987). Figure 1 illustrates the hormonal patterns of twin sisters while living in the family group and after being paired with a new male. There was a dramatic increase in the levels of both estrone and LH after the females were paired. Female Lew, whose data are shown in the bottom panel, conceived 8 days after she was removed from her family group and paired with a male. Note that in both females there are low, fluctuating levels of estrone and LH prior to removal from the family group. These females had reached puberty and were capable of normal ovulatory cycles and reproduction, but these appear to have been inhibited in the presence of a reproductive female.

Ziegler, Savage, Scheffler, and Snowdon (1987) monitored the hormonal levels of several females from 10 to 19 months of age. We found detectable LH levels beginning at about the 16th month and detectable estrone levels in the 18th to 19th months, although these levels were far below the levels found in a reproductive female. One female whose hormones we had been monitoring died at about 20 months of age. The hormonal levels of this female had been low and acyclic, and histological examination of her ovaries revealed well-formed ovarian follicles which had stopped short of maturation and showed signs of degeneration. There were no signs that ovulation had ever occurred (T. E. Ziegler, unpublished observations). Tardif (1984) reported elevated levels of serum progesterone occurring at about 20 months of age in females living in a family group. Thus, we suspect that puberty occurs at about the 18th month of age.

Whether a female can express her reproductive potential is dependent upon her social environment. We have studied some females who have lived in family groups through 4 years of age and have found no indications of ovulation. It appears that some reproductive suppression is taking place. Further evidence for an active suppression of ovarian function comes from an example reported by French, Abbott, and Snowdon (1984), illustrated in Figure 2. When her mother died, female YV began to show normal ovarian cycles and increased rates of scent marking. When YV's father was mated with a new female, YV's hormonal levels decreased rapidly, as did her scent marking. When YV was removed from her father and stepmother and given a mate of her own, her scent-marking behavior and hormonal levels rapidly returned to normal. The reversal of ovulatory function in the presence of a reproductive female suggests that some factor in the reproductive female suppresses reproduction in other females.

What might be the mechanism used by reproductive cotton-top tamarin females to suppress fertility in other females in the group? Since females scent mark in response to intruders (French & Snowdon, 1981), and since the best developed scent glands and highest rates of scent marking are found in reproductive females (French & Cleveland, 1984), it seemed likely that the scent mark might be the mechanism of reproductive suppression. Savage et al. (1988) exam-

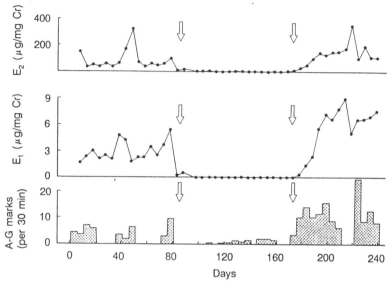

FIGURE 2. Levels of estrone, estradiol, and anogenital scent marking averaged for 5-day periods in female YV, who was housed alone with her father after her mother died. At the time indicated by the first set of arrows, a new female was introduced who became the father's mate. At the time indicated by the second set of arrows, YV was removed from her father and stepmother and paired with a male. E_1 = estrone; E_2 = estradiol; Cr = creatinine. (From French, Abbott, & Snowdon, 1984.)

ined six females while they were living in family groups and after they were paired with new mates. Three of the females received daily transfers of maternal scent marks on wooden planks during the first 60 days after pairing, and the other three received presentations of unmarked wooden planks. Although the mother's scent was presented only once a day, and although the newly paired females scent marked over their mother's odor, there was still a significant effect on reproduction. The females receiving transfers of their mother's scent took significantly longer to reach their first ovulation ($\bar{x}$ = 52.67 ± 17.80 days versus $\bar{x}$ = 20.0 ± 13.1 days—see Figure 3), and none of these females conceived during the 60 days of the scent transfer. In contrast, all of the females in the control condition conceived. At the end of 60 days, the conditions were reversed, with the females in the control condition receiving the maternal scent. However, once a pregnancy was established, the maternal scent transfer had no subsequent effect. Thus one mechanism for reproductive suppression appears to be olfactory cues from the mother. Epple and Katz (1984) reported on a scent-transfer experiment with one saddle-back tamarin with similar results. Hormonal levels increased, but no ovulation was seen during the time of the scent transfer. Once the scent transfer was terminated, the female ovulated immediately.

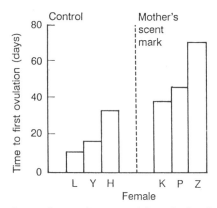

FIGURE 3. Time to first ovulation after removal from the family group and pairing with a mate in females that were presented with a control plank each day (left) and those who were presented with a plank scent-marked by their mother each day (right). Females L and K and females Y and Z are twins.

There appears to be little direct aggression between the reproductive female and subordinate females in our captive family groups. However, de la Ossa et al. (1988) reported severe fights, especially among females, leading to death when five well-established pairs were released together in a large outdoor enclosure, indicating that prior reproductive experience can influence the severity of aggression displayed between individuals.

Savage et al. (1988) showed that postpubertal subordinate females in a family group were social isolates. Despite the presence of many other group members with whom to interact, subordinate females showed low levels of contact, huddling, and grooming behavior. When these same females were subsequently paired with a new male, the levels of all three affiliative behaviors increased greatly. Levels of contact and grooming behavior are quite high in long-term established pairs (Figure 4).

Although olfactory cues from the mother may be necessary to maintain reproductive suppression, it is not necessarily true that removal of maternal olfactory influences are sufficient to induce normal reproductive function. We must also consider the possible stimulating effect of males. Several lines of evidence imply the importance of stimulation by the male in inducing reproductive function. Females removed from the family and kept by themselves showed an immediate increase in hormonal levels, but these levels did not become organized into normal ovarian cycles. Figure 5 shows the hormonal data from a 3-year-old female, Hed, who was housed by herself in proximity to, but not in contact with, males. Hed's levels of estrone and LH were quite high, but quite variable, until she was mated to a male. She then displayed normal cycles immediately, and she conceived on her first ovulation. We have found similar

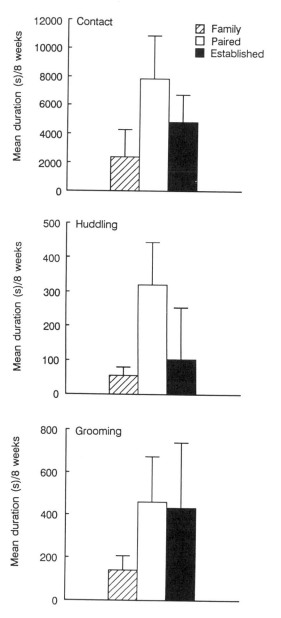

FIGURE 4. Mean duration (in seconds) of time spent in contact, huddling, and grooming with other animals by focal females while in a family and after being paired with a novel male. Data for established pairs are from other females who had produced several infants. Observations took place for 30 minutes each day, 5 days a week, for 8 weeks. (From Savage, Ziegler, & Snowdon, 1988.)

results in other females that we have isolated for brief periods prior to mating (Ziegler, Savage, Scheffler, & Snowdon, 1987).

Males might be able to stimulate precocious development. Tardif (1984) found that females removed from a family group and paired with a male showed an earlier appearance of serum progesterone than did females remaining in their natal groups. Ziegler, Savage, Scheffler, and Snowdon have found similar results. A young female paired at 10 months of age with an adult male developed levels of estrone and LH at 11 months of age that were equivalent to levels seen at 18 months of age in females remaining in their families. Epple and Katz (1980) have found that both male and female saddle-back tamarins showed an acceleration of reproductive development when paired with a reproductively mature animal of the opposite sex.

Thus in cotton-top and saddle-back tamarins, there is a complete reproductive suppression of young females that appears to be maintained by chemical cues from the reproductive female in the group, and there is an acceleration of puberty induced by pairing young animals with reproductively mature animals. Do these findings also hold for other callitrichids? There appear to be different routes by which reproductive suppression is maintained. In common marmosets, about 50 percent of young females living with their mothers show evidence of ovulation, although none of these females ever becomes pregnant. If peer groups are formed of marmosets of similar age, however, only one female will ovulate (Abbott, 1984). There is a rapid switching on and off of ovulatory function in conjunction with a common marmoset's social status. If a subordinate female is housed alone,

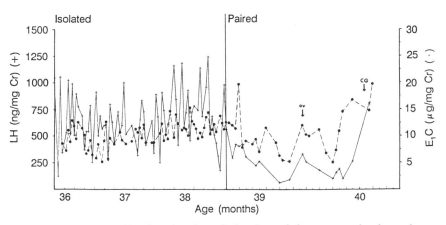

FIGURE 5. Hormonal levels in female Hed when housed alone in partial isolation from other monkeys and when paired with a male. Note the organization of estrone and luteinizing hormone into normal conceptive cycle patterns after pairing. LH = luteinizing hormone; E_1C = estrone conjugate; Cr = creatinine; ov = ovulation. (From Ziegler, Savage, Scheffler, & Snowdon, 1987.)

she will ovulate in about 10 days. As soon as she is placed back into a social group, her hormones fall to undetectable levels within 2 days. (Note that common marmosets, in contrast to cotton-top tamarins, will ovulate when alone; the presence of a male does not seem to be crucial to ovulation.) Abbott (1987) has found that the mechanism of this switch is due to the suppression of the release of gonadotropin-releasing hormone from the hypothalamus, and Abbott hypothesizes that the suppression of this hormone in subordinate females is due to stress.

In the golden lion tamarin, French and Stribley (1987) have found that daughters will ovulate in synchrony with their mothers; thus, there is no evidence of hormonal suppression of reproduction. Presumably there must be behavioral mechanisms that prevent the subordinate females from mating at the same time as their mothers. In pygmy marmosets, I have seen both mothers and daughters in the same group pregnant at the same time (C. T. Snowdon, unpublished observations). But in every such case so far, there has been severe aggression between the two females late in pregnancy, and the daughter has aborted. Thus, there are a variety of patterns and mechanisms in the callitrichids that lead to one consistent result: only a single female in a group will produce viable offspring.

We have detailed information on reproductive suppression of females, but we have few comparable data on males. Intensive observational studies of males in their family groups indicate that subordinate cotton-top tamarin males show little sexual interest or activity, although Epple (1978) has established groups of two males and one female saddle-back tamarin where at times both males are observed to mate with the female. Little is known about the hormonal status of subordinate males.

The phenomenon of reproductive suppression raises an important question: Why should subordinate animals remain with their families rather than disperse at puberty? The answer to this question is dependent on information concerning the ontogeny of parental care.

Extensive infant care by fathers and siblings

Many studies have reported the involvement of fathers and older siblings in infant care in marmosets and tamarins (common marmosets: Box, 1977; Ingram, 1977; golden lion tamarins: Hoage, 1977; saddle-back tamarins: Epple, 1975; cotton-top tamarins: Cleveland & Snowdon, 1984; McGrew, 1988; Tardif et al., 1986). These reports have indicated a great variety in the timing and in the extent of infant caretaking by males and older siblings. Ingram (1977) reports that the choice of measures affects the degree of caretaking observed, and found that, in general, mothers did more carrying of infants than did fathers. Tardif et al. (1986) found no sex differences in infant carrying in common marmosets. Epple (1975, 1978) reports great individual variability among groups of saddle-back tamarins in the degree of male or sibling involvement in infant care. In cotton-top tamarins, both Tardif et al. (1986) and Cleveland and Snowdon (1984) found that males gave more infant care than females did.

McGrew (1988) has suggested that one source for the variance in infant caretaking by fathers might be the number of older siblings present. He found that the amount of infant caretaking time observed in both fathers and mothers decreased in proportion to the number of sibling helpers in the group. Cleveland and Snowdon (1984) reported that the amount of time the mother spent carrying infants was significantly reduced when sibling helpers were available (Figure 6). Recently, Dixson and George (1982) have shown that male common marmosets have higher levels of prolactin while carrying infants than when infants are not present. Whether the prolactin elevation is a cause or a consequence of infant care is uncertain, but further study of a possible hormonal basis of paternal care would be very important.

How do marmosets and tamarins acquire interest in caring for infants? There is an extensive literature indicating that these animals must acquire parental care skills not simply through growing up in a social group, as Harlow, Harlow, Dodsworth, & Arling (1965) indicated for rhesus macaques (*Macaca mulatta*), but by direct hands-on contact with someone else's infants. Epple (1978) has shown that 77 percent of the infants born to female tamarins inexperienced in infant care were dead or mutilated within a day after birth. In contrast, the infant mortality rate was only 20 percent for mothers that had grown up in a social environment where they could care for other infants. Experience was equally important for fathers. Experienced females with experienced males had a 100 percent success rate with infants. Experienced females with inexperienced males had a 78 percent success rate, and when both parents were inexperienced, only

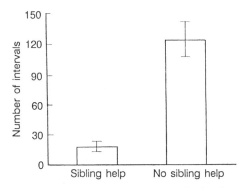

FIGURE 6. Number of 30-second intervals during which infants were carried by mothers during the first 10 weeks of life as a function of whether older siblings were available as helpers. When helpers were not available, maternal carrying time equaled paternal carrying time.

15 percent of the infants survived. A survey of all of the published colony data for cotton-top tamarins (Snowdon, Savage, & McConnell, 1985) showed similar results; Tardif et al. (1984) have also found similar results.

Given that direct infant care experience is essential for good parental care, how is such experience acquired? Cleveland and Snowdon (1984) observed who carried infants in cotton-top tamarin groups. They found that all siblings 14 months and older participated as much as adults did in infant care (Figure 7). However, siblings less than 14 months of age did not carry infants. These younger siblings were very important in initiating play with the infants. Cleveland and Snowdon suggested a two-stage model of acquiring parental care skills. At first, siblings get involved with infants through extensive play interactions that teach them how to interact with infants. When the next set of infants arrives, these siblings, now 14 months of age, begin to carry them in an adult way. We now keep siblings in a family group until they have had experience with two successive sets of infants; this appears to be sufficient experience for developing competent parental care skills.

In addition to carrying infants, other group members help with the weaning process. Several studies (Brown & Mack, 1978; Cleveland & Snowdon, 1982;

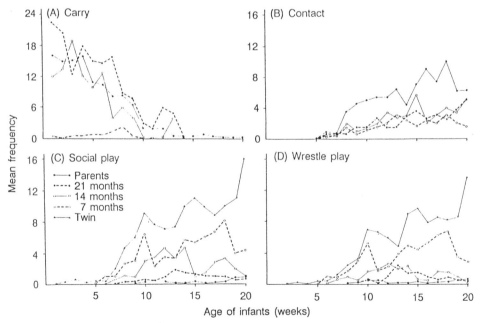

FIGURE 7. Age differences in carrying, social contact, and play behavior with new infants. Seven-month-old siblings did little carrying, but were involved in initiating play with new infants. (From Cleveland & Snowdon, 1984.)

Feistner & Chamove, 1986; Ferrari, 1987) have reported that group members transfer foods to young infants. Sometimes infants beg for food, and often adults give special calls that attract infants for food transfer (Cleveland & Snowdon, 1982). Feistner and Chamove reported that cotton-top tamarins shared food most often when they were hungry or when they were eating highly preferred items. Thus, food sharing appears to be an altruistic behavior.

INTEGRATION

Now that I have presented a large number of research results on the maintenance of monogamy and the development of infant caretaking competence in marmosets and tamarins, it is time to return to the initial questions of this chapter: why do male marmosets and tamarins take so much interest in infant care, and what are the mechanisms that lead to this active involvement? Answering these questions requires the use of each of Tinbergen's levels of analysis.

Function

Let us start with possible functional explanations. It is relatively easy to induce tamarin groups to adopt infants from other groups (Dronzek, Savage, Snowdon, Whaling, & Ziegler, 1986), so tamarins do not seem to base parental care on parental certainty. (However, in the wild, the highly territorial tamarins might rarely, if ever, encounter infants that they were unrelated to; thus, there may have been no selection pressure for recognizing offspring—see Beecher, this volume, for additional discussion.) While we have no evidence as yet that females can communicate their estrous states to their mates, the notion that paternal care evolved from concealed ovulation seems quite unlikely on logical grounds. The most parsimonious explanation is that since females are unable to rear any offspring without extensive help, males who desert females before infants are reared will have a lower reproductive success than males who help (see also Hrdy, 1986; Lancaster, 1985).

The energetic demands on a tamarin female are great. She produces twins that together at birth weigh approximately 25 percent of her own weight (Leutenegger, 1973). We have shown that females have a postpartum estrus at a mean of 19 days after parturition, while they are still nursing their current infants, and that 80 percent of these ovulations result in conception (Ziegler, Savage, Scheffler, & Snowdon, 1987). Current observations of wild tamarins (Anne Savage, personal communication) indicate that this high fecundity is found in the wild and is not an artifact of captivity. Since tamarins are arboreal, infants must be carried continuously until they are able to move about on their own. Thus, the energetic burden on a female is extraordinary, and the burden is reduced by having other group members carry the infants.

Under these conditions, infant care must be communal. In our captive environments, a single male and female can rear infants alone, but Goldizen's (1987) observations suggest that at least one additional helper is useful, and thus polyandry might be adaptive in groups without older sibling helpers. We have shown (Figure 6) that females do much less infant carrying when helpers other than the father are present, and McGrew (1988) has shown that helpers relieve for both parents.

While the presence of fathers and siblings as helpers may be adaptive to the female and her infants, why should the siblings stay in the group in a nonreproductive state past puberty? There are several possible adaptive reasons. First, several studies have demonstrated the importance of early infant caretaking experience for the development of parental competence. Snowdon et al. (1985), Tardif, Richter, & Carson (1984), and Epple (1978) have found a greater lifetime production of offspring among parents who had experience in infant care prior to their own parenthood than among parents without this experience. Thus, remaining in the group to acquire infant care skills is critical. Second, tamarins are highly territorial animals that use clear aggressive displays (Dawson, 1979; McConnell & Snowdon, 1986; Neyman, 1977; de la Ossa et al., 1988; Anne Savage, personal communication). There may be few open territories where animals could form new groups. Thus, tamarins may be best able to acquire a territory and breeding status by staying in a helper role in an established group and waiting for the reproductive animals to die or leave. This type of pattern has been well documented for the Florida scrub jay (Woolfenden & Fitzpatrick, 1984).

Phylogeny

It is not yet possible to derive the phylogenetic history of monogamy and paternal care. Comparison of cotton-top tamarins with their close relatives of the same family has revealed several interesting differences. Although all species of marmosets and tamarins are similar in having only a single reproductive female in a group, the mechanisms of maintaining this status vary greatly. It would be misleading to generalize from the results in one species to the entire family. Different species show different responses to intruders. Both male and female saddle-back tamarins show intrasexual aggression toward intruders. Cotton-top tamarin females scent-mark to intruders of both sexes, while males threaten and attack intruding males. Golden lion tamarin females are highly aggressive to intruders, but males appear nonaggressive toward other males. An understanding of the different modes of reproductive suppression may help to explain these different results. Cotton-top tamarin females can use scent marks to suppress ovulatory function in subordinate females; they need not display aggressive behavior in order to preserve their status as reproductive females. On the other hand, a novel male can stimulate rapid reproductive development in subordinate females, and thus a male intruder could be highly disruptive to a cotton-top tamarin group.

Golden lion tamarin females cannot suppress ovulation in subordinate females, so they must use behavioral mechanisms. Thus, females should be quite aggressive toward intruders. There is no obvious reason to explain why males are not aggressive toward intruders. The combination of different responses to intruders and different mechanisms of maintaining reproductive exclusivity suggest different patterns of dispersal: one would predict that female dispersal would be more likely in cotton-top tamarins and male dispersal more likely in golden lion tamarins. Thus, studies of captive populations can lead to testable hypotheses for field research.

Gestation length varies greatly, from about 132 days in golden lion tamarins (the largest species), to 134 days in pygmy marmosets (the smallest species), to 183 days in cotton-top tamarins (which are intermediate in size). Pygmy marmosets can have two females in a group pregnant at the same time, with only one pregnancy surviving to term, while subordinate cotton-top tamarin and saddle-back tamarin females display a complete lack of ovulation. These great differences in gestation length and in the mechanisms of reproductive suppression are as yet unexplained. The differences illustrate the importance of treating each species separately and not assuming that results from one species will automatically generalize to another related species.

Causation

An understanding of causation is critical in order to avoid making misleading inferences. The development of techniques for monitoring hormonal levels in our tamarins has prevented us from making several errors. Had we used the common expectations of gestation length, we would have concluded that there were clear signals of ovulation, when in fact the increased scent marking and copulation observed was in mid-pregnancy. A precise determination of the time of ovulation is necessary for a precise determination of whether ovulation is concealed or not; inference alone will not suffice. The discovery of different mechanisms of reproductive suppression resulted from long-term hormonal measurements on reproductive and subordinate females. Without these measurements, we would not have had any inkling of the richness of variation between species in mechanisms of suppression, nor any idea of the rapidity with which reproductive suppression can be removed or reinstated.

Ontogeny

Finally, the study of ontogeny is important. Male care of infants cannot be explained simply as a genetic predisposition to desert or to remain with infants. A major component of male interest in infants is the early ontogenetic environment of the individual. Those animals with early experience in taking care of another animal's infants are much more competent and more likely to rear their own offspring successfully.

Some authors (Sussman and Garber, 1987) have noted that marmosets and tamarins show high levels of movement between groups, and they suggest that females must mate promiscuously in order to insure that they have enough males to assist in infant care. Although polyandry has been demonstrated in some individual saddle-back tamarins (Goldizen, 1987), it is not necessary to assume that polyandry or promiscuity is a tactic necessary for a female to gain helpers. Reproductively subordinate animals can benefit themselves by caring for someone else's infants, whether related or not. In a stable family group, the subordinate animals would most likely be aiding in the care of their own kin, but even if extensive movement between groups is common, it would still be adaptive for an animal to care for infants other than its siblings, since the experience of caring for infants will lead to greater reproductive success. Thus, a good understanding of ontogeny can suggest alternative adaptive mechanisms for paternal care. The integrated focus on all four of Tinbergen's levels leads to a better understanding of the phenomenon of paternal care than a focus on only one or two levels would.

RELEVANCE TO HUMAN PATERNAL CARE

Trivers's theory of differential parental investment (1972) has led many sociobiologists to conclude that human males are biologically predisposed against parental care. One writer has even suggested that human males have "love 'em and leave 'em genes" (Barash, 1979). Studies of marmosets and tamarins, however, indicate that, for some primates, paternal care does appear adaptive. Two questions arise with respect to human paternal care: Do males have a biological aversion to infants? Under what circumstances might we expect to find paternal care expressed in human beings?

Surveys of primates of many families, with a variety of mating systems, indicate that male interest in infants may be much greater than originally suspected (Snowdon & Suomi, 1982). In polygynous and promiscuous species like baboons (*Papio cynocephalus*), Altmann (1980) has described special relationships between males and females with infants that may or may not be the offspring of that male. Thierry and Anderson (1986) reviewed the literature on primate adoptions and found that males were the main adopters of postweaning orphans. Taub (1984) presents several papers describing male adoptions of orphaned infants. Berman (1982) reported that in several cases, a male rhesus monkey was the first to adopt an orphaned infant.

In an experimental study, Gibber and Goy (1985) presented juvenile male or female rhesus monkeys with young infants, and found surprisingly few sex differences in response to infants. However, when an infant was presented to a male and a female together, the female took charge of the infant (see also Mitchell & Brandt, 1972; Redican, 1976). Lande, Higley, Snowdon, and Suomi (unpublished data) found that the extent of prior experience with infants was more important than sex in predicting affiliative responses of rhesus macaques toward a videotape of a young infant. All of these studies indicate male interest in infants, even in species where field studies reveal almost no contact between adult males and infants. In each of these demonstrations it has been necessary to break the bond between infant and mother (either experimentally or through the natural death of the mother) in order for males to display paternal care. Males of all types of breeding systems show an interest in infants, but in many species mothers prevent males from having much contact with their infants.

The critical difference between polygynous or promiscuous species and monogamous species is not the issue of paternal certainty, but that females in monogamous groups are more likely to relinquish some control of infant care to fathers and other group members. This occurs in monogamous species where females are more likely to require active participation by other group members in order to rear infants successfully (Hrdy, 1986; Lancaster, 1985; Snowdon & Suomi, 1982).

The limitation of food resources to a defensible area and the inability of males to defend against predators may lead to increased paternal care in monogamous species. Wright (1986) studied monogamous titi monkeys (*Callicebus moloch*) and night monkeys (*Aotus trivirgatus*), and found that both species used more restricted food resources, traveled shorter distances throughout the day, and had smaller home ranges than polygynous species in the same habitat. Wright suggested that economic features relating to food distribution and the small body size of males made them unable to defend against predators. In this situation, males can be more useful by carrying infants in order to allow the mother to obtain adequate food resources.

There are several lines of evidence that suggest similar mechanisms might be operating in human behavior. A survey of parental care in a wide variety of cultures illustrates that human fathers are more likely to become involved with their children when mothers are more able to make an economic contribution to the family by doing tasks other than child care. Thus, in hunter-gatherer pygmies (Hewlett, 1987) and in the !Kung San (Draper, 1976) in Africa, where females' food gathering provides 60 percent of the family's nutrition, there is extensive male involvement in infant care. In highly developed areas such as Sweden (Hwang, 1987), Great Britain (Lewis, 1986), and North America (Leibowitz, 1978) there is increased male involvement in infant care when mothers have opportunities for good employment outside the home. In contrast, in countries such as Italy (New & Benigni, 1987) and Japan (Schwalb, Imaizumi, & Nakazawa, 1987), where mothers have little opportunity to work outside the home, fathers' involvement with infants is minimal.

Leibowitz (1978) notes that monogamy has appeared at both ends of the economic spectrum. In hunter-gatherers, both parents are needed to support the family at a marginal level. In agriculturalist societies, polygyny is frequent, since one male with cattle and productive fields can support several wives and children. In industrialized societies, it is not sufficient to supply a child with food and shelter until the child can cope on its own. Parents must provide consumer goods and education for 4–12 years after a child would have been independent in a preindustrial society; thus, the economic demands of child rearing are greatly increased. When a mother can contribute equally to this economic support, then both parents must share infant care or hire others to provide a significant proportion of infant care. Thus, paternal care is more likely the greater the economic value of the mother is outside the home.

However, ontogenetic influences are as important as economic influences. Several studies indicate that preschool boys and girls show an equal interest in young infants and have equivalent knowledge about how to care for them. However, by the second grade, boys show less interest in infants, although they still have knowledge equal to girls' about how to care for them (Melson, Fogel, & Toda, 1986). Studies of fathers and mothers interacting separately with their infants indicate that both sexes are equally competent in infant care. However, when both parents are with the infant, the father relinquishes caretaking to the mother (Parke & O'Leary, 1976). This result exactly parallels those of Gibber and Goy (1985) for rhesus macaques.

The survey of nonhuman primate species leads to the conclusion that males are very interested in infants, but that they can display this interest only with permission from the mother. The data from marmosets and tamarins and other monogamous species show that mothers in these species are more likely to relinquish care of their infants to adult males and other group members than are females in polygynous species. I suggest that this difference between monogamous and polygynous females is due to the inability of monogamous females to rear offspring alone. Males are not immunized against parental care by the Y chromosome. Whether males express parental care is a function of their early rearing environment and the degree to which mothers need helpers to assist in infant care. Monogamy is not a bizarre mating system, nor is paternal care a bizarre behavior. Both are adaptations to an environment where one parent is not sufficient for successful infant rearing.

SUMMARY

This chapter has argued that direct or substitutive paternal care is common in monogamous primates. In the cotton-top tamarin, the extensive direct paternal care exhibited appears to be a response to the high fecundity rate of females. Only with the presence of the father and additional helpers can young marmosets and tamarins be reared successfully. Older siblings are reproductively inactive, but they must acquire parental care skills through direct experience with infants. The reproductive female actively suppresses fertility in other females through a chemical signal. A young female can be reproductively active only in the absence of another reproductive female and with the stimulation of a novel male. Young males show no signs of sexual activity while living in their natal group, but we do not yet understand the mechanisms causing this lack of activity. Both adult males and females actively defend their territories, and males show high levels of aggression toward intruding males. Females, however, do not show direct aggression, but scent-mark extensively to intruders. Thus, both sexes defend the monogamous relationship, but with different methods.

A monogamous mating system promotes, but does not guarantee, direct paternal care. Some monogamous species show little paternal care, or paternal care is expressed only after weaning. Males of many polygynous species also display interest in young infants when there is no female to provide infant care. The key to direct paternal care appears to be economic. When a female can rear infants by herself, she allows little or no male involvement. Only when the demands on the female are so great that helpers are necessary are males allowed to care for infants. A corollary of this idea explains much of the variance in paternal care in humans. In societies where females can make significant economic contributions to the family through work unrelated to infant care, fathers are much more involved in direct infant care than they are when females are able to make little economic contribution outside of infant care.

BIOLOGICAL TIMING MECHANISMS WITH SPECIAL EMPHASIS ON THE PARENTAL BEHAVIOR OF DOVES

Rae Silver

Whether animals are nocturnal, diurnal, or crepuscular (active at dawn and dusk), their behavior and the multiple internal metabolic adjustments of their bodies must be appropriately timed with respect to daily events in the environment. Most species must adopt a typical temporal niche that complements their ecological spatial niche. Regular daily rhythms of activity increase the likelihood that species can avoid predators and locate food, thereby maximizing the likelihood of survival.

The occurrence of daily cycles of activity in plants and animals has been known for centuries, but for a long while this observation drew little interest. In fact, the match between the environmental cycle of light and dark imposed on the earth by its rotation on its axis and the activity–inactivity cycles of animals is so close and so obvious that it was only in the present century that scientists realized that the daily activity cycle of organisms was not driven by environmental events. Instead, it involves an internal timekeeping mechanism, or "biological clock."

The behavior of the bees indicates that animals can use endogenous clocks to measure time, much as we consult our wristwatches for this purpose. Even more remarkably, in some instances, biological timekeeping involves not only a "clock" but also a "calendar." In temperate-zone species, young are born in spring and early summer, the times of year when food is available and the likelihood of survival is greatest. To achieve this, hamsters and other small mammals with short gestation periods must mate in the spring, while sheep and other large mammals with long gestation periods must mate in the fall. In order to produce young at the optimal time, animals must anticipate or predict the changing of the seasons. For seasonally breeding species, there is an annual cycle of gonadal growth and regression, with the testes and ovaries actively producing gametes and supporting sexual and parental behavior only at restricted times of the year. Recent research has shown that in some species the biological clock that determines daily activity cycles is also consulted to predict the optimal time for gonadal growth and breeding, thus providing a "biological calendar." (See Moore-Ede, Sulzman, & Fuller, 1982, or Turek, Swann, & Earnest, 1984, for a readable textbook discussion of this topic).

In the years since the 1950s, an enormous research effort has increased our understanding of the formal properties and physiological mechanisms underlying daily activity cycles. Evidence of this burgeoning literature lies in the existence of several journals devoted to the study of biological rhythms, including the *Journal of Biological Rhythms, Chronobiologica, Chronobiology International,* the *International Journal of Chronobiology,* and the *Journal of Interdisciplinary Cycle Research,* as well as several meetings devoted exclusively to the analysis of biological rhythms.

Enormous strides have been made in the understanding of biological rhythms and underlying clock mechanisms at the physiological and formal levels. Far less effort has been directed at understanding how an animal's daily behaviors are influenced and organized by the biological clock(s), and how the biological clock(s), in turn, is influenced and organized by behavioral events. Recent research has provided experimentally rigorous ways to investigate questions of this form.

This chapter reviews the status of our understanding of the physiology of biological clocks, with a view to describing how an endogenous circadian ("about a day") clock might function to organize the daily activities of an animal. Recent evidence suggests that an animal's activities can themselves influence the functioning of the clock. The consequences of feedback between endogenous timing mechanisms and behavior provide for new avenues of inquiry into behavioral organization.

My own interest in problems of biological timing emerged from research on sex differences in the parental behavior of ring doves. In order to rear their young successfully, parent doves must coordinate the needs of their eggs and altricial young with the behavior of their mates and with the demands of their environment. Ring dove parents both share in the building of their nest and in the incubation, brooding, and feeding of their young. Doves partition their time on the nest, with the male incubating and brooding in the middle of the day, and the female caring for the young the rest of the time. One goal of this chapter is to discuss the ways in which an understanding of circadian rhythms contributes to our knowledge of parental behavior, and how our understanding of parental behavior clarifies our notions of the functions of biological clocks. To this end, for each question raised about parental care, I indicate how similar processes have been studied in other species (generally in a nonsocial context), and then describe how the question can be understood in the context of the social system of parent doves.

TIMEKEEPING BEHAVIOR

The conceptual breakthrough in understanding timing behavior, and the impetus for an exciting and very active area of scientific research, came from the realization that animals actually measure the passage of time and predict future events by means of biological clocks. There are many instances of behavior involving biological timekeeping. One of the earliest known examples of time-keeping behavior is seen in the foraging activity of bees.

Bees will return to forage at a given patch of flowers at the same time of day each day (see Saunders, 1977 for a review). Furthermore, bees can be trained to feed at a sugar source at a particular time of day—in fact, they can be trained to go to each of several different sugar sources at different times of day, and will continue to go there for several days after the sugar is removed. This behavior persists in the absence of cues from the environment (i.e., in constant temperature, humidity, or light), suggesting an endogenous timekeeping mechanism. Proof that internal timekeeping is involved comes from an experiment in which bees were housed in a special enclosed chamber and trained to get food between approximately 8:00 and 10:00 P.M. Paris time. The bees were then quickly translocated to New York and tested in an identical chamber. The bees continued to feed at the same Paris time, even though they had been displaced 5 hours in their new New York location. This indicates that they were not reacting to subtle local temporal cues, but were indeed using endogenous timing mechanisms. Of course, if they had been released into the New York environment, they would have adjusted gradually to local time, using cues from the sun, and would forage 5 hours later. Bees behave as though they "know" what time it is at all times. This "time sense" in honeybees allows them to forage for food at the appropriate time of day. Parent birds seem to have a similar time sense, as described below.

TIMEKEEPING BEHAVIOR OF
PARENT DOVES DURING INCUBATION

Reproductively mature doves will court each other, build a nest together, and incubate and care for their young together. Doves incubate their eggs and brood their newly hatched young without interruption, and they do so in a highly stereotyped manner: the male sits on the nest for a block of time in the middle of the day, and the female sits for the rest of the time. The nest is rarely left unattended (Wallman, Grabon, & Silver, 1979).

The sex difference in the timing of incubation behavior is not unique to ring doves, but is characteristic of the whole pigeon family. Lorenz (1937/1970) described the sex differences in the timing of parental care in the pigeon family as typical of the order and seen in no other order of birds; it is as characteristic a feature as any morphological character. It is important to note that the main features of the behavior seen in the laboratory have been reported in field studies of wild and feral doves (Figure 1). Taken together, these observations suggest that parent doves use some kind of biological clock to determine whose turn it is to incubate, but do not indicate the nature of the timing mechanisms that are used. Also, the descriptive observations indicate neither why the male and female consistently incubate at different times of day, nor whether the male, the female, or both partners have the presumed biological clock mechanism. Finally, we do not know whether the clock is an "hourglass" type of interval timer, set from dawn, dusk, or some other environmental cue, or whether it involves an endogenous circadian "oscillator" or "pacemaker," a clock mechanism that can measure time in the absence of external periodic cues, of the type that bees use to determine optimal foraging times. (See Silver & Bittman, 1984, for a discussion of circadian and interval timing mechanisms.)

Though individual pairs of birds differ in the precise amount of time each partner will incubate, the male of each pair incubates for a block of time in the middle of the day (Wallman et al., 1979). To analyze the factors controlling this sex difference in the timing of incubation, we examined the behavior of same sex partners (Silver & Ramos, 1989). In male pairs, there was little to analyze, as these birds simply fought with one another and ignored the nest and eggs that had been provided. Female pairs did incubate the eggs that were provided, but no prediction could be made as to which of the pair would be incubating at any particular time.

Role of sex hormones

The role of hormones in mediating the normally occurring sex differences in timing of incubation was demonstrated in an experiment where adults were gonadectomized and treated with heterotypical hormones (hormones characteris-

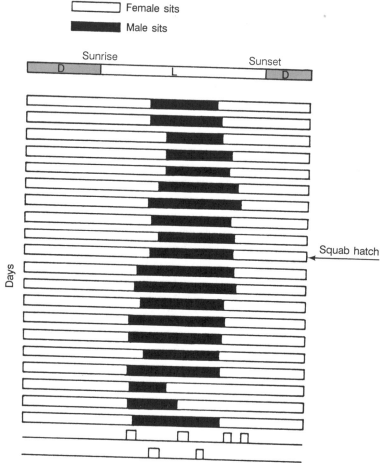

FIGURE 1. The timing of sitting during incubation of eggs by feral ring doves in Florida from the day the first egg is laid until the young are about 12 days of age. The male (depicted by a black bar) sits for a block of time in the middle of the day, and the female (depicted by an open bar) sits the rest of the time. The same temporal pattern is seen in laboratory-housed birds. L = light; D = darkness. (From Silver & Norgren, 1987.)

tic of the other sex). Gonadectomized males treated with the female sex hormones estrogen and progesterone and paired with intact males incubated eggs at the time of day characteristic of females. Gonadectomized females treated with testosterone and paired with intact females incubated at the time of day characteristic of males. The adult sex hormones are apparently involved in setting the time or phase of expression of incubation behavior.

Which partner controls timing? A series of experiments directed at understanding whether the male or the female controlled the timing of incubation proved to be amusingly difficult. In the first experiment, the partners were separated, and each mate was provided with a nest and eggs. The results did not reveal which mate normally timed incubation, as each mate incubated alone for several days and then quit sitting altogether (Silver & Gibson, 1980). It seems that the sex-typical pattern is seen only in paired birds.

In the next futile attempt to determine which parent was timing incubation, we gave the birds a large nest bowl in which to incubate their eggs, so that either partner, or both partners, could sit at whatever time they wished. In this instance, the experiment failed because both birds tried to incubate the eggs together much of the time. They were both in the nest bowl at the same time, and they fought each other for access to the eggs, resulting in an irregular timing of incubation (Silver, unpublished data).

A successful experimental strategy finally came about after we had the opportunity to watch feral doves incubating their eggs in Florida. In several instances, we saw the nonincubating female partner leave the feeding area, located about a mile from the nest, and go to the nest area at about the time she was ready to incubate. This suggested that we might learn more about the dynamics of which parent controlled timing behavior by studying attempts to gain the nest, rather than the time of actual sitting on the nest.

By building a two-chambered cage with a hallway between the chambers, and by placing miniature transmitters on each bird and an antenna beneath the hallway and the nest, we were able to use a computer-monitored telemetry system to detect which bird was nesting and which was approaching the nest at all times of day (Kahn, Fifer, & Silver, 1984). With this apparatus in place, we were able to evaluate the distinct roles of the sexes in determining the time of nest exchange.

The first important result showed that most nest exchanges were initiated by the nonincubating bird (Ball & Silver, 1983). The sitting bird virtually never abandoned the nest, but instead left only when the nonsitting bird approached to take its turn at the nest. We had already noted that the onset of the male's daily incubation bout in the morning tended to be more variable than the onset of the female's bout in the afternoon. Observations of the approaches to the nest area (Figure 2) indicated that the male entered the nest area repeatedly from the time of lights-on until nest exchange several hours later. When the male was prevented from repeatedly approaching the nest until the usual time of exchange, the timing of the subsequent nest exchange and sitting bout were not altered, indicating that the male's visits to the nest are not a prerequisite for subsequent nest exchange. It was not at all clear why the male approached the nest so frequently before the time of nest exchange. One possibility is that the male does not time his bout onset, but instead starts to sit whenever the female permits. Another possibility is that there is some imprecision in the male's timing mechanism.

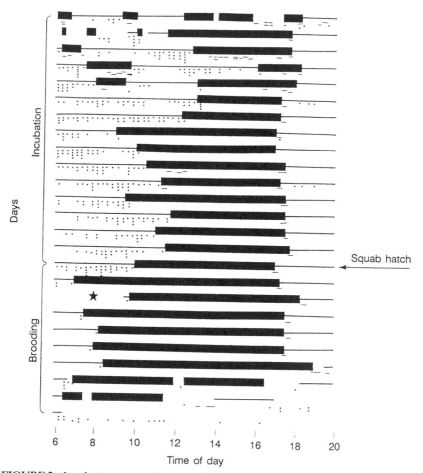

— Female sits
■ Male sits
★ Blackout
— Female approaches
· Male approaches

Squab hatch

FIGURE 2. Incubation pattern for a pair of doves on successive days following egg laying. The doves were housed in a two-chambered cage with a hallway leading from the feeding area to the nesting area. The male's incubation bout is depicted by a black bar. Approaches to the nest area by the male are shown by a dot, while approaches by the female are shown by a horizontal line. The results indicate that the male approaches the nest many times prior to achieving the nest, while the female generally approaches only once, just before starting her incubation bout. (From Ball & Silver, 1983.)

Unlike the male, the female rarely approached the nest, and when she did approach, nest exchange usually ensued, suggesting that she was using a relatively precise timing mechanism in determining the onset of her daily incubation bout.

In the next experiment, we examined the mechanism mediating timing of incubation, again taking advantage of the two-chambered cage. The onset of the male's bout was delayed in the morning by placing a gate in the hallway connecting the nesting and feeding chambers (Gibbon, Morrell, & Silver, 1984). The question of interest was whether the male would end his incubation bout at the usual time in the afternoon, or whether he would try to stay on the nest later into the afternoon. The experimentally imposed delays in the start of the male's sitting bout in the morning resulted in a (smaller) delay in his readiness to leave the nest in the afternoon (Figure 3). The female, however, approached the nest to start her bout of incubation at the usual time in the afternoon, even though she had ended her incubation bout later than usual that day. The male's behavior can be accounted for by an interval timing mechanism, started when the male begins his sitting bout; such a mechanism would control the duration of the bout. The attempts to regain the nest by the female probably reflect a different mechanism, not influenced by duration of the previous sitting bout.

These experiments leave us with clear evidence of the existence of daily timekeeping behavior by both parent doves. They also suggest that doves use a multitude of rules, rather than a single timing mechanism, to determine the sharing of parental duties. To begin a dissection of clock mechanisms, simpler experimental systems in which the timing mechanisms of each animal could be studied separately were needed. In this way, the complexities of analyzing two interacting animals, each capable of using different timing mechanisms, could be avoided. These experiments might provide insight into how timing mechanisms might function when individuals are paired, or when they meet in larger social groups. Attempts to study ring doves housed individually in constant environmental conditions were unsuccessful, as isolated doves tend to become inactive in the absence of photic cues, as discussed later in this chapter. Fortunately, a great number of studies have been done on circadian rhythms in other species. In the following paragraphs, work on circadian rhythms in other systems will be described in order to establish a framework for thinking about the behavior of doves.

CIRCADIAN RHYTHMS IN MODEL SYSTEMS

In contrast to doves, some animals have activity rhythms that are very easy to measure in constant environmental conditions. It is assumed that the biological clocks of these animals are similar to those of other species, like doves, that are

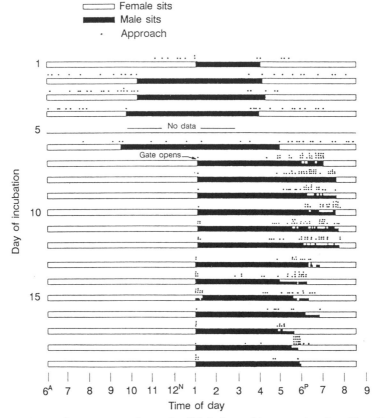

FIGURE 3. Incubation pattern for a pair of birds (housed in a two-chambered breeding cage as in Figure 2) on successive days of incubation. This pair was permitted to exchange places freely during the first 6 days of incubation. Beginning with Day 7, each evening after lights-out, a gate between the nesting and feeding area was closed until 1:00 P.M., delaying the start of the male's sitting bout by about 3 hours. The male's sitting bout is indicated by a black bar; the female's, by an open bar. A dot above the bar indicates an approach to the nest area by the nonincubating bird. (From Silver & Norgren, 1987.)

hard to study. Clear demonstrations of circadian activity cycles are seen in hamsters and flying squirrels (DeCoursey, 1960; Zucker, 1980). If a hamster is housed in a cage containing a running wheel, food, and water, and exposed to a photic regimen of 12 hours of light (L) and 12 hours of darkness (D) (L:D 12:12), it shows an extremely organized pattern of daily activity (Figure 4, upper portion). The hamster, a nocturnal animal, begins running in the wheel soon after dark each day. This behavior appears to be driven, or controlled, by the L:D cycle. If, however, conditions of constant darkness are imposed, and all other cues from

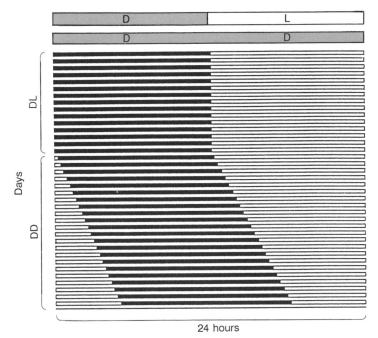

24 hours

FIGURE 4. Schematic illustration of a hamster running record in 12 hours of light and 12 hours of darkness (DL), then in constant darkness (DD). Each horizontal strip represents 24 hours; the solid dark bars represent sustained wheel running. In the nocturnal hamster, wheel-running occurs almost exclusively during the dark hours. In constant darkness, the locomotor activity period free-runs, with the animal starting its bout of running slightly later on each consecutive day.

the environment are removed, the hamster continues to run with an extremely regular cycle of activity and rest (Figure 4, lower portion). The period of the hamster's activity cycle (time from the onset of activity from one day to the next) is slightly longer than 24 hours; this can be seen in the rightward drift of the running record with the passage of time in constant darkness. It seems that the hamster's endogenous clock has a "free-running" period slightly greater than 24 hours (For a more detailed discussion, see Zucker, 1980).

Entrainment

If their biological clocks have a period longer than that of the 24-hour period of the environmental L:D cycle, why don't hamsters (and other small rodents) drift out of phase with their worlds and start eventually to become active during the day and sleep during the night? The answer lies in the ability of the endogenous clock to shift its phase so as to become entrained to the L:D cycle. This can be seen in an experiment where the L:D cycle is phase-shifted so that the lights are turned off several hours earlier than previously (Figure 5). In response, the animal starts to run earlier and earlier each day until its running activity is once again in phase with the onset of dark. Thus, the setting or phase of the endogenous clock is adjusted so that it remains in synchrony with, or "entrained" to, the environment. While a number of environmental cycles can serve as "zeitgebers" (time-givers) which entrain circadian rhythms of mammals and birds, the L:D cycle is one of the most effective and best studied.

To imagine how this might work, think of yourself on a trip from the east coast to the west coast of North America. You have to phase-shift by 3 hours, or go to sleep 3 hours later than is your custom. Generally, you do this by phase-delaying, or shifting your activity to later and later times. On your return to the east coast, you have to phase-advance, or wake up earlier than usual.

The phase response curve

Those who study circadian rhythmicity would like to study clock mechanisms directly, but are unable to do so. The responses influenced by the clock are accessible, but the clock itself is not. However, by examining the various responses, researchers have been able to deduce the properties of the clock. For

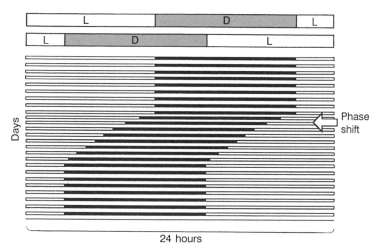

FIGURE 5. Schematic illustration of a hamster running record in an L:D cycle. When dark onset is advanced by 4 hours (indicated by arrow), the activity rhythm shifts correspondingly. As previously, each horizontal strip represents 24 hours; black bars indicate wheel-running.

example, the adjustment of behaviors to new environmental cycles of day and night provides cues about how the clock mechanism might work. Light will induce a delay, an advance, or no change at all in an animal's activities, depending on when the time cue is received. This key property of entrainable circadian systems—a changing sensitivity to light—was precisely quantified by Pittendrigh and Bruce (1957) in *Drosophila*. The main features of the phase response curve, with phase delays in early subjective night and phase advances in late subjective night, are similar in both diurnal and nocturnal species, from single-celled algae to primates (Figure 6). (For more information about phase response curves, see Moore-Ede et al., 1982.) The phase response curve for the response to a pulse of light permits the prediction of how an environmental cue will shift the timing of a behavior, thereby informing us about the state of the circadian pacemaker itself. Without knowing the locus or structure of the biological timekeeping mechanism or pacemaker, we can have an idea of what the pacemaker must be doing by observing its effect on behavior.

As seen in the phase response curve for a nocturnal animal depicted in Figure 6, the sun rising at mid-subjective day does not affect the activity rhythm. A light pulse in the animal's late subjective day or early subjective night tends to produce a phase delay, with activity beginning later (Figure 6, schematics 2 & 3). Light falling at dusk during late subjective night or early subjective day (Figure 6, schematics 4 & 5) causes a phase advance, with the animal continuing activity longer. In this way, the natural daily cycle is constantly nudging an animal's circadian clock forward in the morning and backward at night in every 24-hour day. These experimental manipulations, using brief daily pulses of light at discrete times in the circadian cycle, give us an idea of how environmental zeitgebers can set the phase of the endogenous clock.

Phase shifts in nocturnal animals

One might ask, however, how animals that live in burrows and become active only at night can possibly use environmental L:D cycles to entrain their daily activity bouts. By choosing a suitable experimental subject, and by controlling many features of the environment, it is possible to address questions of this type. A lovely example of the resetting of biological clocks by light is seen in the work of DeCoursey (1986) with flying squirrels, which have very precise rhythms. The flying squirrel is nocturnal, and lives in hollow trees or attics, so it is exposed to light only when it emerges from its nest. DeCoursey housed wild-caught flying squirrels in simulated dens which had three compartments: a darkened nest chamber led to a dark tunnel, which in turn led to an activity chamber with a controlled L:D cycle, a running wheel, food, and water.

The behavior of the squirrel can be described as follows: When it awoke, the squirrel quickly left the nest chamber and ran through the tunnel to the sampling

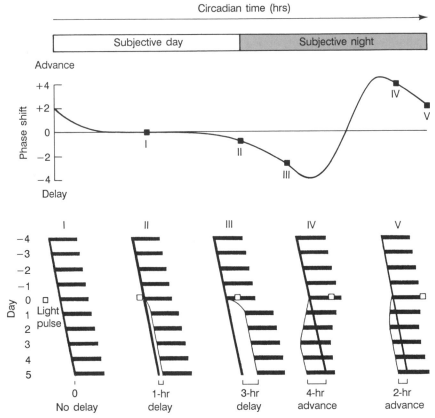

FIGURE 6. Schematic illustration depicting five experiments (I–V) with one individual nocturnal animal. The black bars at the bottom of the figure represent the period of locomotor activity, and illustrate the advance or delay in the onset of activity. A free-running activity rhythm with a period of 25.0 hours is seen on days − 4 to − 1. On Day 0, a light pulse is given at mid-subjective day (I), at late subjective day (II), at early subjective night (III), at late subjective night (IV), and at early subjective day (V). The light pulse in mid-subjective day (I) has no effect, whereas the light pulses in late subjective day and early subjective night (II and III) produce phase delays of the activity rhythm that are complete within one cycle. The light pulses in late subjective night and early subjective day (IV and V) produce phase advances that have several cycles of transients before reaching a steady state. The upper part of the figure illustrates the direction and amount of phase shifts plotted against the time of light pulses, to obtain a phase response curve. When light pulses are given at frequent intervals throughout subjective day and night, the waveform for the phase response curve follows the solid line. In mammals, there is normally a gradual transition between the maximum phase delay and maximum phase advance, with a point at mid-subjective night (like the one in mid-subjective day, I) where there is no phase shift. (From Moore-Ede, Sulzman and Fuller, 1982.)

porthole at the entrance to the activity chamber. If it saw light, it remained immobile just inside the porthole for a few seconds to a few minutes, then returned to the nest box for a brief nap. After about an hour, the squirrel returned to the sampling porthole again to test light conditions, and repeated this series of behaviors until darkness was encountered at the sampling hole. At this point, the squirrel entered the wheel almost immediately and started spinning it rapidly (Figure 7). In summary, upon arousal, the animal checked photic conditions. If

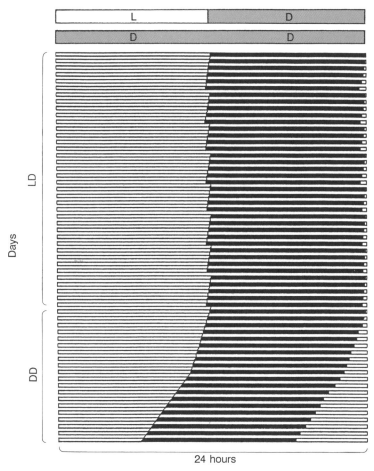

FIGURE 7. Schematic illustration depicting entrainment of activity in a flying squirrel housed in a simulated den cage. The pattern of the lines drawn through the daily onset of activity in the L:D cycle (LD) shows the "zigzag" pattern of light sampling and phase resetting. In constant darkness (DD), the animal's activity free-runs. (After DeCoursey, 1986.)

it was dark, activity ensued. If it was light, a nap ensued, and an immediate delay phase shift was induced. Thus, in the hole-nesting nocturnal flying squirrel, entrainment consists of a free-running state with discrete, instantaneous delay phase shifts brought about by light at the time of brief, daily light sampling.

Entrainment by nonphotic cues

In nature, animals must deal with environmental cues far more complex and more numerous than brief pulses of light. They must seek food from highly variable sources, find mates, care for young, and avoid predators and conspecific competitors. How might circadian timing systems function in the natural world, where there are such a wide variety of external cues and such a large number of constraints and demands on behavior?

Nonphotic environmental cues can entrain circadian rhythms, though they are generally less effective than photic cues (reviewed by Regal & Connolly, 1980). For example, Menaker and Eskin (1966) and Gwinner (1966) both showed that the circadian locomotor activity of birds could be entrained by playing the tape-recorded song of a conspecific to a bird housed in constant environmental conditions. Similarly, people kept in constant environmental conditions in underground chambers were entrained by social cues (Aschoff et al., 1971). The mystery presented by results like these is, What kind of information from these "social" cues reaches the circadian pacemaker and entrains it? Does the social cue entrain by means of auditory, visual, or tactile stimuli? Could some other factor associated with social cues be involved?

In recent experiments, Mrosovsky and Salmon (1987) showed that behavioral events alone could influence phase shifts in animals placed in new L:D cycles. They showed that if hamsters were moved to running wheels at the time of the phase shift, they entrained to a new L:D cycle much faster than they did if they did not exercise at the time of placement in the new environment. Certain drugs, like triazolam, a benzodiazepine, are known to produce phase shifts in activity, and it had been thought that these agents act directly on the circadian clock (see review by Turek & Van Reeth, 1988a). However, more recent evidence suggests that triazolam acts on locomotor behavior to produce phase shifts. Triazolam causes animals to become active and to run. If hamsters are restrained at the time of injection with triazolam so that they cannot run, they do not phase-shift their activity. It is the drug's effect on running behavior, not the drug's effect on the clock itself, that produces a phase shift (Turek & Van Reeth, 1988b). (The effects of light on entrainment are not mediated by changes in activity, but light does seem to act directly on the clock). The demonstration that activity provides feedback between the clock and behavior provides a new avenue for exploring the effects of social factors, such as predator and competitor avoidance, on timing mechanisms.

Precision in the circadian system

Flying squirrels and hamsters provide clear demonstrations of precise free-running endogenous clocks, but these animals are exceptional. Some species, including mice and rats, lack the precision of the hamster, and express much greater variability in the daily onset of running. As noted previously, other animals, such as doves, are even harder to study because they tend to become immobile and go to sleep in constant darkness. In constant very dim illumination, ring doves show a quickly dampened circadian activity rhythm (Figure 8). Initially, one can see the start of a free run, and within 1 or 2 weeks, a daily activity rhythm cannot be detected. The same damping of the circadian pattern is found if one monitors daily cycles of body temperature in the dove. Similar damping of circadian rhythmicity is shown by cultured pineal glands of chickens

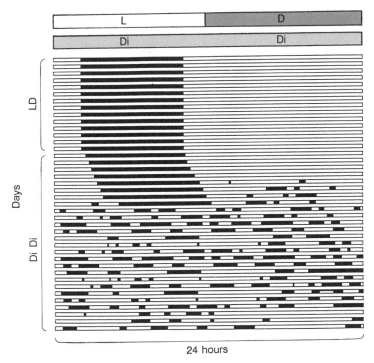

FIGURE 8. Schematic illustration of damping of locomotor activity of doves housed in constant dim illumination. Each horizontal strip represents 24 hours. The black bars represent periods of locomotor activity. In the diurnal dove, activity is restricted to the light portion of the L:D cycle. In constant dim illumination (0.5 lux; Di Di), locomotor activity initially free-runs, and soon becomes arrhythmic.

kept in constant darkness, while glands kept in an L:D cycle will continue to produce melatonin according to a circadian rhythm (Takahashi & Menaker, 1984).

Variability or damping in the expression of locomotor activity does not necessarily mean that the clock itself is imprecise or absent. The circadian system may be considered to be composed of several components, including a photoreceptor, an oscillator or circadian pacemaker, an efferent coupling mechanism from the oscillator to the effector site(s), and the effector site(s).

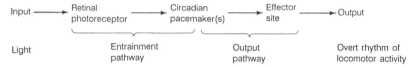

It may be that the source of imprecision is the coupling mechanism whereby the output of the clock is linked to the neural system controlling locomotor activity. Alternatively, the imprecision may be introduced at the effector site itself. Damping of responses may occur when the clock function itself is unaltered, and the end response we are using to monitor the clock's "movements" (i.e., locomotor activity or melatonin production) is not reflecting the clock's activity. Another possibility is that the circadian rhythm of the individual cells that make up the pacemaker continue to oscillate, but are out of synchrony with each other.

CIRCADIAN RHYTHMS IN RING DOVES

The experimental protocols developed in studies of isolated animals can be used to elucidate circadian rhythms used in more complex behavioral systems, such as the timing of incubation in ring doves.

Entrainment

In one series of experiments, the influence of photic conditions on the timing of incubation was monitored. Doves were exposed to an L:D cycle of 14:10 (lights on at 6:00 A.M., off at 8:00 P.M.) and allowed to incubate uninterrupted for the first 5 days following egg laying. After that time, the L:D cycle was phase-shifted so that the middle of the day became the middle of the night. Within a few days, the doves adjusted their time of incubation so that the male sat once again in the middle of the L:D cycle and the female sat the rest of the time, indicating that photic cues can entrain the behavior of the doves (Figure 9).

Effect of photoperiod duration

The phase-shift experiment, however, left open the possibilities that the doves were using circadian phase to time the onset of their incubation bouts, or that

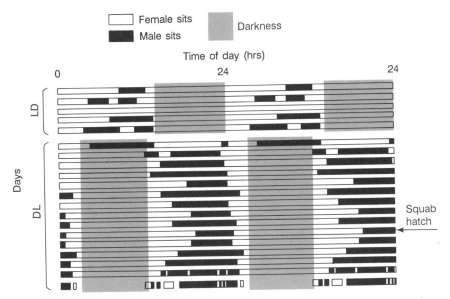

FIGURE 9. Incubation following phase shift in doves. The shaded area represents the dark, while the open bars represent the light portion of the cycle. For the first 5 days of incubation, the doves were housed in an L:D cycle of 14:10. On Day 6, the lights were adjusted so that the middle of the day became the middle of the night (DL). The doves adjusted the timing of their sitting so that the male still sat in the middle of the light period. (From Silver & Norgren, 1987.)

they were timing an interval from dawn or dusk to determine when to incubate. We asked whether the male (or female) timed the start of his (or her) sitting bout from dawn or dusk—that is, did the doves always start to sit a constant number of hours after dawn? If so, males housed in shorter or longer day lengths should continue to begin their daily sitting bouts at about 4 hours after lights-on. In his thesis research, Kahn (1989) examined the duration of incubation by doves housed in a variety of different L:D cycles. Males exposed to day lengths ranging from 6 to 18 hours of light continued to incubate for a block of time in the middle of the day. Though the duration of the day across the various experimental groups changed, the duration of incubation did not vary significantly among groups (Figure 10). Nor did the birds incubate at a constant phase with respect to dawn or dusk, again suggesting mediation by an interval timing mechanism.

Free-running rhythms

Is there any evidence of endogenous circadian rhythmicity in the timing of incubation bouts? By placing parent doves in constant dim illumination, we were able to determine that they could express free-running rhythms of incubation in

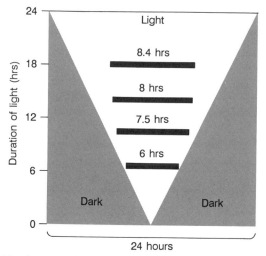

FIGURE 10. The duration of incubation by the male dove in photoperiods of various durations. The black bars depict the time during which the male incubates in L:D cycles of 18:6, 14:10, 10:14, and 6:18. The female (not shown), sits whenever the male is not incubating. (After Kahn, Fifer, & Silver, 1984.)

the absence of environmental cues (Figure 11, upper panel). This indicated that at least one of the mates exhibited circadian rhythmicity; but which one? Or do both mates do so? We reasoned that under constant conditions, the mate that did not have access to a circadian pacemaker might approach the nest to try to incubate at random times with respect to the onset of its daily sitting bout, while the mate with the clock would only approach the nest at the appropriate time. The results were unambiguous. In conditions of constant dim illumination, each partner approached the nest just before the start of its incubation bout, and did not approach the nest at other times (Figure 11, lower panel). Both sexes expressed circadian rhythms in constant conditions.

These results suggest that the doves use more than one mechanism in timing incubation bouts. The overriding rule is that if the mate is not present, the non-incubating dove continues to sit. Each nonsitting mate tries to gain access to the nest at particular times of the day. The male generally achieves the nest several hours after dawn. Once the male starts his sitting bout, he continues to incubate for a minimum duration. If he is prevented from starting his sitting bout for several hours, he will extend the duration of sitting that day, implying an interval timing mechanism. The onset of the sitting bout by the female is determined by a circadian pacemaker mechanism. She generally approaches the nest once, and starts her sitting bout several hours before dusk in the afternoon. Whether or not she sits for a minimum duration is not yet known. We do know that there is no

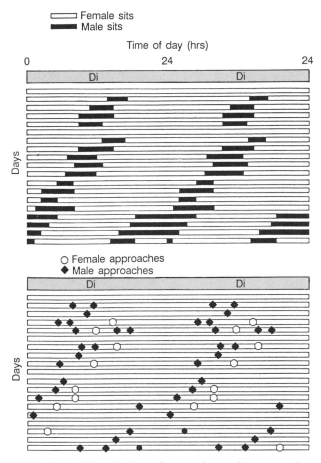

FIGURE 11. The timing of incubation and approaches to the nest area by parent doves housed in constant dim illumination. The figure is double-plotted to show 48 consecutive hours of activity. The determination of which mate is at the nest was made by computer-controlled telemetric monitoring by an antenna at the nest. Upper panel: The black bar indicates sitting by the male, the open bar indicates sitting by the female. Lower panel: Approaches by the male (shown by a diamond) and by the female (shown by an open circle) were automatically tracked by the computer. Note that the approaches to the nest area by both partners are largely limited to the time preceding nest exchange.

maximum duration, as the female will continue to sit until her mate appears, even when he is later than usual. In the absence of photic cues from the environment, both sexes can express a circadian rhythm in onset of incubation. The phase of their circadian rhythms is set by the sex hormones, and can be reversed by administering heterotypical hormones.

Dissection of the rules for whose turn it is to incubate makes it clear that this highly organized, apparently simple and efficient behavior of parent doves has many determinants. What do we know about the underlying brain mechanisms? Why do we care about the underlying brain mechanisms?

PHYSIOLOGY OF THE TIMEKEEPING SYSTEMS

Hebb (1951) pointed out that while "it has been suggested that physiology 'can not cast any vote' in the choice of psychological principles, . . . it always has." One of the factors that instills great confidence in the investigators of circadian rhythmicity in mammals is the fact that specific brain nuclei, the suprachiasmatic nuclei (SCN), have been identified as the locus of the biological pacemaker or clock.

There are two functions that must be achieved by a circadian pacemaker (or pacemakers). First, it must generate self-sustained endogenous rhythms with a free-running period of about 24 hours. Second, it must have access to environ-

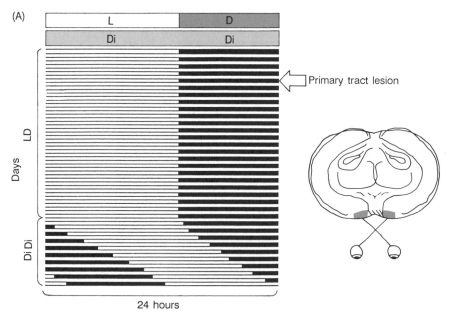

FIGURE 12. (A) Schematic illustration of the consequences of destruction of the primary optic tract in a hamster. Though the hamster was unable to perform certain visual tasks after lesioning, its activity rhythm (left) was entrained by the L:D cycle, and free-ran in constant dim illumination (Di Di). (B) Schematic illustration of the consequences of removal of the SCN in a hamster. Before the SCN lesion, wheel-running activity (left) occurred only during the dark hours. After lesioning, activity also occurred during the

mental time cues, so as to entrain the endogenous rhythm. Many lines of evidence support the view that the SCN is a biological pacemaker, and that photic input from the retina to the SCN mediates entrainment.

The mammalian circadian oscillator

One of the first strong clues to the location of the biological pacemaker came from the discovery that the SCN, lying above the optic chiasm, receive a direct retinal projection. Since that time, many lines of evidence converge to indicate that the SCN serves as a biological pacemaker (see Moore, 1979, 1983; Rusak, 1979; Shibata & Moore, 1988; Zucker 1980, for review). Entrainment is not lost following removal of the primary visual system, as long as the retinohypothalamic pathway from the eye to the SCN is left intact (Figure 12A). On the other hand, removal of the SCN itself results in a loss of circadian rhythms in many responses, such as drinking and locomotor activity (Figure 12B). Electrophysiological studies indicate a daily rhythm of electrical activity in the SCN, with high

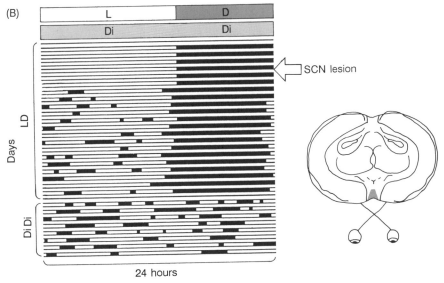

light phase; unlike control animals, this animal showed little change in its activity cycle in response to an L:D cycle, and did not show a coordinated free-running circadian rhythm in constant dim light. Instead, activity occurred sporadically. The primary optic tract remained intact, and the animal could discriminate between white and black squares. This indicates that the retinohypothalmic projection to the SCN, rather than the primary optic tract, is essential for photo-entrainment of circadian rhythms. (After Zucker, 1980.)

multiunit activity in the light period and low multiunit activity in the dark period. If the SCN is surgically isolated from the rest of the brain, rhythmic electrical activity inside the island continues, and none is seen in the tissue outside the island (Inouye & Kawamura, 1979), suggesting that endogenous cycles of activity are not dependent on neural input from other brain regions. There is also a circadian rhythm in the SCN's metabolic activity, which can be measured by its uptake of radioactively tagged 2-deoxyglucose, and which has been shown to continue in constant conditions. Finally, transplantation of fetal tissue containing the SCN into adult animals whose SCN have been removed will restore circadian rhythmicity (Lehman et al., 1987; Sawaki, Nihonmatsu, & Kawamura, 1984). This physiological evidence of circadian pacemakers in rats and hamsters gives credence to the idea of a biological clock, and fuels the interest of investigators in studying it more directly. It also suggests questions about the behavioral significance of circadian clocks, and about the physiology of circadian clocks in other species.

AVIAN CIRCADIAN OSCILLATORS

The pineal gland

The evidence of a neural oscillator in rats and hamsters naturally fueled my interest in the role of such a nucleus in regulating the timing of incubation behavior in doves. However, very compelling evidence had been published by Zimmerman and Menaker (1975) showing that the pineal gland is an important circadian oscillator in birds. In an elegant series of studies, they showed that circadian locomotor rhythms can be restored to an arrhythmic, pinealectomized sparrow by transplanting a pineal gland into the anterior chamber of its eye. Furthermore, the phase of the locomotor rhythm assumed by the recipient animal is that of the donor animal.

In an unpublished study done in my laboratory, we pinealectomized doves and then permitted them to proceed through the reproductive cycle. To our disappointment, the incubation behavior of pinealectomized and intact control animals was not distinguishable. Perhaps this result is not surprising. Circadian rhythms survive pinealectomy in some species (see Menaker and Binkley, 1981; Rusak, 1982, for review). For example, pinealectomized starlings (Gwinner, 1978) and chickens (Menaker & Binkley) continue to show rhythmic locomotor behavior.

Hypothalamic pacemakers

In order to study the nature of sex differences mediating the timing of incubation in doves, we explored the possibility of a brain oscillator. On cytoarchitectonic grounds, a medially lying hypothalamic nucleus (termed, for simplicity, the medial hypothalamic nucleus, MHN) whose location is similar to that of the SCN in a number of mammals (Figure 13), had been designated the SCN (see Norgren and Silver, in press-a, in press-b, for review). Prior to studying the role of the SCN in the timing of incubation, we planned to delimit the precise location and extent of the SCN by identifying the retinorecipient (receiving afferent input from the retina) hypothalamic nucleus, much as had been done earlier in the rat by Moore and Lenn (1972), and in many other mammalian species (Moore, 1973). We used a sensitive anterograde tracer, horseradish peroxidase, applied intravitreously in the eye for this purpose. Much to our surprise at that time, there was no retinal input to the medial hypothalamic region that so resembled the mammalian SCN; instead, there was substantial direct retinal input to another, more laterally lying hypothalamic region termed here the lateral hypothalamic retinorecipient region (LHRN). At that time, we thought that this laterally lying nucleus might be the avian SCN, since it received direct retinal input (Cooper, Pickard, & Silver, 1983). While Cassone and Moore (1987) concur with that view, based on their extensive immunohistochemical evidence, more recent work has made me realize that we lack the definitive evidence needed to declare which hypothalamic nucleus serves as a pacemaker. The MHN does not receive retinal input in any of the species of birds we have studied, namely, quail, budgerigars, starlings, sparrows, and doves (Norgren & Silver, in press-a), suggesting that retinal input to the LHRN and not to the medial hypothalamic region is a universal feature. The avian LHRN region is reminiscent of the lateral hypothalamic projection described in rats (Riley, Card,

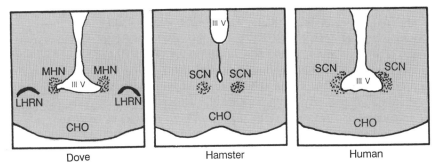

FIGURE 13. The location of the SCN in comparative perspective: comparable coronal sections through the anterior hypothalamus of three species. The hamster and human sections show the SCN located bilaterally, lateral to the third ventricle (III V) and dorsal to the optic chiasm (CHO) in each species. In the dove, the MHN and the LHRN are depicted. Each of these avian hypothalamic nuclei has been termed the SCN. (After Moore-Ede et al., 1982.)

& Moore, 1981), which has recently been shown to be prominent early in development in that species (Speh & Moore, 1988). The function of this lateral retinorecipient region has not yet been studied in avian or mammalian forms. Finally, neither the MHN not the LHRN resemble the mammalian SCN in the distribution of the neuropeptides vasoactive intestinal polypeptide (VIP) and vasopressin (VP) (Norgren & Silver, in press-b), two of the peptides characteristic of the mammalian SCN. Neither VIP nor VP occur in the LHRN or the MHN, though they do occur in nearby regions (Cassone & Moore, 1987) and are fairly widespread in the avian hypothalamus (Cloues, Ramos, & Silver, 1988; Norgren & Silver, in press-b; Yamada, Mikami, & Yanaihara, 1982). In contrast, VIP occurs only in the SCN in the rat and hamster hypothalamus.

If either the LHRN or the MHN serve a function similar to the mammalian SCN, circadian rhythmicity should be disrupted, entrainment should be lost, and seasonal gonadal cycles should be abolished following selective lesions of one or the other nucleus. Lesion studies of the LHRN have yet to be done. The MHN has been the object of lesion studies in quail (Simpson & Follett, 1981) and sparrows (Ebihara & Kawamura, 1981; Takahashi & Menaker, 1979). Although animals became arrhythmic following these lesions, the results are difficult to interpret, because arrhythmicity, at least in the case of the house sparrow, was apparently most often seen in animals with very large lesions in which both the LHRN and the medial hypothalamic nucleus was damaged (see Cassone & Moore, 1987, for the presentation of this evidence).

Need for functional evidence

If a clock function is to be established for a hypothalamic nucleus in birds, we will need the kinds of evidence that have been gathered in mammals. It remains to be established that in birds circadian rhythms are lost following lesion of the hypothalamus restricted to the "SCN," and verification of a complete and discrete lesion is needed. In addition to functional studies, it remains to be verified that an avian hypothalamic nucleus sustains circadian rhythms in metabolic activity and in electrophysiological activity, that it can be transplanted into a lesioned host animal, and so on. In other words, the work needed to verify the existence of a neural oscillator in the hypothalamus of birds remains to be done.

SUMMARY

Ring dove parents share in all aspects of parental care. They both perform the same behaviors at the appropriate phases of the reproductive cycle. They both care for their young during incubation and brooding. The analysis of how dove parents care for their young is an unfinished tale. The studies completed to date establish that photic cues are important in determining which parent will incubate and brood the young. If the L:D cycle is phase shifted, parent doves will adjust their behavior so that the male continues to incubate for a block of time in the middle of the day. In constant dim illumination, in the absence of environmental cues, parent doves can express a free-running rhythm of incubation, with each parent timing the onset of its bout of sitting. Administration of heterotypical hormones to gonadectomized animals indicates that the sex hormones influence the time of expression of incubation. Doves seem to have an overriding rule that in the absence of the mate, each parent will continue to incubate, at least for several days, irrespective of photic or endocrine conditions (see Silver & Norgren, 1987, for review). There is evidence that there is a minimum interval for which the male tries to sit each day. (The parallel question has not been studied in the female.) The foregoing behavioral studies raise the interesting questions of how the various cues that affect circadian rhythms and the expression of behavior are integrated, and how and where photic and non-photic cues reach the neural pacemaker(s) to influence the phase of a response.

Our search for the anatomical loci controlling the timing behavior of parent doves has led to a search for a hypothalamic "clock" and the avian analog of the mammalian SCN. Evidence for a circadian clock in rats and hamsters is based on converging electrophysiological, metabolic, transplant, and lesion studies, all of which suggest that the SCN are neural pacemakers. In contrast, the locus of the hypothalamic pacemaker in birds remains to be established. The evidence for a neural oscillator rests on a few lesion studies. There is a need for more systematic analyses of the hypothalamic region in birds, of the type that have established the function of the neural oscillator in mammals.

A question that looms large is that of the generality of pacemaker systems. Are there similarities in the organization of timing mechanisms across species? Are the differences described above, among avian species and between mammals and birds, due to differences in the importance of one or another pacemaker, but based on a universal "blueprint" featuring redundant, multiple pacemakers? Opportunities to contribute to resolving these issues abound.

COMPARATIVE DEVELOPMENT OF VERTEBRATE SEXUAL BEHAVIOR: LEVELS, CASCADES, AND WEBS

Celia L. Moore

There is an extraordinary diversity of reproductive mechanisms in the animal kingdom. Among these, sexual reproduction is distinguished from its asexual alternatives by the process of fertilization, during which genes from two separate gametes join to produce a new genetic combination in offspring. The two gametes typically come from two separate individuals, but this is not necessarily the case: self-fertilization is found in some animals. Although it is possible for fertilization to involve two gametes of the same size, it is typical to find a bimodal distribution in gamete size within a species, with one kind of gamete that is relatively small, numerous, and mobile (sperm) and another kind that, though fewer in number, is larger, richer in cytoplasm, and less mobile (eggs). Therefore, individuals within a species are typically divided into two kinds: males (which are defined by sperm production) and females (which are defined by egg production), with varying degrees of other differences between them. Again, however, this is not necessarily the case: hermaphrodites produce both eggs and sperm, either sequentially or simultaneously, and may either self-fertilize or cross-fertilize, possibly taking turns fertilizing one another's eggs during the same mating episode (Williams, 1975). Interesting as it is, the diversity in fertilization methods is far surpassed by the remarkable array of behavioral patterns used by animals of various species to achieve the common goal of fertilization. The study of sexual behavior poses a real challenge to comparative psychologists searching for orderly ways to describe and understand similarities and differences among species.

Comparative psychology is concerned with identifying the components that underlie behavior and understanding how they work in relation to one another to produce functional behavior. It is, as Schneirla (1966) said, the study of behavioral organization, and this *organization*, rather than the surface appearance of specific behavioral patterns, is the focus when different species are compared with one another. Further, comparison of developmental processes across species is extraordinarily useful for revealing similarities and differences in behavioral organization. Developmental research looks back in ontogenetic time for antecedents to a behavior that were there in advance of the fully organized behavior. By including ontogenetically earlier and simpler systems, a developmental perspective facilitates a close look at behavioral organization. The organization of complex behavior, difficult to discern in its fully developed form, will be more readily revealed by following its progression during ontogeny. Perhaps this is why Schneirla also claimed that the study of development is the "backbone of comparative psychology" (1966, p. 284).

Where there are both sexual reproduction and the presence of two sex classes, as there are in most vertebrates, three questions arise that are amenable to a comparative developmental analysis: How does sexual ability develop? How is sex determined? How do sex differences arise? These questions provide the context for the comparative analysis of sexual behavior that will be presented in this chapter. A comparative developmental perspective will be adopted to describe similarities and differences in the organization of sexual behavior among both closely and distantly related vertebrate species. The development of masculine sexual behavior in Norway rats will be examined in some detail as an example of this approach. Finally, some suggestions will be offered as to how a detailed analysis of this sort may reveal developmental sources of novel patterns of organization that arise during evolution.

SEX DETERMINATION, SEXUAL DIFFERENTIATION, AND SEX DIFFERENCES

Sex determination

Among species with two sex classes, there is a variety of mechanisms for deciding whether one will become male or female (Bull, 1983). Many animals have special sex chromosomes, with morphological differences among the chromosomes in the set, and sex is determined at conception by chromosomal complement. Mammals, for example, typically have two sex chromosomes, with males heterogametic (XY) and females homogametic (XX). There are also genetic sex-determining factors that are not associated with morphologically different chromosomes, and sex determination in some species is based on a number of these factors scattered among several chromosomes. Sex can also be determined by extrachromosomal factors in the cytoplasm, inherited in the egg. In some cases, neither genotype nor cytoplasm differs for males and females, and sex is determined by environmental factors external to the zygote; in yet others, the sex of individuals that differ in genetic sex determinants may be determined by overriding environmental factors.

Although genetic mechanisms are far more common, environmental sex-determining factors are found in some vertebrates. These factors include such physical variables as the temperature, photoperiod, or pH in which the zygote develops (Bull, 1983). For example, if map turtle eggs are deposited in the cool shade of vegetation, they will develop into males, but if deposited in the warmer, unshaded sand of the same beach, they will develop into females (Vogt & Bull, 1984).

Social stimuli are also used as environmental sex determinants. Remarkable examples are provided by several species of sequentially hermaphroditic fish, which develop first as males or females on the basis of one kind of determinant, then, after maturity, go through a period of reorganization into the opposite sex on the basis of social determinants (Demski, 1987). Both male-to-female and female-to-male changes are found; the first sequence is adaptive in situations where females are more successful when they are larger (because they can pro-duce more eggs) and the second sequence is adaptive in situations where males are more successful when they are larger (because they can compete more successfully with other males).

One socially controlled pattern has been described in detail for the Pacific coral reef fish, *Anthias squamipinnis* (Fishelson, 1970; Shapiro, 1983). This little fish lives in social groups where females significantly outnumber males. Each individual develops first as a female, and some later reorganize into males, which involves not only a change in gamete type, but also changes in coloration and behavior. A complex of behavioral cues related to the number of males in the group provides the environmental determinant for sexual reorganization.

Sexual differentiation and sex differences

Identification of a sex-determining factor does little to explain the development of sexual function, because it specifies only what initially tips the course of development into somewhat different directions for males and females. A developmental analysis would explain how an organism progresses from early stages with neither male nor female sexual capacity to later stages of sexual competence. This is the process of *sexual differentiation*. Sexual differentiation may be elaborate and may involve many aspects of the organism and an extensive behavioral repertoire, or it may be simple and restricted to gonads, a few accessory structures, and rudimentary behavior.

The phenomenon of simultaneous hermaphroditism demonstrates graphically that there is no inherent conflict in the coexistence within the same organism of fully differentiated masculine and feminine systems. Nevertheless, two sexes with some differences between them are typical. Somewhat confusingly, the term sexual differentiation is often used to refer not only to the development of sexual function but also to the processes by which the sexes become different. The sex differences that arise during the course of sexual differentiation are often secondary to the development of masculine or feminine sexual function (i.e., physiology, anatomy, and behavior pertaining to production and transport of sperm or eggs, respectively, and to joining with the complementary gamete). I will use *differentiation* to refer to the development of sexual function, in a sense parallel to that used to refer to the development of vision or ingestion, with no necessary implication of differences between the sexes.

Consistent with the important role they play in reproductive maturation and adult functioning, gonadal steroids are extremely important to vertebrate sexual differentiation. Gonadal tissue is able to synthesize androgen and estrogen very early in ontogeny; in chick embryos, for example, these hormones can be synthesized by embryonic day 6. Studies have shown that gonadal steroids secreted during this very early period can regulate the further differentiation of the gonadal anlagen into fully organized testes or ovaries capable of sperm or egg production and continued steroid synthesis. Sex differences in available androgen and estrogen during early embryogenesis may be the developmental regulator for most vertebrates that translates sex-determining factors into the development of two sexes. (Males of placental mammals are an important exception. These animals have a testis-organizing gene carried on the Y chromosome that regulates the differentiation of spermatogonia, which occurs before the differentiation of the androgen-producing Leydig cells.) (For reviews, see Resko, 1985, and Yahr, 1988).

These early embryological events represent two themes that are repeated frequently among vertebrates: estrogen and androgen are key regulators of sexual development, and sex differences in the pattern of development can usually be traced to differences in the availability of androgen or estrogen to males and females at important stages. When hormones present at one developmental stage contribute to changes in the organism that endure beyond the secretory period into later stages, they are said to have *organizing* effects. Hormonal organizing effects have been reported for an impressive variety of morphological (including neuroanatomical), physiological, and behavioral characteristics in many vertebrate species (Adkins-Regan, 1985; Baum, 1979; Goy & McEwen, 1980; Moore, 1985a; Yahr, 1988). These effects figure importantly in the differentiation of reproductive behavior, which includes not only copulation, but also finding, attracting, or competing for mates, and parental care of offspring.

ALTERNATIVE PATTERNS AND LEVELS OF BEHAVIORAL ORGANIZATION

Alternatives in sexual patterns

The divergent development of males and females in most vertebrates is a major example of alternative patterns of organization that, once adopted, preclude reorganization into a different pattern. That is, the alternatives are mutually exclusive, and there is a loss of developmental plasticity once a decisive step is taken during the course of ontogeny. Other alternatives in sexual pattern are mutually exclusive, but plasticity is maintained so that animals can switch between alternatives. A common example of this second kind of pattern is the change from nonreproductive to reproductive condition that occurs sequentially, often repeatedly, in the life history of an animal. Sequential hermaphroditism is a more dramatic example, as in the sequentially hermaphroditic fish mentioned above. Reorganization may involve not only behavioral change, but anatomical and physiological changes in gonads as well: gametogenic and hormonal aspects of gonads may alternate between functional and regressed states and, in sequential hermaphrodites, between male and female types. Alternative developmental pathways to gonadal organization and mating behavior are summarized in Table 1.

Not all alternative patterns in behavioral organization need imply divergent

TABLE 1. Alternatives in the Development of Vertebrate Sexual Patterns

Pattern	Single outcome	Multiple outcomes
Initial gonadal organization	Divergent: ♂ or ♀ (typical)	Simultaneous: ♂ and ♀ (atypical)
Mature gonadal organization	Maintenance of functional ovary or testis	Regression and recrudescence as same gonad at regular or irregular periods
		Regression and reorganization as other gonad in response to age-related or social cues
Mating pattern	One pattern	Sequential development of more than one pattern
		Simultaneous development of more than one pattern

developmental pathways. Organisms sometimes have multiple alternatives available to them at any one time, and species differ in the degree of this flexibility (or plasticity in a second sense). Given a particular situation, some animals are able to select one of several possible behavioral patterns from a relatively rich repertoire; others have only a limited repertoire from which to select. This individual flexibility extends, in rare cases, to the two sex classes. The simultaneously hermaphroditic sea bass (*Serranus subligarius*), for example, is capable of switching between male and female behavioral and coloration patterns within minutes, during the same mating episode (Demski, 1987).

Some vertebrates develop more than one pattern for mating, yet retain the same sex, or gamete type, throughout life (Dunbar, 1982). Sometimes alternative mating patterns are developed divergently, in separate individuals; sometimes the same individual develops more than one pattern, either simultaneously or sequentially. (Some evolutionists refer to these alternative patterns with the military metaphors of "strategy" or "tactic.") Individuals with more than one pattern available to them may select among the patterns on the basis of context. Waterfowl, for example, typically form pair bonds. In some species of ducks and geese, males copulate with their mates using one set of behavioral patterns, and, during the same reproductive period, use a different set of behavioral patterns to copulate with other females (McKinney, Derrickson, & Mineau, 1983). Frogs and toads have polygynous mating systems, and males typically attract mates by calling. On a given night, several males can be found courting in the same pond. In some species, individuals switch between the calling pattern and an alternative "satellite" pattern of sitting quietly near a calling male and then attempting to copulate with females that are attracted to the caller (Arak, 1988; Gerhardt, Daniel, Perrill, & Schram, 1987).

When alternative mating patterns have physiological or morphological characteristics associated with them, alternatives tend to be found either in different individuals or in different life stages within an individual. Perhaps the simplest morphological change is size, which is related to age. Just as some sex changes in sequential hermaphrodites can be related to size, so can some changes from one within-sex pattern to another (e.g., from "satellite" behavior when small to territorial competition when large in males of various species) (Ghiselin, 1974). More dramatic changes involve altered production of behavioral and nonbehavioral social signals. Female mimicry is an interesting case in point. Males that show this pattern retain their sperm and testosterone production and their attraction to females as mates, but they make use of some developmental patterns typical of females. Female mimics in red-sided garter snakes, unlike other males, release a chemosignal normally released by females and used to attract males. When produced by a mimic, the signal diverts other males from real females to the mimic, and apparently provides him with a competitive edge in fertilizing the female (Mason & Crews, 1985). Female mimicry is also found in bluegill sunfish, where some males look and behave like females. The female mimics act as satellites to larger, morphologically different males that maintain nests and territories. Males of both varieties mate with females (Dominey, 1980; Gross & Charnov, 1980).

It will be very interesting to determine the role of gonadal steroids in the development of different mating patterns within the same sex. These hormones are clearly important both for differentiation and for performance of masculine and feminine behavior in many species, but there are marked species differences in such details of hormonal effects as time of action, the effective form of hormone, and the type of tissue that is affected (Adkins-Regan, 1985; Baum, 1979; Beach, 1971; Crews, 1984). Gonadal steroids may regulate the transition from one sex to another in hermaphroditic fish, although the evidence is still unclear (Adkins-Regan, 1985; Demski, 1987). Gonadal steroids may also be important developmental regulators of female mimicry. In red-sided garter snakes, the ability to release male-attracting chemicals apparently requires exposure to estradiol in infancy (Crews, 1985). The fact that female mimics possess female-typical signals and may behave in some ways like females, yet are attracted to females and copulate like males, suggests that different aspects of sexual function are regulated independently in development. Experiments with zebra finches support this idea. When treated with estradiol during the hatchling stage and with testosterone as adults, female zebra finches sing as males typically do, but do not copulate like males (Adkins-Regan, 1985).

Structure–function relations and behavioral plasticity

During the process of differentiation, the cells and tissues that make up neuroanatomical and other structures typically become committed to a particular form (Jacobson, 1970). Although growth and progressive differentiation of cells and tissues may occur throughout life, the possibility of radical regression and redifferentiation is usually confined to early embryonic stages. This is because the integration of cells and tissues to form organized structures imposes limits to reorganization which arise out of the interdependence of components. When the complexity of this integration is greater, as it is in more complex vertebrates, such limitation becomes greater.

Successive hermaphroditism requires individuals to retain structural plasticity in gonadal tissue, and it is interesting that this sexual pattern has been reported in fish, but not among more advanced vertebrates. Plasticity has also been reported in organs used to produce social signals in successive hermaphrodites, and it would be very interesting to know whether there are neuroanatomical changes that accompany the behavioral changes. Such neural changes might also be expected among the less complex vertebrates in correlation with sequential alterations in mating patterns. The feasibility of such neural changes is supported by the fact that in canaries, seasonal differentiation and regression of neurons occur in the brain regions that control song. These changes have been related to changes in song type on the one hand and control by testosterone on the other (Nottebohm, Nottebohm, & Crane, 1986).

For more complex species, it is not necessary to hypothesize changes at the structural level to account for alternative mating patterns; in species with a higher level of behavioral organization, variation in behavior is made possible by the use of the same structure in different ways. Differentiation of structural supports for the full range of species-typical mating patterns probably occurs in all individuals within a species, although there are often factors that prevent expression of a particular sexual pattern. Males and females undergo much the same development: there are few genetic differences between the sexes, and developmental constraints ensure that males and females share many common features, even when they make no functional sense in one sex. From this view, it is not surprising that when mammals are put in the right context, males will perform feminine sexual behavior and females will perform masculine sexual behavior (Beach, 1971).

Species differences

Although clearly understandable on functional grounds because of sharp differences in ecology, it is often puzzling on phylogenetic and developmental grounds when closely related species exhibit obvious behavioral differences. The alternatives available within one species provide insight into the ways that species differences can emerge rapidly. Sometimes when animals are subjected to what are, for them, unusual conditions, a capacity emerges that is not usually expressed in their species, but may be typical of others. For example, when the differentiated left ovary is removed from a female chicken, the undeveloped right gonad often differentiates as a fully functional testis (Witschi, 1961), thus demonstrating a potential for hermaphroditism that is normally kept in check. Another example can be drawn from the estrous cycles of Norway rats, which are normally timed by an endogenous clock. Placing females in constant light interferes with the functioning of the clock, causing them not to cycle but to show continuous high levels of estrogen. In this state, the estrous cycle can be triggered by mating with a male (Brown-Grant, Davidson, & Greig, 1978), a pattern atypical of rats but typical of several other rodent species. With no great change in neurobehavioral mechanisms, either a change in sensitivity to (or availability of) stimuli linked to the brain–pituitary–gonad axis, or a change in sensitivity to (or availability of) stimuli that regulate an endogenous clock, can shift a species from regular to irregular reproductive cycles, or vice versa. Such variability is probably more common within species than has previously been recognized (Bronson, 1987).

Substantial differences in the organization of behavior may sometimes result from small differences in developmental processes. For example, an excellent case for the importance of differences in the timing of otherwise similar developmental events has been put forth by Gould (1977). Some relationships between the timing of sexual maturation and species differences in the organization of sexual behavior will be considered in the next section.

LENGTH OF DEVELOPMENT AND BEHAVIORAL COMPLEXITY

Length of development and life history

The length of development before sexual maturity is correlated with a number of other characteristics, such as adult body size, longevity, metabolic rate, quality of diet, and size of litter, that together make up the life history of a species (Eisenberg, 1981; Geist, 1978a; Gould, 1977). Characteristics are found bundled together in an organism, in part because the adoption of one may constrain the adoption of others, sometimes for simple allometric reasons. Thus, metabolic rate is inversely related to size in homeothermic vertebrates, because heat is lost more rapidly with the large surface:volume ratio found in smaller animals. Characteristics are also found in similar clusters in different taxa because of the ramifying effects of natural selection. For example, unpredictable fluctuations in resources typically mean that it will be adaptive for an animal to reproduce rapidly when resources are available. This may entail all of the following: large numbers of offspring produced at once, a short gestation time, little parental care, rapid resumption of readiness to reproduce again, and a short reproductive life. Under more predictable conditions, in contrast, one often finds fewer offspring produced at once, a longer gestation time, postnatal feeding by parents, substantial parental care, and a relatively long reproductive life.

Because vertebrates have neuroendocrine mechanisms that allow regulation of the reproductive rate by social and physical environmental conditions (within limits set by other organismic characteristics such as body size), two closely related and therefore morphologically and physiologically similar vertebrates that come to live in different ecological conditions can change their rate of reproduction by a relatively simple initial expedient, such as shifting the age of sexual maturity or the length of intervals between reproductive cycles. This initial change, in turn, provides part of the context within which further change occurs. Therefore, for example, the extent of parental care is likely to be reduced in species with short intervals between successive offspring.

Both ecological and organismic factors must be considered in a comparative analysis of behavioral development. This is illustrated by the different possibilities available to reptiles, birds, and mammals for changing the length of postnatal development and its correlates, such as parental care. In both reptiles and birds, a rapid rate of reproduction is consistent with precocity in the young, which rapidly attain adultlike, independent feeding and predator defense abilities. However, reptiles are ectotherms, and must gain heat by behavioral means such as basking. They do not have the option of producing altricial young, because such young would not have the sensorimotor ability to thermoregulate by behavioral means and the parents would be unable to generate heat for them. Therefore, parental care is rare in reptiles, and the young engage in adultlike behavior shortly after hatching (Burghardt, 1988).

Like mammals, birds are endotherms and can produce altricial young which are warmed with parental body heat; relatively slow development assisted by parental care is often found in birds. However, commitment to homeothermy in birds and mammals limits the rate of reproduction to one below that possible in other vertebrates, because some time and energy must be devoted to parental care to regulate the temperature of developing eggs or altricial young. Unlike birds, mammals combine endothermy with lactation and, in placental mammals, internal gestation. There are, of course, limits to the total mass that can be gestated at once; thus, rapid reproduction in placental mammals is achieved by producing relatively large litters of relatively small, altricial young. Precocity is not associated with rapid reproduction in mammals, but with long gestation of a single fetus or small litter, characteristics found more frequently in larger mammals such as ungulates or primates (Eisenberg, 1981). Humans, altricial because of neoteny and extremely slow development, are an interesting exception (Gould, 1977).

Conditions for behavioral complexity

When postnatal parental care is provided, developing offspring are ensured a social environment with predictable features that can figure in species-typical development. Both birds and mammals provide such care, and with it, reliable sources of social stimulation. However, the small size and high energy requirements of birds are factors that limit the length of the period of dependency on parents in comparison with that possible in the larger mammals.

Slow development, delayed maturity, and parental care are associated in the evolution of mammals with increased brain growth relative to body growth (encephalization quotient) (Eisenberg, 1981). Larger and more complex brains permit more complex neurobehavioral organization and a structural basis for high levels of behavioral flexibility. It is perhaps not surprising that juvenile play and exploration are behavioral patterns that are prominent in larger mammals, but are rare or absent in other vertebrates (Burghardt, 1988; Fagen, 1982; Simpson, 1976).

Perhaps the most important role of play in development is to allow behavioral organization to develop to more complex levels. Controlled rearing experiments have shown that animals that play and explore have greater flexibility in behavioral organization than conspecifics prevented from playing (Fagen, 1982). Simpson (1976) has argued that play allows complex animals such as primates to increase their general information base, and to learn about the uses of different action patterns in different contexts. When large-brained, playful animals with time and energy to spare undergo a long period of development in a social world that includes parents and other companions of varying ages and is characterized by numerous rule-governed interactions, conditions are right for behavioral organization with a high level of complexity. With respect to sexual behavior, one should expect such animals to have more mating patterns available than the two or three alternatives in the finite repertoire found in less complex vertebrates. In addition, one should expect their sexual behavior to be organized more complexly, in the sense of being integrated with other behavioral patterns in complex ways. Humans provide an extreme instance of this trend, with highly diverse sexual patterns, which, to be understood, must be considered along with politics, religion, economics, tradition, pathology, playfulness, and many other aspects of human society and psychology.

Social contributions to sexual development

Because it is parsimonious to do so, developmental processes are likely to make use of social stimuli in behavioral organization whenever they are reliably present in ontogeny. Social stimuli do contribute to many aspects of sexual development in vertebrates, ranging across sex determination, priming the secretion of gonadal hormones, restricting mate choice, and integrating sexual patterns into broader social patterns found within complex groups. In taking a comparative look at social contributions in any of these aspects, it is important to remember that social contributions to sexual development may occur at different levels of behavioral organization and that different kinds of effects may occur in animals with different levels of behavioral complexity.

An example of these species differences is provided by comparing the effects of rearing in social isolation on Norway rats and rhesus monkeys (Moore, 1985b). In neither species is sexual motivation impaired by isolation, but, in both species, males reared in isolation have what appear to be similar problems in orienting to and mounting a female (Harlow, 1965; Larsson, 1978). Rats overcome their difficulties with practice, but monkeys do not. Because monkeys excel at learning motor tasks, the species difference cannot be accounted for in these terms. The greater difficulties experienced by isolated monkeys become more comprehensible when their sexual behavior is thought of as part of a complex social repertoire. Rearing away from social companions eliminates many of the monkey's opportunities for establishing social patterns of any kind, and, perhaps more importantly, for working out the contextual rules for selecting one social pattern rather than another. It was this deficiency, rather than sexual incompetence per se, that prevented successful mating in the socially isolated monkeys; this was demonstrated by the fact that sexual practice with adult partners did not succeed in reversing the deficit, but more general social therapy with younger monkeys did (Novak & Harlow, 1975). Rats, on the other hand, had only to practice mounting by following the cues provided by the female's soliciting behavior and odor zones on her body.

CASCADES AND WEBS IN DEVELOPMENT

Analyzing the process of development in psychobiology requires us to think simultaneously about the interrelation of many different factors. To manage this conceptually difficult task requires us to use metaphors (Lakoff & Johnson, 1980), no one of which can do the job alone. The structural metaphor of *levels* of organization has been used repeatedly in this chapter to communicate something about differences in complexity realized by the process of development at the time when some behavioral capacity has been achieved. Different metaphors are needed to discuss the *process* of development. Two structural metaphors that capture different aspects of the process are *cascades* and *webs*. A cascade can be used to represent the fact that some key elements or events have effects that ramify in an ever widening way during the course of ontogeny, perhaps through the mediation of intervening elements or events. A metaphoric web is useful for visualizing interconnections of events and elements that are present in an organism at any temporal cross-section during the course of ontogeny. In this section, these two metaphors will be used to take a closer look at some aspects of masculine sexual development, with a focus on the Norway rat, a relatively simple, rapidly developing mammal. Although principles that emerge from this analysis can be applied to other species, diversity in details of development will undoubtedly prove the rule, and differences in levels of organization will remain important.

Cascading effects of testosterone in sexual differentiation

Like any other mammal, a developing male rat is first exposed to testosterone from his own testes during fetal life, after the Leydig cells differentiate to functional status. Fetal levels of circulating testosterone are relatively high during the last week of gestation, with a surge on Day 18, followed by a drop which continues until birth (Day 22) (Weisz & Ward, 1980). Neonatal males continue to secrete testosterone through the early period of development, while still in the nest (Dohler & Wuttke, 1975). Females also have circulating testosterone during fetal life, which is apparently synthesized by nontesticular tissues, and perhaps also comes from the dam or from male siblings sharing the uterus, but they have neither the prenatal surge nor the high levels of postnatal testosterone characteristic of males (Dohler & Wuttke, 1975; Weisz & Ward, 1980). Many studies in rats and other laboratory mammals have clearly demonstrated that perinatal testosterone plays a crucial role in masculine sexual differentiation and that the sex difference in early levels of testosterone is the origin of sex differences in anatomy, physiology, and behavior that appear later in development (Goy & McEwen, 1980; Moore, 1985a; Yahr, 1988).

The neural mechanisms through which perinatal testosterone has its effects on behavioral development have been the focus of intensive research during the past two decades, and several of its lasting effects on the central nervous system have been found in various vertebrate species. Of these, perhaps the most attention has been excited by a series of reports, beginning with Raisman and Field (1971), of morphological effects on the brain and spinal cord. The regions in which the changes have been found are involved in various aspects of sexual function, but no necessary relationships between morphological changes and particular adult sexual behavior or neuroendocrine regulation have yet been determined in rats (see Yahr, 1988 for review and discussion). The correlation between morphology and behavior is clearer in Mongolian gerbils, where a sexually dimorphic nucleus in the preoptic area has been linked with both masculine sexual behavior and scent-marking behavior (Commins & Yahr, 1984). Even more striking correlations between testosterone-regulated anatomical differentiation and adult behavior have been found in the control of zebra finch song (Arnold, 1980; Gurney & Konishi, 1980). Testosterone also affects many tissues outside the central nervous system as they differentiate during ontogeny. These include muscles, liver, various accessory sex organs, and genitalia, all of which may contribute importantly to later sexual behavior, either directly or indirectly.

Much of the effect of early testosterone on later sexual behavior may be accounted for by effects on genitalia (Beach, 1971). Sexual behavior in male rats consists of approximately seven ejaculatory series performed during a period of one to two hours. An ejaculatory series consists of several mounts with intromission, separated by intervals of about a minute, then a terminal mount with ejaculation. Each series is followed by a refractory period of several minutes before a new series begins. (An observer can identify intromission and ejaculation by the typical motor patterns associated with them, but the motor patterns can occur independently of actual intromission or ejaculation; thus, they can be observed in females and males with little phallic development). Genital status does not affect a male's interest in females or mounting behavior, but surgically or chemically desensitized or incompletely differentiated genitalia reduce the likelihood of his performing intromission and ejaculatory patterns (Beach, Noble, & Orndoff, 1969; Lodder & Zeilmaker, 1976). On the other hand, fully differentiated genitalia are not sufficient by themselves to account for all aspects of masculine sexual behavior. It is possible to produce a morphologically complete penis by providing dihydrotestosterone, a metabolite of testosterone, to neonatal rats while depriving them of testosterone and its estrogenic metabolites. After treatment with testosterone in adulthood, such animals mount females and perform intromission patterns, but do not perform the terminal mount with the ejaculatory pattern (Booth, 1977; Hart 1977).

In addition to affecting the central nervous system and genitalia, the presence of testosterone in infant rats leads to the production of chemosignals that in turn affect the nature of maternal care. Maternal rats are able to distinguish their male and female pups on the basis of chemosignals in the urine, which are produced, at least in part, by the preputial gland (Moore, 1985c; Moore & Samonte, 1986). The chemosignals produced by males stimulate higher levels of maternal licking than those from females (see Figure 1.)

Maternal licking provides a pup with extensive tactile, vestibular, and thermal stimulation. Thus, chemosignals produced by males ensure relatively high levels of stimulation from this source. In order to determine whether this stimulation contributes in any way to masculine sexual development, the capacity of

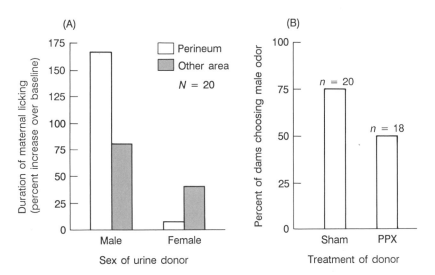

FIGURE 1. (A) Introduction of a drop of pup urine into a nest increased maternal licking of the pups in both perineal and other skin regions. Urine from a male pup was more effective. (After Moore, 1985c.) (B) In simultaneous choice tests where investigation of urine traces was measured, more dams chose male pup urine if the pups were intact (sham surgery) but not if the preputial glands had been removed (PPX). Apparently, the preputial gland produces chemosignals that contribute to the effectiveness of male pup urine. (After Moore & Samonte, 1986.)

some dams to smell their pups was diminished experimentally, with the result that they provided lower levels of licking to their offspring. When tested for masculine sexual behavior as adults, the male offspring performed all elements of masculine copulation, but they did so at a significantly slower pace; for example, both ejaculatory latencies and the refractory periods between ejaculatory series were longer than those of normal males (Moore, 1984) (see Figure 2). Similar results have been obtained by applying a masking odor, which reduces both licking received by neonates and their copulatory rate as adults (Birke & Sadler, 1987). Conversely, providing females with artificially enhanced stimulation during early development increases the rate with which they perform intromission patterns when tested for masculine sexual behavior as adults (Moore, 1985b). Taken together, these studies lead to the conclusion that the adult performance of masculine sexual behavior is facilitated by the behavior normally shown by dams to males.

Relatively small differences in the details of copulatory behavior set by differential maternal stimulation may have important consequences for the reproductive success of male rats. The temporal pattern with which copulation occurs is very important in stimulating the endocrine events that allow pregnancy in females (Adler, 1978), and males may differ in their ability to induce the appropriate neuroendocrine changes. Furthermore, the mating system of this species is such that several males may copulate with the same female during a single mating session. Thus, competition among males takes place within the reproductive tract of the female, through the relative amount of sperm provided during repeated ejaculations (Dewsbury, 1984d) or through the use of penile reflexes to displace the sperm plugs left by other males (Hart & Melese-D'Hospital, 1987). Again, individual males may differ in their capacity for multiple ejaculations or in the adequacy of penile reflexes used either to place sperm for efficient transport or to dislodge sperm deposited by other males.

The contribution of maternal behavior to the reproductive success of sons has not yet been tested directly, but it is an interesting possibility that is indirectly supported by a recent study. Male rats were reared by mothers that provided relatively low levels of maternal licking, then given extended opportunities to mate as adults. These males performed fewer ejaculations before sexual exhaustion than similarly tested, normally reared males (Moore & Power, unpublished data).

Both sex differences and individual differences within a sex in the performance of sexual behavior have been related to variation in the availability of gonadal steroids during early development. Masculine sexual behavior is not as fully developed in males experimentally deprived of typical levels of testosterone, and is more completely developed in females provided with exogenous testosterone (Yahr, 1988). Furthermore, individual variation in prenatal exposure to testosterone, such as might occur during natural development, has been linked

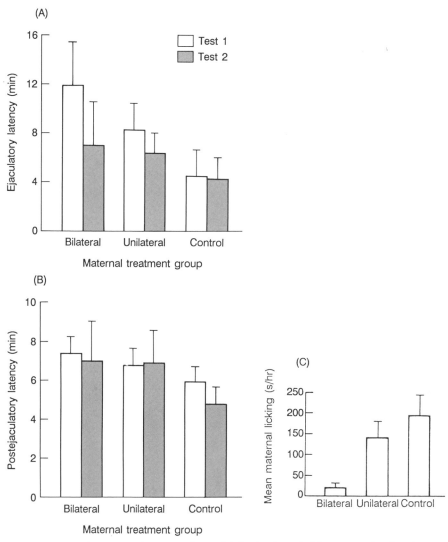

FIGURE 2. The temporal pattern of sexual behavior in male Norway rats is related to stimulation they receive from the dam as neonates. When maternal licking was reduced by blocking the dam's access to pup odors with intranasal polyethylene tubing, both latency to first ejaculation (A) and latency to resumption of intromission after first ejaculation (B) were significantly increased (median and semi-interquartile range) in the sons of the impaired dams. Consistent results were found on two separate tests with females in estrus. Bilaterally placed tubes resulted in a greater reduction of maternal stimulation, and a greater effect on offspring sexual behavior, than unilaterally placed tubes. (C) shows mean maternal licking of pup perinea in the three groups. (After Moore, 1985c.)

with individual differences in sexual behavior. For example, females that develop next to male siblings in the uterus are exposed to more testosterone prenatally than their female siblings without a nearby brother; when adult, their masculine sexual behavior is better developed (Clemens, Gladue, & Coniglio, 1978). Conversely, males gestated by dams that are stressed while pregnant experience a disruption in the normal pattern of testosterone secretion (Weisz & Ward, 1980) and may have deficiencies in masculine sexual behavior (Ward, 1972).

If maternal stimulation is a mediating step in the cascading effects of testosterone on the development of masculine sexual behavior, then it should be possible to manipulate maternal licking by altering the hormonal condition of infants. Such manipulation has been achieved. When female rats were injected with testosterone on the day of birth, they received levels of maternal licking equivalent to those of males when observed both one and nine days after injection (Moore, 1982). Furthermore, male rats gestated by dams that were subjected to stress during pregnancy were no more effective than females in eliciting maternal licking, apparently due to a change in their chemosignal production (Power & Moore, 1986). In Mongolian gerbils, another species in which males are licked more than females, females that had developed near males in utero received more maternal licking as infants than females gestated at a distance from males (Clark, Bone, & Galef, 1989). In general, therefore, hormonal manipulations during early life that are known to increase masculine sexual behavior also have the effect of increasing maternal licking, and manipulations that are known to decrease masculine sexual behavior also decrease maternal licking.

The ramifying effects of testosterone do not end with weaning. Juveniles groom themselves, and the grooming pattern shown by males differs somewhat from that in females. Males devote more of their grooming time to their genitalia, thus providing themselves with stimulation which, in turn, contributes to the rate at which puberty is reached, as measured by accessory organ development (Moore & Rogers, 1984).

Juvenile rats also engage in social play, beginning at about 3 weeks of age and continuing until sexual maturity about 5 weeks later. Males typically engage in more play than females, a pattern that can be reversed by treating neonatal females with testosterone (Meaney & Stewart, 1981). Play is not essential for the development of masculine sexual behavior, but even under supportive laboratory conditions, males that have had social experience as juveniles outperform those that have not (Gerall, Ward, & Gerall, 1967), an advantage that could well be useful in a competitive mating encounter in the more challenging natural environment.

In summary, the additional testosterone available to males in their early ontogeny can be thought of as the origin of a developmental cascade that courses over a variety of separate elements at different ontogenetic times to shape the differentiation of sexual behavior as expressed by sexually mature males (Figure

3). This image, while illustrating an important aspect of the developmental process, fails to capture the interrelations of these elements at each onto-genetic stage in a causal web that includes diverse elements, only some of which are affected by testosterone. For this, a different metaphor is needed.

A causal web in neonatal rats

As indicated in the previous section, maternal licking of pups is affected by testosterone-dependent cues from the pups. However, this maternal behavior is affected by multiple, interacting factors, some originating in the dam and others in the pups (Figure 4). To analyze it further, it is necessary to distinguish two different licking patterns: licking and nuzzling of the entire body surface and licking directed specifically to the perineum or anogenital region. Licking of the anogenital region constitutes a large percentage of total maternal licking behav-ior, and it is the component which is addressed more to males (Moore & Morelli, 1979).

Altricial, nestbound rat pups are unable to urinate and defecate on their own. One of the major consequences of maternal licking is to stimulate the release of

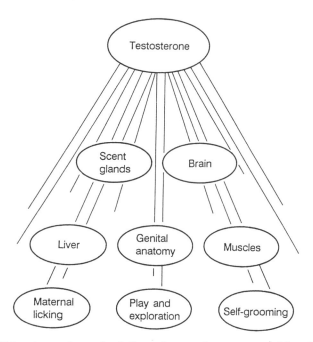

FIGURE 3. A partial cascade of effects of perinatal testosterone. Although not pictured, an effect on one element may in part mediate effects on others.

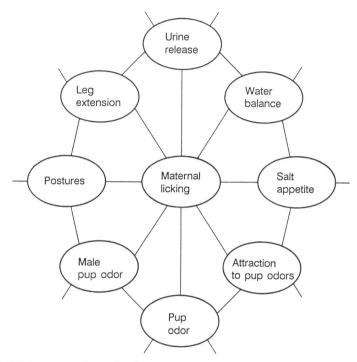

FIGURE 4. A partial causal web centered on the maternal behavior of licking pups, in which some of the interconnections are shown. Both dam and pup contribute elements, not all of which are identified in the diagram.

urine and feces, which are then ingested by the dam; thus she maintains nest cleanliness and recycles important water and salt resources that can be used for further lactation (Gubernick & Alberts, 1983). This maternal pattern is affected by the water balance and the salt appetite of the dam: dams deprived of water spend more time licking the perineum of pups (Friedman, Bruno, & Alberts, 1981), and dams provided with saline to drink spend less time in this behavior (Gubernick & Alberts, 1983). Both water and salt requirements are increased by lactation, a physiological state that is in part maintained, through neuro-endocrine loops, by stimuli associated with the suckling of the pups (Grosvenor & Turner, 1960). Suckling leads to milk intake, which results in, among other things, the production of urine by the pups. These facts are true for pups of both sexes, but interestingly, male infants produce more urine and release it more slowly than females in both rats and gerbils (Clark, Bone, & Galef, 1989), characteristics which could contribute to the more extended licking that males receive in both these species.

Intermingled with the set of water and salt resource exchange relationships is another set of relationships involving chemosignals. Dams are attracted to odors produced by pups, and pup odors stimulate both whole-body and anogenital licking (Moore, 1985c). Some odors are produced by both males and females and are not affected by perinatal testosterone. Others apparently require male-typical levels of testosterone (Moore, 1982; Power & Moore, 1986). Maternal licking, particularly of the perineum, is affected in an additive way by these odors. Therefore, both male and female pups receive licking elicited by their odors, but males receive more of it.

Pups are not passive recipients of maternal licking, but contribute actively to the behavioral interaction. Both they and their dams make postural adjustments that facilitate the initiation and maintenance of the behavior or that lead to its termination. One response to perineal licking shown by both male and female pups is leg extension, in which the body is held rigidly with hind legs extended and tail deviated. The body is typically also supine, which has the effect of exposing the perineum and preventing urine from spilling into the nest before it can be ingested by the dam. It may be significant that male pups assume this posture more readily than females (Moore & Chadwick-Dias, 1986).

Other aspects of development while in the nest also facilitate learning about the stimulus characteristics of conspecifics, which may be relevant for later mate choice (D'Udine & Alleva, 1983). Brush stimulation of the skin of pups, which mimics some aspects of maternal licking, can serve as a reinforcer for classical conditioning. Neutral or negative odors paired with brush stimulation become attractive to pups, who will seek contact with the odor (Coopersmith & Leon, 1988; Pedersen, Williams, & Blass, 1982). The possibility that male pups develop an attraction to adult female rat odor as a result of its frequent pairing during infancy with stimulation provided by the dam is of particular relevance for sexual behavior, and this idea is supported by a study in which male rats showed enhanced sexual behavior toward partners bearing the same artificial odor that had been applied to their mothers (Fillion & Blass, 1986).

At the same time these events occur in the behavioral realm, the central nervous system is undergoing rapid differentiation. The development of the hypothalamus, in particular, is affected by the testosterone present in males. It is possible that stimulation arising from mother–infant interactions plays a role in hypothalamic differentiation. Functional afferent connections to the hypothalamus are present in newborn rats (Almli & Fisher, 1985), providing a mechanism for the delivery of maternal stimulation to relevant brain regions. Furthermore, pharmacological studies in which afferent input to the hypothalamus has been blocked lend strong support to the idea that stimulation of some kind is essential to the neuronal changes that originate with perinatal testosterone (Beyer & Feder, 1987). It remains for future work to identify the neurophysiological consequences of specific kinds of stimulation encountered by infant rats.

Research of the kind described here begins to identify some of the ways in which external stimulation can contribute to behavioral organization at levels close to that of neural structure. Further, it is possible to see how a small difference in one or more components (including external stimulation) of the complex causal webs to which developing animals are exposed can eventually lead to different patterns of behavioral organization. What appears in overt behavior as qualitative differences between the sexes (e.g., lack of an ejaculatory pattern in female rats) or among related species (e.g., differences in the typical number of ejaculations) may well hinge on very small differences at the level of the underlying mechanism which can be conceptualized in quantitative terms (Moore, 1985a; Sachs & Dewsbury, 1978). For example, the failure of female rats to perform the complete ejaculatory pattern unless tested with unusually high doses of hormone or unusually intense stimulation can be interpreted as a sex difference in threshold (Emery & Sachs, 1975; Krieger & Barfield, 1976).

It is intriguing to speculate that some species differences in sexual behavior may have arisen during evolution through a simple change in ontogenetic mechanism. Attention to developmental processes may help to explain the ability of a species to respond rapidly to changes in selective pressure by an apparently radical change in behavioral organization. Many heterogeneous elements are interconnected in ontogenetic webs, so it is entirely possible that a change in sexual behavior may result from a change in any one of these elements. Maternal stimulation is one of these elements, and should not be ignored. Differential stimulation of males may be widespread in rodents. It has been reported in laboratory mice (Alleva, Caprioli, & Lavioli, 1989) and Mongolian gerbils (Clark, Bone, & Galef, 1989) as well as in rats. The evolution of a quantitative change in maternal stimulation of males, which could be achieved by a number of different mechanisms in rodents, might underlie some differences in the copulatory patterns of these species.

SUMMARY

The sexual behavior typical of vertebrates was examined from a comparative developmental point of view. Diversity and general themes were found in both distantly and closely related vertebrates and were related to ecological, life history, phylogenetic, and organismic factors. Diversity within a species is found in the two sex classes, in reproductive and nonreproductive life stages, and in alternative patterns of mating within a sex class. Differences that arise during development may be permanent, or individuals may retain the plasticity to change from one pattern of organization to another. In some species, more than one sexual pattern is developed simultaneously.

It was argued that behavioral differences and similarities should be addressed by focusing on underlying behavioral organization, which was described using three metaphors: levels, cascades, and webs. It was also argued that developmental analyses using these ideas could help reveal mechanisms by which closely related species evolve differences in behavior in response to ecological changes.

The metaphor of levels was used to describe species differences in the complexity of behavioral organization. Higher levels of organization permit behavioral flexibility without requiring reorganization at the structural level. One important factor that contributes to a high level of behavioral complexity is length of development; another is parental care. Thus, sexual behavior is likely to be subsumed within a larger set of social skills in mammals with a long period of dependency.

Because effects can multiply and ramify, a single factor or event can lead to a cascade of developmental influences. The cascading consequences for Norway rats of testosterone secreted during early life were described. This cascade includes the social environment, because testosterone-dependent odors produced by the young male elicit a specific pattern of maternal licking which, in turn, contributes to the development of masculine sexual behavior.

Despite the importance of some key factors, behavioral organization at any point in development is shaped by a web of elements and events, some internal and some external to the organism. The metaphor of web was chosen because it underscores the interconnection of these heterogeneous factors. Thus, when the cascading effects of testosterone on masculine sexual development are put in context, they are found to accentuate developmental events that have multiple supports. For example, licking of pups is promoted by the dam's salt and water appetite and by pup behavior as well as by testosterone-dependent odors. Effects like these help to explain why female mammals also develop masculine sexual behavior.

CHAPTER 13

LITTERMATE INFLUENCES ON BEHAVIORAL AND PHYSIOLOGICAL DEVELOPMENT IN SPINY MICE

Richard H. Porter

The early social environment of young mammals includes their mother, and, in many species, other classes of close kin: namely, littermates, older siblings, and possibly their father. Mother–infant interactions and maternal influences on ontogeny have long been favorite topics of study by animal behaviorists. Moreover, numerous accounts of male parental care (paternal investment) have been reported (reviewed by Dewsbury, 1985b; Elwood, 1983; Kleiman & Malcolm, 1981). In contrast, until recently, the contributions of siblings to the physical and behavioral development of mammalian young have received relatively little attention (e.g., Bekoff, 1981; West & King, 1987).

This neglect of sibling influences is particularly curious when one considers the natural history of species giving birth to litters containing more than one offspring. On inspecting a newly born litter of rodents or carnivores, for example, one is likely to find the young huddled together in a single clump (e.g., Alberts, 1978; Rheingold, 1963). Even if passive, such physical contact may have important ontogenetic consequences—for example, by reducing heat loss before effective endothermy is achieved. Close physical proximity and frequent interactions among littermates may continue until weaning, or even beyond in some species (e.g., McLean, 1982; Sherman, 1981). From birth through weaning, young mammals may actually have more contact with their littermates than with their mother. In extreme instances, as in tree shrews and rabbits, the mother is routinely absent from the nest for long intervals, and returns only for brief nursing bouts (Denenberg, Zarrow, & Ross, 1969; Eisenberg, 1981; Martin, 1974). Therefore, based upon sheer duration of social encounters and physical contact, we might expect littermates to exert a unique influence on one another.

Furthermore, because of the physical and behavioral disparities between adults and young, interactions between littermates, as well as their ultimate effects on each other's development, may be qualitatively different from parental influences. Littermates may engage in interactions not observed among parents and offspring, such as competition over food and various aspects of social play (e.g., Bekoff, 1981; Mendl, 1988b). Early reciprocal littermate interactions could therefore afford singular opportunities for learning and practicing adaptive behavioral patterns to be displayed during subsequent encounters with agemates. This same observation would also apply to potential broodmate effects among avian nestlings that remain together for long portions of the daylight hours while their parents forage for food. Within other taxonomic groups that do not exhibit posthatching or postpartum parental care, early social encounters may be restricted primarily or solely to full (and possibly half) siblings. Likely examples of the latter may include some species of toads and frogs whose larvae (tadpoles) form aggregations coinciding with low dispersal from the oviposition site, or identifiable sibling schools in laboratory and field experiments (Blaustein, Bekoff, & Daniels, 1987; Waldman, 1982).

An additional rationale for studying interactions among full siblings is provided by the close genetic relationship between members of this kin class. On average, mammalian full siblings share 50 percent of their alleles as a function of direct descent from the same parents (the corresponding value for half siblings is 25 percent). The *mean* coefficient of relationship (r) for full siblings equals the *exact* value for parents and offspring ($r = .50$ in both cases) (Barash, Holmes, & Greene, 1978). Because of their high degree of relatedness, full siblings are a useful model for investigating nepotism, the evolution of social behavior, and the theory of kin selection. Littermate siblings are salient features of a young animal's environment that are themselves partial manifestations of the latter individual's own genotype (at least of the alleles that they share).

The primary aim of this chapter is to present an overview of a series of studies concerning littermate influences on the development of Egyptian spiny mice (*Acomys cahirinus*). These experiments grew out of a long-term project focusing on the ontogeny of sibling recognition and social preferences in A. *cahirinus* (reviewed in Porter, 1986, 1987, 1988, and see below). Aside from summarizing the data from the research program, it is hoped that this chapter will illustrate various experimental manipulations that allow one to gain insights into sibling/littermate influences on physiological and behavioral ontogeny.

PUPS RAISED WITH VERSUS WITHOUT LITTERMATES

One strategy for assessing littermate effects on development is to compare animals raised in litters of various sizes (see Mendl, 1988a, for a recent review). In an early study by Seitz (1954), newborn rats were reared in litters containing either 6 or 12 pups each. The mean body weight of the small-litter pups was significantly greater than that of the pups from the large litters by 3 weeks of age, and this weight disparity continued well beyond sexual maturity. Rats from the large litters also differed from rats from the small litters on a number of behavioral measures, including food hoarding, feeding competition, and exploration of a novel environment. Similar retarded weight gains, as well as deficits in learning a visual discrimination task, were observed in rats that had been raised in experimentally created litters of 18–22 pups (Fleischer & Turkewitz, 1979).

Optimal litter sizes have been proposed for several species of rodents. Gerbil pups raised in groups of three agemates displayed more rapid behavioral and physical development than did conspecifics from litters of one or five (Elwood & Broom, 1978). Fertility of *Peromyscus leucopus* was greatest for individuals from four-pup litters and declined linearly with increasing deviations from that intermediate value (Leamy, 1981). When rat litters were abruptly culled to a single pup before Day 10 postpartum, the remaining pup usually died (Leigh & Hofer, 1973). A likely explanation for this result is that single pups do not provide sufficient stimulation to maintain maternal milk production. More gradual reduction in litter size over several days resulted in reduced mortality among remaining 7-day-old singletons (Hofer & Shair, 1987). Overt maternal behavior (in laboratory rats and mice) likewise varies according to number of pups in the litter, and such mother–infant interactions may mediate at least partially the relationship between litter size and offspring development (Grota, 1973; Priestnall, 1972). The inverse relationship between gestation length and litter size observed in rats, gerbils, and deer mice (Dewsbury, 1985c; Norris & Adams, 1979), might also contribute to the ontogenetic differences in pups from large versus small litters.

The experiments in my laboratory were designed to elucidate the effects of rearing in the presence versus the absence of littermates on the development of social responsiveness in *Acomys cahirinus*. This muroid rodent is indigenous to arid regions of the Near East, and gives birth to small litters of precocial offspring following a gestation period of 38–39 days. In my breeding colony, litter sizes range from one to six pups, with a median of two or three pups. Unlike the pups of altricial rodents, such as rats, single *A. cahirinus* pups evince no problems in physical growth or rate of survival. Family members (i.e., mated adult male and female, suckling offspring, and weanlings from previous litters) housed together in laboratory enclosures frequently interact with one another (Porter, Cavallaro, & Moore, 1980; Porter, Moore, & White, 1981). There is little information concerning the social organization and behavior of free-living spiny mice.

Huddling by unfamiliar agemates

Huddling is an unambiguous indicant of social attraction in rodents. With the approach of weaning, A. *cahirinus* pups become increasingly discriminating in their choice of huddling partners, preferring familiar littermates over unfamiliar agemates (Porter & Wyrick, 1979). Although pairs of unfamiliar pups may still huddle if their littermates are not present, such dyadic pairings follow an age-related decline similar to that of suckling (Porter, Tepper, Baumeister, Cernoch, & Matochik, 1982). A series of experiments was conducted to determine whether this same age-dependent measure of social responsiveness varies according to the rearing history of the subjects (Porter et al., 1982).

We tested A. *cahirinus* pups that had been raised in two treatment conditions: *singly reared* pups, which had no experience with agemates prior to testing; and *litter-reared* pups, which had been raised in litters of two to four siblings. All of the subject pups were born in the laboratory breeding colony and were housed in individual home cages with both parents. At the beginning of the test session, two age-matched, unfamiliar pups from the same rearing condition were removed from their respective home cages and placed together in an observation terrarium. Each pair of pups was then observed repeatedly for 2 consecutive days, and the frequencies of dyadic huddling were recorded. Eight pairs of singly reared and eight pairs of litter-reared pups were observed in this manner on Days 14–15 postpartum, and two additional groups of eight pairs each were tested over Days 16–17. The results are summarized in Table 1. The most interesting result in the present context is the difference in overall huddling by litter-reared as opposed to

TABLE 1. Mean Huddling Frequencies
for Pairs of Unfamiliar Unrelated Pups

| | Age at testing[a] | | |
Rearing condition	14–15 days	16–17 days	Total over both age groups
With littermates			
M	43.9	31.8	37.8
SD	31.1	30.7	23.6
Singly reared			
M	17.0	0.3	8.6
SD	21.1	0.7	16.8

Note. Adapted from Porter, Tepper, Baumeister, Cernoch, & Matochik, 1982.
[a]N = 32 pairs (8 pairs per age group for each condition).

singly reared animals. Over the 2-day test periods, unfamiliar agemates that had been raised in litters huddled more frequently than did those reared without littermates.

Feeding competition

The manner in which an animal responds to others of its species can have profound implications for its immediate well-being and ultimate reproductive success. For example, an effective mating sequence involves locating a suitable partner, participating in species-typical courtship behavior, and copulating. Likewise, acquisition of necessary resources may depend upon the outcome of competitive interactions with conspecifics. We hypothesized that A. cahirinus weanlings that had been reared with littermates might have an advantage over single pups when placed into competition with an unfamiliar agemate. Singly reared pups that have had no experience with others of their age should find such an encounter completely unfamiliar, and might also be less capable of decoding relevant social signals (Mendl, 1988a; Porter et al., 1982). To test the above hypothesis, A. cahirinus weanlings were deprived of food for a 24-hour period. Immediately afterwards, these hungry animals were tested in pairs composed of one animal reared in a litter of two to four pups and one singly reared animal, both unfamiliar with each other. Each pair was placed in an observation cage with a food cup situated on the center of the floor. To obtain food, it was necessary for an animal to perch on the top of the cup and gnaw on the food pellets contained inside. A perforated metal lid prevented intact pellets from being removed from the cup while still allowing animals to feed. The dimensions of the cup were such that two animals could feed simultaneously; however, if they did so, they would be forced into physical contact with one another.

Test pairs were observed for 20 minutes, and the following measures recorded for each animal: latency until climbing onto the food cup, and feeding duration (total time spent perched on the cup). As Table 2 shows, litter-reared weanlings were more successful than singly reared animals in competing for access to a restricted food supply. Across the 10 pairs of weanlings tested in this manner, the animals reared in litters displayed significantly shorter latencies until mounting the food cup, and remained perched on the cup for longer periods of time, than did those raised without littermates.

Results from the huddling and food competition tests suggest that A. cahirinus weanlings that have been raised in the presence of littermates are more socially competent than conspecifics reared without agemates. Pups growing up with littermates experience an interacting complex of sibling and maternal stimulation that differs from the social stimulation provided solely by the mother of a single pup. Animals raised in litters are exposed continuously to cues

TABLE 2. Results of Feeding Competition Tests for Unfamiliar Animals Tested in Pairs

	Rearing Condition[a]	
	Without littermates	With littermates
Feeding duration (s)		
M	186.7	292.5
SD	137.2	234.0
Mean latency until climbing onto food cup (s)		
M	700.3	492.9
SD	336.1	392.5

Note. Adapted from Porter, Tepper, Baumeister, Cernoch, & Matochik, 1982.
[a]N = 10 pairs (each comprised of 1 singly reared and 1 litter-reared weanling).

emanating from their littermates, and engage in frequent overt interactions with them, such as huddling and agonistic and competitive encounters. Littermates may thereby exert a direct influence on one another's behavioral and physiological development. Furthermore, as mentioned above, multiple-pup litters may elicit patterns of maternal behavior that differ from those exhibited by mothers of single offspring. Differential maternal treatment is likely to interact with the direct effects of littermates in mediating differences in social behavior between pups reared with versus without littermates.

LITTERMATE EFFECTS VARY ACCORDING TO THE INDIVIDUAL CHARACTERISTICS OF ANIMALS

There is no basis for assuming that litters are homogenous groups whose individual members exert identical influences on one another's development. Rather, behavioral and physiological ontogeny may vary according to the characteristics of others with which an animal is raised. Susceptibility to the qualities of one's littermates may actually begin prenatally. For example, some postnatal attributes of female mice, rats, and gerbils are correlated with the sex of the fetuses contiguous to them in the uterus. Female mice that are located between two male fetuses are exposed to high levels of testosterone (vom Saal & Bronson, 1980), and therefore develop masculinized behavioral and physiological traits (Gandelman, vom Saal, & Reinisch, 1977; Hauser & Gandelman, 1983). In rats, female fetuses are masculinized by neighboring males located caudally in the same uterine horn (Meisel & Ward, 1981). Mongolian gerbil females that were adjacent to one or two males in utero subsequently exhibited delayed sexual maturation (vaginal opening) compared with females lacking such uterine proximity to male fetuses (Clark & Galef, 1988).

Effects of atypical littermates

To assess the relationship between postnatal littermate characteristics and behavioral development, A. *cahirinus* pups were raised with foster pups that differed qualitatively from their biological littermates.

Litters containing pups of different ages. In the first experiment, pups differing in age by 15 days were housed together with the same lactating female to determine whether experience with an older or younger littermate would have any observable influence on social behavior (Porter, Cernoch, & Matochik, 1983). One-day-old A. *cahirinus* pups were individually fostered onto females that had a single 16-day-old pup of their own. These three-animal groups were routinely observed until Day 20 postpartum for the younger foster pup. Females with their own two offspring served as unmanipulated controls, and an additional control group was composed of females whose offspring were removed on day 17 postpartum and replaced with two 1-day-old neonates. This latter condition controlled for fostering per se and for pups being reared by a female whose postpartum interval differed from the age of the pups she was nursing.

Comparisons of agemates across the three conditions on various categories of social interactions indicate that the younger foster pups were more affected than the older pups by the age of the littermate with which they were raised. The observed frequencies of mother–infant interactions for the pups raised with an older littermate differed from those of the pups raised with agemates. Foster pups housed with older littermates suckled less frequently and huddled more often with the adult female alone than did agemates in the control conditions, and were also more frequently alone (physically separate from both the mother and the older littermate).

Litters containing pups of two different species. The fostering of rodent pups onto heterospecific mothers is a common experimental manipulation for studying maternal influences on development (e.g., Bols & Wong, 1973; McCarty & Southwick, 1977; McDonald & Forslund, 1978; Quadagno & Banks, 1970). In a variation of this procedure, we investigated the effects of heterospecific and conspecific "littermates" on the behavior of A. *cahirinus* and *Mus musculus* pups, all of which were reared by A. *cahirinus* females (Porter, Cernoch, & Matochik, 1983).

In the second experiment, we observed pups raised in three treatment conditions that varied according to the composition of "littermate" pairs: *Mus/Acomys* litters, in which individual *Mus* pups were fostered, on Day 10 postpartum, onto *Acomys* mothers whose own litters had been reduced to a single pup; *Mus/Mus* litters, in which the biological offspring of *Acomys* mothers were replaced with two *Mus* pups of the same age on Day 10 postpartum; and *Acomys/Acomys* litters, in which *Acomys* mothers reared their own litters of two biological offspring each. Each group of three animals remained together throughout the observational study.

Observations of mother–infant interactions were conducted for all three conditions over Days 10–28 postpartum. The species of the littermate had markedly different influences on the behavior of *Mus* and of *Acomys* pups. *Mus* pups housed with a conspecific agemate maintained frequent physical contact with that littermate. *Mus* pups raised with an *Acomys* agemate, however, displayed reduced littermate contact, but increased bodily contact with the foster mother (relative to pups in the *Mus/Mus* condition), including higher rates of suckling. *Acomys* pups, in contrast, displayed similar frequencies of suckling and physical contact with mother and littermates across the *Acomys/Acomys* and *Mus/Acomys* conditions. Thus, *Acomys* pups showed no evidence of being differentially affected by the presence of a *Mus* versus *Acomys* littermate, at least on the measures of social interactions recorded in this study.

The observed species differences in susceptibility to heterospecific littermate influences may be related to the marked disparity in the degree of physical development of *Mus* and *Acomys* pups during the perinatal period. At the age when the foster-pup treatment began (Day 10 postpartum), precocial *Acomys* pups are ingesting solid food, and their sensory modalities have all been functional since the day of birth. Compared with *Acomys* neonates, altricial *Mus* pups are physically smaller as well as motorically and perceptually delayed; on Day 10, their visual and auditory systems are just beginning to become functional, and their locomotor capabilities are limited (Gottlieb, 1971). The period of optimal sensitivity to littermate effects might vary concomitantly with the rate of physiological and behavioral development in these two species.

The behavioral sequelae associated with the presence of an older or heterospecific pup could arise either from its direct influence on its littermate and mother, or from its failure to provide the same stimulus properties as a conspecific agemate. Accordingly, the absence of a conspecific littermate might be as important as, or even more important than, the presence of an atypical littermate per se in mediating the observed results. Regardless of the underlying mechanisms, it is evident from the above two experiments that littermate characteristics are correlated with interactions among the pups themselves as well as with the frequency of interactions of the pups with other social partners (i.e., their mothers).

Influence of normally developing young on impaired littermates

As discussed above, rodent pups that appear healthy and otherwise normal at birth may nonetheless benefit from being reared with littermates. The simultaneous presence of several young is necessary to sustain weight gain and survival in altricial rats (Leigh & Hofer, 1973). Although single (precocial) A. *cahirinus* neonates have high survival rates, they manifest deficient social behavior at weaning. Rearing in the presence of intact littermates may likewise enhance the development of pups suffering marked perceptual deficits. *Mus* pups whose olfactory bulbs were ablated 24 hours after birth failed to suckle unless their unoperated control littermates were already feeding (Cooper & Cowley, 1976). Because bulbectomized (anosmic) pups provide the mother with inadequate suckling stimulation, intact littermates may also be necessary for the maintenance of lactation.

Physical development in ZnSO₄-treated pups. The ameliorating influence of normally developing littermates on pups with olfactory deficits was investigated further using A. *cahirinus* as the subject species (Porter, Sentell, & Makin, 1987). It was hoped that precocial *Acomys* pups would be more likely to survive early experimentally induced olfactory impairment than altricial rodent pups are. Intranasal irrigation with zinc sulfate ($ZnSO_4$) solution, which is a reliable means of disrupting olfactory sensitivity in rodents (Alberts, 1974), was the treatment used in this experiment. On Day 2 postpartum, litters containing three pups each were randomly assigned to two treatment conditions: (1) a *single* pup in each litter of three was treated with $ZnSO_4$, then immediately returned to its home cage containing its two control littermates and both parents; or (2) all three pups in each litter were treated with $ZnSO_4$ and were then returned to their home cage.

According to the original design of this experiment, pups in both conditions were to be weighed at 2-day intervals through Day 26. All pups were closely monitored, and any that were wounded, appeared ill or emaciated, or displayed poor motor coordination were immediately sacrificed. The pups in the litters in which all three neonates were treated with $ZnSO_4$ had a very high mortality rate, with 50 percent failing to survive to Day 4. As a result of this excessive mortality rate, the condition was not run to completion, but was discontinued after 10 litters. On Day 22, only 2 of the original 10 litters were intact (with all three pups alive and appearing healthy). A significantly greater proportion of the litters in which only one pup was treated with $ZnSO_4$ survived intact through Day 22 (i.e., 12 of 20 litters). These data suggest that litters containing intact pups may afford a more adequate source of maternal nutrition for the impaired pups, and may also provide visual and tactile guides facilitating effective location of the mother's nipple by the latter pups.

Activity in a novel environment. Heightened locomotor activity is a measurable consequence of anosmia in laboratory mice and rats (Hofer, 1976; Raskin, 1982). Similarly, 2-day-old pairs of A. *cahirinus* littermates treated intranasally with $ZnSO_4$ evince greater ambulation scores when removed from their home cage and placed into a novel environment than do pairs of untreated control littermates (Porter, Sentell, & Makin, 1987). This difference between $ZnSO_4$-treated and control pups is attenuated when a pair of littermates, one treated with $ZnSO_4$ and one untreated, are tested together—there is no reliable difference between their ambulation scores. Thus, by the third day after birth, A. *cahirinus* pups are responsive to their littermates and coordinate their own behavior to some extent according to that of other members of their litter.

Location of food by hungry weanlings. Throughout their lives, rodents rely greatly on their sense of smell for locating food. It is therefore not surprising that hungry A. *cahirinus* weanlings treated with $ZnSO_4$ have difficulty discovering food pellets hidden from view (Porter, Matochik, & Makin, 1986; Porter, Wyrick, & Pankey, 1978). Might weanlings with olfactory deficits be more likely to find limited food sources when in the presence of unimpaired littermates? We tested 24 experimental pairs of littermates in two conditions: in 8 of the experimental pairs, both littermate siblings were treated intranasally with $ZnSO_4$; the remaining 16 pairs consisted of one $ZnSO_4$-treated weanling and one untreated control animal. The animals were deprived of food for 24 hours, then tested together in a series of interconnected cages. One of these cages contained food pellets buried under 4 centimeters of bedding material.

During the 10-minute test session, 7 of the 16 $ZnSO_4$-treated pups tested with an untreated control littermate discovered food pellets and began to eat. In each of these instances, the $ZnSO_4$-treated sibling only succeeded in finding a food pellet after the untreated littermate had already uncovered it. *Buried* food pellets were never located by the $ZnSO_4$-treated weanlings in this condition. Of the 16 weanlings tested in homogeneous $ZnSO_4$-treated pairs, only one animal located and chewed on a food pellet. Overall, a significantly greater proportion of $ZnSO_4$-treated pups were observed eating when paired with an untreated control littermate than when paired with a second $ZnSO_4$-treated sibling. The pups with olfactory deficits capitalized on their intact littermates' proficiency in uncovering hidden food pellets to gain access to that food supply. Perceptually impaired A. *cahirinus* pups may thereby continue to benefit from interacting with intact littermates even after weaning.

LITTERMATE RECOGNITION AND NEPOTISM

Social interactions among animals that grow up together (most commonly littermate siblings) often differ noticeably from those involving other classes of conspecific agemates. In general, familiar littermates interact more amicably than do unfamiliar nonkin—they engage in more frequent huddling and have fewer agonistic encounters (for a recent review see Blaustein, Bekoff, & Daniels, 1987). By treating close kin differently than nonkin, an animal may increase the likelihood of survival and reproduction of its relatives and thereby enhance its own inclusive fitness. Nepotism thus provides a mechanism other than the production of offspring per se for increasing the representation of one's alleles in future generations.

Ground squirrel alarm calling in the presence of siblings is a dramatic example of presumed nepotistic behavior (Davis, 1984; Schwagmeyer, 1980; Sherman, 1977). A correlation between mate choice and kinship has also been documented in a variety of rodents (e.g., Agren, 1984; Dewsbury, 1988b; D'Udine & Alleva, 1983; McGuire & Getz, 1981); littermates engage in less reproductive activity with one another than unfamiliar unrelated agemates do. In this manner, animals may avoid the deleterious consequences of inbreeding. Whether these same species also avoid extreme outbreeding, and thereby display optimal choice of mates of intermediate relatedness (e.g., Bateson, 1983), has yet to be determined.

The theoretical importance of nepotism in the evolution of social behavior has served as the impetus for a corollary interest in kin recognition. As originally suggested by Hamilton (1964), effective nepotism would be facilitated by an ability to discriminate between kin and nonkin. Laboratory and field investigations have demonstrated complex kin recognition capabilities in a host of vertebrates as well as in invertebrates (for recent reviews see Fletcher & Michener, 1987; Hepper, 1986; Porter, 1987; Sherman & Holmes, 1985; Waldman, 1987).

A straightforward technique for testing for littermate discrimination is to place several pups from each of two or more litters together and record the ensuing social interactions. When A. cahirinus sibling pairs from two different litters are removed from their respective home cages and housed together, each pair of siblings typically forms a discrete dyadic huddle (Porter, Wyrick, & Pankey, 1978). Over observation sessions lasting from 5 to 8 days, familiar siblings tend to pair with one another (maintain physical contact), but there are very few instances of pairings by unfamiliar unrelated agemates. Based upon such preferential behavioral interactions, one can infer that littermates recognize one another (i.e., discriminate between littermates and other agemates not previously encountered).

In subsequent studies, we sought to elucidate the phenotypic cues (signatures) and ontogenetic mechanisms underlying littermate recognition in A. cahirinus.

By exchanging pups between two litters, so that unrelated young are raised together, one can assess the relative importance of familiarity versus genetic relatedness in the development of social recognition. Results of such cross-fostering experiments consistently indicate that littermate recognition develops through a process of exposure and familiarization; animals respond discriminatively to those with which they have been raised, regardless of whether they are biological siblings or unrelated agemates (Porter, Tepper, & White, 1981).

Aside from becoming acquainted with individual littermates through direct exposure, animals may also discriminate others who bear a resemblance to familiar conspecifics. Thus, individuals may discern a resemblance between a familiar animal and that same animal's (unfamiliar) full sibling (Porter, 1988; Porter, Matochik, & Makin, 1983), and pups suckling from the same female may detect the common maternal label that they each carry (Porter, Tepper, & White, 1981). This form of recognition can be characterized as resulting from *indirect* familiarization, since the individuals being discriminated have not themselves been previously encountered (Porter, 1988).

To date, there is no evidence that sensory modalities other than olfaction are involved in A. *cahirinus* littermate recognition. Animals rendered anosmic through $ZnSO_4$ infusion show no signs of recognizing their full siblings with which they were reared prior to the experimental treatment (Porter, Wyrick, & Pankey, 1978). Close kin, because of their genotypic similarity, appear to manifest discernibly similar odor signatures (Porter, 1988; Porter, Matochik, & Makin, 1983). Nevertheless, olfactory signatures of individual members of a kin class are not identical—intact animals can distinguish between individual full siblings (Porter, Matochik, & Makin, 1986). The fact that such intralitter discrimination is absent in anosmic animals is further evidence of the involvement of olfactory cues. Discrimination among the odors of individual full siblings presumably reflects the genetic variability within this kin class. Individually acquired environmental factors may also interact with genotype in determining an individual's odor phenotype. Even unrelated unfamiliar animals interact preferentially if fed the same unique diet differing from that of others in the test situation (Porter, 1986).

The role of experience in the development of littermate recognition does not argue against the evolutionary significance of this phenomenon. Animals that grow up together and suckle from the same female are most likely to be siblings; therefore, an ontogenetic rule of thumb whereby familiar littermates are to be treated preferentially would be functionally equivalent to discriminative sibling nepotism.

An obvious question in keeping with the primary theme of this chapter is whether A. *cahirinus* littermates gain any obvious advantages by recognizing one another. That is, aside from huddling preferentially, do littermates engage in cooperative or altruistic behavior not seen among other conspecifics? The few accounts of rodents aiding their kin (other than parental investment) include nepotistic alarm calling (Schwagmeyer, 1980; Sherman, 1977) and cooperation in agonistic encounters with conspecifics (e.g., Sherman, 1981). Research on adaptive interactions among A. *cahirinus* littermates has focused on a less conspicuous category of behavior: sharing of limited food resources.

Location of limited food sources

Rodents typically engage in an initial period of exploratory behavior when placed in a novel environment. As a consequence of this behavior, animals become familiar with the locations and salient features of resources in their surroundings. For A. *cahirinus* weanlings, the presence of a littermate has a facilitating effect on exploration and location of necessary resources (Porter, Moore, & White, 1981).

Pairs of food-deprived weanlings were placed into a starting cage connected to a similar enclosure by a Plexiglas tunnel. Food was available only from a container situated in the center of the second cage. The tunnel between the starting and food cages was wide enough to allow animals to move back and forth, but too narrow for one animal to pass the other. The behavior of littermate pairs and the behavior of pairs containing two unfamiliar agemates was recorded during 20-minute test sessions.

In comparison to the pairs of unfamiliar weanlings, littermate sibling pairs were more efficient and more simultaneously active in exploring an environment with limited food availability (see Table 3). Animals in the sibling pairs spent more *total* time in the food cage and were both in that cage *together* for longer periods than the nonsibling pairs. In the unfamiliar pairs, one animal tended to dominate the food cage, while the second animal remained outside as if intimidated by its conspecific. There was less disparity between the members of littermate pairs in the time they spent inside the food cage.

Cooperative feeding

The previous study was concerned with locating and thereby gaining potential access to food, rather than food sharing per se. An additional experiment tested the prediction that hungry littermates should feed more cooperatively than unfamiliar weanlings (Porter, Moore, & White, 1981). Twelve pairs of weanling littermates (familiar full siblings) and 12 pairs of unfamiliar nonsiblings were deprived of food for 24 hours. Then a single food cup was introduced into each observation terrarium, and the two animals were observed for 20 minutes. As in the feeding competition experiments described above, the animals could eat only by perching on top of the food cup and gnawing on pellets through a perforated metal lid. Because of difficulties in accurately recording ingestion of food, the primary dependent variable was the amount of time that each animal spent perched on the food cup ("feeding duration").

TABLE 3. Mean Time Spent in Food Cage by Littermate and Unfamiliar Agemate Pairs

Group[a]	Total time in food cage (s) (summed across both animals in a pair)	Time both animals simultaneously present in food cage (s)	Time in food cage for less active animal in each pair (s)
Littermate pairs			
M	1,018.8	180.5	340.5
SD	297.6	174.8	233.9
Unfamiliar pairs			
M	773.8	62.8	139.3
SD	279.8	69.9	167.8

Note. Adapted from Porter, Moore, & White, 1981.
[a]N = 24 pairs (12 pairs for each group).

The mean length of time that both animals in a pair were together on the food cup (*simultaneous* feeding) was significantly greater for littermate pairs than for unfamiliar weanlings (means = 198.3 and 91.0 seconds respectively). In the unfamiliar pairs, the dominant animal usually remained on the cup, and the second animal usually had a low feeding duration score: the subordinate animals had a mean feeding score of 193 seconds, contrasted with a mean of 390 seconds for the less active feeders in the littermate pairs. In 4 of the 12 unfamiliar pairs, the more active feeder responded aggressively when its cagemate approached the food cup, chasing and biting at the subordinate animal. Agonistic interactions of this sort were never observed in any of the littermate pairs.

Food sharing, or cooperative feeding, as observed in this study, is a relatively passive form of altruism. Nepotism, in this context, involves the lack of or inhibition of aggression directed towards kin, or the failure to impede kin's access to a limited food supply. Such behavior could be of critical importance for the continued survival of the interacting individuals.

CONCLUSIONS

It is clear from the experiments reviewed in this chapter that littermates are a significant feature of the early environment of A. *cahirinus*. From the perinatal period through weaning, pup development reflects the simple presence or absence of littermates as well as the individual characteristics of those with which an animal is reared. At the present time, however, our understanding of sibling influences in A. *cahirinus* (and other species) is extremely limited. The initial research has identified specific littermate influences, but many questions remain:

for example, what are the mediating links between littermate presence or characteristics and observable behavioral and physiological sequelae? As discussed previously, littermates may have a direct effect on one another (for example, they may serve as a guide to a food source or help to maintain body temperature by huddling), and may also have an impact on the mother's physiological processes and behavior, which in turn could have additional implications for continued pup development.

The range of behavioral and physiological consequences of differing littermate experiences needs to be investigated further. One would expect that littermate influences would vary across species and according to ecological variables within a species. There may also be age-dependent periods of optimal susceptibility to littermate-produced stimulation. While this chapter has emphasized positive or beneficial littermate influences, interactions among littermates may not always be amicable. When ecological conditions demand it, siblings may compete for limited resources and even kill one another. However, the best-documented accounts of siblicide have been reported for avian rather than mammalian species (reviewed by Mock, 1984). Agonistic behavior among littermate siblings does not necessarily argue against the theories of kin selection and inclusive fitness, since an individual carries more of its own genes than it shares with any full sibling (excluding monozygotic twins, triplets, etc.). Therefore, if forced to choose between oneself or a full sibling, self-interest at the expense of one's sibling is the better strategy from a strictly genetic perspective.

Considerable research efforts will be required to begin to unravel the subtleties and complexities of littermate effects on development. In the meantime, investigators working with litter-producing species should consider the likelihood of littermate influences when designing and interpreting studies, and keep in mind that the litter provides a dynamic, interactive social environment that is a unique reflection of the number and qualitative characteristics of its constituent members.

SUMMARY

Littermate influences on the development of precocial *Acomys cahirinus* pups were reviewed. Pups that had been raised with littermates appear more competent in social interactions than do singly reared pups. Littermate effects are not of an all-or-none nature, however. Specific sequelae of being reared with other young are correlated with the individual characteristics of those animals. Pups evince observable differences in behavior as a function of the age and species of their littermates. The presence of normally developing conspecific agemates facilitates the physical growth of pups suffering olfactory deficits and enables them to adapt more efficiently to a novel environment than pups in entirely anosmic litters.

Littermates show discrimination in their interactions with one another, including preferential huddling and nepotistic sharing of limited food resources. Recognition of littermates by A. *cahirinus* pups develops through exposure and familiarization with olfactory phenotypes.

Pups growing up with littermates are exposed to a different constellation of stimuli and experiences than are pups raised singly. Littermates may exert a direct effect on one another, and maternal responsiveness (behavioral as well as physiological) may also vary with the number or qualities of the offspring the mother rears.

PART IV

Communication and Social Behavior

As has been hinted at throughout this book, animals live in organized societies where the communicative signals used by each individual in furtherance of its own survival and reproductive success also serve to bind the society together. What has been ground thus far becomes figure in this section. The first three chapters deal with the development of communication, and thus blend nicely with the concluding chapters of the previous section. The final two chapters are concerned with communication and social behavior in adults.

The topic of the first two chapters is bird song, a line of inquiry that has achieved major significance in the study of animal behavior in recent years. King and West's research (Chapter 14) concerns cowbirds, a species that practices brood parasitism—females lay eggs in the nests of other species, and the young are thus raised by members of other species. This situation presents unusual challenges for the development of species-typical behavior such as song. Significant advances are being made in the study of bird song, and our understanding of the underlying processes is growing rapidly. Earlier research was focused on imitation and mediation via the auditory pathways. The significant early insights provided the foundation on which a more solid understanding is being constructed.

By using videotape analysis of social interactions as juvenile males learned songs, King and West discovered a subtle female behavior that they term *wing stroking* . Females give the wing stroke display only in response to certain songs. Males observe females and alter their singing patterns in ways that increase the number of wing strokes. Thus, song learning is seen as a very social process, in which females affect male song learning via the visual input they provide. Males are thus perfecting their songs during interactions with conspecifics even though they grow up in a heterospecific nest.

King and West took the study of cowbird song "on the road" and studied a variety of populations in different geographic regions ("microphyletic expeditions"). The diversity they observed was interesting in and of itself, and also affected subsequent research. Individual differences within populations were seen in a new light. King and West summarize a useful, three-stage procedure for studies of intraspecific variation: preparation of communication protocols, studying inherited niches, and calibrating ecological time. Their comments on individual and ecological time in humans and cowbirds are especially thought-provoking.

This research provides an excellent example of the virtues of applying the comparative method within species as well as among species. As new results are obtained, the ideas providing the foundation for the approach are being modified.

Like King and West, Petrinovich (Chapter 15) is interested in the development of song in birds. However, his primary concern in Chapter 15 is to use his research on that critical form of animal communication to raise important methodological and conceptual issues.

The research focus here is another example of the ways in which good comparative psychology gets done. Petrinovich derives his problem from behavior in the field and works to create laboratory environments that allow the unfolding of the behavior in a controlled, yet biologically realistic, situation. The pivotal research entails an expansion of earlier results, which showed that young birds that learned songs from audio tapes played to them display a critical period during which exposure to the song must occur. The inference made on the basis of these findings was that the process of song learning is quite limited. These classical studies did much to stimulate interest in the study of song learning. However, the more recent results of Petrinovich and his associates suggest that, while those results are valid, they apply only to a limited range of situations. Thus, when live birds, rather than tape recordings, are used as tutors, song learning occurs at a much later age than was found in the earlier research. This, in turn, has important implications for the way song is used and modified in the field. Birds moving into areas with dialects that are different from the one in which they were raised may be more flexible in acquiring a new song than previously thought.

Petrinovich regards comparative psychologists as ideally suited to develop a synthetic understanding of animal behavior. He reasons that reductionistic thinking is ineffective in explaining phenomena at higher levels than the processes under study. Thus, although we have much to learn from physiological analyses and should attend to them, the processes affecting integrated behavioral patterns are unique and require a different level of analysis. Petrinovich develops some methodological approaches based on some early views of Egon Brunswik that may be especially appropriate in the study of animal behavior. He contends that comparative psychologists work at the interface of levels and are thus in an ideal position to recognize both ultimate and proximate causes of behavior and to develop integrative understanding.

Beecher's contribution (Chapter 16) is focused on parent–offspring recognition or, more specifically, how and when parents recognize their young. He provides an excellent example of the use of the comparative method in testing hypotheses. Beecher reasoned that colonial species, those that nest in clusters, ought to show greater recognition of young than noncolonial species. The likelihood of confusion among young is much greater where birds nest closely together than where nests are dispersed; hence selective pressures for parent–offspring recognition should be greater in colonial species. Beecher and his associates embarked on a comprehensive program combining field and laboratory work in seeking the proximate mechanisms utilized in this ultimately adaptive behavioral complex.

Beecher presents three sets of observations gathered in the field. He begins with observational data, showing that situations in which offspring recognition would be adaptive really do occur in colonial species. He then reports results of field experimentation using the cross-fostering technique, which showed that only the colonial bank swallows showed evidence of recognition, selectively rejecting foster young. Conversely, noncolonial barn and rough-winged swallows reacted indiscriminately to foster and control chicks. In a third experiment, chick calls were recorded and played to parent birds, whose responses were observed; again, the colonial swallows were more responsive.

More precise analysis of these functional behavioral differences that had been documented in the field required study in the laboratory. The structure of swallow chick calls was analyzed acoustically, and a measure of their information-carrying capacity was developed. Beecher concludes that the calls of colonial cliff and barn swallow chicks contain about 20 times more potential information than those of the noncolonial cliff swallows. When parents were tested for discrimination among calls, there was little difference among species. Adults of different species discriminated between the calls of two chicks of a given species equally well; the difference lay in the calls, not in the parents.

Beecher makes some insightful observations on the study of natural selection. In essence, he argues that comparative psychologists can predict situations in which evolutionary solutions will have developed, but cannot predict the proximate means by which the solution is effected; the latter requires empirical study. The combination of attention to both proximate and ultimate and to work in both laboratory and field, while using the comparative method, provides an excellent example of a powerful method for understanding animal behavior.

Johnston (Chapter 17) concentrates primarily on one species, Syrian golden hamsters, and one sensory modality used in communication—olfaction. He describes the unveiling of the complexity of the control of a number of responses related to communication and reproduction, beginning with some models of communication presented in classical comparative psychology and ethology. Progressively more complex relationships and interactions in the control of the systems under study are found, necessitating the recasting of thought about communication.

Johnston's work provides a fine example of the way in which concern with functional aspects of behavior can guide studies of proximate causation. In the first part of his chapter, Johnston discusses both flank-marking patterns and the vaginal-marking patterns of females. After describing each pattern, he discusses its proximate causation and function. It appears that flank marks advertise to others the presence of hamsters of a particular species, sex, and individual identity, and Johnston is able to relate the complex pattern of flank marking to a particular neurotransmitter functioning at a particular locus in the brain. Vaginal marking by females generates attraction from a distance, ultrasonic calling, elevated testosterone levels, and sexual arousal in males. Studies of the factors that affect vaginal marking suggest that the marks are directed primarily at males.

The remainder of Johnston's chapter is concerned with the olfactory control of behavior. He deals especially with flank marking, vaginal marking, ultrasonic calling, and individual discrimination. Using modern neurobiological techniques, Johnston unravels some of the olfactory influences on these behavioral patterns. Among the fruits of the chapter is a fine example of the progress that can be made with a systematic and integrated program of research on the immediate causation of behavior when guided by an understanding of the functional significance of the behavior under study for the life history of the organism.

Blanchard and Blanchard (Chapter 18) are concerned with social behavior, and in particular with aggressive interactions. The Blanchards' approach is focused on the use of biologically relevant, species-typical behavioral patterns studied in situations appropriate for their elicitation. They demonstrate the power of the experimental method used within such contexts.

The behavioral pattern on which the Blanchards focus is aggression in rats. They reveal the misunderstandings about behavior that can arise if one does not pay sufficient attention to the fine structure of the behavior of concern. In the present case, it is critical that the offensive and defensive aspects of agonistic interactions be distinguished. The key elements in aggressive interactions of rats are the attack toward and defense of the back. The various postures and movements in aggressive interactions can be seen as tactics on the part of the attacker to bite the back of the other animal and on the part of the defender to protect its back. This forces a reinterpretation of earlier work done before these distinctions were made. Thus, the much-used "pain-elicited aggression" test is seen not as eliciting aggression, but as a somewhat contaminated index of defensive behavior. Next, the Blanchards examine aggression in the contexts of the costs and benefits potentially accruing to the contestants in conflicts over limited resources. Consideration of the variables of which aggression is a function supports this economic interpretation. The results are relevant to analyses of stress and stress responses of the body and to the functioning of dominance hierarchies. The Blanchards' careful distinction between offense and defense has also proven useful in pharmacological and neural analyses.

CHAPTER 14

VARIATION IN SPECIES-TYPICAL BEHAVIOR: A CONTEMPORARY ISSUE FOR COMPARATIVE PSYCHOLOGY

Andrew P. King and Meredith J. West

Phrases such as "the human," "the animal," or "the rat" recur frequently in psychology textbooks, and are rightly regarded as innocuous scientific fictions. These phrases are needed to advance the reader to the more central concerns regarding the nature of psychological processes. But if the textbook is on comparative psychology, then phyletic liberties such as "the monkey" or "the bird" or "the carnivore" must be taken more seriously. At an organizational level, macrophyletic nomenclature causes few problems. But when it comes to the task of looking for mechanisms underlying species-typical adaptations, the use of such general terms may be misleading, leaving the impression that we know more about phylogenetic networks than is actually the case. Distinguishing primates from birds or rodents is easy, too easy, often amounting to nothing more than distinguishing the proverbial apples and oranges. Most contemporary comparative psychologists, however, face a harder task, because they tend to labor within small phyletic patches, studying the proverbial peas in a pod. By looking within narrow phyletic units, comparative psychologists hope to detect the kinds of variation that constitute the material of natural selection.

As an example of patch size, consider our own research. We work with birds, of which there are over 8,000 species, arranged into 29 orders and 155 families. If we specify the behaviors of interest to us, vocal communication by song, the possible number of species of interest is reduced to around 5,000. We possess expert knowledge of only several populations of one species within one family of one order of one class. Can we then claim to be comparative psychologists? We believe we can, and hope to demonstrate why in this chapter by explaining analyses of intraspecific differences in avian communication.

We encountered the issue of intraspecific diversity while studying the ontogeny of song in cowbirds (*Molothrus ater*). After more than a decade of research, we find that even so specific a designation as "the eastern subspecies of the brown-headed cowbird" blurs distinctions in the very processes we want to study, i.e., relationships between song production in males and song perception by females. Here we review data illustrating the nature of the differences we uncovered. We then consider three psychobiological concepts that may facilitate the process of microphyletic comparison.

COWBIRDS: PROFILES IN DIVERSITY

If female cowbirds had calling cards, they would read: "Have eggs, will travel." The female cowbird deposits her eggs in the nests of other species, delegating to them the duties of incubation and postnatal care (Friedmann, 1929). By allocating caregiving to other species, cowbirds create unusual ontogenetic challenges for their young. How will young cowbirds find other cowbirds? How will they acquire species-typical behavior? Cowbirds have long have been presumed to be ideal examples of closed genetic programs that reduce the need to acquire species-typical behavior through experience with conspecifics (Mayr, 1974). Our research confirms that naive males and females display impressive communicative competencies that should facilitate species identification. But the precise nature of the male's or female's communicative capacities depends on the population being described. To put the differences in perspective, we first review what we know about the nature of song communication in North Carolina (NC) cowbirds (*M. a. ater*), stating at the outset that we take our bearings from this population only because it is the one we know best.

First, a few remarks are required to explain some basic methods. To reveal naive male cowbirds' vocal capacities, we raise males from the egg or from fledgling age in social environments that provide no opportunities to hear conspecifics sing. We provide avian companions, such as female cowbirds or other songbirds, to prevent a confounding of social and auditory deprivation. We analyze the males' songs for structural parallels to the songs of normally reared or wild males. We also use two procedures to assess the functional properties of males' songs. The first procedure consists of playing back songs to captive male-deprived females who are in breeding condition. This technique provides a measure of song potency, i.e., the percentage of playback trials on which a song elicits a copulatory posture from a female. The procedure also contains a double play: it allows us to probe females' perceptual attributes. We can test the sensitivity of the females to the songs of different males or to different songs from the same male. If we find differences in potency, we can test which acoustic features are most crucial to female discrimination (King & West, 1983a).

The second test of the functional properties of songs comes from observing how song is used by males in captive colonies during courtship and mating. By recording vocal behavior, social relations, and courtship patterns, we can assess the "fate" of certain songs and validate the significance of females' differential responsiveness to songs in playback trials. The contextual demands of life in a resident colony force males to attend to the dual obligations of male–male competition and courtship of females, and force females to assess singers as well as songs (West & King, 1980; West, King, & Eastzer, 1981). Although colony life cannot approximate many of the demands on free-living birds, it appears to elicit many behaviors similar to those observed in the wild. Captive females lay fertile eggs and parasitize nests; males and females show nonrandom polygamous patterns of mating, with copulations occurring after a period of active courtship; and residents maintain a diurnal cycle of early morning courtship and afternoon feeding (King & West, 1984).

By using these two methods, we have found that acoustically deprived NC males require no experience with adult males in order to sing effective songs, and that NC females need no exposure to conspecifics to discriminate cowbird songs from those of other songbirds or to discriminate among cowbird subspecies (King & West, 1977, 1983a, 1983c). Moreover, even juvenile males' acoustically primitive precursors to song (often labelled "subsong" or "plastic" song) evoke species-typical copulatory responses from adult females (West & King, 1988b). However, although naive males can produce effective songs without ever having heard any male cowbird songs but their own, they proceed to alter the potent songs of their youth, with the nature of the alterations depending on their social surroundings. During interactions with other males, dominance relations are established that ultimately affect song production. Males learn that singing too effective a song can have deadly consequences, because dominant individuals may attack subordinates that sing highly potent songs (West & King, 1980). But singing cannot be avoided if reproduction is to occur. Females do not mate with a male unless he has sung to her for several days, a phenomenon also seen in wild populations (Rothstein, Yokel, & Fleischer, 1986; West et al., 1981; Yokel, 1986). Moreover, females are quite discriminating about the kinds of males they prefer, choosing the more dominant males that tend to sing the most potent songs (West, King, & Harrocks, 1983).

Social interactions with conspecifics prior to the breeding season affect more than song potency. Adult males sing two to seven song types, that is, distinctively different melodic patterns. The song types developed during a male's first spring depend largely on social feedback from the singer's audience, including females.

Although females do not sing and thus cannot serve as fellow performers, they can serve as social critics and conductors of the process of vocal composition. They do so by providing social feedback during the winter and spring, well before courtship begins.

To learn how females communicated about song, we videotaped males housed individually with females in late winter and early spring. This is the time (from mid-March through April) when wild birds from North Carolina return to their prospective breeding grounds and presumably begin to interact with the females with whom they may mate. We looked at what NC females did when NC males sang. Over 90 percent of the time, the females appeared to do nothing: an observer would not know by looking at the female that she had just heard a song sung a foot away. But the female's apparent indifference served to call attention to the times when she did react. A particular form of reaction involved a rapid extension and retraction of one or both of the female's wings, a behavior we term "wing stroking" (West & King, 1988c).

Changes in the male's singing patterns suggested the importance of wing stroking. Instead of employing the species-typical pattern of cycling through two to seven song types in succession, with little or no repetition, the males repeated the song that had elicited a wing stroke as many as four times in the next eight songs produced. The repetition of that song type by males suggested to us that wing stroking represented positive feedback, i.e., that the females' displays were responses to potentially potent songs. A playback experiment, using a new sample of females exposed to songs that had or had not elicited wing stroking, confirmed that the wing-stroke-eliciting songs were highly effective releasers of copulatory postures, as were the songs repeated after the wing stroke (West & King, 1988c). Thus, taken together, the studies suggest that in the NC population, song development is a synergistic process in which both males and females are active participants.

These data are exciting to us because they reveal concrete linkages between male production and female perception. Although conceptual linkages have long been acknowledged (Marler, 1976), the ontogeny of bird song has been studied too often and with too many species without ever permitting the major participants to meet, let alone mate. To learn more about the female's role, we looked at female perception from several perspectives. First, as mentioned earlier, we documented NC females' native song preferences, a bias found in both captive and wild females (King & West, 1983c). Second, we probed for modifiability of song preference by housing naive NC females with adult males from the second cowbird subspecies, *M. a. obscurus*, which had been collected in south Texas (TX). After a year's social housing, the NC females responded to playbacks of NC song (which they had never heard) significantly more often than to TX song. Even an acoustically naive hybrid female (NC mother × TX father) preferred NC song.

These manipulations involved a level of discrimination not normally experienced by NC females, i.e., listening to NC versus TX song. Thus, we also looked for evidence of perceptual stability at a local level by measuring perceptual concordance of song preferences within and across local females. Did females from a given area perceive all variants of local song as equally potent, and if not, did females "agree" with one another about which songs are the most or least effective?

In answer to the first question, we found that not all males' songs were equally effective. In general, dominant males, successful in courting females, possessed the largest repertoires of effective songs, although even these males included in their repertoire songs to which females responded infrequently. Thus, females were discriminating at a local level (West & King, 1986).

With respect to the second question, we found that local females showed high levels of agreement about which songs were most or least potent. To test concordance, we chose 12 NC songs previously played back to females, 6 of which had elicited many responses (high-potency songs) and 6 that had elicited few responses (low-potency songs). We asked whether a new group of NC females would "agree" with the previous group in terms of their relative responsiveness to the songs. They did, producing significant positive rank-order correlations with the playback preferences of the original cohort. A year later, after living with different NC males for 9 months, the females' playback preferences for the 12 songs were retested, and again showed a comparable level of concordance (West & King, 1986; King & West, 1988). Thus, if NC females can be said to screen males (sensu West-Eberhard, 1983) on the basis of song, they appear to do so using shared criteria.

NORTH CAROLINA COWBIRDS: THE EXCEPTION OR THE RULE?

The data presented thus far hold two lessons for the understanding of behavior. First, the data demonstrate that the brood parasitic habits of cowbirds have not ruled out learning as a means of acquiring species-typical behavior. Second, the data suggest potentially new mechanisms of learning, mechanisms never before postulated for any songbird. The results show that cowbirds can learn by means other than imitation: males do not alter their songs by copying wing strokes, but by attending to their "meaning." Thus, vocal imitation cannot be assumed to be "the" learning mechanism for "songbirds" (Kroodsma, 1982). The experiments also indicate that audition is not the only sensory pathway guiding song development. Thus, the data challenge current views of the role of underlying sensory templates, and call for the mapping of neural regions that receive visual information. As such, data from a single pea in one avian pod render many textbook explications of "bird song" potentially misleading: clearly, there is more than one way to achieve vocal competence.

The emphasis on imitation and on vocal stimulation is, to a large extent, a methodological consequence of framing research questions about song from the male's perspective. The singer-dominated approach is especially apparent in studies of geographic variation (Canady, Kroodsma, & Nottebohm, 1984; Krebs & Kroodsma, 1980). Although the functional significance of song variation is still the subject of active debate (Baker & Cunningham, 1985), until recently, few data existed on female variation in song responsiveness. Until playback procedures with females were developed (King & West, 1977; Baker, Spitler-Nabors, & Bradley, 1981), direct measures of female perception of song were scarce. Female perception has now become the topic of scrutiny in a number of songbirds and will eventually lead to a proliferation of theories of song acquisition (e.g., Baker, 1983; Baker et al., 1981; Baker, Spitler-Nabors, Thompson, & Cunningham, 1987; Catchpole, Dittami, & Leisler, 1984; Ratcliffe & Weisman, 1987; Searcy, 1984; Searcy & Marler, 1981, 1984; Searcy, Marler, & Peters, 1981).

It was our ability to ask females questions that provided the opportunity to study intraspecific variation. Once we had discovered linkages between NC males and females with respect to song ontogeny, we asked whether we could find evidence of this in other parts of the cowbird's extensive range. The answer is a qualified "yes." We qualify the answer for two reasons. We have yet to study other populations as thoroughly as the NC population, so many loose ends remain. But we also qualify our response because we have uncovered a multidimensional array of differences among populations, and we are still searching for optimal ways to organize these data into coherent themes. We are partially hindered in this task because few words exist in the songbird researcher's lexicon to describe differences in receptivity. When males sing different songs in different areas, terms such as "dialects" or "geographic variants," terms borrowed from human linguistics, are employed. When females from different areas respond differently, in the ways to be described, what words are appropriate? The field of human linguistics is quite impoverished when it comes to the behavior of listeners. What is the receptive equivalent of a dialect, perhaps a "dia-cept?"

The geographic points of our empirical compass appear in Figure 1. A quick glance suggests that the south central United States is important territory for cowbird researchers. There are several attractions. The population density of cowbirds is highest in the prairie and in the Great Plains, their ancestral sites, which originally contained buffaloes (the cowbird was, in fact, formerly known as the buffalobird, then the cow-pen bird) (Coon & Arnold, 1977). A second attraction of these areas for cowbird researchers is that taxonomists have drawn the subspecies border between the *M. a. ater* and *M. a. obscurus* subspecies within the state of Texas (Figure 1). The major morphological difference is size,

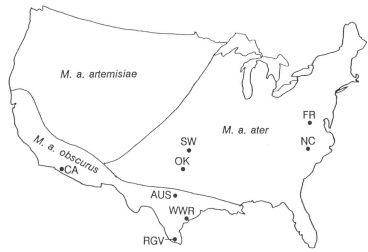

FIGURE 1. Sites at which cowbirds were recorded, collected, and, in most cases, transported to the laboratory in North Carolina for study. The initials stand for the following sites: FR = Front Royal, Virginia; NC = Mebane, North Carolina; SW = Stillwater, Oklahoma; OK = Willis, Oklahoma; AUS = Austin, Texas: WWR = Welder Wildlife Refuge, Sinton, Texas; RGV = Rio Grande Valley, Texas; and CA = Santa Barbara, California.

with some additional differences in the plumage of the smaller, *M. a. obscurus* subspecies. But the songs of the two subspecies also differ (Figure 2). Males in the *M. a. obscurus* range include a cluster of notes before the terminal whistle which we term the midsong element (MSE). This song element is never found in the songs of *M. a. ater* males (sampled from 11 locations), making it a valuable acoustic marker of subspecies identity (King, West, & Eastzer, 1980). (The third subspecies, *M. a. artemisiae*, the sagebrush cowbird, occupies western North America and is not yet a topic of inquiry for us (but see Rothstein, Verner, & Stevens, 1980).

   Thus, to put the sites of Figure 1 into perspective, cowbirds in the center of the United States represent older and denser populations, whereas the NC and California (CA) populations represent some of the newest areas of expansion. Cowbirds have been breeding in North Carolina only for the last 50 years (Potter & Whitehurst, 1981), as opposed to hundreds of years in the central plains and prairies (Grinnell, 1909; Mayfield, 1965; Oberholser, 1920), and they have been breeding in southern California for 80 years and northern California for 50 years (Rothstein et al., 1980). We do not presume to know at this point how to organize the ecological and evolutionary variation subsumed by these sites. But we present it to indicate the potential richness of microphyletic variation.

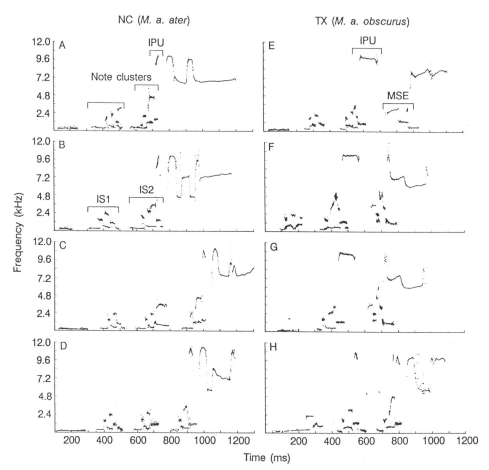

FIGURE 2. A sound spectrogram of *M. a. obscurus* song and *M. a. ater* song. The song components labelled are IS1 and IS2, introductory syllables 1 and 2; IPU, interphrase unit; MSE, midsong element. *M. a. obscurus* songs almost always contain MSE's, *M. a. ater* songs do not. The rhythm differences found in OK songs consisted of differences in the timing of peak-to-peak amplitude on the low and high voice notes in the first syllable. Specifically, the duration of the high to low voice interval (H2 to L4) was found to be a multiple of the previous low to high voice interval (L2 to H2). Differences in syllable diversity among TX *M. a. obscurus* populations referred to the number and arrangement of notes within IS1 and IS2.

PERSPECTIVE FROM THE PRAIRIE: FEMALE FLEXIBILITY

We begin the comparative tale with studies of cowbirds in Oklahoma (OK), the population closest to NC in phyletic terms, as both are classed as the same subspecies (*M. a. ater*). Even though the OK populations live in closer proximity to the *M. a. obscurus* subspecies, OK females, like NC females, respond selectively to their own subspecies' songs in comparison to *M. a. obscurus* songs (King, West, & Eastzer, 1986; King & West, 1987). Other similarities also exist. Acoustic examination of the songs of the two populations suggests common ancestry. On many measures of frequency, duration, and timing, it is difficult to differentiate OK from NC songs. Playback tests to NC females give the same impression. NC females respond as often to OK songs as they do to NC songs. But OK females do not show a comparable tolerance for NC songs. They clearly discriminate between OK and NC songs, preferring the former by a significant margin. Thus, NC and OK females possess different patterns of perceptual breadth, with the OK females displaying more specificity (West & King, 1988a).

Structural analyses of OK and NC songs reveal that OK songs are characterized by a higher degree of stereotyped rhythm in the introductory syllables (King et al., 1986). To study the relevance of this characteristic to the perceptual differences between NC and OK females, we selected a group of NC songs and manipulated the rhythm parameters to mimic those naturally found in OK songs. We played back the manipulated and unmanipulated versions to NC and OK females. The addition of the OK rhythm produced a significant increase in the response of the OK females to the NC songs, but had no effect on the NC females. The sensitivity of the OK females to this feature suggests that the vocal ecology of OK has led to the need for finer levels of discrimination. The greater density of males in OK may have led to this need, as OK females come into contact with a larger numbers of potential mates, which may confer an advantage on those females with very finely tuned discriminative abilities.

Two other differences are noteworthy. First, we looked at intrapopulational concordance with respect to song potency in the OK population. We had found high levels of concordance among NC females, yielding rank order correlations greater than +.80 across multiple cohorts (West & King, 1988c; King & West, 1988). In contrast, OK females showed considerably less concordance, producing nonsignificant correlations. Retesting of the same females after a year's social housing with OK males revealed a strong bias toward OK songs, but not necessarily to the same songs that had elicited the most responses in the previous year.

The relatively lower level of perceptual concordance in OK fits with a second finding. In an attempt to look at flexibility in OK females' perceptual preferences, we housed juvenile OK females for a year with *M. a. obscurus* TX males, repeating the procedures used with juvenile NC females, except that the TX males had been captured at different sites (see King & West, 1987). We found that after a year's social housing, the females responded significantly more often to TX songs than did normally reared OK females (King et al., 1986). Thus, social housing apparently has different effects in OK than in NC, broadening the former group's tolerance for song to include variants characteristic of the second subspecies. In a subsequent year, we repeated the procedure of social housing with TX males using adult OK females as subjects. We obtained the same result—an equal tolerance for OK and TX song.

The difference in flexibility between NC and OK females may relate to the evolutionary age of their respective populations, or it may be a consequence of proximate differences in their respective environments, or both. An explanation in terms of evolutionary age might be that the longer history of the OK population in their prairie setting has allowed an open system of perceptual learning in females to develop. The evolutionary odds that OK cowbirds would meet and learn from other cowbirds grew so high that postnatal learning became the more efficient strategy.

The proximate explanation might be that differences imposed by the physical expanse of the grasslands or the more populous social ecology led to differences in the fine structure of the males' songs. As stated earlier, the songs of OK males are more stereotyped in terms of their rhythm: they have differences too subtle for humans and for NC females, but not for OK females, calling for a flexible ontogenetic program to "tune" the female's perceptual system to tighter acoustic specifications. In any case, taken together, the data show that OK and NC females can be differentiated on several perceptual attributes, suggesting that dissimilar geographic addresses dictated the need for dissimilar perceptual capacities.

CROSSING THE SUBSPECIES BORDER:
NEW DIMENSIONS OF DIVERSITY

The studies of NC and OK females revealed several dimensions on which to compare females: perceptual specificity, concordance, and flexibility. Our studies of females from the second subspecies, *M. a. obscurus*, have added another: female responsiveness to song. Despite the differences in perceptual selectivity and modifiability just detailed between NC and OK females, both populations appear equally responsive to native song in playback tests. In operational terms, this means that when NC or OK females hear native songs, they respond positively on 51 percent and 53 percent of all trials respectively (calculated as a mean percentage of positive responses per individual, with a maximum of one per trial, across all songs, divided by number of playback trials).

But responsiveness to song is lower in populations of *M. a. obscurus* collected in TX and California (CA) and tested using the same procedures employed with OK and NC birds. The TX females responded to approximately 36 percent of native songs, the CA females to about 20 percent. We were especially curious about the lowered threshold for song in TX because we knew these females used song in many of the same ways as NC and OK females did. *M. a. obscurus* females from south TX, for example, respond preferentially to native song. Such females are also able to influence the song development of NC males. When NC males were housed with *M. a. obscurus* females, the males developed bilingual repertoires, composed of prototypical NC and TX songs. The major changes in the males' songs involved inclusion of a midsong element, a cluster typically not present in *M. a. ater* songs (Figure 2). It is a feature to which *M. a. obscurus* (but not *M. a. ater*) females appear especially sensitive in playback tests (King & West, 1983b). Moreover, when *M. a. obscurus* females are given a "choice" of males to mate with, they copulate most often with males whose repertoires contain the most songs with midsong elements (West et al., 1983).

Thus, the females from the second subspecies appear to be able to influence male song and to use male song to assess males. So, too, *M. a. obscurus* males, housed with NC females, alter their songs in ways that make them less effective to *M. a. obscurus* females, suggesting that they too are stimulated by communicative signals from females. Both subspecies therefore appear to be able to "read" each other's communicative signals, even though they prefer different song variants.

We were struck by the differences in absolute responsiveness between the two subspecies. Two lines of research offered a means of tying the differences in song perception to differences in song production. In extensive analyses of the acoustic structure of male song in the two subspecies in sites ranging from NC through TX, Eastzer (1988) documented a relevant difference within TX *M. a. obscurus* populations. Males in the TX *M. a. obscurus* range displayed more intrapopulational diversity with respect to the acoustic structure of the introductory syllables of their songs than *M. a. ater* populations did (see Figure 2). To be more precise, *M. a. obscurus* males included more diverse note clusters in the first two syllables than *M. a. ater* males did. Thus, TX *M. a. obscurus* males develop more diverse vocal material during song ontogeny. Are social responses by females responsible? Several leaps of faith are needed to connect Eastzer's data to such a conclusion, but we are prepared to make the leap in light of other knowledge about *M. a. obscurus*.

The first source of knowledge originates in observations across two breeding seasons of captive TX *M. a. obscurus* females being courted by TX *M. a. obscurus* males and by NC *M. a. ater* males (King & West, 1984). What was most striking was the passivity of TX females, compared to NC females, in response to song. While NC females terminated 88 percent of social interactions including a song after the delivery of only one song, the TX females departed before a second song during 50 percent of social encounters, permitting males to sing a second or third song during half of all song-related encounters. Males also sang in closer physical proximity to TX females, delivering the majority of their songs while within six inches of the female. In contrast, males courting NC females sang the majority of their songs at distances greater than 1 foot, and often while flying. Courtship of NC females appeared to be a frenetic affair involving innumerable aerial pursuits and many brief encounters. Courtship of TX females occurred at a more leisurely pace, and involved less flight and more songs. The end result was that TX females received more song stimulation in absolute terms, although the number and rate of copulations observed did not differ for the two subspecies.

The second line of evidence comes from studies of the ontogeny of song of NC males housed with *M. a. obscurus* females, and includes acoustic analyses of over 10,000 songs (King & West, 1988). We have already described the major outcome of such housing: the NC males come to sing considerable amounts of prototypical TX song. But another striking effect concerned the rate of song development, i.e., the pace at which the males proceeded from the production of variable and diverse song precursors to crystallization of repertoires composed of two to seven song types. In contrast to NC males housed with other species or with *M. a. ater* females, NC males housed with *M. a. obscurus* females retained plastic, that is, noncrystallized, song longer. The same result was obtained when NC males were housed with TX females but tutored with NC song. The males housed with TX *M. a. obscurus* females retained plastic song longer than males tutored with the same NC song but housed with females of other species. So, too, the NC males with *M. a. obscurus* females sang less of the tutor song, developing more original and more diverse repertoires (King & West, 1988).

These data lead us to speculate that Eastzer's (1988) finding of greater heterogeneity in syllable content in TX *M. a. obscurus* represents the operation of female influence early in ontogeny, leading to vocal alterations on the part of the males to deal with the relatively lower level of female responsiveness to song. By including more variation in their songs, the males may give the songs more potential to arouse the less reactive females.

COASTAL PERSPECTIVES:
CHANGES IN COMMUNICATIVE FUNCTION?

Data from a final geographic point are relevant to this hypothesis. As stated earlier, we have also tested the playback responsiveness of another *M. a. obscurus* population, females from southern California. Their playback responsiveness to CA songs was almost half that of their TX counterparts to TX song. Although our sample of males was small (5), we then looked for any possible associated differences in the songs of CA males.

When we housed CA females with juvenile CA males, by the late spring, when TX or NC males' repertoires are in final form, the CA males were still singing highly variable song, with much of it not meeting a criterion of stereotypy sufficient to call it crystallized song. The nature of the acoustic variability was striking: most of the songlike vocalizations were fragments of songs consisting of recombinations and duplications of individual song elements—vocal behaviors seen in NC or TX males in late fall or early winter, but never in the late spring. The simplest explanation appears to be that the CA males' song development occurred at a very slow rate, with some males entering the breeding season possessing primarily plastic or variable song, fitting with observations by Rothstein et al. (1986) that some juvenile males do not breed in their first year.

The developmental data on CA birds are too scant to form many conclusions. But Rothstein and his colleagues have also studied this population's vocal behavior and have found other lines of evidence to suggest that CA males possess a different vocal program than NC or TX males. Most notably, Rothstein has evidence that another male vocalization, the flight whistle, which is used to signal departures and flight movements, is quite modifiable through the male's first breeding season (Rothstein & Fleischer, 1987). Evidence also exists to suggest that flight whistles may play a direct role in eliciting copulations in CA populations (Rothstein, Yokel, and Fleischer, 1988). While our aviary observations and other field observations suggest that copulations are always preceded by song in the eastern subspecies, CA females appear to copulate when immediately cued by only a flight whistle. Although Rothstein et al. find ample evidence of the use of courtship songs, the songs appear to occur in a different proximate relationship to the elicitation of copulatory postures in wild females.

Thus, the lowered responsiveness of CA females to playback of songs and the delayed development of song in CA males may reflect a functional shift in the use of vocal signals in the western part of the cowbird's range. Rothstein et al. speculate that the larger ranges in the west may have favored increased use of long distance signals, such as the flight whistle, which transmit better across greater distances than the courtship song. Thus, the whistled vocalization may have come to have more salience in coordinating male–female interactions.

Rothstein has not yet tested CA females' playback responsiveness to flight whistles. We have tested the responsiveness of TX females to flight whistles from four areas and have found no responses at all (West & King, 1989). We have more limited data on NC females, but we have never been able to elicit a copulatory response to a flight whistle. If Rothstein finds CA females to be responsive to whistles, it would represent significant converging evidence of yet another instance of interrelationships between female perception and male production in relation to differences in ecology.

INDIVIDUAL DIFFERENCES IN RESPONSIVENESS

Our travels from NC to CA have uncovered a number of perceptual variables on which females may differ. We have also uncovered ways in which such differences may be linked to male song production. We have recently completed a study with NC birds in which we tried to test some implicit assumptions about interrelationships between female responsiveness and male song production (King & West, 1989). To do so, we exploited the range of individual variation among NC females in song responsiveness. In 15 years of playback testing of females, we have routinely recorded individual differences in playback responsiveness. Every year, we find a range of females, from those who respond on 80–90 percent of all trials to those who respond on 20–30 percent of all trials. Although, on a relative basis, the females prefer the same songs, some express their preference more frequently than others.

To see if individual variation in playback responsiveness produced local effects that paralleled populational effects, we housed several naive juvenile NC males each with an adult female of known playback responsiveness (King & West, 1989). We deliberately selected female companions who varied considerably in their level of responsiveness. One female had responded to only 7 percent of all playback songs, two had responded to fewer than 20 percent, three had responded to between 50 and 60 percent, and two to more than 75 percent. To introduce some standardization in acoustic stimulation, we tutored all the males with the playback songs on which the females had been tested. After allowing the males and females to interact from late August until the next breeding season, we looked at the nature of the males' song production. We also retested the females' preferences for the playback songs to see if social housing had had any effects.

As in all past work with NC females, we found no evidence of changes in the females' responsiveness: the rank orderings of the females from high to low were unchanged a year later. But noteworthy differences were apparent in the vocal production of the males in relation to the "nature" of their female companions. In line with the populational findings, males housed with relatively unresponsive females developed larger repertoires and included more diversity in their introductory note clusters. In contrast, males with females who responded very frequently developed smaller and less diverse repertoires. And thus we were able to approximate in the laboratory what Eastzer (1988) had found in the field: an association between female responsiveness and syllable diversity.

We have also been able to trace the process one step further. Playback responsiveness is a measure of behavior during the breeding season—females do not adopt copulatory postures at other times of year. Could we connect playback responsiveness to other indices of song reactivity outside of the breeding season? In particular, is there a discernible relationship between playback responsiveness and wing stroking? Although our sample was small (8 females), we did find a positive correlation between playback responsiveness and wing stroking, suggesting that the wing stroke may be a behavioral precursor to a copulatory posture.

And thus we are back where we started—looking at the proximate dynamics of interactions between NC males and females. But we are doing so armed with many new questions. As stated earlier, we had noted individual variation in frequency of responding for 15 years, but it was only after the geographic comparisons that we developed a testable hypothesis. Every comparative psychologist who studies the same population and the same individuals knows that his or her animals have different "personalities," but it is sometimes hard to know what to make of some of the differences—are they statistical noise or empirical signals? Looking at new populations but asking the same questions can put old data in a new light.

MANAGING INTRASPECIFIC VARIATION: THREE CONCEPTUAL TOOLS

Thus far, we have studied only a half-dozen populations in any depth, and we have uncovered 10 communicative variables. In females, perceptual selectivity, specificity, concordance, responsiveness, and reactivity may differ. In males, the rate and content of vocal production, sensitivity to female signals, modifiability, and imitative ability can vary. And how the five female parameters interact with those of males is a another level of possible variation. We are in the process of attempting to negotiate our way through this array of differences. We have locked onto three concepts to help navigate the forest and the trees. We describe them below because we believe they may provide guidance to other investigators as well.

Communicative profiles

In attempting to compare the behavior of 45 different rodent species, Dewsbury (1988a) developed "adaptive profiles" to contrast the "personality–motivational structure of a given species" (p. 24). We have opted for a similar strategy, constructing communicative profiles of males and females from different populations. The aim is to find suites of behavior that seem to be natural units, such as low responsiveness in females and high modifiability in males. In such a way, we hope to be able to identify the mechanisms that couple male and female communicative traits so that the desired outcome, mating, is obtained. Adherence to a profile also helps us avoid the tendency to view bird song or vocal communication as a unitary concept. Among the behaviors embedded within bird song are the motoric skills necessary to articulate sound, orienting and attention mechanisms, trial-and-error learning, rehearsal of vocal material, long-term memory, vocal imitation, improvisation, and invention. And then there are the receptive capacities of listeners detailed earlier. Learning how all these behaviors are joined is similar to learning how the various compartments within a honeybee hive serve to create a society. The physical presence of a hive, however, is a constant reminder that, in the end, everything fits together. It is more difficult with bird song, because the physical signal does not encapsulate the underlying phenomenon of interest: communication.

Inherited niches

After creating profiles, the next step is to look more carefully at the habitats inherited by different populations of the same species. Elsewhere we have proposed the concept of inherited niches to represent the ecological and social legacies transmitted to the young (West & King, 1987). We deem a formal name necessary to give exogenetic inheritance equal status with its genetic cognate. The term *niche* captures the physical requirements necessary for the existence of a species, as well as the particular role or occupation of that species within the broader ecological community. If profiles describe capacities, then niches reveal possibilities for translating capacities into capabilities.

For example, in cowbirds, some of the differences between populations may be explained by focusing on variation in their physical and social ecologies. For example, in field studies of CA cowbirds, Rothstein, Verner, & Stevens (1984) documented a distinctive diurnal pattern: CA cowbirds engage in parasitism and mating in the morning, then fly considerable distances in the afternoon to feed in large pasture lots, during which time minimal, if any, courtship is seen. Females may thus be separated from males for many hours each day, especially while the females are engaging in egg removal, egg laying, and surveillance of potential host nests, activities in which the male does not participate. Such naturally occurring deprivation of the sight and sound of a mate could alter the salience of cues from him. In particular, as these daily experiences may lower the female's threshold for mating, they might render the details of specific song structures less important to the elicitation of copulation, although still making song essential to the original choice of the male as her consort. In contrast, in a prairie population in the Midwest, Elliott (1980) described feeding and mating taking place in the same locale. In areas where feeding and courting are not physically separated, especially in dense populations, females may become over-stimulated, and thus males may need to outdo one another vocally to compete for a female's attention. Thus, in OK, for example, it may be important for females to be maximally sensitive to fine differences in song structure, a sensitivity improved by postnatal tuning of perceptual preferences.

Another source of niche variation in cowbirds is migration, a variable linked to differences in learning opportunities in other songbirds (Kroodsma, 1983). The *M. a. obscurus* populations we have studied the most tend to breed and over-winter in the same vicinity, whereas more northern and eastern *M. a. ater* populations may travel a thousand or more miles to wintering roosts. One impact of migration may be in the amount of time males have to "work" on their songs when they return to breeding sites. So, too, females may have more or less time to influence or become sensitized to local songs. NC males and females are migratory, returning to their breeding sites in mid-March, the time at which we have found captive females reactive to song and males capable of modifying their song in response to social cues (West & King, 1988c).

The above scenarios are just that—possible sequences of events predicting different relationships between male production and female perception depending on the properties of the niche. We provide them to illustrate correlations between ecological heterogeneity across the range of cowbirds and heterogeneity in the ontogeny of vocal communication.

Ecological clocks

Whereas ontogeny is often measured in terms of time or age, ecology is often appraised in terms of physical resources. But an animal's ecology also has temporal dimensions, and thus we come to the final concept, ecological clocks. Temporal readings of a population are in and of themselves triadic entities, recording the passage of phylogenetic, ontogenetic, and individual time. For many species, phylogenetic time estimates are, however, too crude to be direct value to the comparative analysis of behavior. Only minuscule movements of evolutionary time can be accurately tracked. In the case of cowbirds, however, we can trace in general form the species' radiation throughout North America. By following humans' efforts to clear land for pasture and livestock, the ancestral path of cowbirds from South America becomes visible. And, as birdwatchers are also a venerable lot, as quick with their pens as with their eyes, records exist to mark cowbirds' exploitation of the deforestation of the United States (Friedmann, 1929; Grinnell, 1909; Mayfield, 1965; Oberholser, 1920). As stated earlier, the ancestral part of the cowbird's range lies in the central United States; records of their presence date back to the earliest European settlers (Friedmann, 1929). In contrast, cowbirds have resided in North Carolina for only half a century (Potter & Whitehurst, 1981). Cowbirds are also new to California and the Far West (Rothstein et al., 1980). Thus, our studies of cowbirds span populations whose ecological clocks register discernibly different evolutionary times. The significance of this may be considerable in light of work on other animals suggesting that "older" and "newer" populations may possess different ontogenetic mechanisms (Mayr, 1982).

A recent theory concerning human diversity at microphyletic levels may illuminate the use of ecological clocks in comparative analyses (Plomin, 1986). Consider a common question about humans: Why are children in the same family so different (Plomin & Daniels, 1987)? Given genetic relatedness and physical proximity, why is it that parents readily remark on personality differences among siblings that to them seem as conspicuous as they are intractable? Plomin and Daniels argue that siblings may share parents and genes and homes, but they do not share environments. Systematic environmental differences include family composition, sibling interactions, parental treatment, and extrafamilial resources. Nonsystematic variation arises from birth spacing and gender differences, accidents, illnesses, divorce, physical and economic traumas, and exposure to peers, teachers, and television. Thus, children within the same family, by virtue of age differences, run on different ecological clocks.

If we extend the concept of the nonshared temporal environment to the life of a species, it is possible to think of the ancestral populations as firstborns and recent settlers as later-borns. Thus, NC cowbirds attempting to colonize North Carolina in 1930 faced different selection pressures than did their OK counterparts, which have now been settled in their "home" for hundreds of years. NC cowbirds are new kids on the evolutionary block, afforded neither the same opportunities nor the same obstacles.

Students of development are perhaps most used to noting the passage of intragenerational time, especially the portion spent as an infant or child. As important as experience early in ontogeny may be for understanding development, the nature of such experiences may have caused developmentalists to ignore later, equally influential periods. When considered in terms of timing, cowbirds may not be as different from nonparasitic songbirds as one might think. Although they do not experience conspecific parental care as nestlings, they interact with conspecifics at all other times of year. And, since adult male cowbirds do not cease to sing at the end of the breeding season as many other songbirds do, juvenile cowbirds can experience species-typical stimulation naturally once they are settled, at 50–60 days of age, into cowbird flocks. Thus, although stimulation from adults may be "time-shifted" relative to some other songbirds, it is not necessarily less effective. There is considerable evidence to suggest that song learning is not restricted to the natal period as much as previously thought for nonparasitic songbirds (Petrinovich, 1988b). Many songbirds leave the nest and parents at about the same time cowbirds do, and appear to learn many of their songs from unrelated neighbors the following spring. So, too, female songbirds' preferences may not be directly attributable to natal experience: knowing the songs of a female's father or brother may not be sufficient to explain later mate choice (Petrinovich & Baptista, 1984). Thus, the hours most important for cultural transmission must also be considered in a less age-limited manner, rendering the cowbird's pattern of development potentially less idiosyncratic.

In summary, we have proposed three activities necessary to the interpretation of intraspecific variation: preparation of profiles, knowledge of niches, and calibration of clocks. We suggest that they serve to make microphyletic differences especially fertile ground for the formulation of principles of behavioral adaptation. We are hardly the first to emphasize the need for such studies, but we feel compelled to repeat the call, because the question of the value and meaning of psychological comparisons between humans and other animals is still a current topic.

We suspect, judging from our own experiences, that simple inertia also impedes the pace of intraspecific comparisons. Once a phenomenon is settled into a home, thoughts of uprooting it may provoke anxiety. In our case, some of the anxiety stems from insecurity: How should we manage the diversity uncovered to date? We empathize with the New England homeowner, who, in organizing his attic, set aside a box filled with tiny pieces of string. The inscription on the box read: "String too short to be saved" (Hall, 1983). As we sort through data, it is sometimes difficult to know which bits and pieces will ultimately hang together and which ultimately should be set aside. But, for the present, we save them all. With threads of knowledge from many sources, a fine enough net may be woven to hold even the smallest of fruits from microphyletic patches.

SUMMARY

In this chapter, we describe variation in the perceptual and learning capacities of female cowbirds with respect to discrimination of and responsiveness to male song. We also present evidence to suggest that differences in the acoustic structure of males' songs within and across populations represent vocal adjustments to female cues. We attempt to relate these patterns of diversity in female perception and male production to differences in the natural history of cowbirds across their extensive range.

We propose three concepts to help organize evidence of intraspecific diversity: communicative profiles, inherited niches, and ecological clocks. We argue that the study of microphyletic variation is essential to understanding the responsiveness of ontogenetic systems to naturally occurring changes in a species' habitat.

CHAPTER 15

AVIAN SONG DEVELOPMENT: METHODOLOGICAL AND CONCEPTUAL ISSUES

Lewis Petrinovich

The research I describe here reflects my early background, which involved training as a psychologist in the disciplines of animal learning, motivation, and physiological psychology. My interest in the physiological mechanisms of memory storage and retrieval led me to laboratory studies of song development in the white-crowned sparrow (*Zonotrichia leucophrys nuttalli*). Because it was necessary to collect nestlings in the field, I had to learn something of the breeding system of the birds, and this led me to make systematic observations of the territorial behavior of males and females during the breeding season, and to a series of field experiments in which I studied the habituation of territorial pairs to the playback of song.

The field observations of sparrows that I made during this time convinced me of the value of systematically studying the population dynamics and reproductive success of field populations, and of understanding and using the procedures and insights of my ethologist and ornithologist colleagues. Finally, I have returned to laboratory studies of song development to realize the benefits of the increased understanding gained from this breadth of experience at the different levels of study with the members of this fascinating avian species. Throughout all of the later years of this research, I have attempted to bring to bear multivariate statistical methods on the complex data fields involved, and to cast my research designs in a manner that captures as much as possible the representativeness of the ecological situations within which the birds must operate.

In this chapter, I consider some of the problems involved in constructing

340

adequate explanations of behavioral processes, especially as they relate to the development of song in birds. In particular, I consider levels of explanation that are used in the sciences of behavior and some problems with the idea of reductionism, and I emphasize the importance of considering the distinction between proximate and ultimate causes of behavior. I then discuss some ideas concerning the paramount importance of understanding problems in measurement, sampling strategies, and processes of generalization. These ideas are illustrated by examples drawn from my field studies of habituation. I also concentrate on a case history based on my studies of the development of song in the white-crowned sparrow to provide a concrete illustration of how conceptual factors can influence the manner in which behavioral explanations are framed. Finally, I argue that psychologists, especially comparative psychologists, are equipped to play a major role in the development of general explanations of behavior at adequate levels of complexity.

REDUCTIONISM

It seems an inescapable conclusion that the reduction of behavioral processes to those of physiological mechanisms is neither a necessary nor a sufficient step to achieve an adequate explanation of a behavioral event. It is clear that behavioral events can be discussed in terms of lower levels of physiological organization, and it is undeniable that behavioral events are constituted of physicochemical events. However, there are organizational principles at higher levels that are different from those at lower ones, and the descriptive languages at the different levels are independent of one another. An excellent discussion, with illuminating examples, has been provided by Beckner (1974), who discusses the descriptive languages involved in describing an event using the example of the execution of a last will and testament. D1 (executing the will) and D2 (moving the hand in a certain way) can both be descriptions of the same event at different levels. However, there is a context involved, and that context could make the events totally different. D2, making the series of hand movements, could be done while signing a love letter, and D1, executing a will, could be done by marking an X. Thus, D1 and D2 each determine a class of events, and an event in either class may or may not be the same as an event in the other. The important consideration that determines the context of executing a will (D1) is on a level involving a legal concept and a theoretical structure not entailed at the level of D2. Descriptions of hand movements involve a descriptive set which is neutral regarding function or achievement. This example is intended to demonstrate that neither level of explanation is more or less "real" than the other: they constitute different aspects of a contemporaneous reality, but neither can fully replace the other.

In the biological realm, Beckner has illustrated the problem of using constitutive reductionism when considering an event such as predation. Predation is a biological process, as well as being constructed of a series of physicochemical events. However, the biological concept of predation is a construct with surplus content that is not contained in, nor is it admissable to, the level of physicochemical processes. In addition, the theoretical vocabularies of the biological and the physicochemical realms are not comparable. A cat's mouse hunting is a biological, not a physical, action: textbooks of chemistry do not mention mouse hunting, nor does the vocabulary of chemistry contain the terms *cat*, *mouse*, or *hunt*. The events can be, at one level, physicochemical, but the biological concepts cannot be reduced to concepts at the lower physicochemical level. Likewise, because of this inherent difference in the conceptual structures, the higher-level biological event cannot be reduced to the lower-level physicochemical event structure. This irreducibility, then, is conceptual, and is not due to a lack of dependence of the higher process event on the lower.

It is clear that the issue of reductionism is of concern not only when considering the explanation of behavioral events in terms of physiology. The reductionism issue arises whenever one attempts to explain any molar behavioral phenomenon (such as cognition) by events at a lower behavioral level (such as conditioning). The points regarding reductionism are important to keep in mind as well when considering the nature of explanation in terms of proximate and ultimate levels. The term *ultimate*, as used in the evolutionary sense, refers to the survival value of a behavior in relation to the organism's environment, and its operative characteristics are expressed in terms of fitness and reproductive success: explanation at this level suggests the end toward which the evolved behavior is focused. The term *proximate* centers on the mechanisms producing the behavior, and its characteristics are couched at the level of such things as hormonal or neural events, or of the environmental circumstances influencing the behavior: explanation at this level is focused on the structural and operating characteristics of the underlying mechanisms. An investigator legitimately might choose to couch an explanation in terms of the neurophysiological mechanisms that produce a behavior, and move toward a molecular reduction of a complex behavioral episode to the underlying physicochemical processes. On the other hand, one might just as legitimately choose to couch an explanation in terms of overriding evolutionary principles that are expressed in the organization of behavior, and move toward what I have called a molar reduction to these overriding principles (Petrinovich, 1976).

A complete explanation of behavior has to include terms at both proximate and ultimate levels of reality, and neither level is sufficient unto itself. One can describe and explain an event at either level, but a description at either level is no more complete than the earlier example of executing a will using a specific set of hand movements. It will be argued below that when events are considered at proximate as well as ultimate levels, each level can complement and strengthen the other, and that investigators concerned with one level should always have the other in mind to ensure that the reality at one level is not violating reality constraints imposed by the other.

PROBLEMS IN DESIGN AND GENERALIZATION

There are several problems in the song development research to be discussed here, primarily because a single method of presenting song material was used in the initial experiments. This specific limitation, however, is but one instance of a set of problems that are encountered when attempting to construct theories that reflect the behavior of organisms in their environment. Many of these problems can be resolved if attention is paid to the methodological arguments of Egon Brunswik.

An overview of Brunswikian behavioral biology

Elsewhere (Petrinovich, 1980), I presented some of my research within the framework of probabilistic functionalism, as outlined by Egon Brunswik. Brunswik's psychology was a functionalist psychology concerned with the nature of the organism's adaptation to its environment. The relation between the organism and the environment, rather than the nature of the organism itself, was to be the object of study in psychology. Brunswik (1952, 1956) argued that the progress of science has been impeded by an almost exclusive reliance on a type of systematic design that employs the logic of the single variable. This logic is based on the assumption that science is best pursued by isolating variables, and then manipulating a single one through a series of magnitudes while holding all of the other variables constant; then, the variable that has been manipulated is held constant and another is manipulated systematically, until all have been studied in turn.

Brunswik argued that the only method adequate to develop a science sufficient to understand the behavior of organisms in their environment is that of representative design. This type of design is based on the assumption that research should be conducted in settings that are representative of those to which the theoretical generalizations are intended to apply. Thus, one should take care to represent variables and their interaction in the density with which they appear in the universe of concern and with their natural intercorrelations preserved as much as possible. Only in this manner can the probable importance of different variables be assessed, because each occurs within the context of all other variables of importance, and each is interacting with all of the others as it does in the situations to which one wishes to generalize (see Petrinovich, 1979, 1981, for a detailed comparison of systematic and representative designs).

To illustrate the power of representative design, I have characterized my research on the process of habituation to the playback of territorial song by birds in their breeding territories in terms of the salient characteristics of representative design. I have described my attempts to obtain representative samples of situations, subjects, and behavior in these experiments, and have advocated the use of statistics that avoid the pitfalls of aggregating over time or subjects (Petrinovich, 1980). My research was aimed at understanding the role habituation plays in maintaining social systems. In addition, I sought to develop quantitative theory to permit the understanding of the functional processes presumed to produce behavior in territorial birds in response to the playback of recorded song in the field setting. The research was done by studying behavior in the natural (representative) situation and allowing variables to interact with a minimal degree of influence on the part of the observers. A large number of the salient features of the environment were noted, and the birds were permitted a full range of responses to the song stimuli. A few of the principles of representative design used in the research are explained below.

Situational sampling

Care was taken to sample the situations in which the behavior of interest occurred. Experiments were started throughout the day. The loudspeaker was located within the birds' territory, and the male had access to his normal singing perches in the region of the speaker. Experiments were run under all weather conditions except high winds and heavy rains, when the birds, quite sensibly, take cover rather than singing and flying in response to the playback or confronting neighboring birds. The distance of the speaker from the nest, the time of day, and the weather conditions were all recorded, and if they had been related to any of the responses, this would be determined in later statistical analyses. Thus, situational variables were either systematically sampled (time of day), allowed to vary randomly (weather), or were varied representatively in accordance with the nature of the territory (distance of the speaker from the nest).

Subject sampling

Subjects were selected by performing experiments as the nests were located. Because the research continued throughout the breeding season, some pairs of birds were tested when the female was incubating eggs, some when she was brooding nestlings and the male and female were feeding them, and some after the young had fledged and both parents were feeding them. After the experiments were completed, it was found that the stage of the breeding cycle during which the experiments were conducted had a major influence on the response topography for both the male and the female.

The detailed results of the research program on habituation are summarized in Petrinovich (1984). Briefly, the results indicated that a male whose mate is brooding eggs responds to the playback in a manner similar to that of a paired territorial male prior to the nesting season. He sings and flies about a great deal and engages in aggressive behavior (trills and flutters) at the outset. A female incubating eggs has no young to warn, is not visible very often, and issues very few fright calls.

A female with nestlings is in view very little, and when she is, she flies about but emits few fright calls, trills, or flutters. In short, she is cryptic; if she is in the nest bush when the playback begins she stays there quietly, if she is out of the nest bush foraging at the start of the experiment, she remains concealed away from the nest. The male flies about and sings somewhat, but is fairly unresponsive at this stage of the reproductive cycle.

A female with fledglings is in view most of the time and issues a large number of fright calls. When either of the parents makes fright calls, the fledglings stop moving and stop making begging calls, thus enhancing their concealment in the face of disturbance within the territory. The female also trills and flutters at a high rate. The male sings and flies more than he does in the other two stages of the breeding cycle. He initially flutters but stops as the trials progress.

The changes in response levels that were observed had to be considered against these different background levels. If a response is at a low baseline, no habituation can be observed. Conversely, if the response levels are high, habituation can be obtained. However, certain behaviors that contribute to the survival of the young might be very difficult to habituate because of their significance to the adaptation of the species. Only by studying behavior within a representative sample of situations can the importance of a theoretical entity such as habituation be understood.

Without going into details, the initially bewildering patterns of behavior observed during the playback experiments were easy to comprehend in the context of the ongoing behavior during the different stages of the reproductive cycle. If no attention had been paid to reproductive condition, a major modulating influence would not have been recognized. These influences were not expected because experimenters traditionally conduct field experiments of this type over a relatively short time period, which would minimize the variability of breeding conditions sampled in this synchronously breeding species. Also, there has seldom been any attempt to locate the nests of experimental subjects, or even to find the female. Breeding condition is, then, an uncontrolled variable, and if it is not considered, the usual methods of assessing statistical reliability will consign their effect to the error term; when such systematic and reliable variance is not identified, it remains part of the unexplained statistical variance.

Through the use of representative sampling throughout the breeding season, it was possible to recognize the importance of a variable, reproductive condition, that accounted for over 10 percent of the total variance in behavior in response to playback. When reproductive condition was added to the number of playbacks presented, it was possible to account for as much as 18 percent of the total variance with only the two variables. The general conclusions regarding the relationship of behavior patterns to reproductive condition were cross-validated in an independent study (Patterson & Petrinovich, 1979), an important consideration when using correlational analytic procedures.

Stimulus sampling

The songs used in playback experiments differed for different birds. Songs from the same dialect group as that of the parent birds were used, but the songs were chosen to be unfamiliar to the individual birds. Kroodsma (1989) has emphasized the importance of using an adequate sample of songs in playback experiments in order to avoid effects due to the particular salience of the physical components of individual songs.

Behavior sampling

There was no attempt to sample selected response types on any a priori theoretical grounds or because they had been studied by other investigators. All behavior that two observers were able to record reliably was monitored continuously. Thus, the birds were allowed a free range of behavior, and we attempted to take a completely representative sample of their behavior.

The choice of response measure is an extremely important one because the effects of repeated playback of song on the different responses turned out to be quite complex. A decrement occurs for some responses with the repeated playback of recorded song, but not for others. If only one, or a selected few, of these variables had been chosen arbitrarily for the study, it would be possible to argue, for example, that there are no differences in response level as a function of reproductive condition (if male flutters, trills, and attacks were chosen), that there is a large difference in response level (if female trills and time in view were chosen), that birds with eggs respond more than those with young (if male flights and partial songs were chosen), or that birds with fledglings respond more than any other group (if female time in view were chosen). Similarly, by selecting variables, I could conclude that the response level does not change over trials (if male flights, female trills, and female time in view were chosen), or that it decreases over trials (if full and partial songs and male and female fright calls were chosen). By allowing the animals to express their behavior freely, I have arrived at some understanding of the organization of the behavior in the context of the entire behavioral repertoire.

Statistical procedures

Statistical methods have been developed that preserve the nature of the behavioral patterns of individual birds as much as possible. In addition, an attempt is being made to utilize exploratory factor analysis to aggregate the large number of behaviors observed during the playback experiments into a small number of independent factors, and to express the behavior in terms of these independent factor scores. A method has been devised to develop a regression equation for each individual subject (Petrinovich & Widaman, 1984) and then to group the equations statistically for the subjects in terms of similarity of regression weights. When such an individual characterization has been done, it is also possible to aggregate the individual regression equations into experimental treatment groups in a manner that does not mask the individual response characteristics of the different individuals (Petrinovich, 1989).

Thus, through the judicious use of powerful statistical procedures, it has been possible to develop a more complete description and understanding of the role of habituation in the regulation of the responsiveness of territorial males and females to the playback of song, and to explain the patterns of habituation to ongoing natural behavior throughout the reproductive cycle. I suggest that psychologists should begin to give more attention to the use of representative multivariate designs and the application of multivariate statistics to the data fields generated. The use of such complex design and analysis, combined with an attention to understanding individual differences in response style, could provide tools sufficient to arrive at major conceptual breakthroughs in the development of theories adequate to allow us to understand the behavior of organisms in their environment.

My methodological arguments have been based on Brunswik's belief that we should adopt research strategies that are appropriate to understand complex, molar behavior in representative situations. Because behavior takes place in a world that contains cues of limited trustworthiness that can be substituted for one another, the adequate research strategy must be one that allows the resulting inherent probabilism in causal mechanisms to express itself. Given that the organism is confronted with a welter of cues at any given time, that it has acquired a set of central dispositions on the basis of inheritance and experience, and that there are a number of satisfactory ways to behave in any given situation, research designs should be chosen that allow the detection of multiple mediation of information, probabilistic processing, and variable outcomes of behaviors.

I have developed the Brunswikian argument as an exercise in sampling theory (Petrinovich, in press). Traditionally, in behavioral science, it has been agreed that it is essential to obtain a representative sample of subjects on which to base psychological laws that will have general applicability. It has been argued that it is equally important to obtain an adequate sample of environmental stimuli; this is often referred to as contextual or situational sampling. Thus, to construct psychological theories at an adequate level of complexity, it is necessary to study representative samples both of subjects and of the situations to which these psychological laws are intended to apply.

Universes of generalization

To obtain representative samples of subjects and situations, one must define carefully the universe from which these samples are drawn. Clearly, we cannot sample a universe adequately if we have not taken pains to define its characteristics. If we have defined a universe, and obtained adequate samples from its domain, variables will be represented with their natural density and covariation expressed, a point of considerable importance when the interaction of variables is to be examined (see Hammond, 1954; Petrinovich, 1981).

This concept, which I call the universe of generalization, is of paramount importance and must be considered carefully. The concept is based on the ideas of Cronbach, Gleser, Nanda, and Rajaratnam (1972). They considered an observed score to be a representative of a universe of conditions (e.g., raters, tasks, stimuli presented, time of day, week, or year, settings) and of subjects. In this view, an observation should be regarded as a representative of a number of different universes of generalization; the observation might provide adequate support for some generalizations and be inadequate for others.

Just as an observation can be conceptualized as a member of several universes of conditions, a theory should be conceptualized in the same way. A theory is always a general statement about some specific set of occurrences. This set of occurrences, and the theory that collects them, could be conceived (depending on our interest) to be universal, to apply widely, to apply only in certain situations, to apply only to certain kinds of individuals, to apply only to certain individuals at certain places and times, or to apply only to this individual in this place at this time. A theory always applies to some universe of occurrences, and the question of sampling representativeness always arises whenever theories are about anything—as they always are.

The development of sound conceptualizations is of paramount importance if psychological theory is to progress. When we propose general theory, we want to understand the probable importance (effect size) and the interaction of a set of variables in a broader context than the ones we have studied. If we only wish to describe these things in the places we have observed them, we remain at the level of empirical generalization, and we have not moved toward theory in any significant sense.

Extending the idea of universes of generalization beyond measurement into the realm of theory introduces the concept that observations must be considered in relation to a theoretical universe, which can be construed as a population of propositions whose variance is represented as unity: 1.0. Then it is possible to consider a theory in terms of the proportion of the theoretical variance that can be accounted for, using the variables we now understand, and for which we have measurements: the ideal theory will approach the limit of 1.0. This view leads one to consider representativeness as a requirement for an adequate definition of the universe of instances and situations of the intended theoretical generalization.

The definition of the universe of generalization must lead to an adequate operational translation of the theoretical constructs involved if we are to relate theoretical propositions to observables and the different theoretical propositions to one another. This endeavor perhaps can be best accomplished by utilizing the procedures recommended to establish construct validity (Cronbach & Meehl, 1955), using the multitrait–multimethod approach (Campbell & Fiske, 1959; Hammond, Hamm, & Grassia, 1986). In the following section, I will use the findings regarding the development of song in the white-crowned sparrow to illustrate and exemplify the points I have made above.

DEVELOPMENT OF SONG IN THE WHITE-CROWNED SPARROW

A little natural history

The sedentary Nuttall subspecies of the white-crowned sparrow is found in the San Francisco Bay region. Most adult male white-crowned sparrows have a single 2-second-long song, the physical elements of which are organized into a relatively few phrases. The song is quite prevalent when the males are settling on their territories in January. Singing persists until the males obtain mates, then there is a resurgence of song when the females begin nest building and copulation occurs, and it persists until the young of the last brood are fledged (see Blanchard, 1941, for an authoritative description). The Nuttall subspecies attempts to raise two or more broods each season.

An interesting aspect of the song of this subspecies is that it has a large number of very noticeable regional dialects within a relatively restricted geographical region. The boundaries of the dialect areas that have been studied in the San Francisco Bay region have been quite stable for a number of years, and the size of each dialect area is small compared to those of the migratory subspecies.

Figure 1 contains a number of sound spectrographs of songs that will be referred to in the text. Several songs of the Nuttall subspecies have been studied carefully. The song of the Presidio dialect is characterized by an initial whistle, a buzz, two paired complex syllables, and several simple, comma-shaped syllables. In an area adjoining the Presidio dialect area one finds the Twin Peaks dialect, which is quite similar except for the slash-shaped simple syllables that have a wider frequency range than is characteristic of the Presidio song. The Lake Merced dialect differs from the first two in the types of syllables it contains and in their ordering. The Inspiration Point dialect is found across the San Francisco Bay in Tilden Park to the east of Berkeley. The Mendocino dialect, found several

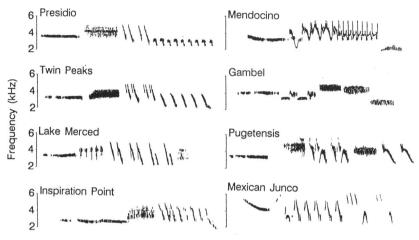

FIGURE 1. Sonagrams of white-crowned sparrow song dialects and songs of other birds discussed in the text. All songs are field recordings from normal singers.

miles north of San Francisco is quite different, and although not used in these studies, it is included to provide a better idea of the range of Nuttall songs.

The song of the alien Gambel subspecies is quite different from the Nuttall songs in that it has fewer discrete complex or simple syllables and concludes with three pronounced vibrato notes. The Pugetensis subspecies song has more syllable types than does the Gambel song, but is quite different in structure from the Nuttall song. One of the alien species songs that has been learned by white-crowned sparrows, that of the junco, is also illustrated in Figure 1.

Some important characteristics of the natural history of the white-crowned sparrow indicate the direction research should take to delineate the proximate mechanisms involved in song development. Nestlings hatch after having been brooded by the female for about 10 days. They remain in the nest for 9 or 10 days after hatching, then fledge from the nest, but remain in the immediate region of the nest for another 10 days or so. The young are fed by both parents until they are 20–30 days of age. They remain in the general region of the nest until they are at least 50 days of age, at which time many disperse from the natal region and can be found in what might become their breeding region.

Fledglings that acquire breeding territories in their natal dialect region sing a song with many of the characteristics of the local dialect, but there is considerable variability in song types within the dialect region. I have found that some breeding males whose father's and neighbors' songs have been recorded sing the same song as their fathers, some sing a song different from that of their fathers, more resembling the song of neighbors, and some sing a song with quite idiosyncratic elements (Petrinovich, 1988a). It can be concluded that males do not necessarily learn their song from their fathers.

It has also been reported that first-year birds newly arrived in an area sing a song with different dialect markers from those of the local region, but change their song to resemble that of the local dialect area (DeWolfe, Baptista, & Petrinovich, 1989). In one particularly compelling instance, a first-year male occupied a vacant territory and sang a song characteristic of a neighboring dialect. After a day or so, he was recorded singing the song of his immediate neighbor as well as his original song. A few days later, he was recorded singing only the song of the neighbor. He obtained a mate and successfully produced young on that territory. This, as well as other instances, indicates that song can be modified after birds leave the natal region, and suggests that social interaction with a neighbor might direct the course of that change.

The female white-crowned sparrow does not sing under ordinary circumstances, although there are field recordings of normal females singing under unusual circumstances, indicating that they are capable of producing song. If wild-caught females receive testosterone when they are adults, most will sing a recognizable version of the local dialect. Only a few hand-reared females sing when treated with testosterone at adulthood, but almost all hand-reared males sing either spontaneously or when treated with testosterone as adults.

It has been suggested (e.g., Nottebohm, 1969) that one function of the learned regional dialects of the white-crowned sparrow is the maintenance of the integrity of local populations that are well adapted to the requirements of their particular breeding habitat. Baker and Cunningham (1985) argued that birds of both sexes may learn the songs of their fathers and that females should choose as mates males that sing the song of their fathers. Mate selection by dialect could promote inbreeding, which would fix genes that adapt individuals to their natal environment, or it could cause a deviation from panmixia (Payne, 1973; Baker, 1982) which could be adaptive (Wright, 1943; Miller, 1947).

In field studies with migratory (Baptista & Morton, 1982) and with sedentary (Petrinovich & Baptista, 1984) subspecies, a male's song was recorded, then his mate was trapped and injected with testosterone and her song was recorded. No tendency was found for females to be mated with males that sang a song of the same dialect as their own. It has also been found that in a sedentary subspecies (Petrinovich, 1988a) and in a migratory subspecies (Baptista & Morton, 1988), females did not preferentially choose as mates males that sang the same song as the females' fathers. Such preferential choice would have been expected if song was being used as a marker to promote positive assortative mating.

The lack of a simple relationship between song type and choice of mate, combined with the finding that song learned when the birds are younger than 50 days can be modified after that age (Petrinovich & Baptista, 1987), suggests that song does not function as a reliable marker of the birds' natal area, thereby making it unlikely that it could serve to promote patterns of positive assortative mating. Data on several other species that demonstrate the ability to alter songs after dispersal from the natal area support the view that, in many instances, song is not used to regulate breeding patterns (e.g., Jenkins, 1978; King & West, this volume; Kroodsma, 1974; McGregor & Krebs, 1982; Payne, 1981, 1983; Payne, Payne, & Doehler, 1987; Rothstein & Fleischer, 1987). Thus, the proximate mechanisms involved in the regulation of song learning seem to be quite plastic for some time after the birds leave the natal area, and, if this is so, song type is unlikely to be a reliable indication of natal area.

Laboratory studies of song development

Now, consider the research evidence obtained in the laboratory with hand-raised, acoustically isolated birds. Marler (1970) reported data for 10 individually isolated white-crowned sparrows of the Nuttall subspecies tutored with recorded song. He concluded that the critical period for song learning is 10–50 days, because birds not exposed to song during that time developed abnormal song, and because exposure to songs of alien species had no effect on song development: in both instances the young sang an atypical isolate song lacking the characteristic phrases of normal song.

I reported data from 40 tape-tutored male birds of the Nuttall subspecies (Petrinovich, 1985) that replicated the above findings of Marler, identified some of the factors involved in song learning, and questioned the generalization that there is a sensory gate that rejects the songs of alien species. The birds learned the songs of the alien *pugetensis* or *gambelii* subspecies, and if they were presented with songs from two different dialects, they would either sing one of them or they would sing a hybrid song. Three male birds were tape-tutored with the song of the alien Mexican junco (*Junco phaeonotus*), and two of the three copied elements of the junco song. This latter finding indicates that with a large number of song presentations, it is possible for young males to acquire elements of an alien species' song, even when a tape recording is used to present the song. The fact that the young birds could learn the song of an alien species indicates that the song is not gated at the sensory level: if presented a sufficient number of times, the alien song can be an effective tutoring stimulus.

An incidental observation that an untutored young bird that was over 50 days of age learned the song of a strawberry finch with which he was caged was the serendipitous event that led us to question both the idea of a 10–50-day critical period and of a sensory gating mechanism involving a song template. We appreciated the profound significance of this late learning of an alien song, and we replicated the finding to establish its reliability (Baptista & Petrinovich, 1984). We then performed a series of studies to investigate the generality of the finding (Baptista & Petrinovich, 1986; Petrinovich & Baptista, 1987), and to establish the general circumstances under which song learning could occur. These findings then led us to question existing views regarding both the proximate mechanisms of song development and their ultimate significance (Petrinovich, 1988a, 1988b).

Baptista and Petrinovich (1984) exposed each of six young male birds to a live tutor singing the song of the alien strawberry finch (*Amandava amandava*) species. All six copied the song of the tutor, whether the tutor was a real strawberry finch or a white-crowned sparrow that previously had learned strawberry finch song. The tutoring for these students did not begin until they were at least 50 days of age. Thus, with a live tutor, the sensitive phase is longer than 50 days, and it is possible for birds to learn an alien song. It seems clear that the initial suggestion that there was a critical period between Days 10 and 50 was an artifact obtained through the use of recorded song as the tutoring stimulus. In fact, if a live tutor is used to present the song, the sensitive phase for song learning extends beyond 100 days of age, and it is very easy for the young birds to learn alien songs. It is apparent that the concept of a sensory gating mechanism, as well as of a genetic blueprint (or sensory template) that serves to map the acceptable song types, was reasonable only because recorded song was used as a tutor stimulus. The reliance on results obtained using recorded tutoring stimuli also led to a mistaken view regarding the role of song in the regulation of the breeding patterns of the species. Because birds leave their natal territories to settle in their breeding territories by the time they are 50 days old (when the critical period would be closed), some thought it reasonable to assume that an adult's song would reveal its natal dialect area. Because birds in the wild are tutored not by recordings, but by live tutors, conclusions regarding the meaning of the distribution of song types in the population were incorrect.

Tables 1, 2, and 3 summarize the available tutoring data for the white-crowned sparrow. These data are based on studies by Baptista & Petrinovich (1984, 1986), Petrinovich (1985), Petrinovich & Baptista (1987), and some as yet unpublished data from my laboratory. Table 1 contains the results of the tutoring of 74 Z. l. *nuttalli* students with songs of their own subspecies. Almost all males (16 of 19) copied the song of either a taped or a live tutor during days 10–50, but only 1 of 8 copied a taped tutor after 50 days of age. In contrast, hardly any females (2 of 25) copied either a taped or a live tutor at any age. The data show that it is possible for males to learn from a live tutor after they have reached the age of 100 days, a finding that agrees with numerous field observations indicating that males can modify their song during their first breeding season.

The results of tutoring with an alien subspecies or species song are shown in Tables 2 and 3. Clearly, it is possible for both males and females to learn the song of their own subspecies, an alien subspecies, or an alien species from either a taped or a live tutor when 10–50 days of age. However, when 50 days old or older, the birds learned only from a live tutor. Copying was seen in live-tutored males even at over 100 days of age. Few females copied a tutor song in the

TABLE 1. Birds Tutored with Taped or Live Songs of the Nuttall Subspecies

Age (days)		Males			Females		
		n	Copying or partial copying	Isolate song	*n*	Copying or partial copying	Isolate song
<50					5	1	4
	Taped	15	12	3			
	Live	4	4	0	2	0	2
50–100							
	Taped	8	1	7	8	0	8
	Live	13	10	3	7	1	6
>100							
	Taped	—	—	—	—	—	—
	Live	9	5[a]	4	3[b]	0	3

[a]Three of these birds had been implanted with a testosterone pellet during tutoring.
[b]One of these birds had been implanted with a testosterone pellet during tutoring.

TABLE 2. Birds Tutored with Taped or Live Alien Subspecies Songs

Age (days)		Males			Females		
		n	Copying or partial copying	Isolate song	*n*	Copying or partial copying	Isolate song
<50							
	Taped	5	3[a]	2	1	0	1
	Live	2	2	0	—	—	—
50–100							
	Taped	2	0	2	1	0	1
	Live	4	1	3	4	0	4[b]
>100							
	Taped	—	—	—	—	—	—
	Live	1	1	0	—	—	—

Note: All birds were tutored with Gambel subspecies song except as noted.
[a]One of these birds was tutored with Pugetensis subspecies song.
[b]One of these birds acquired strawberry finch song in the second year.

TABLE 3. Birds Tutored with Taped or Live Alien Species Songs

Age (days)	Tutor species	Males			Females		
		n	Copying or partial copying	Isolate song	*n*	Copying or partial copying	Isolate song
<50							
Taped	Junco	3	2	1	—	—	—
Live	Strawberry finch	2	1	1	—	—	—
	Song sparrow	8	8	0	1	1	0
	Junco	2	2	0	—	—	—
50–100							
Taped	Strawberry finch	3	0	3	1	0	1
Live	Strawberry finch	7	6	1	2	1	1
	Song sparrow	—	—	—	2	1	1
	Junco	—	—	—	2	1	1
>100							
Taped		—	—	—	—	—	—
Live	Strawberry finch	2	2	0	—	—	—
	Song sparrow	3	1	2	—	—	—

laboratory, although females have been heard to sing in the wild. As mentioned earlier, most wild-caught females can be brought into song in the laboratory using testosterone injections.

It was suggested that our isolated birds were able to learn after 50 days of age only because they had not been previously exposed to song, which delayed the onset of the sensitive phase. If this were so, birds held in isolation until 50 days of age and then subjected to tape tutoring should learn, but they did not. Another way to speak to this objection more directly would be to permit the birds normal exposure to a song during days 10–50, and then to expose them to a live tutor singing a different song. If song experience during days 10–50 opens the song-learning mechanism, then experience between days 50 and 100 should not be effective, because the delay would not have been in effect. Petrinovich and Baptista (1987) exposed birds that learned song during days 10–50 to a live tutor singing a different song after the students were 50 days of age, the age at which they disperse from their natal territory (Blanchard, 1941). It was found that 10 of 13 males altered a learned song when exposed to a live tutor, while none of 9 females did.

The question remains as to whether song could be altered if the young birds were tutored in the normal fashion in the wild. Perhaps the later tutoring could be effective only when the artificial conditions of laboratory tutoring have prevailed. To speak to this question, we trapped six males in their natal area when they were about 40 days of age, brought them to the laboratory, and exposed them to a live tutor singing a song different from the natal dialect. Three of the six altered the song they had learned in the natal area, and three did not. None of five field-tutored females modified their learned song. It is, therefore, possible for males to modify a song learned either in the field or the laboratory if they are exposed to a live tutor when they are over 50 days old. The above findings also make it even more unreasonable to suppose that the successful tutoring found when the birds were over 50 days of age was an artifact produced by the early experience of auditory isolation. The song-learning mechanism remained available even after normal song learning experience in either the laboratory or the field.

CONCLUSIONS AND IMPLICATIONS

The initial deprivation research done with the white-crowned sparrow began with a conceptual focus similar to that developed by ethologists to account for the phenomena of imprinting. This view involved the assumption that the proximate mechanisms of song development involve an inborn system (a sensory song template) that accepts only certain stimulus inputs during an early restricted ontogenetic period, and that the system is irreversible and permanent once it has closed.

The initial song development research was done using tape recordings to present the song stimuli. This method of presenting the songs was chosen to ensure control of the stimulus input: a standard song stimulus could be presented a standard number of times at preset times, with constant control of stimulus quality. Marler (1987) considers live tutors to be "intractable" as experimental sources of learning stimuli. He writes, (p. 103) "Tape-recorded songs . . . are readily standardized and quantified, lending themselves to synthesis and independent control of their acoustic properties." As indicated in the discussion of the laboratory evidence, a set of conclusions was arrived at which was correct given the testing circumstances, but which was method-specific, applying only when songs were presented using tape recordings. The problem is not with the correctness or incorrectness of the conclusions arrived at, but with the lack of generalizability to the naturally occurring behavior of the species. If one is interested in understanding the proximate physiological mechanisms regulating natural behavior, it is essential that the behavioral testing situation be representative of the natural behavior of the species. Similarly, if one is to develop evolutionary arguments that involve ultimate factors, such as the effect of song on breeding patterns and resulting reproductive success, it is essential that the timing of behavioral expression be portrayed accurately.

The seemingly trivial choice of a single method to present song stimuli resulted in an inaccurate view of the song learning mechanism, and led to the postulation of an unnecessary set of physiological entities. As suggested above, if the song of alien species can be learned, it is not necessary to propose sensory gating systems at the physiological level. This inaccurate view of the underlying mechanisms also led to a set of ideas regarding the role of song dialects in the regulation of mate choice by females in the wild. The arguments regarding physiological mechanisms have been pursued in detail elsewhere (Petrinovich, 1988b), and will not be developed any further here. Much of the difficulty in conceptual focus could have been avoided had more careful attention been paid to studies of the distribution patterns and the stability of song types in the breeding population (see Baptista, 1975; Blanchard, 1941; DeWolfe, Baptista, & Petrinovich, 1989; Petrinovich, 1988a; Petrinovich & Patterson, 1982, 1983).

The role of the psychologist

What is the pivotal role that psychologists should play in developing a behavioral science? I have argued (Petrinovich, 1979) that psychology necessarily is involved in the development and utilization of inferential conceptions. Psychologists tend to be identified by the type of inferential process they investigate: memory, learning, perception, personality, etc. Although it is necessary to translate these conceptions into operations that permit measurement at some level, the major concerns are still with the overriding theoretical principles. "One of the unique responsibilities of the discipline of psychology is the development, elaboration, and use of these inferential terms in the explanation of behavior, and this responsibility provides one of the defining qualities of psychology as a discipline." (Petrinovich, 1979, p. 378).

As Hebb (1958, p. 460) so nicely phrased it, "Let us be clear first that there is no possibility of a physiological psychology that can avoid use of 'intervening variables' or 'dispositional concepts'—conceptions that refer not to a specific structure, or activity of a specified kind in a specific locus of the nervous system, but to a property of functioning of the whole nervous system which is known from behavior and which must involve such complexities of unit interactions in the nervous system that it would be impossible to specify them in detail." In fact, as Ayala (1972, p. 8) has phrased it, " . . . laws discovered at a higher level of organization have more frequently contributed to guide research at the lower level than vice versa."

To return to an earlier theme, this pivotal role of psychology will be realized, not by joining the molecular reductionists in their superb science of investigating proximate mechanisms, but by defining concepts, refining measures, and developing theoretical constructs. This should be done at a level of complexity that makes it possible to incorporate factors within the organism, such as sensory and response capacities and integrative mechanisms, with factors outside of the organism, such as adaptation and ecological supports. These concerns must be combined with an understanding of the historical and developmental influences that affect behavior. Such understanding can only be reached by paying careful attention to the details of measurement and quantification and by taking care to establish the construct validity of our different theoretical concepts. The latter will require us to understand what behaviors animals exhibit when in different environmental contexts and to allow this natural range of behavior to express itself as much as possible. If we are going to work within the complicated frameworks constituting the world of organisms, we must pay careful attention to the development and utilization of multivariate statistics, both as descriptive tools and as explanatory and confirmatory devices.

The special role of the comparative psychologist

Psychologists can make powerful contributions to behavioral science by using the methodological and statistical tools which have been forged within the general discipline. The comparative psychologist can make even more significant contributions. We comparative psychologists are cognizant of the statistical and methodological niceties that characterize our basic discipline, and most of us have a background in physiological psychology which alerts us to the importance of physiological mechanisms. We have come to appreciate and understand evolutionary processes, and recently, we have begun to appreciate the importance of ecological factors in the behavioral equation. Thus, we can make important contributions to the development of general behavior theory adequate to understand the behavior of organisms in their environment by our careful examination of the patterns of similarities and differences in behavior between species. In addition, understanding will result from a search for patterns of similarities and differences in mechanisms and adaptations as related to environmental factors that are important in the organism's ecological adjustments. Finally, one can understand behavior in terms of structural factors of the organism that provide constraints on the potentials for behavioral adaptations.

The research bearing on the song of the white-crowned sparrow illustrates several of the general methodological points developed above. It was found that through the use of a single method of presenting song, a misleading picture of song development had been developed. The outcomes of recent studies seem to fit quite nicely with what we know of natural behavior in the field, and the way is now open to develop an evolutionarily relevant understanding of proximate mechanisms, both at the neurophysiological and endocrinological levels.

An attempt is now being made to identify the factors that make it possible for some birds to learn while others fail to do so, even when all receive the same treatment. We are also attempting to identify the factors that make it possible for some tutors to teach effectively while others seem unable to function as effective tutors. These attempts are based on analysis of the behavioral events that seem to occur when animals do learn tutor songs. An attempt is then made to relate individual differences in quality of song learning to the mode of behavioral response to the tutor song.

Finally, more careful attention must be paid to sampling from a representative array of song types when examining the song learning process. Kroodsma (1989) has pointed out that in many tutoring studies, investigators have used only one or a few arbitrarily selected songs, which can produce an unfortunate confounding of treatment condition and song stimulus. It is clear, if one examines the outcome of isolation experiments in detail, that some songs are easier to learn than others, and it is possible that certain song elements within a song are more easily learned than others. By constantly being aware of such things as the use of song in the field, the organization of behavior throughout the year, the normal changes in hormone levels during the year, and the dynamics of breeding patterns in the field, it will be possible to develop more meaningful behavioral and physiological explanations than we have in the past.

SUMMARY

This chapter considers problems encountered in constructing adequate explanations of the factors influencing the development of song in birds. These problems involve levels of explanatory reductionism, differences between proximate and ultimate causes of behavior, sampling, and processes of generalization. The importance of these problems is illustrated through examples drawn from field studies of habituation and song development in the white-crowned sparrow. The role of the comparative psychologist in conducting research that resolves these problems is discussed.

No single research method should be used to develop scientific explanations. Careful attention should be paid to sampling song types in a representative manner when examining behavioral responses to songs. Ecological and behavioral processes should be representative of the universe of generalization toward which theoretical explanations are directed, and explanations should be framed in terms of the proximate mechanisms that stimulate and regulate behavior. At the same time, attention should be paid to the ultimate evolutionary ends that are being served by behavioral adaptations.

CHAPTER 16

THE EVOLUTION OF PARENT–OFFSPRING RECOGNITION IN SWALLOWS

Michael D. Beecher

In this chapter, I discuss our research on the evolution of recognition in swallows, primarily in the context of parents recognizing offspring. There have been many demonstrations that parents recognize their offspring (for a recent summary, see Colgan, 1983), often under extraordinarily difficult conditions (for example, a free-tailed bat mother finds her pup in a maternity cave of a million bats; McCracken & Gustin, 1987). That this should be so is as about as straightforward a prediction as can be made from basic natural selection reasoning: in species where parents increase their reproductive success by providing parental care, they receive this benefit only if they direct the care to their own offspring rather than to unrelated young. It is a small step from this basic natural selection argument and the many empirical demonstrations of parent–offspring recognition to the hypothesis that parent–offspring recognition should be better developed in colonial species than in noncolonial species. After all, in noncolonial species, a parent may be able to restrict its parental care to its own offspring simply by keeping them in the nest, or in a particular place apart from other young. Pure recognition may not be needed, or at least not needed to the same extent. Put differently, it seems reasonable to suppose that colonial species would show adaptations for parent–offspring recognition that noncolonial species would not. The term "adaptation" refers to a trait that the species in question has which other closely related species do not have, and it carries the important theoretical

360

implication that the ultimate cause of this species difference is a history of natural selection on the trait for the function specified: in this case, recognition (see Williams, 1966, for a general discussion of adaptation).

When my colleagues and I first began studying parent–offspring recognition in swallows, we supposed that there was already considerable evidence to support the idea that recognition is better developed in colonial species. We were surprised to discover, however, that there was not, despite generalizations to the contrary in textbooks and other secondary sources. The pattern of positive outcomes (demonstrations of parent–offspring recognition) and negative outcomes (failures to demonstrate it) was anything but consistent. Although most of the colonial species tested gave positive outcomes, not all did, and most of the noncolonial species tested also gave positive outcomes. Moreover, many of the studies were not adequate tests of recognition (I will discuss some of the problems in these tests later). Finally, rarely had a single investigator or group ever tested more than one species, which raises the question of comparability across different studies of different species. This confusing state of affairs is epitomized by the widely cited generalization that in herring gulls (which are colonial and where young intermingle at an early age) parents recognize their chicks, but in kittiwakes (which are also colonial but where the young cannot stray from their nests on narrow cliff ledges) parents fail to recognize their young. This generalization began with Cullen (1957), who compared her kittiwake studies to the herring gull studies of others. It turns out that this generalization is incorrect, and that in all gull species which have been adequately tested, parents fail to recognize their chicks in the early weeks (although chicks do recognize parents; Beer 1969, 1979; Holley, 1984; Knudsen & Evans, 1986; Miller & Emlen, 1975; Shugart, unpublished data).

All of this, taken together, led us to the conclusion that the pattern of positive and negative evidence might have more to do with the particular investigators than with the true state of affairs, and that in any case, there was no evidence that parent–offspring recognition differed in colonial and noncolonial species, or that it was affected by any ecological variable, for that matter. Thus, we began our work on parent–offspring recognition in swallows with three guidelines. First, we felt that the hypothesis that parent–offspring recognition is better developed in colonial species than in noncolonial species was plausible, but had not been confirmed for any group of animals. Second, we felt that the same research group had to look at both colonial and noncolonial species for an adequate test of the hypothesis. Thus, we decided to look in detail at both colonial and noncolonial swallows. Third, the major goal of our research—and this was predicated on the assumption that we would support the hypothesis that parent–offspring recognition is better developed in colonial swallows than noncolonial swallows—was to delineate the adaptations for recognition distinguishing these species.

SOME COMMENTS ON THE STUDY OF ADAPTATION IN ANIMAL BEHAVIOR

It is de rigueur these days to employ natural selection theory in the hypothetico-deductive fashion. While I agree that prediction should be central to the evolutionary approach to behavior, a purely predictive approach is often inappropriate. When the trait under study is complex—as is "recognition," or "mating system," or almost any of the composite traits we study in animal behavior—we may be able to predict general adaptive outcomes, but rarely will we be able to predict the particular adaptive solution which evolution has opportunistically selected from among the many possibilities.

Let me make this argument explicit. A prediction about the outcome of natural selection can be compelling, in the sense that if the argument has been correctly constructed, and if the supporting assumptions are correct, the prediction must be true. Indeed, if the prediction is not supported, we invariably reevaluate the argument and supporting assumptions. On the other hand, a prediction about the specific nature of the adaptations underlying the outcome—about the mechanisms—is inherently less compelling, and is often presumptuous. This is because natural selection is opportunistic. We can predict that animals will have evolved adaptive solutions to problems, but in any particular case, we generally cannot predict, on purely logical grounds, what opportunistic solution natural selection will have seized upon, nor what limitations (constraints on adaptation) this solution may have. In short, some solution to an ecological problem is necessary, but any particular solution is not.

The modern investigator of animal behavior should be a serious student of evolution, capable of constructing cogent natural selection arguments, eagle-eyed in detecting fallacious ones. The investigator, however, should not expect to be prescient, which is what correct "predictions" about mechanisms generally require. It is often rather easy to make an adaptive prediction about behavior, particularly when popular interpretation has set up a group selectionist or non-adaptive straw man. For example, consider the Mexican free-tailed bat mother who must find her pup amidst thousands or millions of other pups in the maternity cave. Several investigators were so impressed by the magnitude of this recognition problem that they concluded mothers must feed pups at random. McCracken, however, made, and subsequently confirmed, the contrary prediction that mothers do recognize their young in these circumstances (albeit imperfectly, see McCracken, 1984; McCracken & Gustin, 1987). It would generally be agreed that the McCracken prediction is a relatively easy, straightforward one by modern standards. Even its demonstration is relatively easy, given the modern technique of electrophoresis (and barring an aversion to bat caves). But the delineation of the actual adaptations which underlie this recognition, which must include evidence that they are absent (or less developed) in closely related bats not facing this recognition problem, is by no means easy. To delineate the adaptations, we are left with the time-honored empirical approach: we simply have get into the trenches and dig hard.

To take a broad example of the relative difficulty of predictions concerning outcomes compared with predictions concerning adaptations or mechanisms, consider research on the evolution of learning. There has been a tremendous interest in this area in recent years, and it has given us many demonstrations of adaptive *uses* of learning by animals. Nevertheless, it has not yet given us a single convincing demonstration of the action of natural selection on some aspect of learning, i.e., of adaptations of learning per se. (For a discussion of adaptive uses of learning versus adaptations of learning, see Beecher 1988b; Sherry 1988.) To take a specific example which will be discussed below, bank swallow parents learn the calls of their young, while, so far as we can tell, rough-winged swallow parents do not. This is certainly an adaptive use of learning by bank swallows, but we have no evidence at this point that learning per se is in any way adapted for this function. Rather, as we shall see below, our evidence so far points to other sorts of adaptations. It would be interesting if we found that bank swallows imprint on chick calls while rough-winged swallows do not, but we have not yet shown that. These would be difficult experiments to do, in fact, and that is precisely my point. Unravelling the specific solutions (mechanisms) shaped by natural selection can be far harder than predicting (and confirming) that some sort of solution has been found.

A GENERAL PERSPECTIVE ON RECOGNITION

In this section, I provide a general perspective on recognition. We have used this perspective as a simple model which suggests the necessary observations and experiments. I use the term "parent–offspring recognition" to refer to discrimination of offspring from unrelated young by parents based on individually distinctive cues. This definition specifically excludes discrimination based on circumstantial evidence (e.g., the location of the young in the home nest). In this chapter I do not treat the reverse process of young recognizing parents (but see Beecher, Stoddard, & Loesche, 1985).

While some researchers in this area prefer not to distinguish between recognition and discrimination, I prefer to use "recognition" as a more general, theoretical term, for the simple reason that an animal capable of discriminating between two individuals (or classes of individuals) may do so in one circumstance but not in another. Furthermore, the "failure" of recognition may be just as adaptive as its "success." Thus, I prefer to use "discrimination" in reference to specific contexts and "recognition" in reference to an underlying ability which may be inferred from the occurrence of discrimination in at least some contexts.

Several examples of successes and failures of recognition in the same animal will be given below (for further discussion of this point, see Beecher, in press-b, and Beecher & Stoddard, in press).

While it is sometimes convenient to speak of "individual recognition" as if it were a simple trait, it is in fact an outcome or a composite of several separate traits. This is easily seen by considering the particular case of parent–offspring recognition as a generalized recognition problem. One animal (the receiver, parent) is seeking another individual (the target individual, offspring) and is confronted by an individual (the sender) that may or may not be the target individual. The recognition process consists of four logically independent components. First, the sender must provide *cues* to its identity ("signature" cues). Although we should not necessarily expect that the sender will always signal "honestly," it is clear that the receiver requires such cues if it is to have any basis for a decision (assuming circumstantial evidence is inadequate). (For a discussion of cases where offspring might be favored to conceal their identity, see Beecher, 1988a.) Second, the receiver must process these cues in order to *perceive* the difference between target and nontarget individuals. Presumably, the receiver compares the signal to some model contained in its memory. Third, the receiver must *decide* whether the sender is the target individual. In theory, the receiver's decision rule should be based in part on the a priori probability of the receiver being the target individual, the costs of the two types of error (i.e., accepting an unrelated chick or rejecting one's own offspring), and the benefits of the two types of correct decisions. For example, in a solitary species, the probability of finding unrelated young in the home nest might be so tiny that selection would have favored the decision rule "Always accept young you find in the nest." Finally, the receiver must take appropriate *action*. For example, if the encounter is in the home nest, and the parent decides that the sender is an intruder, it could evict it, or avoid feeding it. Another class of "recognition behaviors" includes paying attention to signature cues, careful inspection of young in the nest before feeding, and so on.

The key point is that natural selection can promote individual recognition by acting appropriately on any of these four components of recognition: signal, perception, decision, and behavior. (Note that the distinction between signal, perception, and decision rule is straight from signal detection theory; e.g., Green & Swets, 1966). Thus, there are four general ways in which natural selection could shape the recognition process. Selection favoring recognition could (1) increase signature variation among individuals and/or decrease it within individuals, thus making individuals more distinctive; (2) increase perceptual sensitivity or attention to the signature traits, thus allowing receivers to discriminate more readily among senders; (3) modify the receiver's decision rule; and (4) shape recognition behaviors. In the research described below we have tried to use particular studies to dissect out the particular adaptations underlying recognition.

SWALLOWS

My colleagues and I have studied four species of North American swallows: two colonial species of swallows (bank swallows, *Riparia riparia*, and cliff swallows, *Hirundo pyrrhonota*) and two noncolonial species of swallows (northern rough-winged swallows, *Stelgidopteryx serripennis*, and barn swallows, *Hirundo rustica*). The North American swallows are an excellent group for research on adaptations to coloniality, because they are a rather uniform group, with coloniality being one of the major dimensions distinguishing the species. Of the seven North American swallow species, only bank swallows and cliff swallows are unequivocally colonial. By "colonial," I mean that they generally nest in large groups, aggregate their nests, and show reproductive synchrony as well as social coordination of other activities such as nest material collection and foraging. The four study species we chose form two natural comparison pairs. Bank swallows and rough-winged swallows are physically quite similar and share the habit of nesting in burrows. Bank swallows dig their burrows in sandbanks along river cuts and (nowadays) in sand quarries, while rough-winged swallows opportunistically use burrows dug and abandoned by other animals as well as other similar cavities such as drainpipes. In Michigan, where we studied them, rough-winged swallows most often nest in bank swallow colonies, usually with one or two pairs being found at the edge of the colony. Cliff swallows and barn swallows are an even closer comparison, since they are congenerics and even hybridize on occasion (we have found one hybrid at our study sites, and see Martin, 1980).

I should comment on the validity of the colonial–noncolonial distinction, for it is obviously crucial to interpretation of our comparative study. It is probably fair to refer to barn swallows and rough-winged swallows as "facultatively colonial," since in this country one occasionally does find them nesting in groups. Even when one does, however, the groups are typically small, with maximally dispersed nests and no reproductive synchrony. The key point is that all swallows are capable of coloniality because, unlike most passerines, they do not defend food territories, since they feed on unpredictable patches of insects. Thus, one sometimes finds the "noncolonial" swallow species in small groups, probably where suitable nesting sites are in short supply. Although this makes the colonial–noncolonial distinction less black and white, it does not blur the basic issue, which has to do with the evolutionary background of the species in question, not the size of the group in which our subject animals happen to be living. In fact, most of our research on both cliff swallows and barn swallows has actually been on birds living in colonies of about 30–50 nests. But all aspects of their behavior suggest that cliff swallows and bank swallows are adapted to colonial living, while barn swallows and rough-winged swallows are not. It is these adaptations to colonial living we are interested in. The intraspecific variation in group size that we find, however, does allow us to look at the *proximate* effects of group living on recognition.

NATURAL OBSERVATIONS OF RECOGNITION

The presence of colonial living in a species is almost a prima facie case for strong selection for recognition. In almost all colonial species, intermingling of young is inevitable and extensive, and there is great pressure on parents to recognize their young (the cliff-nesting kittiwake is an exception—Cullen, 1957). In the swallow species we have studied, intermingling of young is conspicuous in the two colonial species and rare in the two noncolonial species (Beecher & Beecher, unpublished data; Beecher, Beecher, & Lumpkin, 1981; Medvin & Beecher, 1986; Stoddard & Beecher, 1983).

In all four of the swallow species, parents continue to feed and care for young for some time after fledging. Young fledge after approximately 3 weeks in the nest, and their dependence on their parents wanes gradually over the next 2 weeks or so. Typically, there is a period ranging from a day to a week after fledging during which the young spend some of their time at the nest and some of their time away from the nest. From this point on, the situation diverges for the colonial and noncolonial species. In bank swallows and cliff swallows, this interim stage is usually longer than it is in noncolonial rough-winged swallows and barn swallows, in part because in the colonial species, parents often leave their just-fledged young in "creches" ("nursery" groups) near the colony. Chicks and parents frequently become separated and fly about looking for one another near the colony or nest site. Often lost young fly into the wrong nest. These errant flights present parents with a two-sided recognition problem: first, parents must search for their young in the colony, and second, parents must make sure that the young they find in their nest are actually their own. Interlopers are usually detected and ejected. The other major context for parent–offspring recognition in the colonial species occurs in the creche. We have found that creches are common in bank swallows and cliff swallows, and that parents can indeed locate their young in the creches.

In rough-winged swallows and barn swallows, on the other hand, recognition problems rarely arise because there are generally few or no similar-aged conspecific young nearby. Furthermore, even when the two noncolonial species are found in small groups, or when their nests are relatively clumped, parents avoid mixing their young with others in the early days after fledging. We have never observed creches in rough-winged swallows or barn swallows, although we occasionally see small groups of older fledglings, which are largely independent of their parents.

CROSS-FOSTERING EXPERIMENTS

In our cross-fostering experiments, we exchanged approximately half the chicks between two nests that each contained chicks of the same age. Control chicks were handled in the same way that experimental chicks were, but were returned to the home nest. In these experiments, we say that "recognition" has occurred when significantly more control chicks are accepted than experimental chicks. Field cross-fostering experiments generally provide only a first approximation to recognition, since the criterion of "recognition" is inevitably indirect. It is indirect because we generally cannot monitor the nest and our subjects exhaustively, and so must use "bottom-line" criteria of acceptance or rejection, such as whether the subject is present or absent in the nest 24 hours later.

The age at which the cross-fostering is done is crucial, since even when recognition occurs in a species, it typically does not appear until relatively late, usually shortly before fledging. The only case we will consider here, therefore, is cross-fostering carried out at about the time of first flights. The results are shown in Table 1. Of the three swallow species we tested, only the colonial bank swallow gave clear evidence of recognition (Beecher, Beecher, & Hahn, 1981). In comparable experiments with noncolonial rough-winged swallows and barn swallows, on the other hand, exchanged and sham-exchanged birds were accepted equally (Beecher & Beecher, unpublished data; Medvin & Beecher, 1986; see also Hoogland & Sherman, 1976).

Because bank swallows and rough-winged swallows nest together in sandbanks in Michigan, we were able to carry out interspecific cross-fostering experiments (Beecher 1981; Beecher & Beecher, unpublished data). Normally, such exchanges between species will fail because the chicks are poorly adapted to the heterospecific nest environment. In this case, however, both species are nesting in precisely the same habitat. Moreover, the diets of the two species are highly similar. In these exchanges, we would add a single bank swallow to

TABLE 1. Summary of Intraspecific Cross-Fostering Experiments

Species (Reference)	Percentage of chicks accepted		Number of chicks accepted	
	Foster	Control	Foster	Control
Bank swallow (1)	22	100	18	20
Rough-winged swallow (2)	100	100	12	14
Barn swallow (3)	42	58	36	41

Note. Data from: (1) Beecher, Beecher, & Hahn, 1981; (2) Beecher & Beecher, unpublished data; (3) Medvin & Beecher, 1986. In all experiments, chick exchanges were carried out on or shortly before first flights from the nest. Differing "acceptance" criteria were used in the different experiments. Thus, for example, in the case of the barn swallows, the criterion was that the chick be present at a nest check the following day. Many absent chicks, however, may have flown of their own accord, and thus may have been only temporarily absent from the nest. The bank swallow and rough-winged swallow nests were canvassed more closely.

a rough-winged swallow brood, or a single rough-winged swallow to a bank swallow brood.

We found that rough-winged swallows added to bank swallow nests were typically rejected (5 out of 6), whereas bank swallows added to roughwing nests were invariably accepted (6 out of 6). I should add that we also have seen rough-winged swallow parents feeding bank swallow chicks that had flown into their nest. What these interspecific transfers tell us that the intraspecific transfers cannot is that rough-winged swallow parents do not accept alien chicks purely because they cannot discriminate own from alien. Bank swallow chicks are clearly different from rough-winged swallow chicks (visually and acoustically), and we have seen roughwing parents do visible double-takes before feeding a bank swallow chick. The difference between bank swallows and rough-winged swallows in these interspecific fostering experiments parallels the difference between those passerine species that accept and those that reject cowbird eggs (Rothstein, 1982). The difference between cowbird and host eggs is quite conspicuous, and acceptance of cowbird eggs seems to reflect either a decision rule (possibly adaptive, see Rohwer & Spaw, 1988) or a lack of appropriate eviction behavior (Rothstein 1982), rather than a perceptual inability.

This inference is supported by a second type of cross-fostering experiment we carried out in which we exchanged rough-winged swallow and bank swallow broods from adjacent or close burrows (Beecher & Beecher, unpublished data). We observed that both sets of parents would shortly begin to feed their chicks at the new location. Although the behavior of the two sets of parents in this situation cannot be treated as independent (which is why we generally didn't use this very convenient design), rough-winged swallow parents were clearly attracted to the calls of their young. These experiments suggest that when forced to make a hard choice, rough-winged swallow parents can indeed discriminate conspecific from heterospecific chicks.

One interpretation of these interspecific cross-fostering experiments is that these two species normally employ different decision rules when confronted with the problem of discrimination between their own and alien young. In bank swallows, parents are often confronted with such a problem, and have been selected to base their decisions on individually distinctive cues. In rough-winged swallows, where such discriminations are almost never required, the criterion of "Feed any chick you find in your nest" has been a generally reliable, conservative rule. A chick's presence in the home nest is, of course, strictly circumstantial evidence as to its relatedness, but in rough-winged swallows it is a virtually fail-safe criterion. In bank swallows, however, it is an unreliable predictor of relatedness, at least for chicks near flying age. According to this hypothesis, in the chick substitution test, a rough-winged swallow parent that finds a bank swallow chick in its nest gives priority to the chick's location in the home nest over its unusual appearance and sound, and so accepts it. In the close interchange test, however, the rough-winged swallow parent is confronted not only with an entire brood of transplanted heterospecific chicks in its nest, but also with its own brood of chicks calling at the mouth of a nest close by. It cannot tend to both broods of chicks. In this case, the very large difference in calls and physical appearance is pitted against the very small difference in location, and the parent gives priority to calls and appearance. With regard to this hypothesis, I should point out that we have good evidence for a decision rule of this sort in a species where parent–offspring recognition normally occurs. Caspian tern parents will accept young substituted for their own in the first week of life, yet when given a choice between their own and alien young in nest scrapes on either side of the original nest, they will unfailingly choose their own (Shugart, 1977). Similar results are obtained with egg-fostering experiments in this species (Shugart, 1987).

PLAYBACK EXPERIMENTS

As noted earlier, during the interim period just after fledging, chicks and parents often become separated and fly about looking for one another near the colony or nest site. Reciprocal calling is a conspicuous feature of these events, and one forms the casual impression that these calls are critical to the reunion of chick and parent. The call given by the chick in these aerial reunions is the same begging call it gives before virtually every feeding at the nest, in the air, or (in the case of bank swallows and cliff swallows) at the creche. In the colonial context, many chicks will be calling at any one time. This is true at the creche and at the colony, where chicks sitting at the front of nests and chicks flying near the colony, presumably lost, create a cacophony. Despite the appearance of pandemonium, an observer tracking color-marked birds will discover that parent and chick usually get together. In the noncolonial context, there will usually be very few birds calling, and a parent searching for its young could assume that any chick flying about and calling is ipso facto its offspring. Thus, in barn swallows or rough-winged swallows, a begging call need only be a general "lost" call. In the colonial bank swallows and cliff swallows, however, the call ideally should have identifying or "signature" features as well, as a parent will typically be required to discriminate its calling young from other calling young.

In our playback experiments, we simulated the situation in which chick and parent become separated near the nest. Most often this will occur when the chick flies from, and tries to return to, the nest when the parent is away. On returning to the nest area, the parent must search for the lost chick, and will usually try to lure it back to the nest (although the strategies of parents of different species may differ somewhat; see below). Our procedures for all species were essentially the same, so as to enhance comparability (Beecher & Beecher, unpublished data; Beecher, Beecher, & Hahn, 1981; Medvin & Beecher, 1986; Stoddard & Beecher, 1983).

The experiment was done on nests where young were close to fledging. Some of the young had already taken some trips to and from the nest, or were on the verge of doing so. We began by temporarily removing the young from the nest and placing loudspeakers in or above two empty nests on either side of the empty home nest, 3–4 meters apart. (For barn swallows we sometimes had to install extra empty nests). When one of the parents returned to the home nest, it would begin to search for the missing young, i.e., calling from the nest or calling while flying about in the vicinity. At this point we turned on our playback tapes, and the parent heard calls coming from the two loudspeakers. From one loudspeaker, it heard the calls of its own chicks, recorded the previous day. From the other loudspeaker, it heard the calls of unrelated, similar-aged chicks. Our measure of recognition was the number of approaches the parent made to each playback speaker during a trial. Experimental and control calls were played an equal number of times on each side. Our question was, would parents respond more strongly to loudspeakers playing the calls of their own chicks—would they recognize their young by voice?

The results for all four species are summarized in Table 2. The first response measure is simply the percentage of tested parents that responded more strongly to the calls of their offspring than they did to the calls of the unrelated chicks. The second response measure is the percentage of the total approach responses to the two sets of calls that were approaches to the parent's own offspring. Both measures show that recognition is well developed in the colonial bank swallow and cliff swallow and absent (or at least weaker) in the noncolonial rough-winged swallow and barn swallow.

It is possible that barn swallows and rough-winged swallows normally use visual cues for recognition. Our failure to find parental recognition in the cross-

TABLE 2. Summary of Playback Experiments

Species (Reference)	Number of parents tested	Percentage of parents choosing offspring	Percentage of parental responses to offspring
Bank swallow (1)[a]	12	100	100
Rough-winged swallow (2)	5	40	47
Cliff swallow (3)[a]	7	100	86
Barn swallow (4)	13	61	52

Note. Data from: (1) Beecher, Beecher, & Hahn, 1981; (2) Beecher & Beecher, unpublished data, (3) Stoddard & Beecher, 1983; (4) Medvin & Beecher, 1986.
[a]Colonial species.

fostering experiments with these two noncolonial species argues against this interpretation. In addition, of the four species, only cliff swallow chicks show marked individual variation in face color pattern (see Stoddard & Beecher, 1983). Although we have not investigated whether cliff swallow parents use this visual variation for recognition, this species difference is opposite that expected if the noncolonial swallow species use the visual modality rather than the acoustic modality; additionally, we know of no case in which visual recognition has been shown in birds where the visual variation is not conspicuous to the eye of the human observer.

I should emphasize that in all four species, parents searched for their lost young and were attracted to loudspeaker calls. The difference is that in the colonial species, parents always chose the calls of their young, while in the noncolonial species, parents appeared to choose the calls randomly. Nevertheless, I should note some differences between the searching behavior of parents in these species. Of the two noncolonial species, we made our most detailed observations on barn swallows. Compared to either of the colonial species, barn swallow parents were more likely to stay at the nest and call, less likely to actively search away from the nest, and less strongly attracted to the playback speakers. This difference suggests that barn swallow parents may recognize the calls of their chicks, at least to some degree, but that their normal style of dealing with lost chicks is to call them back home rather than to go out and try to find them via their calls. Or possibly, lost chicks that do not respond to the parental call (as happened in our experiment) represent such an unusual event for barn swallows that selection has not shaped the call-directed searching behavior we see in bank swallows and cliff swallows. These behavioral differences suggest a conclusion similar to the one I drew from our interspecific fostering experiments with rough-winged swallows. The noncolonial swallow species may "fail" our recognition tests (cross-fostering experiments, playback experiments) not simply because they have difficulty discriminating between their own and alien chicks, but also because in their evolutionary background they have not had to make such discriminations. That is, in the normal field context, barn swallows and rough-winged swallows do not normally have to evict alien chicks from their nests, do not have to select their young out of a crowd away from the nest, and so forth, and so natural selection has not equipped them with the necessary behaviors and decision rules that we see in bank swallows and cliff swallows.

SUMMARY OF FIELD STUDIES

The evidence from our field studies (observational, cross-fostering, and playback) supports the generic natural selection prediction that recognition will be better developed in colonial species than in related noncolonial species. Moreover, since the cliff swallow versus barn swallow comparison studies were mostly done on colonies of similar size, this species difference must be traced to the ultimate effects rather than the proximate effects of colonial living, i.e., to the group sizes which were experienced by ancestral cliff swallows and barn swallows, rather than to those experienced by the birds we happened to study.

Our major goal has been to go beyond simple confirmation of the generic natural selection prediction to an analysis of the actual adaptations underlying the coloniality–recognition correlation. To do this, we must look closely at our observational, cross-fostering, and playback studies. Although no one of these rather conventional tools of analyzing recognition permits dissection of the components of recognition (signal, perception, decision rule, and behavior), taken together they provide some strong hints that decision-rule and/or behavioral adaptations are part of the story. For example, rough-winged swallow parents fail to discriminate between bank swallow and rough-winged swallow young when both are present in the home nest, yet they do make the correct choice when forced to do so (when their young and alien young are placed in adjacent nests). Barn swallow parents seem to follow a somewhat different "roundup" strategy than do the colonial swallows, tending to return to the home nest and calling lost young to them, rather than actively searching for and retrieving them. Thus, it would be misleading to summarize the studies described above by saying, "Colonial swallows recognize their young, while noncolonial swallows do not." This statement places all the emphasis on capacity, suggesting that the adaptations are exclusively signal and/or perceptual. We decided, therefore, to examine signal and perceptual adaptations directly via two additional types of study. First, we carried out a signal analysis of the calls used by bank swallows and cliff swallows in recognition and of the homologous calls of rough-winged swallows and barn swallows. We were looking for evidence of adaptation of these calls for "signature" function in the colonial species. Second, we brought cliff swallows and barn swallows into the laboratory to carry out a perceptual analysis of their calls. In the laboratory, we could analyze the birds' perception of conspecific and heterospecific calls, and potentially separate out signal and perceptual adaptations.

INFORMATION ANALYSIS OF SWALLOW CHICK CALLS

Perhaps the simplest hypothesis concerning adaptations for recognition (and thus the first one to occur to me) is that the signals used in recognition have been modified so as to be more individually distinctive in the colonial species. As mentioned earlier, chick calls are a key part of recognition in natural circumstances. Inspection of sonagrams of the calls used by swallows strongly suggested this hypothesis, since the calls of the colonial species appeared more individually distinctive than the homologous calls in the noncolonial species (see Figure 1). Clearly, a method was needed to objectify and quantify these visual impressions.

To evaluate this "signature adaptation" hypothesis, therefore, I developed a model for analyzing the relative information capacities of signals (a preliminary version is described in Beecher, 1982, and the final version is in Beecher, in press-a). The model combines the Shannon information measure (Shannon & Weaver, 1949) and the Model II (Random Effects) of Analysis of Variance (e.g., Sokal & Rohlf, 1981). I provide a brief outline of the model here.

Suppose we are measuring a single variable trait, such as the duration of a call, and have n observations each on k individuals. Then by the model a particular observation, X_{ij}, is assumed to be composed of two independent components: a component B_i, reflecting true differences between individuals, and a "within-individual" or "error" component, W_{ij}, i.e.,

$$X_{ij} = B_i + W_{ij}$$

assuming that the means are zero. Because B_i and W_{ij} are independent, the variances have the simple relationship

$$\sigma^2_T = \sigma^2_B + \sigma^2_W$$

where σ^2_T is the total variance in X and σ^2_B and σ^2_W are the variances in B and W respectively.

H is then defined as the amount of information needed to reduce the total uncertainty to the within-individual uncertainty, which turns out to be

$$H = \log \frac{\sigma_T}{\sigma_W}$$

H so defined has all the properties an information measure should have (see Shannon & Weaver 1949), including the following: (1) Signature information increases directly with σ_B and inversely with σ_W; (2) $H = 0$ when $\sigma_B = 0$; (3) H is an absolute measure with a nonarbitrary zero, the unit of measure being the within-individual uncertainty. The original units of measurement are immaterial. We can compare, say, the amount of signature information conveyed by the amount of dark feathering on the face with that conveyed by the average frequency of a call.

The signature traits typically measured by investigators, however, are inherently multivariate. That is, they can be analyzed into a number of intercorrelated variables. This is certainly true of the calls we are considering here. Studies in this area have generally overlooked the intercorrelations, doing a separate ANOVA on each variable. It is sometimes assumed that the larger the number of significant Fs obtained in such an analysis, the greater the potential signature information. Such an assumption is incorrect, of course, since much of the information may be shared by variables, i.e. may be redundant.

The problem of variable intercorrelations is circumvented by doing a principal components transformation of the original data. The information analysis is

(A) Bank swallow   Roughwing

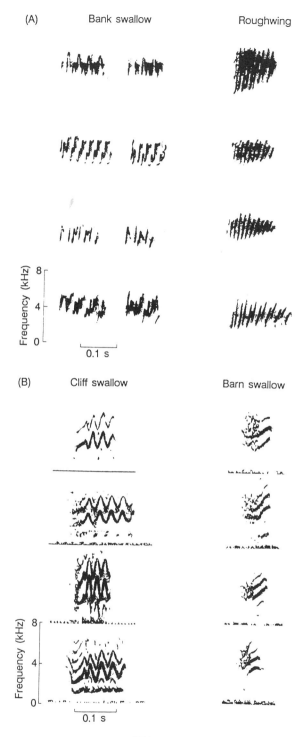

Frequency (kHz)
8
4
0

0.1 s

(B) Cliff swallow   Barn swallow

Frequency (kHz)
8
4
0

0.1 s

374

then done on the principal components, which are uncorrelated and preserve the total nonredundant variance (generalized variance) of the original data set. Then the total information H_S is simply the sum of the information H_i in each of the principal components, and

$$H_S = \Sigma \, H_i = \Sigma \, \log \frac{\sigma_{Ti}}{\sigma_{Wi}}$$

where σ_i is the standard deviation of the ith trait.

The analysis of swallow calls begins with extraction of measurements from sonagrams of calls. We have done the complete analysis only on the cliff swallow and barn swallow chick calls (Medvin, Stoddard, & Beecher, unpublished data). An analysis of a small data set of bank swallow and rough-winged swallow chick calls was done using an earlier, preliminary version of this method (Beecher, 1982); analysis of larger data sets using the final method is in progress (Beecher & Beecher, unpublished data).

The call parameters are chosen so as to describe the call as completely as possible with the smallest number of parameters. We used five parameters for the cliff swallows and four for the barn swallows. With the exception of the fifth parameter (cliff swallows but not barn swallows have a periodic frequency modulation of the call), the parameters were comparable for the two species. This comparability condition is essentially irrelevant for our analysis, for the method allows us to compare apples and oranges, or calls and odors, or whatever signature sets we choose. The key condition is that we extract all of the information in the signatures of the two species being compared, or that if we do not, that we err on the conservative side. We have met the second part of this condition. We evaluated our success in extracting most of the information in the calls with this parameter set by reconstructing the original calls from our measurements. While the replicas we got were somewhat crude, they were better for the barn swallow calls than for the cliff swallow calls. Thus, our error is conservative, given our hypothesis, since it means that our method underestimates the information capacity of the cliff swallow calls more than that of the barn swallow calls.

The acoustical measurements derived from the sonagrams are next subjected to a principal components analysis. Simple ANOVAs are carried out on the principal components and between-individual, within-individual, and total variance estimates are obtained according to the Model II (Random Effects) model. The total information is then computed by the formula given above.

The analyses of cliff swallow and barn swallow chick calls are summarized in Table 3, in terms of the original measurements (means, standard deviations based

◄**FIGURE 1.** (A) Sonagrams of the calls of four bank swallow chicks and four rough-winged swallow chicks. (B) Sonagrams of the calls of four cliff swallow chicks and four barn swallow chicks.

TABLE 3. Acoustical Measurements of Cliff Swallow and Barn Swallow Chick Calls

	Cliff swallows					Barn swallows			
	T	f	Δv	Δf	Pa	T	f	Δv	Δf
Mean	74.4	3.71	1.53	1.25	29.0	67.0	3.84	1.14	0.797
SD Total	31.8	0.395	0.404	0.304	5.12	7.76	0.359	0.183	0.261
SD Within	8.88	0.084	0.142	0.141	0.662	3.62	0.083	0.107	0.151
T	—	−0.42	−0.39	−0.16	+0.37	—	−0.28	−0.53	+0.04
f	—	—	+0.23	+0.58	−0.32	—	—	−0.44	+0.02
Δv	—	—	—	−0.23	+0.50	—	—	—	−0.30
Δf	—	—	—	—	+0.20	—	—	—	—

Note. T = duration of the call (ms); f = peak frequency of the lower voice (kHz); Δv = frequency difference between the upper and lower voices (kHz); Δf = frequency modulation range of the lower voice; P = the period of frequency modulation (ms). Numbers in the bottom half of the table are correlation coefficients based on the between-individual data.
[a]This parameter pertains to cliff swallows only.

on the variance estimates, and the among-individual parameter intercorrelations), not the principal components. Table 3 also provides a brief description of these measurements. The total information capacity, based on the ANOVA of the principal components (not shown in Table 3), is 8.74 bits for cliff swallow calls and 4.57 bits for barn swallow calls. Thus ,as predicted, the information capacity of the signature calls of the colonial cliff swallow is greater than that of the noncolonial barn swallow. This finding of greater information capacity for the colonial species parallels the difference found between the colonial bank swallow and noncolonial rough-winged swallow in an earlier study using the preliminary version of this method (Beecher, 1982). The difference of 4.17 bits between cliff swallow calls and barn swallow calls can be roughly translated to say that approximately 20 times more individuals can be identified, to the same degree of precision, with the cliff swallow signature system.

PERCEPTUAL STUDIES OF SWALLOW CALLS

Several assumptions are implicit in our comparison of the information capacity of cliff swallow and barn swallow chick calls. First, we assume that we have extracted all (or most of) the relevant information from the calls. Second, our method weights all extracted parameters equally (or more precisely, by σ_{Ti}/σ_{Wi}). Third, the method provides a measure of the information capacity of the calls, not of the information extracted by the receiver; in a sense, it presumes an ideal receiver. It should be clear that all of these assumptions relate to a single issue: does our call analysis parallel the birds' perception of the calls? To answer this question, we have carried out a study of the perception of cliff swallow and barn swallow chick calls by cliff swallows and barn swallows, which I will describe briefly here (Beecher, Loesche, Stoddard, & Medvin, 1989; Loesche, Stoddard, Higgins, & Beecher, unpublished data).

We tested the hypothesis that cliff swallow calls are more discriminable than barn swallow calls by training laboratory-reared birds of both species to discriminate among the calls of different individuals of each species. We used the methods of "animal psychophysics" (Stebbins, 1970), training birds to discriminate among calls for a food reward. The reward contingencies (for example, responses to the call of cliff swallow A are rewarded, and responses to the call of cliff swallow B are not) allowed us to circumvent confounding natural contexts and natural decision rules and focus in on signal and perceptual adaptations. On the basis of the call analysis just described, we predicted that cliff swallow calls would be more distinctive, or discriminable, than barn swallow calls.

Our birds were trained as adults to discriminate among chick calls. Birds were trained in a soundproof booth equipped with a loudspeaker, a light, a feeder, and two pecking keys. Pecks on the left, "observing" key turned on a call. In each pair of calls, one was arbitrarily designated the positive (GO) stimulus and the other the negative (NOGO) stimulus. Pecks on the right, "report" key within 1 second of the GO call were reinforced with an opportunity to feed. Pecks within 1 second of a NOGO call, or a failure to respond to a GO call, produced a time-out period during which the houselight was out. A bird received only one pair of calls in a given session, with the two calls always being from different individuals of the same species. The bird was trained on the same pair of calls until it reached a criterion of 85 percent correct responses in a session. Thus, our measure of the discriminability of a call pair was the number of sessions it took to reach this criterion. Training on a new pair of calls began in the next session. The experiment was terminated when a bird had learned five or ten pairs each of cliff swallow and barn swallow calls. We tested two cliff swallows, two barn swallows, and one European starling (*Sturnus vulgaris*), all hand raised. Each of the five birds received unique pairings of calls, and the calls were chosen to be representative of our larger data base for the two species.

The results of the perceptual study are shown in Figure 2. It can be seen that all five birds learned cliff swallow call discriminations more readily on average than they learned barn swallow call discriminations. There is no hint of an advantage for conspecific calls; in fact, the greatest preference for cliff swallow call pairs was shown by one of the barn swallows. These perceptual experiments are consistent with the results of our information analysis of the calls, and they support the hypothesis that natural selection has acted on the chick's begging

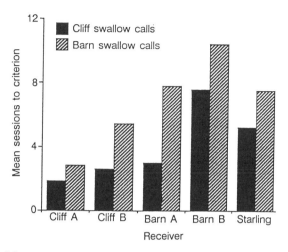

FIGURE 2. Mean sessions to criterion of 85 percent correct responses for discrimination between pairs of cliff swallow calls (dark) and pairs of barn swallow calls (stippled) by two cliff swallows (Cliff A and Cliff B), two barn swallows (Barn A and Barn B), and a starling. Results are based on 10 pairs of calls for the cliff swallow subjects and barn swallow A, and 20 pairs of calls for barn swallow B and the starling.

call in cliff swallows and bank swallows so as to enhance the call's individual distinctiveness. Thus, in these colonial species, this "signature call" is properly considered an *adaptation* for parent–offspring recognition.

At the same time, these studies also show that the difference in discriminability between barn swallow and cliff swallow calls is purely a quantitative one. All birds could in fact discriminate between two calls from different barn swallows. Although these discriminations were presented without the blurring effect of within-individual variability, we believe they show that barn swallow calls can be discriminated, though not so easily as cliff swallow calls.

The one thing we have no evidence for in any of these studies is perceptual adaptations. Our sample size here is too small to rule out such adaptations, and the difficulty of these laboratory experiments, at least with swallows, precludes further attempts to get at such adaptations. Nevertheless, the acoustic sense of passerines is generally highly developed, and it is not clear that there is a great deal of need or room for further perceptual adaptations for this single purpose of better perceiving signature calls. Elsewhere we have argued against the likelihood of perceptual adaptations specifically for analyzing swallow calls (Beecher, et al., 1989; Beecher, Medvin, Stoddard, & Loesche, 1986).

CONCLUSIONS

By combining our various approaches, we have put together a preliminary characterization of the differences among these four species of swallows with respect to the four components of parent–offspring recognition. First, signals are more distinctive in colonial species. The calls of cliff swallow and bank swallow chicks show more individual variation than those of barn swallow and rough-winged swallow chicks. Also, there is face plumage variation in cliff swallow chicks but not in the other species. Second, so far as we can tell, perception of these signals does not differ among the four species. Third, the decision rule used by the noncolonial species appears to be more conservative, giving priority to the location of chicks over signature cues. Fourth, the colonial and noncolonial species use different searching strategies, and eviction and other actions that might be thought of as "recognition" behaviors are seen only in the colonial species. If we imagine that the noncolonial swallows resemble more closely the common ancestors of all four species, then these conclusions form a rudimentary evolutionary scenario as well.

I hope readers will agree that we have gone beyond a simple test of the prediction that colonial swallows should show better parent–offspring recognition than noncolonial swallows and that we have begun to delineate the actual adaptations shaped by natural selection in response to the pressures for recognition. We feel that our summary characterization is charitable, and that we have clearly demonstrated only the "signature" call adaptation. We have just sketched out what I have called "decision rule" or "behavioral" adaptations, and admittedly, the evidence is skimpy. We have argued against "perceptual" adaptations, but again, on the basis of admittedly limited evidence. And of course there are other possible adaptations, such as learning adaptations (discussed in the introduction), which we have not yet investigated.

Finally, I would like to return to the discussion of the relative difficulty of predictions concerning adaptive outcomes as compared to the delineation of actual adaptations or mechanisms. It was straightforward to predict a higher level of parent–offspring recognition in colonial swallow species than in noncolonial swallow species. Had we not found it, we would have suspected that we had some of our basic facts wrong, or that our thinking was muddled in some way. On the other hand, it has not been particularly easy to predict the actual mechanisms—the adaptations—by which colonial swallows solve these recognition problems. I did "predict" signature adaptations, but the point is that this is merely one mechanism by which recognition could be improved, and there are alternatives. If we had failed to find evidence of signature adaptations, the correct course of action would have been to note that such an adaptation is not a *necessary* solution to the problem of recognition, that it might have been *constrained* in some way, and that alternative adaptations (e.g., perceptual) might achieve the same end. The better one's sense of the animals under study, the more likely one may be to correctly "predict" which of several alternative solutions is more likely. For example, elsewhere we have argued that signature adaptations are much more likely than perceptual adaptations in the case of swallow acoustical recognition, essentially on the grounds that there is much more room for elaboration of the calls than for elaboration of the perceptual system (Beecher et al., 1989). But these are hardly predictions of the sort one derives from rigorous theory. Indeed, in these cases it is often hard to disentangle prediction from observation, especially since we tend to shift things into the logical (predictive) format when writing up the research. Did I predict signature adaptations, or did the idea originate in my casual observation that sonagrams of bank swallow calls looked more individually distinctive than those of rough-winged swallow calls? I did decide that the cliff swallow versus barn swallow test was needed as an independent test of this prediction. In the end, however, it makes no difference whether this "prediction" originated in a lucky observation or in good theory. For the value of the results lies not in how we arrived at them, but in whether they ultimately advance our understanding of the evolution of animal behavior.

SUMMARY

I have described a series of studies which tested and confirmed the prediction that parent–offspring recognition is better developed in colonial swallows (bank swallows and cliff swallows) than in noncolonial swallows (northern rough-winged swallows and barn swallows). The primary goal of the studies, however, was to characterize the adaptations underlying the difference. The studies have suggested that elaboration of a chick "signature" call, so that it is more individually distinctive, is one such mechanism. We also provided evidence for adaptations of specific behaviors ("eviction" behavior and searching strategies) and perhaps for adaptations of "decision rules." We provided evidence against perceptual adaptations.

CHAPTER 17

CHEMICAL COMMUNICATION IN GOLDEN HAMSTERS: FROM BEHAVIOR TO MOLECULES AND NEURAL MECHANISMS

Robert E. Johnston

Communication by means of chemical signals, although probably the most ancient mode of communication between organisms, is the least well understood. In this chapter, I will outline what has been learned about this type of communication in one model species, the golden hamster, *Mesocricetus auratus*. This work developed within the context of two fields of study that were quite separate when the work began about 20 years ago, namely, ethology and comparative/physiological psychology. Since the concepts current in those two fields at that time shaped the research strategies used by me and by others working on similar problems, I will briefly review this historical and conceptual context.

Within the field of psychology, communication has always occupied an oddly peripheral position, especially with regard to general theories of psychological function. Perhaps one reason for this is that the study of communication necessarily involves two different levels of analysis: interpersonal interactions, and internal emotions and thoughts. Thus, communication does not fit easily into any one subdiscipline, and does not lend itself to extensions of theory from within such subdisciplines. The study of language, for example, has been carried out primarily by psycholinguists as a subdiscipline within cognitive psychology and by linguists as a discipline almost entirely separate from psychology. Such work has stressed the cognitive and formal aspects of language, but has not been particularly concerned with the social and communicative uses of language. In addition, psychology has traditionally focused within the organism—on the mind, thoughts, emotions, learning, and memory—rather than on behavior and behavioral interactions. Psychological research on facial expressions, for example, has primarily concentrated on how they are related to emotions and on whether people can correctly "recognize" emotions in them, and has until recently almost ignored the actual use of facial expressions and their effect on social interactions (Goldenthal, Johnston, & Kraut, 1981; Kraut & Johnston, 1979).

Given the relative lack of interest in and theory about social communication within psychology during the first 60 years of this century, it is not surprising that comparative and physiological psychologists did not make communication a central focus of their research. They did, however, investigate the mechanisms of social emotions such as fear and anger and of social behaviors such as aggression and sexual behavior (e.g., Morgan, 1965). These broad motivational categories or "drives" were viewed as the basic units of functional organization; individual acts were part of a set of behaviors subserving some motivation or drive. Lesion experiments showed that such drives were mediated by broadly distributed neural networks. For example, social behaviors, such as male copulatory behavior, were shown to be influenced by input from several sensory systems, and communicative signals were seen as just another stimulus that had to be detected and evaluated by generalized, all-purpose sensory systems.

Within the field of ethology, communication was always a central concern. I think this was primarily because the starting point for ethologists was the observation of behavior and, since many of the most spectacular, interesting, and initially puzzling aspects of animal behavior are social displays, it was natural that they came under scrutiny. One of the most far-reaching theoretical accomplishments of classical ethology was a model of the causation of innate behaviors, including signaling acts and responses to social signals. This model proposed the concept of a "sign stimulus," an evolutionarily specialized signal that had a specific effect on the receiver's behavior due to a corresponding perceptual–motivational "innate releasing mechanism" (e.g., Tinbergen, 1951). What was unique about the sign stimulus concept was the notion that only a limited subset of the available stimuli was actually important for eliciting a certain response. This concept implied some mechanism for stimulus filtering or selective perception; such a mechanism could occur at any level of the nervous system, but early research concentrated on specializations of peripheral receptors and sensory organs (e.g., Marler & Hamilton, 1966). Thus, in contrast to the broad motivational categories used by comparative and physiological psychologists, the units of analysis for ethologists were much smaller—often single, discrete behaviors—and their conceptual model proposed highly specialized mechanisms dedicated to these discrete behavioral responses.

One area in which the sign stimulus concept was used successfully was the study of chemical communication among insects; indeed, the concepts developed in this field still have a powerful influence on thinking within the entire chemical communication field. The idea of a sign stimulus found its parallel in the concept of a releaser pheromone: a chemical substance emitted by one animal that causes a specific behavioral response in another individual (Wilson & Bossert, 1963). A pheromone was thought to be a single chemical compound that was detected by specialized receptors and that almost invariably caused specific kinds of responses in appropriate receivers. Initial neurophysiological studies of insect olfactory systems suggested that there were specific receptors for such pheromones and that there were essentially "labeled-line" inputs into the central nervous system whose sole function was to indicate the presence or absence of specific pheromones (Schneider, 1974).

Another aspect of the sign-stimulus, innate-releasing-mechanism model had to do with the causation of behavioral responses to signals. The model was a fairly simple mechanistic one which implied that, given an animal in the proper physiological state, the detection of a sign stimulus would automatically lead to the appropriate response; that is, the stimulus might be sufficient to elicit the response by itself, even in the absence of other seemingly relevant cues, such as the presence of another animal. For example, honeybee drones will approach and attempt to copulate with a cork scented with a pheromone from the queen and dangled in the air (Butler, 1967, 1971). A related implication was that the sign stimulus might also be necessary for the elicitation of a designated response. In the case of the honey bee this may indeed be true, since if the mandibular glands of a queen are removed, the drones' attraction to her and copulations with her are drastically reduced (Butler, 1971; Morse, Gary, & Johansson, 1962). In sum, ethological concepts and research were concerned primarily with highly evolved and specialized mechanisms for control of behavior—specialized signals detected by specific, dedicated sensory mechanisms that are in turn connected to specialized response systems.

These characterizations of ethological and psychological views are both, of course, oversimplified. Nonetheless, I think they suggest a core of ideas that has been influential in the study of the mechanisms of animal social behavior and communication. My own research, as well as that of many others in this field, was in part stimulated by the great intellectual excitement that followed the initial clashing of these two fields, a ferment that was initiated by books by Marler and Hamilton (1966) and Hinde (1966).

In this chapter, I present a summary of my own and others' work that has attempted to understand chemical communication in a model mammalian species, the golden hamster, at a variety of levels of analysis. In the first part of the chapter, I review investigations into the communicative process itself: specifically, into the causation of two scent-marking behaviors, flank marking and vaginal marking, the functions of these two scents, and the chemical analysis of the vaginal secretion. The latter part of the chapter deals with recent work on the segregation of function in the sensory systems that mediate communication by odors and, specifically, the differences in function between the main olfactory system and the vomeronasal system. Issues relating to specialization of function versus general-purpose mechanisms arise in various guises throughout.

NATURAL HISTORY OF THE GOLDEN HAMSTER

The golden hamster, *Mesocricetus auratus*, is one species of a tribe of related species of hamsters, at present classified into six or seven genera that contain approximately 70 species and subspecies. Very little is known about the behavioral ecology of this tribe, but the available information suggests that most species are nocturnal. Only one species, the common European hamster (*Cricetus cricetus*) has been studied in any detail in the field (Eibl-Eibesfeldt, 1953). Murphy (1971) collected and dug up golden hamster burrows in Syria, and his observations support the notion of a solitary lifestyle. Golden hamster burrows are most commonly found near cultivated fields; large stores of grain have been found within burrows. Murphy also reports trapping data from Hamar on the Roumanian hamster, *Mesocricetus neutoni*, which suggests that individuals live solitarily in burrows and that both males and females have home ranges of approximately 2000 square meters. Home ranges of opposite-sex individuals overlap extensively, often by 50 percent or more, but home ranges of same-sex individuals overlap very little (Murphy, 1977). Laboratory observations of golden hamsters living in large enclosures also indicate that they nest by themselves, hoard food in their nests, and defend the nests from others (Johnston, 1975c; Lisk, Ciaccio, & Catanzaro, 1983). In a series of unpublished observations, I placed four golden hamsters in a 16 × 20-foot environment that provided plenty of nest boxes and other places to hide. Males were extremely aggressive toward one another; often, if there were two males present, one male was killed. Males were not aggressive toward females. Females were aggressive toward other females and males, but not as aggressive as males were. All individuals in these environments nested alone.

THE CAUSATION OF FLANK-MARKING BEHAVIOR

One of the primary sources of chemical signals in golden hamsters is the flank gland, a clearly circumscribed region of enlarged and darkly pigmented sebaceous glands on the dorsal flank. The glands of males are much larger than those of females, a sex difference that is androgen dependent (Vandenbergh, 1973). Hamsters have a specialized, stereotyped behavior pattern for depositing the scent from this gland that I call *flank marking* (Figure 1) (Dieterlen, 1959; Johnston,

FIGURE 1. A sequence of photographs, taken at 1/3-second intervals, that show stereo-typic flank marking behavior being performed by a male golden hamster. Note the raised tail in the initial frame, the arched back, and the way the hamster pushes its side forcefully against the walls.

1970; 1975a; 1977a). This behavior occurs in a variety of circumstances. Hamsters engage in marking as part of their routine maintenance behavior; they flank-mark, for example, when they first awaken and emerge from their nests in the evening (Johnston, 1975c). Occasional flank marking also occurs during the course of moving about in a familiar environment.

Flank marking is stimulated by the odors of conspecifics that are potentially antagonistic. For example, males flank-mark in response to the odors of other males or of nonestrous females (Figure 2A) (see Johnston, 1975a). High rates of marking are associated with a high level of agonistic tension or motivation; the highest rates of marking are observed just after agonistic encounters, and if a clear dominance relationship is established, the dominant individual marks more frequently than the subordinate (Figure 2B) (see Johnston, 1975a, 1975c, 1977a). Females mark most vigorously in response to contact with another female or the odors of another female (Johnston, 1977a). Sexual motivation, on the other hand, tends to reduce the tendency to flank-mark: females mark less often in the

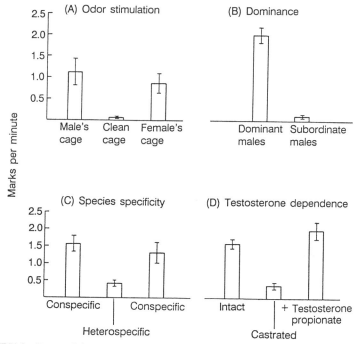

FIGURE 2. Some of the factors influencing flank marking by male hamsters. (A) Odor stimulation: marking by males in temporarily vacant cages. Odors in the cages of males and nonestrous females stimulate flank marking relative to the odors in a clean cage. (Reanalyzed data from Johnston, 1975a.) (B) Correlation with dominance status: marking by males repeatedly exposed to one another in a neutral arena and tested immediately after these encounters in the opponent's vacant cage. Dominant males mark more than subordinates do. (Reanalyzed data from Johnston, 1975a.) (C) Species specificity: marking by males when tested in the vacant cage of a conspecific male, then in the cage of a male Turkish hamster (*Mesocrecetus brandti*), and finally in the cage of a conspecific again. (Adapted from Johnston & Brenner, 1982.) (D) Testosterone dependence: marking by males when intact, 6–25 days after castration, and 27–36 days after replacement therapy with testosterone propionate. (Adapted from Johnston, 1981.)

presence of the odors of males when they are estrous than when they are not, and males mark less often in the temporarily vacant cages of estrous females than in the cages of the same females on nonestrous days (Johnston, 1977a; 1980). In addition, marking in males is specifically inhibited by the presence of vaginal secretions, a source of sexually attracting and arousing odors (Johnston, 1970; 1975a).

The scent from the flank gland seems to be the most important stimulus in inducing another animal to mark. One hamster tends to mark where other animals have previously marked (Johnston, 1970, 1975b), a phenomenon that is common among mammals and is sometimes called "overmarking." Males mark much more frequently in the temporarily vacant home cages of intact males than in the cages of males that have had their flank glands removed (Johnston, 1975b). These results suggest that the primary scent stimulus for flank marking is the odor of another individual's flank gland, at least in the case of males.

Flank marks are selectively directed at and stimulated by conspecific hamsters or their odors. Males and females both mark more often in the vacant cages of males of their own species than in the cages of males of a closely related species, the Turkish hamster, *Mesocricetus brandti* (Figure 2C) (Johnston & Brenner, 1982). Since the odor from the flank gland is the most important stimulus for marking, these results suggest that the scent produced by the flank gland differs across species and is used for species discrimination.

Hormones also modulate the tendency to flank-mark. In males, testosterone is an important internal stimulus that facilitates marking. Intact males showed significantly higher rates of marking in response to the cage odors of stimulus males than the same males did 16 to 25 days after they had been castrated (Johnston, 1981b). When they were given testosterone replacement therapy, their marking rates gradually increased; their marking rates 15 to 24 and 27 to 36 days after the onset of the treatment were significantly higher than their rates after castration, but not significantly different from their rates of marking before castration (Figure 2D). Thus, flank marking by male hamsters in response to conspecific odors appears to be highly testosterone dependent (Johnston, 1981b), a result consistent with studies of similar marking behaviors in a wide range of species (Thiessen & Rice, 1976). However, flank marking at high rates is not completely dependent on the presence of the testes: under some testing conditions, castrated males may engage in aggressive encounters with one another and may display levels of aggressive and flank-marking behaviors similar to those shown by intact males (Whitsett, 1975). The hormonal influences on flank marking in females have not been systematically investigated.

In retrospect, it is remarkable how consistent flank-marking rates have been when males have been tested in a similar manner, often by different observers. Marking rates for intact males investigating the temporarily vacant home cages of intact stimulus males fall between 1.1 and 1.9 marks per minute, even when the experimental males have had remarkably different experiences or testing histories, (Johnston, 1975a, 1975b; 1981b; Johnston & Brenner, 1982). The finding that flank marking was not completely eliminated by castration or by testing in environments lacking optimal odor cues suggests that there is an endogenous level of marking that is independent of specific external causes and internal steroid modulation. Consistent with this interpretation is the fact that low levels of marking are associated with maintenance activities such as grooming (Johnston, 1975a; Dieterlen, 1959).

Flank marking by male hamsters is perhaps the only complex mammalian behavior pattern for which a mediating neurotransmitter acting in a discrete neural locus has been discovered. The injection of arginine vasopressin into the medial preoptic area results in an immediate increase in flank marking (Ferris, Albers, Wesolowski, Goldman, & Luman, 1984). The injection of a vasopressin antagonist into the same area blocks the marking elicited by vasopressin injection as well as marking elicited by the odors of other males (Ferris, Pollock, Albers, & Luman, 1985). Additional studies of other peptides and other antagonist drugs have led to the conclusion that the receptor is similar to the pressor-type receptor that is associated with some other functions of vasopressin (Albers, Pollock, Simmons, & Ferris, 1986). The location of the sensitive neurons has been determined by using microinjections of kainic acid, which kills neuronal cell bodies. Such injections into the ventromedial area of the anterior hypothalamus– medial preoptic area drastically reduce flank marking in response to odors of other males and in response to arginine vasopressin injections. Injections of kainic acid into the third ventricle or into other areas of the hypothalamus have no effect on marking (Ferris, Meenan, & Albers, 1986). Thus, flank marking in male hamsters is dependent upon vasopressin-sensitive neurons in a localized region of the hypothalamus. It should be possible to describe the neural circuit in control of this behavior, especially since we have characterized the sensory system responsible for the stimulation of marking (see below).

In summary, experiments on the causes of flank marking in hamsters show that the behavior is exhibited during low-arousal-level maintenance activities and at greater frequency and intensity during high levels of agonistic arousal. Such a pattern suggests that flank marking might have both general, information-providing functions and specific functions relating to competition and aggression (Johnston, 1985a). It would be interesting to know if the high levels of marking elicited by vasopressin injections are specific to agonistically motivated marking.

Functions of flank marking

What is the significance of the flank gland and of flank-marking behavior? When I began these studies, it was assumed by many that marking behaviors that were associated with agonistic motivation must have functions related to aggression, such as the defense of a home area. Some scientists assumed that the functions were "territorial," even though little may have been known about the actual spatial organization of the species in question. This was, at best, an oversimplified assumption. Signals such as scent marks that are "broadcast" into the environment are likely to have a variety of functions, depending on the situation and the individuals involved. Bird song is analogous in the sense that it is broadcast relatively indiscriminately into the environment and in that it has a variety of functions. Most scent marks are likely to be even more all-purpose, since once they are deposited, they may remain detectable for long periods of time, and therefore are available for use in contexts other than those in which they were deposited (Johnston & Schmidt, 1979). Thus, scent marks may advertise the presence of an individual in an area, and may provide information about the marking animal's species, sex, relatedness to the receiver, and individual identity, as well as other information such as reproductive status, health, and age class. Indeed, such information may be necessary for the scent mark's use in additional functions such as defense of a home area or burrow, defense of a food hoard, or selection of a mate. Flank marking in hamsters has been shown to have some of these functions.

First, the flank gland appears to be an important source of species-specific cues, as mentioned above (see Figure 2C). Second, there is evidence that flank gland odor may be important for individual discrimination. After a male hamster mates to satiety with one female, he can be stimulated to begin mating again by the introduction of a novel female (Bunnell, Boland, & Dewsbury, 1977). We showed that this effect was based on chemical cues by allowing males to mate to satiety with one female and then, after an 8-minute break, presenting each male with two anesthetized females, the original partner and a new partner. The males attempted to mount the novel female but not the original partner, just as they had done in a previous experiment with awake females (Johnston, 1983; Johnston & Rasmussen, 1984). In order to determine what sources of scent might be most important in this discrimination, we again allowed males to mate to satiety with one female, then presented them with two scents, one from the original partner and one from a novel female, and compared the amount of interest the males displayed in the two scents. There was no difference in the time the males spent investigating vaginal secretions or head-region scents from the two females, but there was a significant preference for the scent of the flank gland of the novel female, suggesting that this scent is sufficient for individual discrimination and that the other two scents are less salient for such discrimination. Halpin and McCurdy (cited in Halpin, 1986), using a habituation procedure, provide independent evidence for individual discrimination using flank gland scent.

The role that flank marks play in agonistic interactions is still not clear. The scant evidence available from the field on the Roumanian hamster (*M. neutoni*) suggests that the home ranges of opposite-sex individuals overlap extensively, but those of same-sex individuals overlap very little (Murphy, 1977). It is thus possible that this species and the closely related golden hamster display intrasexual territoriality. What seems much clearer is that golden hamsters and the other species of the genus *Mesocricetus* nest solitarily and probably defend their burrows and the large quantities of food that they hoard there (Johnston, 1975c; Murphy, 1977). Are flank marking and the flank-gland scent used for such defense? In captivity, hamsters flank-mark in burrows and at entrances to nesting areas, indicating that scent is placed in the appropriate places for advertising that a nest area is occupied (Johnston, 1975c). Furthermore, the scent from flank marks persists for long periods of time—in laboratory conditions, flank marks on glass are detected and responded to for up to 40 days after they are deposited (Johnston & Schmidt, 1979). Thus, flank gland scent also has the appropriate chemical properties to function as an advertisement of occupation.

Attempts to demonstrate that flank marks repel another individual or limit its movements have met with mixed success. One question that has been addressed is whether the presence of flank-gland scent from one hamster renders another hamster less likely to enter an area. In one experiment, it was found that experimental males did take longer to enter an area marked by an intact male than an area marked by a flank-glandectomized male (Alderson & Johnston, 1975), but in subsequent experiments using slightly different procedures, this effect was not found (Alderson, 1976; Fullenkamp, Fischer, & Vance, 1987; Johnston & Kwan, 1984). Indeed, it is rather naive to expect that one would find such an effect in the absence of an appropriate social context. From the point of view of the intruder, a marked area should be avoided only if the scent is associated with aggressive interactions. For example, I have observed animals that, having just engaged in and lost an aggressive encounter with another, were extremely reluctant to enter the victor's vacant cage, often sitting with teeth chattering for minutes at the threshold of the cage (Johnston, 1970, 1975a, 1977a). Experiments that more realistically model situations hamsters encounter in nature are needed to determine the role of experience in the functions of the flank-gland scent.

Another way in which I attempted to test the home-defense hypothesis was by placing two males together in an arena that contained the flank-gland scent of one of the males to find out whether the presence of his own scent gives a male an advantage in aggressive encounters. Despite careful matching of the weights of the males paired, and despite providing each male with the same amount of experience in an arena of his own prior to pairing, several experiments of this type yielded no effect of flank-gland scent in the test arena (Johnston, unpublished data). Negative results such as this, however, are not very instructive, since there may be many reasons why the laboratory design does not sufficiently mimic or model the natural environment.

To summarize briefly, the flank gland and flank marking behavior appear to have a number of functions, not all of which are fully understood. Flank marking may be specialized to provide information about individual identity and possibly other types of classificatory information. It does not appear to have a threat or intimidation function by itself, but may serve such functions in appropriate circumstances.

Many scent-marking behaviors that have been studied in other mammals are similar to hamster flank marking in various ways: they are sexually dimorphic, they are androgen-dependent in males, and they have a relatively broad range of probable functions (for reviews see Eisenberg & Kleiman, 1972; Johnson, 1973;

Ralls, 1971; Thiessen & Rice, 1976). There is considerable variation among species in the use of the glands, just as there is in the use of vocal or visual signals, but a discussion of the similarities and differences among species is beyond the scope of this chapter.

VAGINAL SECRETIONS AND VAGINAL MARKING

The hamster vagina is a specialized secretory organ that produces a discharge with a rich, pungent odor. The distal vagina has two lateral pockets specialized for the storage and release of this secretion. Dieterlen (1959) first reported a genital marking behavior in females that I studied in detail and called *vaginal marking* (Johnston, 1970, 1977a): females press the genital region against the substrate and move forward, usually 1 to 3 centimeters, leaving a streak of thin, watery secretion behind. The voluminous nature of the secretion was noticed by endocrinologists, who discovered that it changed in amount and consistency with the estrous cycle and that these changes could be used as a method of monitoring the cycle (Orsini, 1961). Interest in the functions of this secretion was sparked by a report by Murphy and Schneider (1970) that indicated that males with olfactory bulb lesions failed to mate. The vaginal secretion was thus suspected of being a source of aphrodisiac pheromones.

The causation of vaginal scent marking also suggests that it has sexual functions. Vaginal marking is stimulated by the presence of males or their odors (Figure 3A) (see Johnston, 1977a). These findings suggest that the marks are directed at males, and that they may have special significance for males. A female's endocrine state also modulates the tendency to mark. The dramatic swings in the frequency of vaginal marking with the estrous cycle are illustrated in Figure 3. Females mark at intermediate rates on cycle days 2 and 3, and mark at the highest rates on the day before they are receptive (Johnston, 1977a), but they rarely mark when estrous. Females do not mark while pregnant or early in lactation, but begin to mark during the second half of lactation (Figure 3B). By the end of lactation, marking rates are comparable to those that occur 2 and 3 days before estrus. The final levels of marking observed on the day before estrus (Day 4) can be viewed as the culmination of a trend to mark more and more frequently as the period of receptivity approaches (Johnston, 1979). I have interpreted this pattern as a means of sexual advertisement.

One curious aspect of this pattern is the lack of marking on the estrous day itself. I initially hypothesized that for a solitary species, it would be important to advertise well before the time of receptivity in order to ensure the presence of a mate. Subsequently, it was observed that in laboratory enclosures, the female entices the male into her burrow near the end of the dark phase before estrus, sleeps with him during the day, mates during the estrous period (during the next dark phase) and shortly thereafter chases the male out (Lisk, Ciaccio, &

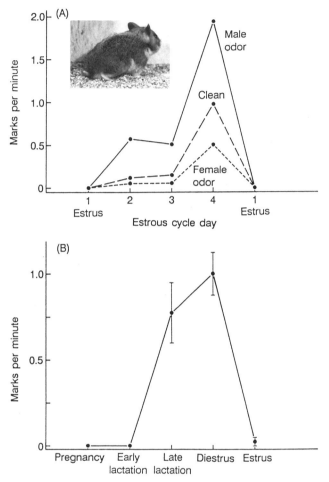

FIGURE 3. Vaginal marking by females during different reproductive states. Inset: Female hamster marking. (A) Mean number of marks during 10-minute trials for each cycle day in three different odor conditions. Females mark significantly more frequently in the male odor condition than in the female odor condition or in clean cages. They mark more frequently the day before their receptive day than on other cycle days. (Adapted from Johnston, 1977a; Johnston, 1985a.) (B) Mean number of marks by females in several reproductive states during 4-minute trials in the presence of conspecific odors. Females late in lactation mark at about the same rate as diestrous females. Note the expanded scale. (Adapted from Johnston, 1979; Johnston, 1985a.)

Catanzaro, 1983). Thus, the peak marking frequency seems to correspond to the time when the female is likely to accept a male into her burrow.

Despite these dramatic cyclic changes in vaginal marking frequency, the hormonal control of this behavior has not been thoroughly investigated. During the estrous cycle, there is a good correlation between marking rate and estradiol levels when progesterone is low; the decline in marking during receptivity suggests a suppressive effect of progesterone (for hormone data see Baranczuk & Greenwald, 1973, 1974; Bast & Greenwald, 1974; Leavitt & Blaha, 1970). These hypotheses are partly supported by experimental studies in which estradiol was implanted in the brains of ovariectomized females: implants in the ventromedial nucleus, medial preoptic area, or suprachiasmatic nucleus caused increased levels of vaginal marking. However, systemic injections of progesterone did not inhibit vaginal marking in these implanted females, suggesting that progesterone does not have a direct inhibiting effect on vaginal marking (Takahashi & Lisk, 1985; Takahashi, Lisk, & Burnett, 1985). This interpretation gains support from the lack of correlation between marking levels and progesterone levels during pregnancy and lactation: progesterone levels remain high throughout these reproductive states (Baranczuk & Greenwald, 1974; Leavitt & Blaha, 1970), whereas vaginal marking varies considerably (Johnston, 1979; Leonard, 1972). Thus, high levels of vaginal marking may be stimulated by relatively high levels of estradiol, but other hormonal factors that modulate this type of marking are not yet understood.

As might be expected for a signaling behavior that has sexual advertisement functions, vaginal marking seems to be directed primarily at conspecifics. Females mark much more frequently in areas smelling of conspecific males than in areas smelling of males of the closely related Turkish hamster, *M. brandti* (Johnston & Brenner, 1982). The higher level of response to conspecific males suggests that some kind of species recognition process influences the tendency to mark. This selectivity in marking is supported by a similar selectivity in actual mating preferences. Females of three species of *Mesocricetus* do prefer to mate with conspecific males and may completely reject heterospecific males, even in a highly constrained laboratory situation in which they are presented only with heterospecific males (Murphy, 1977, 1978).

Functions of vaginal marks

Males and females respond quite differently to vaginal marks. Females show little or no overt response upon encountering another female's marks; at most, they will briefly sniff them and may mark over them. In contrast, males display a whole repertoire of responses, including attraction to the marks from a distance, sniffing and licking, ultrasonic calling, and hormonal responses.

Upon encountering a mark, a male stops and sniffs and licks the mark for several seconds. This tendency is so powerful that he will even stop following a female to sniff and lick vaginal marks, although by doing this he may lose track of the female. The vaginal secretion is highly attractive to males, as shown in a variety of testing situations. It is clear that the volatile components can attract males from moderate distances (35 to 76 centimeters in actual experiments, but probably at least several meters in nature; Johnston, 1974; Johnston & Kwan, 1984; Kwan & Johnston, 1980; Murphy, 1973). Although the amount of material deposited by vaginal marking is quite small and dries within about a minute on glass or slate, males were preferentially attracted upwind into the arm of a Y maze that was marked 5 minutes previously, suggesting a prolonged release of volatile components. Males were not attracted toward an arm of the maze marked by a vaginectomized female (Johnston & Kwan, 1984). Since vaginectomized females have all of the other sources of odor that intact females do, we are confident in concluding that the primary source of the odor that attracted males from a distance was the vaginal secretion.

Some progress has been made in the chemical analysis of components of the vaginal secretion that have attractive properties. Dimethyl disulfide is the only component so far identified that elicits sniffing investigation (Singer, Agosta, O'Connell, Pfaffmann, Bowen, & Field, 1976); other identified volatile components, either alone or in mixtures, are not attractive to males and do not enhance the attractiveness of dimethyl disulfide (O'Connell, Singer, Macrides, Pfaffmann, & Agosta, 1978). The highest concentrations of dimethyl disulfide occur during estrus, and it is attractive to males in femtogram (10^{-15} gram) amounts (O'Connell, Singer, Pfaffmann, & Agosta, 1979; O'Connell, Singer, Stern, Jesmajian, & Agosta, 1981). Dimethyl disulfide does not, however, produce the intensity of attraction that the entire secretion does; fewer males respond to it, those that do spend less time investigating it, and qualitatively, their responses lack the vigor and level of arousal shown toward the entire secretion (Johnston, 1977b; Singer et al., 1976). Although dimethyl disulfide has been touted as a sexual attractant, its effectiveness in attracting males from a distance has not actually been assessed. As I have argued previously, the behavioral assay used to assess the attractiveness of this substance is more appropriate for measuring detection and investigation of a new odor in a familiar environment (Johnston, 1981a). At present, it is not clear whether the addition of a few as yet unidentified components to dimethyl disulfide could cause the full level of responsiveness, or whether a very complex mixture of odors, producing a multidimensional "gestalt" or "odor image," is necessary.

Males also respond to the odors of females by emitting ultrasonic vocalizations, a response that seems to be primarily a response to vaginal secretions, since males call more frequently in an area marked by an intact female than in an area marked by a vaginectomized female (Johnston & Kwan, 1984). Estrous females are likely to call in response to hearing a call, and both sexes are attracted to the source of such calls (Floody & Pfaff, 1977b; Floody, Pfaff, & Lewis, 1977). Thus, the detection of vaginal marks by a male may set off a sequence of behaviors that bring a male and an estrous female together. Other responses of males to vaginal marks may also have this effect. Males become notably agitated upon sniffing at vaginal marks, and appear to search for the marker by moving about, sniffing, and calling. In large enclosures, the density of marks is greatest near females' nests, and males may follow such concentration gradients to locate females (Lisk, Ciaccio, & Catanzaro, 1983).

Another male response to vaginal secretions is an increase in testosterone levels. Exposing sexually experienced or sexually naive males to females or to the odor of vaginal secretions causes a doubling in their circulating testosterone levels within 30 minutes; exposure to another male has no effect (Macrides, Bartke, Fernandez, & D'Angelo, 1974; Pfeiffer, 1988; Pfeiffer & Johnston, 1986, unpublished data). Although vaginal secretions are sufficient to cause such responses, they are not necessary; sexually experienced males interacting with vaginectomized females still show increases in testosterone levels (Pfeiffer, 1988; Pfeiffer & Johnston, 1986, unpublished data). The functions of these androgen surges are not known either for hamsters or for other mammalian species that show similar responses. Hypotheses range from the suggestion that these surges may have subtle effects on behavior to the possibility that they may influence sperm production or keep the hypothalamic–pituitary–gonadal axis "in tune." Alternatively, it may not be testosterone that is active in these situations, but one of the hormones that elicits the testosterone response, such as gonadotropin-releasing hormone. At present, there is no convincing evidence for any of these proposed theories. Tests of possible behavioral functions have, however, concentrated on copulatory performance. In a solitary species like the golden hamster, it is likely that males often encounter vaginal secretions well before they encounter females; if so, hormone surges in response to the secretions might influence precopulatory behavior.

Finally, vaginal secretions have powerful sexual arousal effects. Normally, male hamsters attempt to mount only female hamsters; however, if intact or castrated males are scented with vaginal secretions, other males will attempt to mate with them (Darby, Devor, & Chorover, 1975; Johnston, 1975d). This is an extremely powerful and striking effect, since male hamsters are usually quite aggressive toward one another (Johnston, 1975a, 1985c). Thus, it is also clear that vaginal secretions have a strong inhibitory effect on the aggressive tendencies of males. This probably accounts for the relatively low levels of aggression shown by males toward females throughout the estrous cycle and perhaps during other reproductive states as well.

Both volatile and nonvolatile components of the vaginal secretion contribute to the aphrodisiac effect (Frey, 1978; Johnston, 1977b; O'Connell & Meredith, 1984). Relatively little research has been directed at the volatile fraction, but it is known that dimethyl disulfide does not have a sexually arousing influence (Macrides, Johnson, & Schneider, 1977). Separation, assay, and purification of the nonvolatile, high-molecular-weight fraction of the vaginal secretion has yielded a relatively pure protein with a molecular weight of 17,000 daltons, which has an aphrodisiac effect when placed on the hindquarters of an anesthetized male stimulus animal. The level of sexual response to this protein is significantly greater than to control (water or saline) applications, and indeed, is not significantly different from the level of response to an application containing the entire high-molecular-weight fraction of the secretion (Singer, Agosta, Clancy, & Macrides, 1987; Singer, Macrides, Clancy, & Agosta, 1986). The protein itself appears to be the stimulus—it is highly purified, and researchers believe that no smaller molecules bound to it that could be the "real" stimulus. Responses to this protein appear to be mediated via the vomeronasal organ (see below) (Clancy, Macrides, Singer, & Agosta, 1984; Singer, Clancy, Macrides, & Agosta, 1984).

Responses to both the high-molecular-weight fraction and to the purified protein are, however, less robust than those to the whole vaginal secretion. This suggests that either there are some additional specific components of the aphrodisiac signal, or, as suggested above of the attraction properties of the secretion, the entire secretion is the signal—the secretion, in all its complexity, forms a unique odor image that is necessary for full-scale responsiveness. In the far simpler sex pheromone systems found among insects, it is becoming clear that blends of components, rather than single compounds, appear to constitute signals (Linn, Campbell, & Roelofs, 1987).

The predictability and robustness of sexual responses toward artificially scented partners is the clearest example of the effect of a simple behavioral "releaser" pheromone known for mammals. Many such examples are known in other taxa, especially in insects, in which such pheromones may be both sufficient and necessary for particular behavioral responses. It is therefore interesting to ask to what degree hamster vaginal secretions have this type of tightly linked control over male copulatory behavior—can these secretions elicit copulatory attempts in the absence of other cues from females, as, for example, honeybee pheromones do when placed on a small cork that is dangled in the air (Butler, 1971; Gary & Marston, 1971)? Experiments in which vaginal secretions were placed on glass jars of approximately hamster dimensions (Darby, Devor, & Chorover, 1974) or on a homemade stuffed animal made to resemble a female in lordosis (Johnston, unpublished data) were not successful in eliciting any sexual responses; males just sniffed and licked at the secretion, as they would do if it were placed on any artificial object. Therefore, we can conclude that some other information is necessary for the elicitation of sexual responses, such as information indicating that the partner is alive, animate, or is a hamster of the appropriate species.

Even if vaginal secretions are not sufficient to elicit copulatory behavior, they could be necessary for such behavior. In some insects, such as the honeybee, removal of the queen's mandibular gland drastically reduces both the attraction of drones to queens and mating behavior (Butler, 1967, 1971; Gary & Marston, 1971; Morse, Gary, & Johansson, 1962). In hamsters, a functional sense of smell is necessary for male sexual behavior. If males are rendered anosmic by ablation of the olfactory bulbs or by separate lesions of the main olfactory mucosa and of the vomeronasal organ, they stop mating entirely (Murphy & Schneider, 1970; Meredith, 1980). Indeed, a male can be almost instantly turned from a non-copulator into a copulator; if just one olfactory bulb is ablated, and the nostril on the side opposite the ablated blub is clipped, rendering him anosmic, he will not mate, but if the clip is then moved to the other nostril, he will regain his sense of smell and will begin copulatory attempts (Devor & Murphy, 1973).

It would seem possible that, since vaginal secretions have such a powerful influence on sexual arousal, the elimination of vaginal secretions from females might also eliminate mating attempts by males. However, this is not the case. When males interact with vaginectomized, estrous females, they still attempt to mate with them. There are statistically significant reductions in mounting attempts, but the effect is slight (Figure 4) (Johnston, 1986; Kwan & Johnston, 1980; Pfeiffer, 1988). Thus, unlike releaser pheromones in the classic ethological view, the vaginal secretions of female hamsters are neither sufficient nor necessary for male copulatory behavior; instead, these secretions have a profound effect on male behavior, but do so in the context of other, perhaps partially redundant, information from females (Johnston, 1986).

The fact that nasal chemoreception is necessary for male sexual behavior, but that the sexually arousing pheromones in vaginal secretions are not, suggests either that other chemical cues are important for the stimulation of male sexual behavior or that methods of eliminating olfactory input create other, nonspecific effects on arousal that interfere with sexual and other behaviors. What other

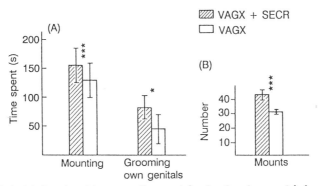

FIGURE 4. Median (semi-interquartile range) levels of male sexual behaviors toward vaginectomized females (VAGX) and toward vaginectomized females to which vaginal secretions were applied (VAGX + SECR) during 12-minute trials. Absence of vaginal secretions results in small but significant reductions in sexual behaviors. (A) Time spent (in seconds) in sexual behaviors. (B) Number of mounts by males. $* = p < .050$; $*** = p < .005$. (Adapted from Johnston, 1986.)

chemical signals might be involved? Might there be one other source of arousal pheromones or do all sources of scent provide information that influences male behavior? In a series of experiments in which we removed from females not only the vagina but also the flank glands, Harderian glands, and/or ear glands (all of which have been shown to be sexually dimorphic, sexually discriminable, or both), we found that no one of these sources seemed especially important. As more sources of scent were eliminated from females, however, we tended to observe less sexual behavior by males, suggesting that there is not a single source of relevant cues (Johnston, 1986). In a preliminary experiment in which we attempted to create "odorless" female hamsters by washing vaginectomized females with detergent and rubbing them with an organic solvent, we found that males' copulatory attempts were drastically reduced, and that a few males did not mate with them (Johnston, 1986). These results suggest that chemical information is necessary for male copulatory behavior. A more vigorous and sustained approach to creating an "odorless" female might provide stronger evidence for this hypothesis.

The vaginal secretion of the female hamster is one of the most thoroughly investigated and best understood chemical signals in any mammalian species, especially with regard to chemical analysis and behavioral functions. Nonetheless, we are far from a thorough understanding. It is clear that this scent has powerful and predictable effects on behavior, but the signals do not act alone to cause behavioral or hormonal responses. Instead, the scent is one of many cues that male hamsters rely upon to guide their social interactions. Likewise, although much of its chemistry is known, it is not clear exactly which components or mixtures of components of the scent are needed for maximal responses. Is there any response for which the best signal is a single component, or is complex perception of odor images always involved? To what extent do the signals and the perceptual mechanisms differ for different functions? My guess is that most functions require some form of "hamster recognition" information that is based on a signal composed of many compounds and a general-purpose perceptual mechanism. In addition, some functions, such as hormonal responses or copulatory arousal, may also depend on a specialized signal that has some effectiveness by itself. There may well be a combination of evolutionarily specialized mechanisms specific for a few chemical compounds and an all-purpose pattern recognition system that evaluates chemical mixtures.

OLFACTORY AND VOMERONASAL MEDIATION OF CHEMICAL SIGNALS AND COMMUNICATORY BEHAVIORS

The olfactory system has proven remarkably recalcitrant to analysis by the methods traditionally employed by sensory physiologists, psychophysicists, and other biopsychologists. One of the major reasons for this is the complexity of the stimuli. Unlike visual or auditory stimuli, odor has no underlying dimensions (such as wavelength) that are clearly understood and upon which stimuli can be ordered. Because of this, the systematic investigation of the mechanisms of sensory coding of odor quality is fraught with uncertainties; no unifying theory has emerged. Another major factor in the delay of understanding of the olfactory system has been that the behavioral capacities and functions of olfaction have not been well understood. Now that we are beginning to understand some of these functions, approaches to the structure–function relationships of the olfactory pathways are more promising.

One of the bright spots in the study of the vertebrate olfactory system is the fact that the neuroanatomy of the olfactory bulb and its central connections is relatively well known (Price, 1987). With regard to structure–function relationships, one of the most exciting areas of recent research has been the elucidation of the separate functions of the main and accessory olfactory systems, an endeavor that got its impetus from neuroanatomical discoveries. Although it was believed for some time that the vomeronasal organ was a sensory organ and had neural connections with the accessory olfactory bulb, the significance of this separate area of the olfactory bulb were not appreciated. In the 1970s, Scalia and Winans (1975, 1976; Winans & Scalia, 1970) demonstrated that the first-order central projections of the accessory olfactory bulb were entirely separate from those of the main olfactory bulb, suggesting functional differences between the two. The characterization of the similarities and differences in function of these two nasal chemosensory systems remains an exciting area of research (for reviews see Johnston, 1985b; Meredith, 1983; Wysocki, 1979). In the remainder of this chapter, I describe the progress made in this area using golden hamsters as subjects.

The first function described for the vomeronasal organ in a mammal was its role in the copulatory behavior of male golden hamsters (Powers & Winans, 1975; Winans & Powers, 1977). Following up on reports that demonstrated the dependence of male mating behavior on olfactory function, these authors showed that by cutting the nerves that link the vomeronasal organ to the accessory olfactory bulb, one could cause deficits in male copulatory performance; indeed, most of the lesioned males stopped mating entirely. These results proved controversial in the sense that later studies, using techniques such as removal of the vomeronasal organ, which do less damage to the main olfactory system, have found much smaller deficits; in fact, most such studies have found little or no deficit in mating after organ removal alone. All reports are consistent in showing that lesions of the olfactory mucosa alone result in no substantial deficits, but that if both systems are eliminated, mating is eliminated. Thus, it is clear that both systems play significant roles in sexual arousal and performance in male hamsters (Johnston, 1985b; Meredith, 1980, 1983a).

These two components of nasal chemoreception may nonetheless have some distinct functions with regard to sexual and/or other behaviors. Attraction from a distance to the volatile components of vaginal secretions seems to be primarily a function of the main olfactory system. Males whose vomeronasal nerves have been cut are still quite responsive to these volatile components, whereas males with lesions of the olfactory mucosa are not (Powers, Fields, & Winans, 1979). In contrast, the high-molecular-weight fraction of the vaginal secretion that has sexually arousing effects is primàrily detected by the vomeronasal organ (Clancy et al., 1984; Singer et al., 1984). Thus, the main olfactory mucosa seems to primarily mediate responses to the more volatile components of this secretion, although the vomeronasal organ may also respond to these components (O'Connell & Meredith, 1984; Clancy et al., 1984; Singer et al., 1984).

In my laboratory, we are taking another approach by investigating the role of the main and accessory olfactory systems in the mediation of behavioral and hormonal responses that are less complex than copulatory behavior and less likely to be influenced by a multitude of cues. The hope is that the control of simpler, more discrete responses may have more limited and discrete sensory mechanisms. We have investigated three behaviors—flank marking, vaginal marking, and ultrasonic calling—and one hormonal response, the androgen surges that males show in response to females or their odors. The remainder of this chapter summarizes these experiments.

Vomeronasal and olfactory influences on hormonal responses in male hamsters

Several years ago, Macrides and his colleagues (Macrides et al., 1974) demonstrated that male hamsters experience a twofold rise in testosterone levels when exposed either to female hamsters or to their vaginal secretions. In a recent series of experiments, Cheryl Pfeiffer and I investigated whether these responses are mediated by the olfactory system, the vomeronasal system, or both, and whether sexual experience is an important variable. Males whose vomeronasal organs were removed did not show a rise in plasma testosterone concentration in response to vaginal secretions alone, whereas control males with sham surgery did show such increases (see Figure 5A). This was true for both sexually naive and sexually experienced males. In contrast, males treated with zinc sulfate continued to exhibit testosterone responses to vaginal secretions (Figure 5B; Pfeiffer, 1988; Pfeiffer & Johnston, 1986, and unpublished data). We conclude that androgen responses to vaginal secretions are mediated via the vomeronasal organ—indeed, that its presence is necessary for such responses. The main olfactory system, in contrast, is not necessary.

However, neither vomeronasal organ removal nor zinc sulfate treatment eliminated androgen responses to females themselves. Sexually experienced and sexually naive males, whether intact, lacking vomeronasal organs, or lacking olfactory mucosa, all showed elevated androgen levels when allowed to interact

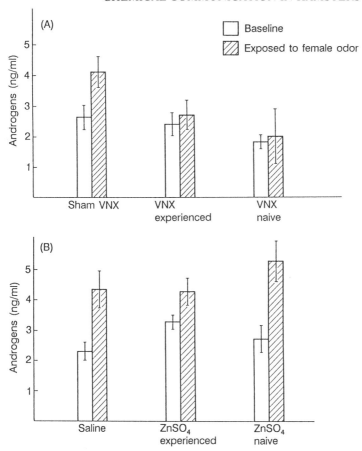

FIGURE 5. Mean androgen levels in male hamsters during resting periods (baseline) and 30 minutes after exposure to vaginal secretions. (A) Removal of the vomeronasal organ eliminates the androgen response to vaginal secretions. SHAM VNX = control males on whom sham surgery was performed; VNX Experienced = sexually experienced males with vomeronasal organs removed; VNX Naive = sexually naive males with vomeronasal organs removed. (B) Despite lesions of the olfactory mucosa with a solution of zinc sulfate, males continued to show androgen responses. Saline = control males treated with saline solution; ZnSO₄ Experienced = sexually experienced males treated with zinc sulfate; ZnSO₄ Naive = sexually naive males treated with zinc sulfate. (Adapted from Pfeiffer, 1988; Pfeiffer & Johnston, unpublished data.)

with estrous females. Thus, neither the vomeronasal organ nor the main olfactory receptors are necessary for hormonal responses to females themselves.

In a further experiment, we combined lesions of the vomeronasal organ and the olfactory mucosa. This procedure eliminated mating behavior in both sexually experienced and sexually naive males, as reported previously by others

(Meredith, 1980, 1983). Sexually experienced males nonetheless continued to show increases in androgen levels after interactions with estrous females, indicating that nasal chemoreception is not necessary for this response; other cues are sufficient. This result also shows that the androgen response mechanism is not the same as the copulatory behavior mechanism. In contrast, sexually naive males with this double lesion did not exhibit elevated androgen levels, indicating that for these males, the androgen response to females is dependent on odor signals and requires nasal chemoreception (see Figure 6). These results suggest that sexually naive males recognize the relevant features of females by their odors and that this capacity is dependent on developmental processes occurring long before adulthood. Sexual experience must provide the means by which other cues become capable of signifying "female hamster." It is interesting that from 10 to 16 days of age, young hamsters are particularly responsive to and interested in a variety of odors, especially vaginal secretions (Johnston & Coplin, 1979). This is the same age at which the final stages in the development of projections from the olfactory bulb to the central nervous system occur (Leonard, 1975). This period may be critical in the development of relatively hard-wired responses to odors.

Olfactory system mediation of scent marking

In an extensive series of experiments, we studied three different communicative behaviors in golden hamsters, all of which are stimulated by conspecific odors.

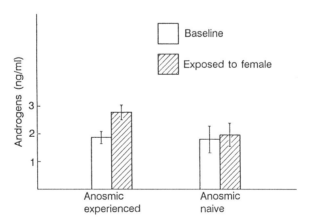

FIGURE 6. Mean androgen levels of male hamsters in a resting state (baseline) or 30 minutes after exposure to an estrous female. Anosmia was produced by combined vomeronasal organ removal and treatment of the olfactory mucosa with zinc sulfate. Sexually naive anosmic males do not respond with an increase in androgen levels, but sexually experienced males do show an increase in androgens. (Adapted from Pfeiffer, 1988; Pfeiffer & Johnston, unpublished data.)

Using the lesion methods described above, we investigated the roles of the olfactory and vomeronasal systems in the mediation of flank marking in males and females and ultrasonic calling and vaginal marking in females. The details of our experimental design cannot be presented here, but in all the experiments, at least 10 animals were used in every group, and each animal was observed during 5- to 8-minute trials on 12 to 16 days in each condition. Some experiments used a repeated measures design and some used an independent groups design; in all cases experimental animals were compared to controls on which sham surgery had been performed (Johnston, Pfeiffer, & Mueller, 1987, and unpublished data).

Vomeronasal organ removal had no influence on flank marking by either males or females or on vaginal marking by females. Destruction of olfactory receptors with zinc sulfate, in contrast, greatly reduced the frequency of flank marking by both sexes as well as vaginal marking by females (Figures 7 and 8). This effect is shown most dramatically in the data for males, plotted as a daily mean marking rate (Figure 7). The sham treatment produced a slight, nonsignificant effect, but the zinc sulfate treatment produced a dramatic effect. The marking rate begins to recover near the end of the zinc sulfate testing period, and indeed, independent tests suggested that the animals' ability to detect volatile odorants was also improving. Figure 8 shows that odor-stimulated flank and vaginal marking by females is greatly reduced by zinc sulfate treatment of the olfactory mucosa. Sensory deficits do not completely eliminate marking, perhaps because there is an endogenous, nonelicited cause of scent marking that does not depend on conspecific odors (as mentioned above, low to moderate rates of marking are observed in a perfectly clean arena). Thus, the main olfactory system

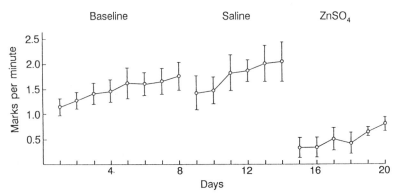

FIGURE 7. Daily mean flank-marking frequency by male hamsters during 7-minute tests in response to the odors of another male during a baseline period, after a control treatment of the nasal mucosa with saline solution, or after treatment of the mucosa with zinc sulfate. Lesions of the olfactory mucosa greatly reduced flank marking frequency. (From Johnston & Mueller, unpublished data.)

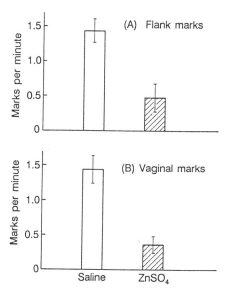

FIGURE 8. Mean scent marking frequency by female hamsters during 5-minute tests. Females with lesions of the olfactory mucosa vaginal-marked less in response to male and female odors (A) and flank-marked less in response to female odors (B). Saline = control females treated with saline solution; $ZnSO_4$ = females treated with zinc sulfate.

is important for mediation of scent marking behaviors, whereas the vomeronasal system has little influence. As explained above, these marking behaviors both depend on recognition of species-specific scent (Johnston & Brenner, 1982). One interpretation of the present results is that main olfactory system lesions disrupt the species-recognition mechanisms, and this lack of information results in decreased marking. This interpretation is consistent with a prior prediction that the main olfactory system should be primarily responsible for social recognition that depends on pattern recognition processes. Previous data are also consistent with these ideas. Cutting the vomeronasal nerve does not change the preference of male hamsters for conspecific over heterospecific females, whereas elimination of the olfactory bulb, which eliminates both olfactory and vomeronasal input, abolishes this preference (Murphy, 1980).

Vomeronasal and olfactory mediation of ultrasonic calling

Both male and female hamsters produce ultrasonic calls in the 30 to 45 kilohertz range (Floody & Pfaff, 1977a). These calls occur primarily in sexual contexts and have sexual functions. Females call most often when they are estrous (Floody et al., 1977). The calls are used in the location of a sexual partner—individuals tend to call in response to hearing the calls of others, and are attracted to the source of a call (Floody & Pfaff, 1977b; Floody et al., 1977). Males also produce calls during intermount intervals, and such calls facilitate the maintenance of lordosis by females (Floody & Pfaff, 1977b). Calling is stimulated by the odors of individuals of the opposite sex (Floody et al., 1977). One of the stimuli that is particularly important in the elicitation of male calls is the vaginal secretion. Males call much more frequently in an area that has been explored and scent-marked by intact females than in a similar area explored and marked by vaginec-tomized females (Johnston & Kwan, 1984).

In our experiments on the olfactory and vomeronasal mediation of ultrasonic calling, we investigated the causes of calling by females in response to odors of conspecifics. Females explored an arena that contained fresh odors of both male and female hamsters for 5 minutes per day for 12 consecutive days, first before and then following lesions of the vomeronasal system or olfactory mucosa. Lesions of either the olfactory or the vomeronasal system reduced the frequency of ultrasonic calling by estrous females (Figure 9), whereas control treatments had no effect. Thus, in contrast to scent-marking behaviors, ultrasonic calling by females is influenced by both vomeronasal and olfactory input. It would be interesting to know if the two systems are responding to the same or to different chemical signals.

Olfactory mediation of individual discrimination

Individual recognition or discrimination in mammals often is mediated by chem-ical signals (Halpin, 1986). It is an extremely interesting process from the point of view of the sensory and central nervous system mechanisms involved, since it must be mediated by some sort of pattern recognition process. Other types of discrimination, such as sex or species discrimination, may have similar under-lying mechanisms, but they could theoretically be accomplished by unique "marker" substances in a scent that would signify each category. For example, the presence of substances unique to vaginal secretions of female hamsters could indicate the sex of a hamster; a unique compound in some other glandular secretion could likewise indicate sex or species. Individual differences in scent cannot be so indicated, because there is no way for the genetic system to code for a unique product for each and every individual. It is likely that each individual has a unique odor "image" due to differing proportions of components in scent secretions, much as the proportions of different facial features makes individual human faces so clearly identifiable.

We have begun to examine the neural mechanisms underlying such discrim-inations by investigating whether discrimination of different female hamsters by males is mediated by the olfactory or vomeronasal system (Johnston & Rasmussen, 1984). The paradigm for this study was the mate-recognition situa-

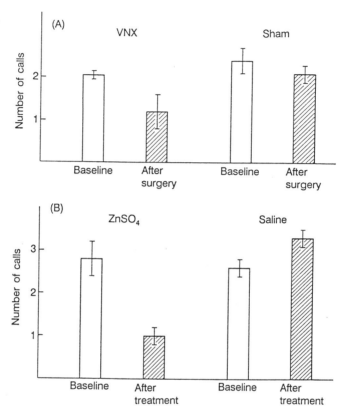

FIGURE 9. Mean ultrasonic calling frequency by female hamsters per 5-minute trial in response to male and female odors. (A) Vomeronasal organ removal significantly reduced calling. VNX = females with vomeronasal organs removed; Sham = females with sham surgery. (B) Lesions of the olfactory mucosa reduced calling. ZnSO$_4$ = females treated intranasally with zinc sulfate. Saline = control females treated intranasally with saline. (From Johnston, unpublished data.)

tion described above, in which a male mated to satiety with one female and then, after a short break, was introduced to a pair of anesthetized females, one the original partner and the other a novel female. Intact males spend much time investigating and attempting to mount the novel female, but spend little time with the familiar female. Males with intact olfactory systems but without vomeronasal organs behave the same way, indicating that the vomeronasal system is not essential for individual discrimination. Males with lesions of the main olfactory mucosa, however, do not display a preference for the novel female; in fact, they show very low levels of sexual arousal in this situation. These experiments indicate that the main olfactory system is essential for mediating individual discrimination and the sexual arousal that is based on this discrimination (Johnston, 1983; 1985b; Johnston & Rasmussen, 1984). It should be noted that this view is controversial, since other investigators have suggested that the vomeronasal system may be involved in discrimination of individuals in different circumstances (Steel & Keverne, 1985). Further experimental work is needed to clarify the interpretations of all of the relevant experiments. Nonetheless, at the present time I think an exciting and possibly correct working hypothesis is that the main olfactory system is primarily responsible for functions based on pattern recognition, and that this is why it seems crucial in mediating individual recognition as well as flank marking, vaginal marking, and ultrasonic calling, all of which depend on species recognition (Johnston, 1985b).

CONCLUSIONS

The progress in our understanding of chemical communication among hamsters and other mammals in the past 20 years is simply astounding. In a review published in 1966, Whitten summarized the literature on scent signals with behavioral functions in less than two pages, and concluded: "The scanty literature on possible mammalian releaser pheromones is reviewed. Before further advances can be made, it will be necessary to quantitate behavioral reactions . . . " This phase of research has been completed, at least for some behaviors, in several species. In golden hamsters, enough has been learned about scent-marking behavior, the chemistry of the scent secretions, and the sensory systems involved that we can now try to answer more fundamental questions about the mechanisms involved—questions that arise out of the original ethological and psychological traditions. In the most general form, the question is, to what extent is the behavior mediated by flexible, all-purpose mechanisms versus highly specialized, dedicated modules? Or more particularly, to what extent are the signals and the sensory and central nervous system mechanisms specialized and dedicated to single, discrete functions? Conversely, to what extent are these mechanisms general-purpose devices that are used, among other things, for communication? At the level of the signals, what does constitute the signal for sexual attraction and arousal? To what extent do the single compounds that have been identified really function on their own as communicative signals? For example, is dimethyl disulfide a sexual attractant or just an interesting odor to a male hamster? Is there a special protein in vaginal secretions that can act alone to cause sexual arousal or luteinizing hormone and testosterone surges? If so, can it act by itself, or must it always be perceived in the context of a "hamster" odor image? If the latter is true, what constitutes the signal for such an image? Are the flank glands really specialized to provide individually distinctive odors, or does phenotypic individuality arise as an automatic consequence of genetic and environmental differences between individuals? Are there any specialized receptors or central nervous system modules for the detection and evaluation of these signals, or do all of the responses to such signals depend on nonspecialized, general-purpose mechanisms? Are there dedicated receptors for dimethyl disulfide or the active protein(s) in vaginal secretions? Do individual recognition and/or other social recognition processes depend on specialized central nervous system modules, or are these functions served by general purpose pattern recognition systems?

At least partial answers to some of these questions should be available in the not-too-distant future and should help to answer fundamental questions about the evolution of the brain–behavior functional system. The degree to which there are limited-function, special-purpose modules in the brain and in cognitive function are presently matters of considerable research and controversy. Animal communication systems, which appear to have some of the properties of both general-purpose systems and specialized systems, should be particularly useful models for understanding these general problems.

SUMMARY

In this chapter, I review what is known about the mechanisms of chemical communication in golden hamsters and attempt to relate these detailed findings to general ideas about communication, the causation of behavior, the nature of chemical communication signals, and the neural mechanisms underlying responses to signals.

Both of the scent-marking behaviors we studied, flank marking and vaginal marking, are used to advertise aspects of the sender to other members of the species. Both are part of the animal's normal maintenance activities, and both are facilitated by cues from conspecifics, but not by cues from closely related species. Flank marking has a broad range of functions that can be summarized as advertisement of an individual's presence; more specific functions may include the communication of species, sex, and individual identity, and defense of a nest area and food hoard. Flank marking is especially frequent in response to the odors or presence of conspecifics that constitute a competitive threat (e.g., most other adult hamsters). Vaginal marking is primarily involved in sexual advertisement. The vaginal marking rate varies dramatically with the female's reproductive condition, peaking just before receptivity. Vaginal marking is stimulated by males or their odors, but not by other females or their odors. The effects of this scent on males include attraction from a distance, reduction in aggressive tendencies, elicitation of ultrasonic calling (used by males and females to locate one another), elicitation of testosterone surges, and increases in male sexual arousal. Thus, the causation of these two marking behaviors relates to both the general aspects of their advertisement functions and more specific functions that each of them serves.

The chemistry of the vaginal secretion has been examined in considerable detail: one highly volatile compound (dimethyl disulfide) has attractive properties, and a protein in the secretion has effects on copulatory performance. These results provide evidence for the evolution of highly specific chemical signals and suggest that specialized perceptual mechanisms may also have evolved. On the other hand, neither of these compounds elicits the level of responsiveness associated with the complete secretion, suggesting that the actual signals are not just single compounds, but depend to some extent on blends or mixtures of compounds that may be perceived by general-purpose pattern-recognition systems.

Aspects of the sensory mechanisms underlying odor-guided behaviors are hormonal responses and are discussed. The main olfactory system is responsible for mediating individual discrimination and scent marking, whereas the vomeronasal system mediates hormonal responses to odors. Both systems are involved in mediation of ultrasonic calling and copulatory behavior—it is not yet clear if the two systems have redundant or different functions in these cases. A hypothesis that may explain some of the differences in function is that the main olfactory system may have a primary role in general-purpose pattern recognition. The vomeronasal system appears to be especially important in mediating responses to large molecules, and may have specific receptors for these molecules; it also seems especially important in responses that relate directly to reproductive function.

The degree to which specialized, highly evolved mechanisms, as opposed to adventitious general-purpose mechanisms, are used in scent communication in hamsters, and, more broadly, in the control of specific behaviors or classes of behavior in other species, is an important issue for the understanding of sensory and perceptual function, brain organization, and the evolution of brain–behavioral systems.

CHAPTER 18

THE COLONY MODEL
OF AGGRESSION AND DEFENSE

D. Caroline Blanchard and Robert J. Blanchard

Unlike many of the other topics covered in this book, aggression research did not develop primarily within the framework of comparative psychology. This difference may in part reflect the anthropocentric origin of much scientific interest in aggression, a focus which has resulted in a very evenhanded division of behavioral work on aggression between human and animal subjects (Crabtree & Moyer, 1977). Moreover, in many cases, animal aggression research has been used specifically as a model for evaluating hypotheses arising primarily from consideration of human aggression phenomena. As one example, the concept that "frustration produces aggression," one of the best known and most influential statements in the history of psychology, came from a group of sociologists and psychologists (Dollard, Doob, Miller, Mowrer, & Sears, 1939) attempting to explain a range of largely human phenomena. Studies explicitly labeled as investigations of the frustration–aggression link have generally used human subjects (52 human to 17 animal studies up to 1975: Crabtree & Moyer, 1977). However, a paradigm designed to provide an analogous situation for use with animals—extinction-induced aggression—has been used many times in specific conjunction with the frustration–aggression hypothesis, producing a literature on "frustrative nonreward" (Gallup, 1965; Tondat & Daly, 1972).

An important goal of most comparative psychology studies is to determine whether the relationships of behavior patterns to important antecedent and consequent events are generalizable across various types of animals. In the typical modeling study, the behavior being investigated is one that is regarded as problematic, and the purpose of the research is to produce results that will ultimately lead to improved control or treatment of the problem as it affects people. This approach involves a very specific focus on the similarity of mechanisms in nonhuman animals to those in humans, and has the very specific requirement that the animal model reflect the same phenomenon that one wishes to understand or control on the human level. Most important action patterns (sexual behavior, maternal behavior, eating, or drinking) have obvious functions (reproduction, successful rearing of offspring, ingestion of food or fluids) that are identical in animals and humans. Although the human and animal behaviors involved are usually fairly similar as well, these common functions serve as the most important criteria for determining that eating, for example, is much the same behavioral phenomenon for rats (*Rattus norvegicus*) as it is for people.

A major problem in aggression research, however, is that there is no such clear and unequivocal function for aggression. The most widely used definition of aggression is that it is a directed harm-giving behavior. One might see the giving of harm as the function of aggression, but this view begs the question of the functional significance(s) of harm giving. The target of the harm-giving activity is also glossed over in most definitions. This target can be a conspecific, an animal of another species (such as a predator, or perhaps a prey animal), or a totally inanimate object.

To complicate these conceptual matters further, while ethological studies have long been concerned with social and dominance relationships within groups of animals, one of the most durable tenets of classical ethology (Lorenz, 1966) is the notion that nonhuman animals have a variety of threat and submission displays or signals which are used to settle intraspecies disputes without physical harm to the combatants. Taken in conjunction with the definition of aggression as harm-giving behavior, this suggests that aggression is directed largely against nonconspecifics and inanimate stimuli, or at least that these targets will prove more useful in measures of aggression, as actual harm-giving behavior against conspecifics is likely to be rare or absent.

In fact, animal aggression research has involved a wide array of different paradigms for producing the behavior, and an equally wide array of targets for it. Crabtree and Moyer's compendium of aggression studies up to 1975 indicated that predatory aggression (attacks on prey) was by far the most extensively investigated paradigm, while pain-induced aggression (object of attack not specified, but clearly including both animate and inanimate stimuli) was second. Intermale aggression, the most commonly used paradigm specifically involving a conspecific stimulus, was fourth on the list of animal aggression paradigms ranked in order of frequency of use. These and many of the other divisions of aggression studies used in the Crabtree and Moyer bibliography closely followed Moyer's (1968) well-known list of kinds of aggression based on the eliciting stimuli involved. This list included, in addition to the three kinds given above, territorial defense, irritable aggression, maternal aggression, and instrumental aggression. Although Moyer related this specific division of various kinds of aggression to different patterns of neural and endocrine factors (Moyer, 1968), the question of the functions of the various types was not addressed, nor (with a few exceptions: Crabtree & Moyer, 1972) was any systematic attempt made to analyze the specific behaviors involved or to use particular behavior patterns as important criteria in the study of aggression. Nonetheless, Moyer's classification represented a significant step in the attempt to understand the relationships among the various behavioral phenomena traditionally lumped under the rubric of aggression.

DESCRIPTIONS OF INTRASPECIFIC ATTACK AND DEFENSE

Against this background of great variability in paradigms and targets of attack and a lack of emphasis on specific behaviors, Grant and his colleagues undertook a very different approach to the study of aggression in animals. These investigators (Grant, 1963; Grant & Chance, 1958; Grant & Mackintosh, 1963) placed pairs of strange adult male rats together, or studied males housed in multimale cages. In each case, however, the focus of the work was a meticulously described set of species-typical social and agonistic behaviors.

It is greatly to the credit of these investigators that, despite their lack of videorecording equipment (such equipment has become something of a microscope for behavior analysis, since it allows behavior to be examined and reexamined in slow motion), this work nevertheless provided a systematic description of fighting and other social behaviors in rats that remains a standard for the area.

The results of these careful observations tended also to agree very well with the classic studies of S. A. Barnett (1958a), who placed groups of wild-trapped Norway rats together and observed a wide range of social and nonsocial behaviors in the groups thus formed. Barnett was particularly interested in stress in this situation, in which many newly introduced rats died in a matter of hours, often without having been seriously wounded. However, overt fighting did occur, and Barnett's illustrations and descriptions of wild rat fighting were strikingly similar to those given by Grant and his colleagues and by Eibl-Eibesfeldt (1958) and Ewer (1971).

Colonies and burrowing habitats

A few years later, colonies of laboratory rats began to be established and maintained in several American laboratories for the purpose of observing agonistic behaviors (Blanchard, Fukunaga, Blanchard, & Kelley, 1975; Luciano & Lore, 1975). The use of mixed-sex colonies, as compared to male-only groups, increased the level and intensity of attacks (Flannelly, Flannelly, & Blanchard, 1984) with the result that a dominance hierarchy among the males was quickly established. When strange males were introduced into these groups, they were vigorously attacked by the colony males. In one such early study (Blanchard, Blanchard, & Takahashi, 1977), we documented the establishment of dominance hierarchies among the males of six groups of rats over a number of weeks after colony formation, and found that the dominant male of each group was also the animal making the overwhelming majority of attacks on intruders, a finding which has since been repeated many times (Blanchard, Flannelly, & Blanchard, 1988).

Polarization of attack tendencies

One interesting feature of these situations was that the dominant male of each group had a history of successful aggression, and appeared to be relatively fearless in its own home area, while other male group members had histories of less successful aggression, and tended to be fearful in the presence of the alpha male. Thus, in encounters with a subordinate colony male or a naive intruder into the colony, the dominant male tended to show a highly motivated, purely offensive attack pattern, while its opponent showed defensive behavior. The within-colony or resident–intruder situation thus *polarizes* the motives and the actions of the two combatants. While this degree of polarization may be somewhat unnatural, it does greatly facilitate the analysis of aggressive or offensive behavior by separating it from the defensive actions of an attacked animal.

Offensive and defensive behaviors

The behaviors observed in these tests were generally similar to those described earlier by Grant and his coworkers. For the attacking rat, the primary elements of the attack or offense pattern are as follows (listed more or less in the order in which they typically occur): The dominant rat approaches an intruder and sniffs its anogenital region, then erects its body hairs (piloerection), becoming visually larger in consequence. It assumes a characteristic lateral attack position, with head lowered and back arched, and moves sideways, crowding against the intruder. This crowding move, sometimes combined with or followed by a forward movement tightly circling the intruder, may bring the attacker within biting reach of the intruder's back. When this happens, the attacker is likely to bite.

Following a bite, the naive intruder's behavior changes dramatically into a defense pattern. It may flee, in which case the attacker chases it. It may rear to a defensive upright or boxing posture, facing the attacker and bringing up its forepaws to interpose them between the attacker and itself. The attacker tends to respond to this with the lateral attack maneuver. The intruder, after receiving a number of bites, often sinks backwards from this boxing posture to lie on its back, and when this happens, the attacker quickly stands over and on top of the supine intruder. These actions are repeated many times in the average 10-minute encounter, but with a consistent synchrony between attacker and defender behavior, almost as if the two animals were doing a sort of dance.

Wound sites

When wounds occurred as a result of one rat's biting another, these wounds were localized on specific areas of the opponent's body (Blanchard, Blanchard, Takahashi, & Kelley, 1977). Wounds on subordinates and intruders, which were very common, occurred almost exclusively on the bitten animal's back and flanks. Bites on the dominant rat, very few in number, tended to involve the head and snout. These initial observations of different, specific target sites for offensive bites and defensive bites have since been consistently confirmed. Figure 1 presents the results of a number of additional studies from this laboratory on bite target sites for wild and laboratory R. *norvegicus* and R. *rattus* examined in both laboratory and real-world situations. These data, which are remarkably consistent across wild and laboratory strains, from R. *norvegicus* to R. *rattus*, and from one type of situation to another, show that between 70 and 90 percent of bites and wounds are on the back. It must be noted that wounds on wild-trapped rats could not be measured separately for dominant and subordinate rats, since we did not know the status of these animals. However, the vast majority of wounds in laboratory settings are associated with offensive attack, so we would expect that a compilation of all wounds on combatants, regardless of their status as dominant rat or subordinate/intruder, would yield a distribution of wound sites not substantially different from that on subordinates/intruders alone. If the same situation exists in the real-world situation in which the wild rats were trapped, then the primary wound locus should be the back. This is indeed what was found when wild R. *norvegicus* were trapped in their natural habitat (sugarcane fields on the island of Hawaii). Some of these animals were trapped in undisturbed habitat, others in disturbed habitat (the margins of a recently harvested and burned sugarcane field). Thus, the latter animals were the displaced survivors of a cataclysmic event. While rats from disturbed habitat had more wounds, the locations of the wounds on the bodies of all the wild-trapped rats were in excellent agreement with those of wounds found on intruders into colonies, with about 80 percent of the wounds on the back.

Since wounds on alpha males made in conjunction with subordinate/intruder defense patterns involved the head and snout, it was interesting to determine the distribution of wounds made by rats biting in response to electric shock. These wounds also show a very strict localization on the head and snout (see Figure 1). This finding strongly suggests that shock-elicited biting is defensive rather than offensive, and thus that the assumption that shock situations produce aggression is essentially incorrect. This issue will be taken up later.

Bite and wound sites have also been examined by a variety of other investigators, with results that are generally in agreement with the above findings. Olivier, Mos, van der Poel, Krijzer, & Kruk, (1984) found that from 70 percent to nearly 90 percent of all wounds incurred in intermale and territorial aggression situa-

(A) Wounds on intruders

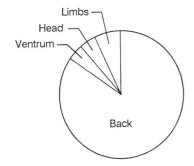

(B) Wounds on subordinates

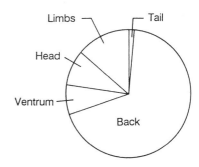

(C) Wounds on alpha males

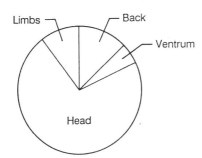

(D) Wounds on wild-trapped rats

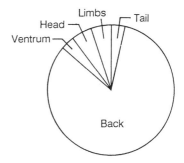

(E) Shock biting

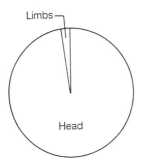

FIGURE 1. Wound distributions for bites by dominant males on intruders (A) and subordinates (B), by intruders/subordinates on alpha males (C), on wild-trapped rats (D), and in a shock biting test (E).

tions were on the back in two different inbred laboratory rat strains. Mos, Olivier, van Oorschot, & Dijkstra (1984) also found typical wound distribution on intruders into both small (about lab cage size) and large (1 meter square) enclosures, but a rather different distribution when an intermediate-sized enclosure was used. We, too, have noted an interesting effect of enclosure characteristics on wound sites: tail wounds frequently occur on intruders and subordinates in burrowing habitats or in a visible burrow system. When the intruder/subordinate seeks refuge in a burrow or tunnel, the dominant male may grab its tail (the teeth being used for this chore) and pull it out. Thus, the association of tail wounds with the availability of tunnels or burrows seems to be easily explained. No ready explanation for the Mos et al. finding is yet apparent, however.

With only a very few exceptions, then, the target site literature appears to be very consistent indeed, strongly suggesting that target site preferences provide a fixed point in the attack pattern of the rat, one which varies little from strain to strain, from wild to laboratory rats, and from colony to real-world situations. These target sites, do, however, vary strikingly between offensive and defensive attacks.

Back attack, back defense

The specificity of this targeting raised an interesting question: To what extent might the specific behaviors involved in attack and defense be aimed at gaining, or denying, respectively, biting access to the defender's back? Could this explain the relationships between the specific attack and defense behaviors that tend to occur together in dyadic attack–defense pairs? Blanchard, Blanchard, Takahashi, and Kelley (1977) analyzed dyadic interactions between dominant colony males and intruders, and found that there were indeed substantial relationships between specific defender behaviors and the attack behaviors of the dominant male. Specifically, chasing never occurred unless the intruder was running away; standing on top of the intruder never occurred unless the intruder was on its back; and lateral attack tended to be much more common when the intruder was boxing. These findings suggest that these offensive behaviors occur in response to the defensive behaviors with which they are associated.

Another way of verifying the close relationships of these specific attack–defense dyads is to describe how they vary together across different types of subjects. Takahashi & Blanchard (1982) measured these (and other offensive and defensive behaviors) for pairs of laboratory rats and pairs of wild-trapped *R. norvegicus*, with the results given in Figure 2. Comparison of attacker offense and defender defense within a given strain (laboratory or wild rat) shows extremely close correspondences within each attack–defense dyad. To provide a comparison point, freezing is not a component of such an intraspecific offense–defense dyad, and its lack of relationship to variation in any of the offensive behaviors (for

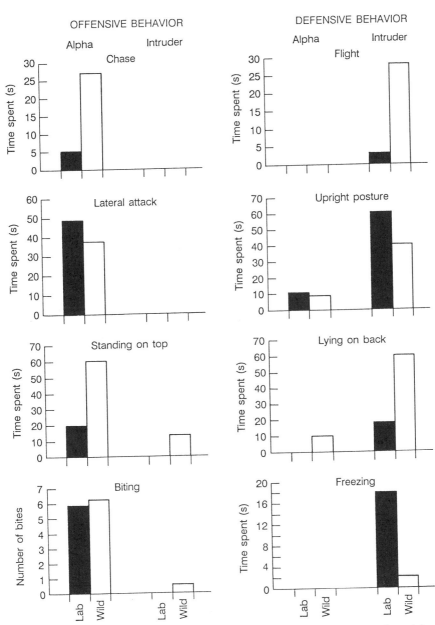

FIGURE 2. Offensive behaviors (left) and defensive behaviors (right) by resident alpha males (Alpha) and intruders (Intruder), in encounters between pairs of laboratory rats (Lab) and between pairs of wild rats (Wild).

lab and wild groups) displayed is obvious. What these findings strongly indicate is that each of the attack–defense dyads represents a functional unit, with the prevalence of each unit varying somewhat for wild and laboratory rats.

The function of the chase–flight dyad seems obvious: the fleeing individual is trying to get away, and the chaser is attempting to gain access to the fleer by a maneuver, chasing, which specifically counters the flight defense. Moreover, exactly the same analysis is possible for the remaining two attack–defense dyads: In the defensive upright posture, the defender is supported by its hind legs with its thorax more or less upright, and maintains a frontal orientation toward the attacker. This protects the back from the attacker's teeth, while exposing the ventrum (chest–stomach), an area which is almost never bitten even when it is freely accessible. The attacker attempts to counter this defensive upright posture, either by crowding in to push the defender off balance, or by rapid, close circling from the lateral attack position, which can bring it around to the intruder's back for a bite. When the intruder is naive, circling is often effective. It is more difficult to bite an experienced subordinate, which will pivot on its hind legs and follow the attacker's trajectory smoothly, keeping its back out of reach. Similarly, lying on the back makes access to the back target very difficult. However, the attacker standing on top of a defender is active in many ways, crowding, pushing, or pulling at the supine defender, which may result in exposure of its back. Thus, although lying on the back sounds as if it would be the ultimate protection, it is not: at least as many *attempted* bites are made (per unit of time) on defenders lying on the back as on those engaged in all other forms of defense, or no apparent defense at all (Blanchard, Blanchard, Takahashi, & Kelley, 1977). As with the defensive upright position, even naive defenders show recognizable lying on the back the first time they are attacked. However, experience makes this pattern much more precise and better coordinated with the behaviors of the attacker and thus more effective in preventing bites.

THE OFFENSIVE ATTACK MODEL

These analyses suggest that the consummatory component of the offense pattern (biting the other animal), the target of this behavior (the back of the opponent), and many of the other behaviors in the offense pattern (lateral attack, chase, standing-on-top-of) form a complex that can best be understood in terms of a strategic principle that we have labelled *back attack* (Blanchard & Blanchard, 1977). The corresponding strategy in conspecific defense is *back defense*, which is similarly associated with a number of specific behaviors (defensive upright posture, pivoting to maintain orientation to the attacker, lying on the back, rolling to keep the back away from the attacker) that function to make the back unavailable for biting. It is particularly notable that the most specific back defense behavior, lying on the back, does not occur in reaction to predator attack, as this would be counterproductive with an attacker that does not target its bites primarily to the rat's back.

This analysis thus suggests a number of different stimulus, organismic, and response characteristics of aggressive or offensive behavior that are different from those of the defense pattern. These include the following:

1. *Eliciting stimuli:* Offense in male rats is especially likely toward a strange male intruder, but also occurs consistently toward subordinate males of the group (Blanchard, Flannelly, & Blanchard 1988).
2. *Situational stimuli:* Offense tends to occur in a situation that is relatively familiar and safe for the subject (Mink & Adams, 1981), and it may be greatly facilitated by the presence of defensible resources of biological significance to the two potential combatants (Blanchard & Blanchard, 1977; Flannelly, Flannelly, & Blanchard, 1984).
3. *Subject characteristics:* Offense is particularly associated with the dominant male of the group, or more generally with animals that have a history of successful offense (Blanchard, Takahashi, & Blanchard, 1977). However, there are strong individual differences in offensive attack tendencies for animals of similar previous experience, and these predict future aggressive behaviors (Blanchard, Hori, & Blanchard, 1988).
4. *Responsiveness to independent variables:* Offense is reduced by fear (Mink & Adams, 1981; Blanchard, Kleinschmidt, Flannelly, & Blanchard, 1984). It is enhanced by sexual experience (Flannelly, Flannelly, & Blanchard, 1984).
5. *Behavior* (the primary criterion): Offense involves bites targeted to the back, plus a set of behaviors (lateral attack, chase, and standing-on-top-of) that facilitate access to the bite target site. Another action uniquely associated with offensive attack is piloerection, which occurs prior to other aggressive actions and increases the attacking animal's apparent size.

Many of the factors listed above, each of which has a definite and consistent effect on offense, produce just the opposite effects on defensive behavior. Thus, testing in a novel situation, or otherwise increasing the level of potential danger of a stimulus or situation, will increase defensiveness and decrease offensive behavior (Mink & Adams, 1981). In other situations, however, offense and defense appear to be relatively independent. For example, all normal rats are extremely defensive in the presence of a cat, and this, as far as is known, does not vary substantially with the level of aggressiveness they display to other rats, which does vary widely across individuals.

In addition, other factors, such as sedation, extreme fatigue, or malnutrition, might be expected to have effects on aggression that are similar to their effects on defense. Most active behaviors decline in a nonspecific fashion in response to reductions in arousal level, metabolic insufficiency, and the like, a situation long recognized by psychologists, who have traditionally provided controls for arousal level and other such effects in their research.

With the predictable exception of such nonspecific factors, offense and defense appear to be separable and distinct at every level studied. The analysis given above illustrates the distinctions in terms of the traditional stimulus–organism–response levels of the psychologist, but many of these same findings clearly apply equally well to the analysis of the different functions of offense and defense. Certainly these differences indicate that offense and defense should be investigated as separate entities. We, in fact, tend to go further. While it is fashionable to treat these topics as if they embody human constructions rather than evolved systems (see Brain, 1988 for a very nice statement of this position), we feel that these biobehavioral patterns constitute real entities which we and others are in the process of discovering, delineating, and describing. While our present descriptions are doubtless oversimplistic and incomplete, nonetheless we have no doubts that they reflect a reality which will become increasingly clear as the research continues.

Attention to the factors listed above as promoters of offensive behavior also enables a high degree of laboratory control over the magnitude of aggressive tendencies for particular subjects. When this is combined with the ability to measure a wide range of offensive behaviors, a very precise model is produced which can be used for further analysis of the relationship of aggression (and defense, though that is less the present topic) to important antecedent and subsequent events.

USES OF THE OFFENSE–DEFENSE MODEL AND RELATED MODELS

One establishes models in order to use them. The colony model of offensive aggression, with its conceptual separation from defense, has been used in many ways over the past decade.

Offense–defense and the "pain-elicited aggression" model

Perhaps the first important question about this model is: how well does the offense–defense distinction fit with other commonly used psychological models for aggression, such as the reflexive fighting and single-subject tube test situations? Blanchard and Blanchard (1977) compared the behaviors and bite sites of colony alpha males and intruders to those of rats in a test of reflexive fighting in response to electric shock, and found that reflexive fighting produced very high levels of defensive responses and little or no offensive behavior. Moreover, the forepaw movements typically interpreted as "striking" in reflexive fighting tasks

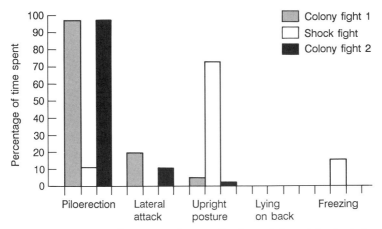

FIGURE 3. Percentage of time spent in two offensive and three defensive behaviors by resident alpha males in encounters with intruders. The first encounter in each group was in the colony, the second in a "reflexive fighting" situation, and the third in the colony again.

also occurred when a single rat was held on the shock grids in a boxing posture and given comparable foot shocks (Takahashi & Blanchard, 1978). The finding that these strikes were very common when no opponent was present suggested that they may be reflexive jerks of the unsupported forelimbs in response to foot shock.

Blanchard, Blanchard, & Takahashi (1978) further refined this comparison by using the same pairs of animals (colony alphas and intruders) first in colony tests, then paired in a reflexive fighting test, then again in the colony. Figure 3 presents the behavior of the alpha males only. Given are two behaviors associated with the offensive pattern (piloerection and lateral attack) and three associated primarily with defense (defensive upright posture, lying on the back, and freezing), for these three sequentially run tests. In both colony tests, the dominant colony males performed as expected, showing relatively high levels of offense and very little defense. All bites were made by the colony alphas, and these showed the expected target site distribution. In reflexive fighting, however, the dominant colony males showed very little piloerection, and lateral attacks were virtually nonexistent. Instead, the alphas showed high levels of boxing and moderately high levels of freezing. Very few bites were seen, and these involved the snout target typical of defensive bites, instead of the back target typical of offensive bites.

Although rats closely confined in a tube test situation are not capable of showing any of the major offensive and defensive behaviors outlined here except biting, Blanchard, Kleinschmidt, Fukunaga-Stinson, and Blanchard (1980) performed a tube test in which bite target sites on the body of a deeply anesthetized conspecific were measured. We found that, even when given tail shock, almost no subjects made bites to the back targets typical of offensive biting, or to neutral areas such as tail or feet. However, these animals readily bit the opponent's snout, strongly indicating that these were defensively rather than offensively motivated bites.

These results suggest that the two pain-elicited aggression tasks have little to do with offense, though they may provide a (somewhat contaminated) index of certain elements of defensiveness, notably, boxing for the reflexive fighting test, and defensive biting for the tube test. Objection has been made to this conclusion on the basis that what is here called defense may in fact represent a lower intensity of aggression, in comparison to the offensive pattern which represents more intense aggressiveness (Hutchinson, 1983). This objection has been answered (Blanchard & Blanchard, 1984) in a manner that will doubtless seem familiar by now: offense and defense are different in terms of the eliciting stimuli or situations, the characteristics of the organism, and, above all, on the basis of behavior.

Causes and functions of aggression

These situations and the rather consistent body of data resulting from them have had an impact on one of the age-old questions of psychology: What causes aggression? This question has been a perennial issue in psychology, receiving answers such as "a death wish or instinct" (Freud, 1940/1949), "frustration" (Dollard, Doob, Miller, Mowrer, & Sears, 1939), or "pain" (Ulrich & Azrin, 1962). What all these putative causes have in common is that they are distinctly unpleasant phenomena of varying levels of concreteness. Perhaps it is the idea that aggression tends to be elicited by unpleasant events generally that has produced the widespread notion in psychology and elsewhere that aggression can be prevented by the simple expedient of reducing the level of unpleasant life events for an individual or for a society.

The sociobiological view of the "cause" of aggression is quite different: aggression involves a resource or dominance dispute (Wilson, 1975). Thus, aggression is the response to a challenge (generally from a conspecific) over important resources (food or water, if these are in scarce supply and in large enough units to make it worthwhile to fight over them, females in breeding condition, a territory or nest site with adaptive advantages, and the like) or over one's position within the group. This view explains why aggression tends to be so clearly a function of such variables as sex and breeding condition (Wilson, 1975). In rats, as in many mammals, males fight more than females do (Blanchard, Flannelly, & Blanchard, 1988). However, females do show unequivocal (and effective: Lore, 1987) fighting when there is a crucial consequence involved. Maternal aggression in rats and mice occurs at a high level during the first 10 days or so of their pups' lives, a time when the pups are particularly likely to be cannibalized by conspecific intruders (Flannelly, Flannelly, & Lore, 1986). Males also show more offensive attacks after sexual experience and in the presence of females (Flannelly, Flannelly, & Blanchard, 1984), and dominant males enjoy priority of sexual access to females (Blanchard, Fukunaga-Stinson, Takahashi, Flannelly, & Blanchard, 1984).

Priority of access to food and, especially, water is less clear for dominant males (Blanchard, Fukunaga-Stinson, Takahashi, Flannelly, & Blanchard, 1984), but this may be misleading. In general, fights over resources appear to be linked to the importance and scarcity of those resources (Wilson, 1975), and it is not clear that these ecological variables have been well modeled in the rat aggression situation. Certainly no one intends to starve laboratory animals, or deprive them of water, to a point at which access to food or water becomes an immediate survival issue. At any rate, the finding that dominant males do have priority of sexual access, but not of access to water (with access to food intermediate between the two, significantly higher for dominant males but not as clearly characteristic as is sexual access), suggests that one important function of conspecific aggression is to enhance access to especially scarce or valuable resources, particularly when these can be successfully defended. For common and abundant resources, the value of the enhanced access that could be gained by aggression is probably quite low. In general, when the value of obtaining access to a particular resource outweighs the potential cost of aggression, then aggression is adaptive. It is obvious that this resource or dominance dispute view of the causes of offensive attack constitutes a rather complex hypothesis that requires attention to the specific ecology of a particular species.

In contrast, defense has the function of protecting the individual from threat. It might, in fact, be more properly called self-defense, since defense of or protection of exclusive access to entities other than the self (for example, Moyer's category of "territorial defense") involves offensive, not defensive, behavior. The defensive threat–attack pattern, the component of the defense system which is most likely to be confused with offensive attack, occurs almost exclusively in the very close presence of an attacker, and generally in the specific context of pain or high-magnitude fear. Defensive threat is adaptive in that it tends to discourage the continued attack of a predator or attacking conspecific, while defensive biting, aimed at particularly vulnerable areas (face, eyes) may hurt or at least disorient the attacker long enough for the defensive animal to flee. Moreover, while defensive attack is doubtless a high-risk activity, it occurs in situations which afford few defensive alternatives (Blanchard & Blanchard, 1989).

Stress

Another use of the offense–defense model involves the relationship between these behaviors, the social-dominance structure of rat groups, and stress. This work stems originally from Barnett's (1958a) observation that stress death may be found only hours after a wild rat intruder is introduced into an established group of wild rats. While wounding might certainly occur, these animals did not in general seem to have sustained the sorts of wounds one would expect to produce death.

Our more recent follow-ups to this work came about serendipitously when we attempted to make our colony enclosures more natural for the animals. We created seminatural habitat systems consisting of an open area (1.0 or .7 meters square) and a contiguous burrow system with tunnels and chambers into which animals could retreat, and which they could possibly defend against attacking conspecifics. At first, we provided a soil substrate into which the rats could burrow (Blanchard, Blanchard, & Flannelly, 1985). This required the rats to dig their own tunnels, and they did so almost immediately. Later, after it became clear that this system was very messy and also that the burrows were hard to see into, we began to use a visible burrow system (Figure 4) which consisted of ready-made Plexiglas tunnels and chambers (Blanchard & Blanchard, 1989). While the open areas were on a 12:12 hour light:dark cycle, the burrows were maintained under red light, and the rats appeared to accept them as dark, although rat movements in the burrows could be recorded using a low-light video system. In both situations, the burrow systems were utilized very quickly, and the animals tended to remain there during the day, coming out at night (lights-off in the surface area) to eat and drink.

After using these more elaborate systems, we began to realize that our subordinate males were not living as long as the dominant males. In our standard colony enclosure—an open box with Plexiglas or wire-mesh sides of approximately 1 meter, with wood shavings on the floor—our dominant rats were living 700 days or more, but subordinates lived to an average of about 500 days (Blanchard, Flannelly, & Blanchard, 1988). In compartments of the same dimensions with the soil substrate, the dominant males again lived 700 days or more. However, the first subordinate male deaths occurred about 30 days after formation of the group, when the subjects were 100 days old. While some of these animals were wounded, others showed relatively little external trauma, again raising the question of the relationship between stress and the early death of subordinates. This early mortality of subordinate males has continued in the visible burrow system, to the point that we now use this apparatus primarily as a short-term testing device, rather than as a standard living area. It is notable that neither dominant male deaths nor female deaths in these mixed-sex groups were different in the open colonies as compared to the soil substrate habitats or the visible burrow systems.

The idea that stress is an important feature of life for male subordinates in these situations is supported by several findings. First, prolonged attack does produce ulcers in rats, even in single tests lasting only 21 hours (Lore & Luciano, 1977). Also, dominant males in burrowing habitats are particularly aggressive in terms of attacks on intruders, providing a potential mechanism for enhanced

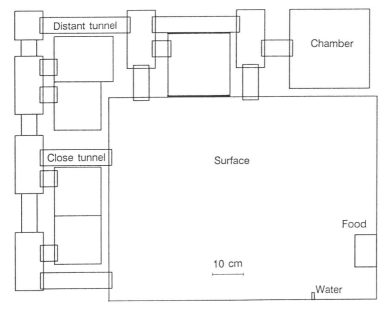

FIGURE 4. Schematic for a visible burrow system. The "surface" area was open and was subjected to a 12:12 hour light:dark cycle. The tunnel/chamber system was shielded from the surface area light by a high wall and was illuminated by red light only.

stress in group subordinates (Blanchard, Blanchard, & Flannelly, 1985). The view that the operative factor is stress also receives support from the finding that subordinates consume alcohol at a higher rate than dominants in group situations (Blanchard, Hori, & Blanchard, 1987).

If, indeed, stress is the factor controlling early subordinate mortality, it is particularly intriguing that the stress seems to be differentially distributed among the subordinates. Although subordinate age at death is much younger in both types of burrow situations than in the open colonies, some subordinates show almost normal lifespans in the burrow situations, while others die very early. The early-dying subordinates, moreover, show behavioral avoidance of the dominant rat beginning several weeks before they die, while the longer-living subordinates show little alpha avoidance at this time (Blanchard, Blanchard, & Flannelly, 1985). Moreover, the early-dying subordinates show a specific decrease in offensive attacks on other subordinate males and females within the colonies, which may be seen in some cases as much as 6 months before they die (Blanchard, Flannelly, & Blanchard, 1988).

We do have some evidence as to why some subordinates may be attacked more than others. Blanchard, Hori, & Blanchard (1988) tested male rats individually for aggressiveness in their home cages, and divided them into high, intermediate, and low aggressiveness categories on this basis. When groups were formed, each consisting of three males and three females, with one male from each of these aggressiveness categories in each group, the previously categorized highly aggressive male predictably became dominant in most cases. What was particularly interesting, however, was that the intermediately aggressive male (or the highly aggressive, nondominant male, in the few groups where the intermediate male became dominant) reliably showed more wounds from these interactions than did the least aggressive subordinate male. We do not yet understand the mechanism involved; perhaps the more aggressive animals are more persistent in dominance fights, or, by being more offensive than defensive in these fights, they may perhaps be wounded more easily. Nonetheless, something is happening that produces a more severe impact on the subordinates that were initially more aggressive, and this might in turn lead to the individual differences in voluntary alcohol intake and early mortality.

The previously mentioned increase in alcohol intake for subordinate males is also highly variable across subordinates, but consistent within individuals (the correlation between consumption levels on tests involving different alcohol concentrations was $r = +.68$ for males, which was highly significant: Blanchard, Hori, & Blanchard, 1987). As Figure 5 shows, some subordinates drank no more than the dominants did, while other subordinates consumed 2 to 3 times as much alcohol as any of the dominant males.

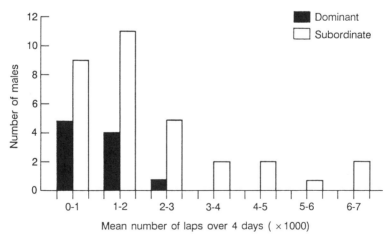

FIGURE 5. Numbers of dominant and subordinate males voluntarily consuming a 4 percent solution of ethanol in various quantities on a daily basis, over 4 days of access to the ethanol solution.

It would clearly be interesting to determine whether this alcohol intake is related to the patterns of dominant attacks on subordinates and of early versus late stress death in subordinates. Specifically, we might expect that the early-dying males are those which the dominant male attacks more severely, and that the more severely attacked males may be those showing higher levels of alcohol intake when alcohol is available.

All these findings suggest that the offensive and defensive behaviors of male rats in groups are involved in the formation of dominance hierarchies, and that some aspect of this combination of behavior and established relationships engenders high levels of stress for the subordinates, particularly in more natural habitats. Thus, the colony and visible burrow system situations may provide a useful model of social stress in conditions specifically designed to be natural for the animals. This pattern of findings, incidentally, is directly contrary to the often-heard view that it is the close confinement and unnatural conditions under which laboratory animals live that makes them fight. In all these studies, increased space and availability of burrow systems has enhanced both the aggressiveness of the dominant male and the resultant polarization of dominant–subordinate relationships.

PHYSIOLOGICAL STUDIES

Pharmacological studies

Perhaps the most extensive use of the offense–defense distinction has been with pharmacological agents, which have been involved in a vast literature using "resident–intruder" or "colony" models. Studies of the pharmacology of aggression have been exhaustively reviewed by Miczek (1987) and cannot even be summarized in the space presently available. It is worth noting, however, that there appear to be a number of pharmacological agents which differentiate between offense and defense, with a recently developed class of "serenics" selectively reducing offensive (Olivier, 1981) and either not changing or perhaps increasing defensive behavior (Kemble, Thornton, & Schultz, 1987).

In this context, what is perhaps more important than a simple dichotomy of offense and defense is the detailed description of behavior patterns for each of them. Ethopharmacology—the use of natural behavior, described and measured in detail, in conjunction with pharmacological manipulations—can provide descriptions of specific drug-based changes in behaviors which are understood in terms of their relationships to major antecedent and consequent factors. This enables a much finer and more precise assessment of drug effects than previously available. Since it is unquestionably the goal of much research involving the effects of pharmacological agents on behavior to provide a rational basis for the use of drugs to control maladaptive behavior in humans, such detailed analyses are very much needed. To give one ongoing example involving defense rather than offense, we are presently investigating the effects of a variety of pharmacological agents on a broad spectrum of defensive behavior, finding, for example, that the effects of benzodiazepines (by far the most commonly used group of drugs for the control of anxiety) appear to differentially impact some defense patterns, while leaving others relatively intact (Blanchard, Blanchard, & Rodgers, in press).

Neural studies

Although research on the neural systems involved in offensive and defensive behaviors has not produced the same enormous literature as pharmacological research, the rapid development of new and sophisticated techniques for analysis of the neural systems associated with particular behavior patterns has produced rapid advancement in this area as well. We have summarized some of these studies in a brief review (Blanchard & Blanchard, 1988), which is, however, already outdated by more recent work. The major conclusion of the application of an offense–defense distinction to this literature is that while the neural and neurochemical systems underlying various defensive behaviors have been and are being well studied (see, e.g., DePaulis, Bandler, & Vergnes, in press; Hammer, Hori, Cholvanich, Blanchard, & Blanchard, in press), offensive aggression is very much underrepresented in this research. A major reason for this situation is that the behavior paradigms typically used in these neural system studies involve testing animals in isolation. A cat, for example, tested alone, is hardly capable of displaying a typical offensive behavior pattern. It can, however, show a very dramatic defensive threat pattern involving screams and hisses and the typical "halloween cat" posture with arched back and erect ears. Thus, the brain stimulation leading to such a pattern, and the brain manipulations eliminating it, can easily be noted and used to develop a body of relevant data. However, manipulations altering offensive attack would almost certainly go unnoticed in such tests. The point is that offensive attack is a complex and specific phenomenon, and if one wishes to understand its neural basis, one must be careful to give attention to the adequacy of the test situation and the measures taken in order to provide a clear baseline offense pattern. If offense and defense are not carefully differentiated, the dramatic defensive threat–attack pattern will likely be used as the major index of "aggression."

SOME COMPARATIVE PSYCHOLOGY: GENERALIZATION OF THE OFFENSE–DEFENSE DISTINCTION

Work on other species strongly suggests that the general principles outlined here for the rat—that offense and defense are different, and that offensive attack is aimed at specific target sites on the body of the opponent, with offensive behaviors facilitating, and defensive behaviors denying, access to these sites—may be true for a variety of mammals. For example, Rushen & Pajor recently (1987) reported that in the domestic pig, the specific target site for offensive attack is the head, ears, and neck, and that intraspecific fighting patterns reduce (for defense) or facilitate (for offense) access to this target. The classic work of Leyhausen (1969) on domestic cats indicated bite and forepaw slash targets again in the neck area; Leyhausen in fact analyzed much of cat conspecific defense in terms of actions which tend to make this neck target site unavailable to the attacker. Ungulates (Geist, 1978b), notably mountain sheep and goats, also appear to have specific target sites for potentially damaging contact, in that they direct powerful head butts at a protective horn or antler structure. These fights are particularly interesting because both the combatants show an offensive attack pattern in prebreeding ruts.

Pellis (1988) has recently provided a survey of diverse taxa (including birds and a range of mammals) in which bites or blows are directed to specific targets. For the majority of these, the same targets appear to be used in serious adult fights and in juvenile play fights, though some animals, including the laboratory rat, show somewhat different attack targets in juvenile fights. In fact, so far as we know, no one who has looked for such targeting in any higher species has yet reported a failure to find it. There is reason to be optimistic, then, that this specific view of intraspecies agonistic behavior will prove to have wide applicability among mammals and perhaps even more widely.

This is not to say that the back attack–back defense model, or, more broadly, the offense–defense distinction, is by any means universally accepted. These are first-step, doubtless simplified, views of some complex relationships, and it is to be expected that they will be subjected to scrutiny and modification. Indeed, when a new hypothesis remains unmodified over a long period of time (and this is especially true in the early stages of the scientific development of an area), it is less likely to reflect that the hypothesis is valid than that it is so dull or vague that no one is seriously trying to investigate or develop it. In contrast to this sad state of affairs, the offense–defense distinction has resulted in a broad array of empirical descriptions and research applications which suggest that if and when it is modified, this will involve increased understanding of the basic processes involved.

SUMMARY

Studies of intraspecific fighting behavior in rats in increasingly more natural situations suggest that aggressive or offensive behaviors are very different from the defensive behaviors of the attacked animal. Offensive behaviors are aimed at a specific target on the body of the opponent: the back. A number of intraspecific rat defenses (not seen in reactions to a predator) result in protection of this site, while a corresponding number of offensive behaviors appear to be functional in thwarting the behavioral defenses and gaining access to this target site. This back attack–back defense view of rat fighting indicates that offense and defense are different in terms of behaviors and targets of attack, in addition to an array of stimulus and organismic factors by which they may be distinguished.

The colony model of intraspecific aggression and defense has been used to investigate a number of aspects of intraspecific agonistic behavior. These studies indicate that aggression is particularly likely in the context of disputes over dominance or scarce and important resources. In contrast, the threat–attack behaviors elicited by pain or high-level and immediate fear are seen as a component of the defense pattern. Aggressive and defensive behaviors are involved in the creation of dominance hierarchies among male rats within groups, and these dominance relationships strongly influence mortality. Subordinate males show greater rates of ulceration and higher voluntary alcohol consumption, and die at increasingly younger ages in more natural situations affording access to burrow systems. These findings suggest that such habitats may provide a model for investigation of stress effects.

Finally, aggression and defense appear to involve very different neuroanatomical and neurochemical systems, and careful consideration of specific behaviors and behavior patterns is required in the interpretation of studies of brain manipulations in terms of their impact on aggression and defense.

Epilogue

COMPARATIVE PSYCHOLOGY: RETROSPECT AND PROSPECT

Donald A. Dewsbury

It is not easy to define comparative psychology. Operationally, it might be taken to include the kind of material that is published in the *Journal of Comparative Psychology*. This includes studies of species-characteristic behavior and learning done both in the laboratory and in the field with a general focus on the relevance of the research to the natural lives of the animals under study. The American Psychological Association publishes two other journals in animal psychology, the *Journal of Experimental Psychology: Animal Behavior Processes*, concerned mainly with general processes of learned behavior thought to be characteristic of a wide range of species, and *Behavioral Neuroscience*, concerned primarily with physiological analyses of behavior. Although there are important areas of overlap in these fields, I think it important to differentiate comparative psychology from these other, different approaches to the study of animal behavior represented in the latter two publications.

COMPARATIVE PSYCHOLOGY IN THE TWENTIETH CENTURY

Although the three fields of animal psychology alluded to above were not always clearly differentiated, it is instructive to view the history of what we now call comparative psychology as distinct from the predecessors of process-oriented learning studies and physiological analysis (Dewsbury, 1984). There were pioneers of scientific comparative psychology already at work at the turn of the century who viewed comparative psychology much as we do today. Further, there is historical continuity in this approach; there have been comparative psychologists, in this sense, throughout the century. This does not mean that they were dominant throughout the century, or that their work was not overshadowed for substantial periods by other approaches in animal psychology. However, it does mean that there is a long tradition for the kind of comparative psychology represented in this book.

Elsewhere I have delineated ten myths that I believe have led to a misperception of comparative psychology (Dewsbury, 1984b). Comparative psychology has often been contrasted with classical ethology as being limited to the use of domesticated mammals in laboratory studies designed to develop principles of learning for application to humans. Comparative psychologists have been characterized as working with a limited range of species, ignoring problems of naturally occurring behavior, and not being cognizant of issues related to the evolution of behavior. Some of these characterizations may be accurate for animal psychology as a whole, and their authors may have been aiming at larger targets in the name of "comparative psychology." Whatever the case, the waters have been muddied, and clarification of the true nature of comparative psychology is needed. We hope that this volume will aid in this effort.

One can distinguish various approaches to comparative psychology, two of which—the study of animal cognition and of "comparative animal behavior"—appear especially active and productive today. Both date from the period of the origins of comparative psychology. The idea of a comparative psychology was made substantial with the development of Charles Darwin's theory of evolution by natural selection. Others, especially Herbert Spencer, had similar ideas and had applied them to psychology. However, it was with Darwin that these notions gained sufficient force to shape significant developments in psychology.

Darwin's associate, George John Romanes, explored the implications of Darwinian thinking about the continuity of species as it affected views of the behavior of nonhuman vis a vis human animals. C. Lloyd Morgan, L. T. Hobhouse, John Lubbock, and Edward L. Thorndike all were contributors in the quest for the understanding of the relationship between human and nonhuman consciousness and mental functioning. The comparative study of mental processes has continued ever since, though the terminology changed—especially during the period when behavioristic approaches dominated psychology.

Another important line in the origin of comparative psychology stemmed from attempts to address what Francis Galton termed the "nature–nurture problem." The problems of instincts and the developmental origins of behavior were fundamental in the early days of comparative psychology. Thus, for example, in advancing the "New Psychology," G. Stanley Hall (1885) recommended studies in "the rapidly-growing science of comparative psychology," because "besides their intrinsic and their practical value, such studies shed light on the nature, and often on the psychic genesis of what is a priori and innate in man"

(p. 122). Studies of instincts and their development were advanced by Douglas A. Spalding, James Mark Baldwin, T. Wesley Mills, and John B. Watson, among others. For E. L. Thorndike, (1900) "the first task of comparative psychology is to find out the instinctive equipment of any animal studied. Instincts are, however, well worth study for their own sake" (p. 58).

Comparative psychologists thus became interested in the study of species-characteristic behavior for a number of reasons. They were interested in instincts and their origins, and thought that an understanding of instinctive behavior was fundamental to the study of the mind and higher processes. Comparative psychologists also became interested in the functions of behavior, which led to the prominent, if somewhat diffuse, school of functionalism in psychology. This too was stimulated by Darwin and his focus on adaptation. An exact understanding of the problems of function and adaptation in psychology is made difficult, in part, by the multiple uses of these terms (e.g., Ruckmich, 1913). A case can be made that much of the work on function in psychology was not directed at the evolutionary process of adaptation in the Darwinian sense. Rather, the focus was on the process of adaptation, or better "adjustment," within the lives of individual organisms in their environments (Sohn, 1976; Buxton, 1985). The interest in this developmental problem of adjustment may stem as much from Herbert Spencer as from Darwin. John Dewey, William James, James Rowland Angell, and Harvey Carr were among the important early advocates of this functionalist psychology. Even a psychologist trained in the older structuralist tradition, Margaret Floy Washburn (1908, pp. 274 ff.), came to view behavior in a functional context. Some of her views fit especially well with the approach taken by Hollis (Chapter 9) in this volume.

Whatever the origins of the field, by the early part of the twentieth century, numerous comparative psychologists were studying species-characteristic behavior in animals within a functionalistic context. John B. Watson compared the nesting behavior of two species of terns in the field; Robert M. Yerkes studied the behavior of mutant "dancing" mice, and Linus Kline advocated a broad comparative base for the field (see Dewsbury, 1984). Contrary to the views of some historians, I believe that this tradition continued throughout the century, although I agree that it was often overshadowed by other approaches. Frank A. Beach, Leonard Carmichael, C. Ray Carpenter, Harry F. Harlow, W. N. Kellogg, Zing-Yang Kuo, Karl S. Lashley, Daniel S. Lehrman, Norman R. F. Maier, Henry W. Nissen, T. C. Schneirla, Calvin P. Stone, Carl J. Warden, and Yerkes were among the important comparative psychologists working within this tradition.

During the 1930s and 1940s, there developed within European zoology the discipline of classical ethology. The focus of this new discipline was on the study of instinctive behavior in a variety of species under field conditions. Although there was initially some hostility between comparative psychologists and ethologists, their interaction has modified both fields in ways that appear beneficial. The arrival of European ethology provided a shot in the arm to comparative psychology at a time when it was being overshadowed by other endeavors in animal psychology in North America. Both fields have continued to evolve, with the most notable recent development being the evolution of the sociobiological approach in the 1970s. The work in the present book should be seen as a part of this long tradition.

COMPARATIVE PSYCHOLOGY TODAY

The Four Questions

The classical ethologist Niko Tinbergen (1951; 1963) proposed a schema for the orderly study of animal behavior. For Tinbergen, such study should begin with the careful observation and description of behavior. Observation and description are not ends in themselves, but they provide the foundation for the study of four classes of questions: immediate causation, development, evolutionary history, and adaptive significance. The study of immediate causation is concerned with the environmental and internal factors important in the short-term regulation of behavior. Developmental questions are concerned with longer time spans in the lives of individual organisms. Questions of evolutionary history concern the evolution of behavior across species and evolutionary time. Questions of adaptive significance concern the role of behavior in promoting survival and reproduction (i.e., adaptation, function). Questions of immediate causation and development are sometimes grouped together as questions of "proximate" causation, and questions of evolutionary history and adaptive significance as treating "ultimate causation."

The boundaries among these questions are not always sharp, as in the gray area between development and immediate causation. However, the delineation of the four questions has had several beneficial effects. It has served to balance attention toward different aspects of animal behavior. It has also promoted clear thinking, as, for example, in the realization that studies of adaptive significance can be scientifically valid, but must be scrupulously differentiated from studies of immediate causation. A plausible function may not be a plausible immediate cause. Further, the "four questions," as they have become known colloquially, have provided an effective basis for organizing studies of animal behavior (e.g., Dewsbury, 1978). They have been cited repeatedly by the authors of this book.

The present volume is not organized in terms of the four questions with good reason. For some time after the formulation of the four questions, individual research programs tended to be focused on one or another of them, and it was rare for multiple aspects of animal behavior to be addressed in a single program. This has changed of late, so that individual research programs transcend single questions and have become difficult to classify. Several of the chapters in the present book that are concerned with several questions illustrate this. Although this has made a clear-cut organization of this book based on the four questions impractical, I believe it a healthy sign.

Snowdon (Chapter 10) emphasizes the interrelations among the four questions. Like Tinbergen, Snowdon believes that all four must be addressed in order to reach a comprehensive understanding of behavior. He argues that, with the advent of sociobiology, an excessive amount of attention has been directed at questions of function and phylogeny. Comparative psychologists, such as the authors of this volume, are in a position to redress this imbalance. A nearly identical point is made by Petrinovich (Chapter 15), who states that a complete understanding of behavior requires analysis of both the proximate and the ultimate. Coming from a different perspective, Hollis (Chapter 9) notes that studies of learning have generally been addressed toward questions of immediate causation. With the advent of the "constraints-on-learning" approach, ultimate questions have received more attention, so that today there is a peaceful coexistence between causative and functional approaches.

Beyond this, a beneficial feedback occurs when multiple questions are addressed. Thus, for example, knowledge of function can provide a guide for research on causation, and vice versa. Kamil and Clements (Chapter 1) make this point effectively in their discussion of their work on patch depletion, which provides an excellent example of the interaction of proximate and ultimate considerations. "Rules of thumb" are seen as effective proximate means by which animals achieve effects that approximate those expected from analyses of what appears optimal. Thiessen (Chapter 4) agrees: after noting the difference between proximate and "distal" factors, he notes the importance of welding the two together. Beecher's research on parent–offspring recognition in swallows (Chapter 16) provides an excellent example of the advantages of attention to multiple questions. His research originated with a functional perspective and a prediction that recognition would be functionally more relevant in colonial than in noncolonial species. Beecher's comparative studies of the mechanisms of recognition and of the development of these processes unite the research into the kind of integrated package envisaged by Tinbergen and by other authors of this present volume. In Chapter 6, I note that the traditional distinction between research on proximate and ultimate causation can become quite narrowed. Consider studies of sperm competition and the consequences of mating order for differential reproduction. Does this concern mechanism, functional significance, or a blend of both?

The most neglected of the four questions in recent years has been that of evolutionary history—the one that Konrad Lorenz regarded as especially fundamental. This trend continues in the present volume, although the approach is certainly represented in Thiessen's discussion of allometry (Chapter 4). Also,

King and West (Chapter 14) provide a nice example of the study of evolutionary history: they can pinpoint the spread of cowbird populations in the United States, and they have worked to relate differences in behavior among populations to the species' geographic expansion.

Even those chapters most directed at the study of mechanisms have a strong functional focus. Silver (Chapter 11) considers the role of biorhythms in the integration of behavior, but it is a functional integration that results in the male and the female effectively sharing brooding duties. Johnston (Chapter 17) stresses the study of mechanisms in his studies of olfactory communication in hamsters; however, he is guided throughout by a functional understanding of the animal and its behavior. The same is true of Galef's studies of social learning and foraging patterns in rats (Chapter 3). Blanchard and Blanchard (Chapter 18) emphasize the immediate causation of aggressive behavior in rats, but blend in a healthy portion of material on the functions of aggression, especially as viewed in an economic context.

Tinbergen's four questions remain an important basis for organizing studies of animal behavior. The most interesting development is the way studies are being designed to bridge the questions and the interaction among the different questions in many studies. However, despite this erosion of once-sharp divisions, there are still important distinctions to be made, and balance among the four domains is still critical.

The comparative method

Although some would define comparative psychology as necessarily entailing overt comparisons among species, such a definition seems needlessly restrictive. Many excellent studies in the comparative tradition are done without overt between-species comparisons. For Konrad Lorenz (e.g., 1950), the use of the "comparative method" necessarily entails the study of evolutionary history. For most researchers, however, a looser definition is useful, with many types of comparison qualifying for inclusion. Comparisons can be made at the "phyletic level" (among phylogenetically quite diverse species), the "species level" (among closely related species), or at the "genetic level" (among groups within a species) (King, 1963). Kamil and Clements (Chapter 1) especially advocate the species level.

There are many reasons for comparing species. For example, one may wish to trace the evolutionary history of a behavioral pattern. Alternatively, however, one may wish to compare the behavior of unrelated species responding to similar ecological pressures or of closely related species responding to different pressures. One may simply wish to explore the generality, including both similarities and differences, of a phenomenon.

Uses of the comparative method. The use of the comparative method clearly is alive in comparative psychology, as demonstrated by the chapters of this book.

Perhaps the most comparative chapter is Thiessen's discussion of allometry (Chapter 4), in which he presents important cautions for comparative study. Any proposed comparison must be considered in relation to possible allometric relationships constraining the evolution of the systems under study. Thiessen envisages the compilation of a "dictionary of allometric equations" that would facilitate comparative analyses. His use of scaling with "broad and delicate strokes" corresponds to study at the phyletic and species levels.

Clearly, the comparative method provides the basis for Beecher's work on parent–offspring recognition in swallows (Chapter 16). His 2×2 experimental design, with two nesting patterns and two replicates at each pattern, provides an ideal approach for the analysis of adaptive correlation. A similar approach is taken by Schwagmeyer (Chapter 8) in her comparisons of mating strategies in different species of North American ground squirrels. Kamil and Clements (Chapter 1) compare the ability to recover cached food in several species of birds with differing degrees of dependence on such food stores. Not surprisingly, perhaps, those species most dependent on cached food were most efficient at recovering it.

An interesting example of the comparison of diverse species appears in Chapter 9, where Hollis contrasts the ardor of blue gourami females with the indifference of female Japanese quail. She relates this to the mating systems of the two species, with gouramis showing polyandry and quail polgyny.

The application of the comparative method at the genetic level is perfected by King and West (Chapter 14). They encourage comparative psychologists to pay attention to "microphyletic," as opposed to "macrophyletic," analyses as a worthwhile route in the field. The approach of King and West can be treated as involving "microphyletic expeditions," in which the same species is observed in different settings. King and West develop a three-tiered research strategy for the investigation of intraspecific variation, involving preparation of communication protocols, knowledge of inherited niches, and calibration of ecological time. Together, these authors, and others in the book, make different, but productive, uses of the comparative method.

Selection of species. The selection of species for study in animal psychology has sometimes been rather arbitrary. Such has not been the case in most of the studies discussed in this book. As Kamil and Clements (Chapter 1) note, one can often select animals because of unique or uncommon characteristics that allow the researcher to address problems less readily approached with other species. Kamil and Clements' blue jays are an appropriate species for studying patch depletion because they are omnivorous foragers that feed in depletable patches. Their nutcrackers are appropriate for the study of cache recovery because such recovery is important to these birds in the field. King and West (Chapter 14) note that there is much interest in the development of song in cowbirds because adults allocate parental duties to other species, thus raising interesting questions about the ontogeny of species-characteristic behavioral patterns. Christenson (Chapter

7) notes several characteristics of the changing social organization of his orb-weaving spiders at different life stages that raise especially interesting evolutionary questions. Johnston (Chapter 17) was searching for a good mammalian "model" species for the study of olfactory communication; the presence of prominent flank glands in golden hamsters suggested their utility in this role.

There are other good reasons for selecting particular species. One is the availability of closely related species for comparative study. The existence of four species of swallows with contrasting nesting patterns was critical to Beecher's work (Chapter 15). In Chapter 6, I note the diversity both of species within the genus *Peromyscus* and of *P. maniculatus* populations in different regions. The choice of a species native to the study area makes it easier to link field data with data collected in the laboratory. When the species under study is endangered, such as the tamarins studied by Snowdon (Chapter 10), there are both special obligations for the researcher and implications for conservation of the results gathered in the research. The selection of the brown tree snake as a research animal yields an applied focus to Chiszar's work (Chapter 5).

Diversity of study species. Diversity of study species is not necessarily a good end in itself. Although psychologists have been criticized for overreliance on white rats and White Carneaux pigeons, much useful research, some of it in the comparative tradition, has been done with these species. Nevertheless, the diversity of species used by the authors of this volume is considerable. Arthropods remain greatly underrepresented; only one study, Christenson's on orb-weaving spiders (Chapter 7) involved them. Hollis (Chapter 9) continues the tradition of research with fish in comparative psychology with her studies of blue gouramis. The herpetological tradition is represented by Chiszar's study of brown tree snakes (Chapter 5).

In recent years there has been much interest in the use of birds in behavioral research. Five full chapters in this volume deal with birds: the studies by Kamil and Clements on blue jays and nutcrackers (Chapter 1), Silver on ring doves (Chapter 11), King and West on cowbirds (Chapter 14), Petrinovich on white-crowned sparrows (Chapter 15), and Beecher on four species of swallows (Chapter 16).

Rodents remain very popular study animals in comparative psychology. They adapt well to the laboratory and are very useful animals for research. Three of the seven chapters dealing with rodents are concerned with laboratory rats: Timberlake's on learning and feeding (Chapter 2), Galef's on social learning (Chapter 3), and Blanchard and Blanchard's on aggression (Chapter 18). Together, these chapters illustrate how research within the comparative tradition can be done with laboratory rats. Other students of rodent behavior include myself, (Chapter 6) working with deer mice, Schwagmeyer (Chapter 8), studying ground squirrels (Chapter 8), Porter (Chapter 13), working with spiny mice, and Johnston (Chapter 17), working with golden hamsters.

Although nonhuman primates have become something of a focus in recent research, there is just one chapter on primate behavior—Snowdon's on cotton-top tamarins (Chapter 10). Thiessen's chapter on allometry (Chapter 4) is so comparative as to be impossible to classify. Similarly, though Moore's own research (Chapter 12) deals primarily with laboratory rats, she reviews literature on a broad variety of species.

Methods in Comparative Psychology

Advances in any field, including comparative psychology, often depend on the methods used. The methods must be appropriate for the problem under study, and new technology should be used as it becomes available and whenever it is truly relevant for the research.

Laboratory and field. At times during the development of the study of animal behavior, there has been conflict between field and laboratory researchers. Field workers bemoaned the artificial conditions of the laboratory and questioned the validity of laboratory observations applied to behavior under natural conditions. Laboratory researchers bemoaned the lack of control of relevant variables under field conditions and questioned the reliability of results. Much of this hostility has dissipated as both groups recognized the advantages of the other approach and the limitations of their own. Both field and laboratory research are legitimate; what is critical is that the method be appropriate to the problem under study.

Some of the research described in this book was done under field conditions: for example, Christenson's work on orb-weaving spiders (Chapter 7). Christenson's work began with observations of natural history and proceeded to tests of hypotheses based on those observations under field conditions, in the tradition of T. C. Schneirla.

Some authors combine field and laboratory work and thus reap the benefits of each. Beecher (Chapter 16) begins with his observations of and experiments on swallows in the field and then describes laboratory research designed for the precise determination of controlling mechanisms. Schwagmeyer (Chapter 8) stresses field observations on scramble competition for mates in thirteen-lined ground squirrels, but notes the need for careful laboratory research on sperm competition to make some of the results interpretable.

The most common approach among the authors of this volume is to model their laboratory research on knowledge gained from field studies. Kamil and Clements (Chapter 1) model both the operant technology used in their study of foraging and the enclosure used in their study of cache location on field observations. Galef's analysis of foraging in rats (Chapter 3) was designed to model central-place foraging in nature. Chiszar (Chapter 5) also modeled his laboratory research on brown tree snakes on field situations. To show a chemical mediation of food searching in this species, Chiszar and his associates placed chemical cues in devices simulating dark burrows, thus making visual inspection of the bait by the snakes impossible. Ropes and dowels were used as substrates to simulate the arboreal locomotion of the snakes in nature. I was careful to set up my studies of sperm competition and dominance (Chapter 6) to simulate reasonable situations that appear to occur in nature.

It is important that laboratory simulations take the natural environment and behavior of study species into account if valid results are to be obtained. Animals that live in individual home ranges should not be treated as if they lived in baboonlike troops. Although paternal behavior may occur in small cages, it may be difficult to extrapolate this finding to the field. The blue gouramis studied by Hollis (Chapter 9) are territorial, so she allowed them to establish territories and simulated the arrival of a rival or mate when conducting tests. Snowdon (Chapter 10) recognized that the behavior of tamarins is greatly dependent on the family group within which they live in nature and simulated these social groups in laboratory enclosures. Silver's analyses of the temporal patterning of shared parental care in ring doves (Chapter 11) were based on an analysis of their natural patterns of shared effort, and she designed environments to enable her to dissect controlling variables in the context of natural patterning. Porter's study of food location by weanlings (Chapter 12) represents a modeling of a situation likely to occur in the field. A message from both King and West's work (Chapter 14) and that of Petrinovich (Chapter 15) is that song learning in birds occurs in a social context, and to fully understand it one must eventually study song learning in social situations similar to those occurring in the field. Johnston (Chapter 17) presents a discussion of the natural history of golden hamsters; he designed his research problems in relation to that natural history.

Blanchard and Blanchard (Chapter 18) stress the importance of combining naturalistic observation with controlled experimentation. Their work shows that specific features of the natural environment must be simulated if the behavior under study is to be observed properly. The relevant features will vary with the species and the behavior. "Naturalistic" environments may not suffice; they may have to be naturalistic in terms of certain dimensions. Such factors as the presence or absence of a burrow can have important consequences for behavior. Petrinovich (Chapter 15) also emphasizes this point. A single poorly chosen test environment characteristic can lead to problematical data for an entire research project. Petrinovich follows Egon Brunswik's approach with regard to the sampling of different conditions.

Two other voices merit citation in this context. Chiszar (Chapter 5) notes that interesting behavior of a species can occur in abnormal environments, and that one may not see the full range of the behavioral capabilities of a species unless animals are tested in a range of environments, some of which may be quite unlike those normally encountered in the field. The "ecological release" involving brown tree snakes on Guam described by Chiszar revealed a variety of interesting behavioral potentials. Timberlake (Chapter 2) notes that natural behavior often occurs in unnatural situations. He emphasizes that it is only when one places an animal in unusual situations that one can analyze precisely the factors controlling behavior. Timberlake would have comparative psychologists recognize, produce, and model critical stimulus and response components relevant to functionally important behavior. One might go a step further to note that those behavioral patterns that ethologists have regarded as instinctive are those that occur in highly abnormal environments, and that such occurrence is one of the primary bases for the inference of instinctive control.

Utilization of technological advances. A frequent message found in these chapters is that one often has to go "back to basics," making careful observations of behavior and considering natural history when designing research. At the same time, however, sophisticated technology is critical to the execution of a great deal of research. Many of the phenomena reported in this book could not have been found without the utilization of such recently developed methods.

The simulations of foraging situations used by Kamil and Clements (Chapter 1) utilized sophisticated operant conditioning technology. Galef's discovery of the role of CS_2 in social learning (Chapter 3) stemmed from mass spectrometric and gas chromatographic analyses of air from the nasal cavities of rats. I used electrophoresis (Chapter 6) to determine paternity after female deer mice mated with more than one male. Snowdon (Chapter 10) developed sophisticated hormone assays for urine, and he and his colleagues developed a method of collecting urine using techniques that were noninvasive and produced minimal disturbance of the animals. The research on vocal communication reported by King and West (Chapter 14), Petrinovich (Chapter 15), and Beecher (Chapter 16) utilized sophisticated auditory equipment for both playback and sound spectrographic analyses, and methods were developed to quantify the visual records obtained with sound spectrograms. Both Petrinovich and Thiessen (Chapter 4) utilize new techniques of mathematical scaling in analyzing behavior.

Two techniques that have become so common in behavioral research that they are often not even mentioned are the computerization of data collection and analysis and the use of videotape. Many of the analyses reported in this book would have been so cumbersome as to be extremely difficult, if not impossible, without the aid of computers. Videotape permits the observer to examine critical behavioral sequences over and over again to see aspects of behavior not observable to the unaided eye—the "instant replay" of comparative psychology. Thus, King and West (Chapter 14) first spotted the "wing stroking" display of female cowbirds using videotape. Blanchard and Blanchard (Chapter 18) made extensive use of videotape in their analyses of the rapidly occurring aggressive interactions of rats.

The rapid advances in neuroscience enable researchers to perform sophisticated analyses of the physiological processes correlated with behavior. Among the techniques discussed by Silver (Chapter 11) that are being used to study internal clocks are electrophysiological recording, analysis of metabolic uptake with radioactively tagged 2-deoxyglucose, anatomical analysis with horseradish peroxidase, transplantation of fetal tissue, and analysis of neuropeptides. Johnston (Chapter 17) used both ablation and reversible disruption of olfaction with zinc sulfate to analyze olfactory mediation of behavior in hamsters.

Psychologists sometimes become so in awe of technological advances in other areas that they undervalue those in their own. Analyses of behavioral patterns have become more detailed and more sophisticated. An excellent example can be found in Blanchard and Blanchard's work on aggression (Chapter 18). Their refined appreciation of offensive and defensive components in agonistic behavior and of the importance of clear specification of both motor patterns and targets of attack has led to a reinterpretation of much of the earlier work in this field. Researchers utilizing contemporary technology must be sure that their research is as sophisticated in its approach to behavior as in its utilization of hardware, software, or physiological techniques.

Research themes

Each chapter in this book is unique, and the individual authors present insights that are specific to their particular approaches and results. Several major themes can be seen in the remarkable and diverse array of results presented here and in their implications for the development of general principles concerning animal behavior.

Adaptation. The notion of behavioral adaptation is central to many of the chapters. In many cases, studies were designed to determine the nature of particular adaptations in the species under study. Galef (Chapter 3) begins with a discussion of the problem of adaptation and uses the phrase "An adaptationist perspective" in his chapter title. Kamil and Clements (Chapter 1) used the presence of specific adaptations as a criterion for selection of species for study. I use my observations of reproductive behavior in deer mice (Chapter 6) to illustrate the principles of natural selection leading to behavioral adaptations. Both Petrinovich (Chapter 15) and Hollis (Chapter 9) stress the importance of the study of adaptations.

The other side of comparative psychology, however, is a certain methodological hardheadedness. There are precautions for the study of adaptation as well. Thiessen (Chapter 4), for example, stresses the use of allometry; one must control for body size and other allometric relationships before concluding that a feature is a true behavioral adaptation. Galef (Chapter 3) discusses the important critique by Gould and Lewontin (1979) along a similar vein. Snowdon (Chapter 10) stresses the importance of avoiding overemphasis on adaptationist approaches in the post-Wilson sociobiological era. Beecher (Chapter 16) notes the limitations of the adaptationist perspective for making predictions: he was able to predict the occurrence of some adaptation to serve parent–offspring recognition, but was unable to predict the nature of that adaptation without an empirical analysis of mechanisms.

The fact is that predictions from adaptationist perspectives sometimes fail. Christenson (Chapter 7) was troubled by several phenomena in which spiders seem to be acting suboptimally, and approached the problem with a modeling technique designed to assess the costs and benefits of alternative behavioral patterns available to his animals. I noted (Chapter 6) that male capacity for mating in deer mice seems less than would appear adaptive and that deer mice are much less discriminating with respect to both kin and mates than other species are or than would be expected in light of adaptationist considerations. Kamil and Clements (Chapter 1) note that birds often remain in a patch longer, or revisit a depleted patch sooner, than predicted from their model; this behavior could serve the function of gathering information necessary for behavioral flexibility with changing conditions. Snowdon (Chapter 10) notes that cotton-top tamarins have a high rate of copulatory activity, though prevalent models suggest low copulatory rates in monogamous species; this is interpreted in relation to the temporal patterning of copulation and the time frame considered.

I believe that the increased utilization of an adaptationist approach has been of substantial benefit to comparative psychology and that its continued widespread use is warranted. However, it should be used with the experimental rigor that has long characterized work in comparative psychology. The occurrence of results inconsistent with predictions may be a positive sign that predictions can indeed fail and that models are indeed falsifiable, even if the first response of the experimenter often is to try to patch up the original model.

The social context of behavior. The research described herein is illustrative of the growing emphasis on the social context within which behavior normally occurs. Study of an isolated animal under controlled conditions is necessary for the discovery of many behavioral patterns, and is often an important first step. However, changes often are seen when the animal is replaced in its normal social environment. This may be most immediately apparent in studies of song learning in birds. Petrinovich (Chapter 15) contrasts song learning in white-crowned sparrows using taped tutors versus live tutors. With live tutors, the sensitive period for learning is extended, because students appear to attend to their tutors as part of a social interaction. In a similar vein, King and West (Chapter 14) show how nonsinging female cowbirds influence the ontogeny of song in singing males; males attend to their audience, responding especially to the female wing-stroke display.

The whole emphasis in Galef's discussion (Chapter 3) is on *social* learning.

Rats do not locate food in isolation; rather, conspecifics are relevant to food location in several contexts delineated by Galef. I begin analyzing deer mouse copulatory behavior (Chapter 6) by studying male–female pairs in small cages, but expand the analysis to stable social groups in larger environments. Male–male aggression is greatly enhanced by the presence of females. The reproductive behavior of Christenson's orb-weaving spiders (Chapter 7) is shaped by the female's control of the web and the presence of multiple males, thus generating male–male competition. Schwagmeyer (Chapter 8) notes that different patterns of male–male competition for females are prevalent in different mating systems, and that the particular pattern that occurs is largely dependent on the spatial and temporal patterning of available receptive females. Snowdon (Chapter 10) discusses research showing that the degree of aggression displayed in marmosets depends on the presence or absence of their mates (i.e., the social context). Blanchard and Blanchard (Chapter 18) describe the historical progression of studies of aggressive behavior in rats leading from studies of individuals or pairs to studies in a colony situation. In mixed-sex colonies, dominance hierarchies are formed and agonistic interactions are increased. The study of naturally occurring aggressive behavior is greatly facilitated with such colonies.

The point may be taken a step further with Chiszar's discussion of brown tree snakes (Chapter 5). In the other studies, the "social environment" includes only members of the same species. In fact, most species live as parts of complex communities, and behavior is affected by the structure of those communities. Chiszar takes a step in what will be a very difficult, but important direction: determining the ways in which the community context affects behavior.

Learning and memory. The study of learning and memory has been a major focus of interest since the dawn of comparative psychology, and perusal of the chapters of this book reveals that it is still a major topic of interest in the field. The first three chapters of the book provide excellent examples. Kamil and Clements (Chapter 1) discuss cache location in birds. When birds of some species place food items in specific places, they are remarkably efficient at retrieving them at a later time. It appears as though the memory systems in these species are specifically adapted to function in this way. Timberlake (Chapter 2) describes a variety of studies in which standard phenomena of the learning literature are reexamined and reinterpreted in terms of preexisting natural behavioral tendencies of the animal subjects. Galef's emphasis (Chapter 3) is on social learning in the process of food acquisition, and he discusses the range of cues that rats are able to learn to use in locating food. Hollis' research (Chapter 9), when viewed as a study of learning rather than of territorial defense and reproductive behavior, is also part of this tradition. She examines the role of associations learned by Pavlovian processes in facilitating territorial defense and mating.

The three chapters on vocal communication in birds all have a heavy emphasis on learning. King and West (Chapter 14) discuss the various factors that affect song learning in cowbirds. Petrinovich (Chapter 15) deals with the sensitive period and relevant modulating factors for song learning in white-crowned sparrows. His results have important methodological implications but are also relevant to the difficult conceptual issues that he raises. Beecher (Chapter 16) discusses the role of learning in parent–offspring recognition in swallows in his studies of cross-fostering and recognition.

Earlier, I differentiated research in comparative psychology from that in the process-oriented learning tradition. In light of the heavy emphasis on learning in the studies in this book, it is fair to ask how this differentiation can be maintained. I believe that the difference lies in the way in which learning is treated. In most of the work discussed in this book, learning is viewed as a part of an animal's evolved life history. The focus in this research is on the natural lives of animals and the factors that affect them. Behavioral plasticity in general, and learning in particular, are as much a part of the natural lives of animals, and are as much adaptations, as any other characteristics. For the contributors to this volume, unique adaptations of particular species are generally welcomed as research challenges rather than dealt with as troubling exceptions to general rules. Process oriented learning research is valid and worthy of continuation; however, it is different from the primary focus of the work included here.

Development. Another focus from the earliest days of comparative psychology has been upon studies of the development of behavior. The earlier dichotomy of nature and nurture has been expanded into more complex and sophisticated analyses of the development of behavior. Galef (Chapter 3) discusses Mayr's notion of closed versus open behavioral programs; the same notion is mentioned by King and West (Chapter 14). There are some behavioral patterns whose development appears well buffered against environmental variation and which develop along very similar lines in a wide range of environments. Other behavioral patterns, those with open developmental programs, are susceptible to various kinds of input during ontogeny. In some cases, the effective input may be quite limited, as may the time during which the input can be effective. The fact that some features of either sensory sensitivity or motor pattern may be well "buffered" and may develop in the absence of specific input by no means excludes important environmental input to other aspects of the pattern.

Moore's discussion (Chapter 12) is centered on the development of sexual behavior. She uses the metaphor of cascades to emphasize the fact that key elements in development can have complex and diverse ramifications over extended periods of time. The metaphor of webs is used to stress the interconnection of many disparate factors and processes in the development of behavior. Her research on the role of stimulation in the development of sexual behavior in rats provides an excellent example of this behavioral complexity.

Developmental themes are prevalent in other chapters as well. Christenson

(Chapter 7) takes a developmental, life-history approach to his orb-weaving spiders. He notes changes as the spiderlings mature and emphasizes the changing role of the web. Snowdon (Chapter 10) notes that the predisposition of male nonhuman primates to display paternal care of young is often quite dependent on their early experience. Animals that gain early experience taking care of the young of other animals are more likely to be competent parents. The strong developmental focus in the three chapters on vocal communication in birds (Chapters 14, 15, and 16) should be readily apparent.

The complexity of development is especially apparent in King and West's studies of cowbirds (Chapter 14). Acoustically deprived North Carolina male birds require no experience with adult males to sing effective songs. Similarly, females need no exposure to song to be able to make effective discriminations between the songs of their own subspecies and other songs. Some researchers would stop at this point; however, this is just part of the story. A wealth of developmental questions remain after this is said, and these are traced in Chapter 14.

The developmental processes of behavioral patterns that are both highly plastic and greatly buffered can be quite complex. Analysis of the complex pattern of webs and cascades in development is indeed a critical part of any comprehensive understanding of behavior and is prevalent in contemporary comparative psychology.

Applications and conservation. Most of the research reported in this volume is basic research designed to be relevant to important scientific questions. The primary concerns of comparative psychology have been to develop a comprehensive science of behavior and to formulate principles that will be applicable to a wide range of situations. Such general principles and theories of behavior should promote the application of the science in a variety of situations. However, this is a slow process, as contrasted with research targeted at immediate goals. When viewed in the long run, it may be an effective strategy. The problems societal forces regard as worthy of intense research effort appear to change rather rapidly. Intense, short-term efforts, in the absence of a solid foundation gained by slow but careful basic research, is unlikely to have the desired payoffs.

Even in the absence of the kind of comprehensive principles we are trying to develop, research results generated by theoretical goals often have considerable applicability. Perhaps the best example in animal psychology is the applicability of operant principles generated in basic research on animal learning. Research on animal reproductive behavior can be relevant to our understanding of human reproduction and to the practical problems of both increasing and decreasing the rates of reproductive activity in nonhuman species as deemed appropriate by societal concerns. Research on biorhythms may be relevant to dealing with problems caused by jet lag. Parallels between the acquisition of bird song and human language learning have often been noted.

Chiszar's research on brown tree snakes (Chapter 5) provides an excellent example of a program of research designed with an applied focus from its inception. The problems caused by these snakes in decimating the local avian fauna and in causing power outages have impact on the welfare of both human and nonhuman species. Work designed to apply principles of behavior to the humane control of these animals can be of immediate practical value. In addition, however, Chiszar shows how applied research can be relevant to the generation of general principles in the understanding of animal behavior. The fact that research may be conducted with an applied focus need not mean that it is without relevance to important scientific issues.

Snowdon's research on cotton-top tamarins (Chapter 10) has practical implications in two directions. First, these animals are seriously endangered. This both places serious obligations on the scientist to treat the animals with special care and provides an opportunity to apply results in a situation where it is impossible to wait for the slow accumulation of theory that characterizes much of scientific development. Laboratory research has revealed ways in which the breeding success of these and other species can be facilitated in captivity. The hope of captive breeding programs is that political and social conditions may someday change so that reintroduction of endangered animals to the field will be possible. Second, Snowdon relates his studies of nonhuman primates to humans. His research suggests that males are generally interested in caring for young but that the extent of actual paternal care may be altered by both the early rearing environment and by economic factors. The same factors may affect the extent to which human males exhibit extensive paternal care.

RETROSPECT AND PROSPECT

Comparative psychologists may be seen as working within a long tradition in psychology. Many of the basic questions addressed in contemporary research have a long history in a variety of disciplines, including psychology, during the century or so during which it has existed as an independent discipline. New questions arise, new methods become available, and new integrating principles are formulated. We need to continue to make use of available technological advances in conducting research in comparative psychology. However, the perspective to be gained from the experiences of those who worked in our tradition earlier can be invaluable in guiding contemporary research toward significant questions and in avoiding dead ends that have been encountered before.

There are no intellectual reasons that progress in comparative psychology should not continue. Comparative psychologists have made effective use of available resources in advancing their science and have produced research results and principles demonstrating the utility of their approach.

Perhaps the major internal threat to the continued advancement of comparative psychology is growing fractionalization. Although many disciplinary squabbles have been settled, research is becoming more and more specialized, with less communication among those working in different areas. If this trend continues, it could make effective synthesis difficult or impossible. The specialized use of new approaches is to be encouraged, but we must not lose our overall perspective.

The further development of the field may be hampered by a variety of interacting societal pressures. First, in times of limited funding, basic research with long-term, rather than short-term, payoffs tends to be short-changed, making effective use of available technology difficult. A second concern stems from pressures generated in the name of animal welfare. Most comparative psychologists are greatly concerned with the welfare of animals; indeed, many became comparative psychologists because of an interest in and affection for animals. However, some extremists in the animal rights movement are exerting pressures to eliminate animal research; and there is a strong anti-science element in this endeavor. One must hope that a middle ground can be reached wherein the concern for animals that scientists and activists share can be balanced with the need for scientific advances. The cause is not advanced by strong rhetoric from either side. Finally, partially as a result of both of the factors just mentioned, changing standards for laboratory facilities are increasing the costs of animal research and making the conduct of research correspondingly more difficult. Most of these changes are well intentioned, and some, though certainly not all, of these changes improve the welfare of the animals under study. Such changes are to be applauded, but one must hope that extraneous requirements with great costs and minimal effect on animals can be pared.

Science must exist and flourish within a societal context, and it is greatly affected by that context. If the field is nurtured and allowed to develop, there is every prospect that future comparative psychologists can greatly advance the sophistication of our understanding of animal behavior and its causation, development, evolutionary history, and adaptive significance. But our endeavor is also capable of being killed by societal forces. Comparative psychology fits within the broad Western intellectual tradition, and is worthy of nurturance. This message needs to be communicated to those empowered to affect the fate of comparative psychology.

Acknowledgements

Chapter 1: Alan C. Kamil and Kevin C. Clements   The preparation of this chapter was supported by National Science Foundation grants BNS 85-19010, which supported the comparative cache recovery research, and BNS 84-18721, which supported the patch depletion research.

Chapter 2: William Timberlake   Preparation of this chapter was supported by USPHS Grant MH37892 and National Science Foundation Grant BNS84-11445. I am greatly indebted to the many people who worked with me on this research, and especially to Gary Lucas. I also profited from the comments of Don Dewsbury and two reviewers.

Chapter 3: Bennett G. Galef, Jr.   The research program described here has been supported since 1968 by the National Research Council of Canada, the Natural Sciences and Engineering Research Board of Canada, and the McMaster University Research Board. I thank the many students, both graduate (Matthew Beck and Steve Wigmore) and undergraduate (Moni Stein, Sylvie Malenfant, Anna Mischinger, Christine Hitchcock, and Katie Gilmour), technicians (Sandra Vegaris, Cathy Maskell, Cecelia Malinski, Elaine Whiskin, and Cathy Hammond), and colleagues (Deborah Kennett, Russ Mason, Jay Bean, and George Preti) without whose collaboration very little of the work described here could have been accomplished. Mertice Clark, Martin Daly, and Don Dewsbury gave helpful advice on earlier drafts of this manuscript.

Chapter 4: Del Thiessen   The writing of this chapter was made possible by NIMH Grant MH 140760-20.

Chapter 5: David A. Chiszar   I thank my friends and colleagues who have participated in this project: T. Fritts, N. Scott, and G. Rodda (all with the U.S. Fish and Wildlife Service), K. Burrows, D. Carrillo, J. Chiszar, D. Drew, R. Lee, S. Reiners, and H. M. Smith (all with the University of Colorado); and K. Kandler (University of Tübingen, Federal Republic of Germany). I hope we shall soon make a contribution to the residents of Guam.

Chapter 6: Donald A. Dewsbury   This research was supported by grants from the National Science Foundation, most recently BNS-8520318. I thank M. D. Beecher, J. M. Bryan, T. E. Christenson, C. J. Manning, A. Salo, P. L. Schwagmeyer, and S. A. Taylor for their comments on earlier drafts of this manuscript.

Chapter 7: Terry E. Christenson   I wish to thank Jeff Cohn, William Dunlap, and Paula Singleton for their help in preparing this manuscript, and Steve Austad, Michael Beecher, Donald Dewsbury, William Eberhard, Susan Riechert, and Trish Schwagmeyer for their incisive comments on various drafts of this paper. Several of the studies mentioned were supported by the National Science Foundation Grant BSN-8317988.

Chapter 8: P. L. Schwagmeyer   I thank D. Dewsbury, T. Christenson, A. Kamil, and D. Mock for their comments on the manuscript, and D. Mock for helpful discussions of the topics covered in it. My research on thirteen-lined ground squirrels has been supported by an NIMH Predoctoral Fellowship, the University of Oklahoma Research Council, and NSF grants BNS8317848, INT8402913, and BNS8619574; during the writing of this review I received financial support from NSF RII8700055.

Chapter 9: Karen L. Hollis   In the 6 years that I have been at Mount Holyoke College, many hardworking undergraduate students have collaborated with me to produce the work described in this chapter. I thank all of them, but especially: Grace Begany, Lisa Cadieux, Stacy Canis, Maura Colbert, Katie Doty, Theresa Gies, Ruth Grahn, Kathy Martin, Sarah Moseley, Karen Roberts, and Jean Zeiler. The research reported here was supported by Grants-in-Aid from the Merck Fund and from the Dana Foundation. Several Faculty Fellowship Grants provided additional support.

Chapter 10: Charles T. Snowdon   The preparation of this chapter and the author's research were supported by USPHS Research Grant MH 35,215 and Research Scientist Award MH 00,177. I am grateful to a group of excellent collaborators, past and present— Jayne Cleveland, Laura Dronzek, A. Margaret Elowson, Jeffrey A. French, Patricia B. McConnell, Anne Savage, Tina M. Widowski, and Toni E. Ziegler—for their stimulating ideas and diligent research. I am grateful to Toni Ziegler, Donald Dewsbury, and Bertrand Deputte for their helpful critiques of this chapter.

Chapter 11: Rae Silver   I wish to thank Peter Balsam, Resit Candelyi, Don Dewsbury, Celia Moore, Cindy Ramos, and Richard Porter for their comments on previous drafts of this manuscript, and Ray Garcia for assistance with the figures. The research on the parental behavior of doves described in this paper was supported by NIMH grant 29380.

Chapter 12: Celia L. Moore   The research from my laboratory described in this chapter was supported by grants BNS-8317796 and BNS-8513687 from the National Science Foundation. I am grateful to George Michel, Jeremy Hatch, Rae Silver, Richard Porter, and Don Dewsbury for their helpful comments on an earlier version of the chapter.

Chapter 13: Richard H. Porter   Preparation of this chapter, including the research summarized herein, was supported in part by grant HD-15051 from the National Institutes of Child Health and Human Development.

Chapter 14: Andrew P. King and Meredith J. West   The work reported here has been supported by grants from the National Science Foundation and the National Institute of Neurological and Communicative Disorders and Stroke. David Eastzer's doctoral work was supported by grants from the National Science Foundation and National Institutes of Mental Health. We thank M. Beecher, D. A. Dewsbury, and L. Petrinovich for their comments.

Chapter 15: Lewis Petrinovich   The original research discussed here was supported by grants from the University of California, the National Institutes of Health (HD-04343 and MH-38782), and the National Science Foundation (BNS-7914126 and BNS-8004540). I wish to thank Patty O'Neill for her comments that greatly improved the manuscript, and to thank Meredith West and Don Dewsbury for their constructive criticism of the penultimate draft.

Chapter 16: Michael D. Beecher   This work would not have been possible without the following colleagues: Inger Mornestam Beecher, Philip Stoddard, Mandy Medvin, and Patricia Loesche. Much of the work was supported by grants from the National Science Foundation.

Chapter 18: D. Caroline Blanchard and Robert J. Blanchard   This work was supported by NIH AA06220, RCMI Grants RR03061 and RR01825, and by the University of Hawaii Research Council.

Literature Cited

Abbott, D. H. (1984). Behavioural and physiological suppression of fertility in subordinate marmoset monkeys. *American Journal of Primatology, 6*, 169–186. [10]

Abbott, D. H. (1987). Behaviourally mediated suppression of reproduction in female primates. *Journal of Zoology, London, 213*, 455–470. [10]

Adkins-Regan, E. (1985). Nonmammalian psychosexual differentiation. In N. Adler, D. Pfaff, & R. W. Goy (Eds.), *Handbook of behavioral neurobiology: Vol. 7. Reproduction* (pp. 43–76). New York: Plenum. [12]

Adler, N., & Hogan, J. A. (1963). Classical conditioning and punishment of an instinctive response in *Betta splendens*. *Animal Behaviour, 11*, 351–354. [9]

Adler, N. T. (1969). Effects of the male's copulatory behavior on successful pregnancy of the female rat. *Journal of Comparative and Physiological Psychology, 69*, 613–622. [6]

Adler, N. T. (1978). Social and environmental control of reproductive processes in animals. In T. E. McGill, D. A. Dewsbury, & B. D. Sachs (Eds.), *Sex and behavior: Status and prospectus* (pp. 115–160). New York: Plenum. [12]

Adler, N. T., & Zoloth, S. R. (1970). Copulatory behavior can inhibit pregnancy in female rats. *Science, 168*, 1480–1482. [6]

Agren, G. (1984). Incest avoidance and bonding between siblings in gerbils. *Behavioral Ecology and Sociobiology, 14*, 161–169. [13]

Albers, H. E., Pollock, J., Simmons, W. H., & Ferris, C. F. (1986). A V1 receptor mediates vasopressin-induced flank marking behavior in hamster hypothalamus. *Journal of Neuroscience, 6*, 2085–2089. [17]

Alberts, J. R. (1974). Producing and interpreting experimental olfactory deficits. *Physiology and Behavior, 12*, 657–670. [13]

Alberts, J. R. (1978). Huddling by rat pups: Multisensory control of contact behavior. *Journal of Comparative and Physiological Psychology, 92*, 220–230. [13]

Alberts, J. R., & Galef, B. G., Jr. (1971). Acute anosmia in the rat: A behavioral test of a peripherally-induced olfactory deficit. *Physiology and Behavior, 6*, 619–621. [3]

Albone, E. S., Blazquez, N. B., French, J., Long, S. E., & Perry, G. C. (1986). Mammalian semiochemistry: Issues and futures, with some examples of chemical signaling in cattle. In D. Duvall, D. Müller-Schwarze, & R. M. Silverstein (Eds.), *Chemical signals in vertebrates: Vol. 4. Ecology, evolution and comparative biology* (pp. 27–36). New York: Plenum Press. [3]

Alcock, J. (1979). The evolution of intraspecific diversity in male reproductive strategies in some bees and wasps. In M. S. Blum & N. A. Blum (Eds.), *Sexual selection and reproductive competition in insects* (pp. 381–402). New York: Academic Press. [8]

Alcock, J. (1980). Natural selection and the mating systems of solitary bees. *American Scientist, 68*, 146–153. [8]

Alderson, J. (1976). *Responses of the golden hamster,* Mesocricetus auratus *to conspecific scents.* Unpublished master's thesis, Cornell University, Ithaca, NY. [17]

Alderson, J., & Johnston, R. E. (1975). Responses of male golden hamsters (*Mesocricetus auratus*) to clean and male scented areas. *Behavioral Biology, 15*, 505–510. [17]

Alexander, R. D., Hoogland, J. L., Howard, R. D., Noonan, K. M., & Sherman, P. W. (1979). Sexual dimorphism and breeding systems in pinnipeds, ungulates, primates and humans. In N. A. Chagnon and W. Irons (Eds.), *Evolutionary biology and human social behavior: An anthropological perspective* (pp. 402–435). North Scituate, MA: Duxbury Press. [10]

Alexander, R. M., Jayes, A. S., Maloiy, G. M. O., & Wathuta, E. M. (1981). Allometry of the leg muscles of mammals. *Journal of Zoology, 194*, 539–552. [4]

Alleva, E., Caprioli, A., & Laviola, G. (1989). Litter-gender composition affects maternal behavior of the primiparous mouse dam (*Mus musculus*). *Journal of Comparative Psychology, 103*, 83–87. [12]

452

Almli, C. R., & Fisher, R. S. (1985). Postnatal development of sensory influences on neurons in the ventromedial hypothalamic nucleus of the rat. *Developmental Brain Research, 18,* 13–26. [12]

Altmann, J. (1980). *Baboon mothers and infants.* Cambridge, MA: Harvard University Press. [10]

Anzelberger, G. (1985). How stranger encounters of common marmosets (*Callithrix jacchus jacchus*) are influenced by family members: The quality of behavior. *Folia Primatologica, 45,* 204–224. [10]

Arak, A. (1988). Callers and satellites in the natterjack toad: evolutionarily stable decision rules. *Animal Behaviour, 36,* 416–432. [12]

Armitage, K. B. (1974). Male behaviour and territoriality in the yellow-bellied marmot. *Journal of Zoology, 17,* 233–265. [8]

Armitage, K. B. (1981). Sociality as a life-history tactic of ground squirrels. *Oecologia, 48,* 36–49. [8]

Armitage, K. B. (1986). Marmot polygyny revisited: Determinants of male and female reproductive strategies. In D. I. Rubenstein & R. W. Wrangham (Eds.), *Ecological aspects of social evolution* (pp. 303–331). Princeton, NJ: Princeton University Press. [8]

Armstrong, D. P., Gass, C. L., & Sutherland, G. D. (1987). Should foragers remember where they've been? Explorations of a simulation model based on the behavior and energetics of territorial hummingbirds. In A. C. Kamil, J. R. Krebs, & H. R. Pulliam (Eds.), *Foraging behavior* (pp. 563–586). New York: Plenum. [1]

Arnold, A. P. (1980). Effects of androgens on volumes of sexually dimorphic brain regions in the zebra finch. *Brain Research, 185,* 441–444. [12]

Aschoff, J., Fatranska, M., Giedke, H., Doerr, P., Stamm, D., & Wisser, H. (1971). Human circadian rhythms in continual darkness: Entrainment by social cues. *Science, 171,* 213–215. [11]

Atz, J. W. (1970). The application of the idea of homology to behavior. In L. R. Aronson, E. Tobach, D. S. Lehrman, & J. S. Rosenblatt (Eds.), *Development and evolution of behavior* (pp. 53–74). San Francisco: W. H. Freeman. [1]

Auffenberg, W. (1981). *The behavioral ecology of the Komodo monitor.* Gainesville: University Presses of Florida. [5]

Austad, S. N. (1982). First male sperm priority in the bowl and doily spider *Frontinella pyramitela.* *Evolution, 36,* 777–785. [7]

Austad, S. N. (1984). Evolution of sperm priority patterns in spiders. In R. L. Smith (Ed.), *Sperm competition and the evolution of animal mating systems* (pp. 223–249). New York: Academic Press. [7]

Austad, S. N., & Thornhill, R. (1986). Female reproductive variation in a nuptial-feeding spider, *Pisaura mirabilis. Bulletin of the British Arachnological Society, 7,* 48–52. [7]

Ayala, F. J. (1972). The autonomy of biology as a natural science. In A. D. Breck & W. Yourgrau (Eds.), *Biology, history, and natural philosophy* (pp. 1–16). New York: Plenum Press. [15]

Babkin, B. P. (1949). *Pavlov: A biography.* Chicago: University of Chicago Press. [9]

Baerends, G. P., & Drent, R. H. (Eds.). (1982). The herring gull and its egg. *Behaviour, 82,* 1–416. [2]

Baerends, G. P., & Kruijt, J. P. (1973). Stimulus selection. In R. A. Hinde and J. Stevenson-Hinde (Eds.), *Constraints on learning: Limitations and predispositions* (pp. 23–50). New York: Academic Press. [2]

Bailey, S., Bunyan, P. J., & Page, J. M. J. (1980). Variation in the levels of some components of the volatile fraction of urine from captive red fox (*Vulpes vulpes*) and its relationship to the state of the animal. In D. Müller-Schwarze and R. M. Silverstein (Eds.), *Chemical signals in vertebrates: Vol. 2. Vertebrates and aquatic invertebrates* (pp. 391–403). New York: Plenum Press. [3]

Bainbridge, R. (1958). The speed of swimming of fish as related to the frequency and amplitude of the tail beat. *Journal of Experimental Biology, 35,* 109–133. [4]

Baker, M. C. (1982). Vocal dialect recognition and population genetic consequences. *American Zoologist, 22,* 561–569. [15]

Baker, M. C. (1983). The behavioral responses of the female Nuttall's white-crowned sparrows to male song of natal and alien dialects. *Behavioral Ecology and Sociobiology, 12,* 309–315. [14]

Baker, M. C., & Cunningham, M. A. (1985). The biology of bird-song dialects. *Behavioral and Brain Sciences, 8,* 85–133. [14, 15]

Baker, M. C., & Mewaldt, L. R. (1979). The use of space by white-crowned sparrows: Juvenile and adult ranging patterns and home range versus body size comparisons in an avian granivore community. *Behavioral Ecology and Sociobiology, 6,* 45–52. [4]

Baker, M. C., Spitler-Nabors, K. J., & Bradley, D. C. (1981). Early experience determines song dialect responsiveness of female sparrows. *Science, 214*, 819–821. [14]

Baker, M. C., Spitler-Nabors, K. J., Thompson, A. D., Jr., & Cunningham, M. A. (1987). Reproductive behavior of female white-crowned sparrows stimulated by two song dialects and hybrid songs synthesized by computer. *Animal Behaviour, 35*, 1766–1774. [14]

Baker, R. H. (1946). Some effects of the war on the wildlife of Micronesia. *Transactions of the 11th North American Wildlife Conference, 11*, 205–213. [5]

Baker, R. H. (1951). The avifauna of Micronesia, its origin, evolution, and distribution. *University of Kansas Publications of the Museum of Natural History, 3*, 1–359. [5]

Balda, R. P. (1980a). Recovery of cached seeds by a captive *Nucifraga caryotactes*. *Zeitschrift für Tierpsychologie, 52*, 331–346. [1]

Balda, R. P. (1980b). Are seed-caching systems co-evolved? In R. Nohring (Ed.), *Acta XVI Congressus Internationalis Ornithologici* (pp. 1185–1191). Berlin: Deutsche Ornitologen-Gesellschaft. [1]

Balda, R. P. (1987). Avian impacts on pinyon–juniper woodlands. In R. L. Everett (Ed.), *Proceedings—Pinyon–Juniper Conference* (U.S. Forest Service General Technical Report INT-215, pp. 525–533). Washington, DC: U.S. Government Printing Office. [1]

Balda, R. P., & Kamil, A. C. (1988). The spatial memory of Clark's nutcrackers (*Nucifraga columbiana*) in an analog of the radial-arm maze. *Animal Learning and Behavior, 16*, 116–122. [1]

Balda, R. P., & Kamil, A. C. (in press). A comparative study of cache recovery by three corvid species. *Animal Behaviour.* [1]

Ball, G., & Silver, R. (1983). Timing of incubation bouts by ring doves. *Journal of Comparative Psychology, 97*, 213–225. [11]

Balph, D. F. (1984). Spatial and social behavior in a population of Uinta ground squirrels: Interrelations with climate and annual cycle. In J. O. Murie & G. R. Michener (Eds.), *The biology of ground-dwelling squirrels* (pp. 326–352). Lincoln: University of Nebraska Press. [8]

Balph, D. F., & Stokes, A. W. (1963). On the ethology of a population of Uinta ground squirrels. *American Midland Naturalist, 69*, 106–126. [8]

Balsam, P., & Tomie, A. (1984). *Context and learning*. Hillsdale, NJ: Lawrence Erlbaum Associates. [9]

Baptista, L. F. (1975). Song dialects and demes in sedentary populations of the white-crowned sparrow (*Zonotrichia leucophrys nuttalli*). *University of California Publications in Zoology, 105*, 1–52. [15]

Baptista, L. F., & Morton, M. L. (1982). Song dialects and mate selection in montane white-crowned sparrows. *Auk, 99*, 537–547. [15]

Baptista, L. F., & Morton, M. L. (1988). Song learning in montane white-crowned sparrows: from whom and when. *Animal Behaviour, 36*, 1753–1764. [15]

Baptista, L. F., & Petrinovich, L. (1984). Social interaction, sensitive phases and the song template hypothesis in the white-crowned sparrow. *Animal Behaviour, 32*, 172–181. [15]

Baptista, L. F., & Petrinovich, L. (1986). Song development in the white-crowned sparrow: Social factors and sex differences. *Animal Behaviour, 34*, 1359–1371. [15]

Baranczuk, R., & Greenwald, G. S. (1973). Peripheral levels of estrogen in the cyclic hamster. *Endocrinology, 92*, 805–812. [17]

Baranczuk, R., & Greenwald, G. S. (1974). Plasma levels of estrogen and progesterone in pregnant and lactating hamsters. *Journal of Endocrinology, 63*, 125–135. [17]

Barash, D. (1979). *The whisperings within*. New York: Harper and Row. [10]

Barash, D. P. (1981). Mate guarding and gallivanting by male hoary marmots (*Marmota caligata*). *Behavioral Ecology and Sociobiology, 9*, 187–193. [8]

Barash, D. P., Holmes, W. G., & Greene, P. J. (1978). Exact versus probabilistic coefficients of relationship: Some implications for sociobiology. *American Naturalist, 112*, 355–363. [13]

Barnett, S. A. (1958a). An analysis of social behaviour in wild rats. *Proceedings of the Zoological Society of London, 130*, 107–152. [18]

Barnett, S. A. (1958b). Experiments on "neophobia" in wild and laboratory rats. *British Journal of Psychology, 49*, 195–201. [3]

Bartecki, U., & Heymann, E. W. (1987). Field observation of snake mobbing in a group of saddleback tamarins, *Saguinus fuscicollis nigrifrons*. *Folia Primatologica, 48*, 199–202. [10]

Bast, J. D., & Greenwald, G. S. (1974). Serum profiles of follicle-stimulating hormone, luteinizing hormone and prolactin during the estrous cycle of the hamster. *Endocrinology, 94*, 1295–1299. [17]

Bateson, P. (1983). *Mate choice*. Cambridge: Cambridge University Press. [6, 13]

Battig, K., & Schlatter, J. (1979). Effects of sex and strain on exploratory locomotion and development of nonreinforced maze patrolling. *Animal Learning & Behavior, 7,* 99–105. [2]

Baum, M. J. (1979). Differentiation of coital behavior in mammals: A comparative analysis. *Neuroscience & Biobehavioral Reviews, 3,* 265–284. [12]

Baylis, J. R. (1981). The evolution of parental care in fishes, with reference to Darwin's rule of male sexual selection. *Environmental Fish Biology, 6,* 223–251. [9]

Beach, F. A. (1971). Hormonal factors controlling the differentiation, development, and display of copulatory behavior in the ramstergig and related species. In E. Tobach, L. R. Aronson, & E. Shaw (Eds.), *The biopsychology of development* (pp. 249–296). New York: Academic Press. [12]

Beach, F. A., Noble, R. G., & Orndoff, R. K. (1969). Effects of perinatal androgen treatment on responses of male rats to gonadal hormones in adulthood. *Journal of Comparative and Physiological Psychology, 68,* 490–497. [12]

Bean, N. J., Galef, B. G., Jr., & Mason, J. R. (1988). The effect of carbon disulfide on food consumption by house mice. *Journal of Wildlife Management, 52,* 502–507. [3]

Beck, M., & Galef, B. G., Jr. (in press). Social influences on the selection of a protein-sufficient diet by Norway rats. *Journal of Comparative Psychology.* [3]

Beckner, M. (1974). Reduction, hierarchies and organicism. In F. J. Ayala & T. Dobzhansky (Eds.), *Studies in the philosophy of biology* (pp. 163–176). Berkeley: University of California Press. [15]

Beecher, M. D. (1981). Development of parent–offspring recognition in birds. In R. K. Aslin, J. R. Alberts, & M. R. Petersen (Eds.), *Development of perception* (Vol. 1, pp. 45–66). New York: Academic Press. [16]

Beecher, M. D. (1982). Signature systems and kin recognition. *American Zoologist, 22,* 477–490. [16]

Beecher, M. D. (1988a). Kin recognition in birds. *Behavior Genetics, 18,* 465–482. [16]

Beecher, M. D. (1988b). Some comments on the adaptationist approach to learning. In R. C. Bolles & M. D. Beecher (Eds.), *Evolution and learning* (pp. 239–248). Hillsdale, NJ: Lawrence Erlbaum Associates. [2, 16]

Beecher, M. D. (in press-a). Signalling systems for individual recognition: an information theory approach. *Animal Behaviour.* [16]

Beecher, M. D. (in press-b). Successes and failures of parent–offspring recognition in animals. In P. G. Harper (Ed.), *Kin recognition.* Cambridge: Cambridge University Press. [16]

Beecher, M. D., Beecher, I. M., and Hahn, S. (1981). Parent–offspring recognition in bank swallows: 2. Development and acoustic basis. *Animal Behaviour, 29,* 95–101. [16]

Beecher, M. D., Beecher, I. M., and Lumpkin, S. (1981). Parent–offspring recognition in bank swallows: 1. Natural history. *Animal Behaviour, 29,* 86–94. [16]

Beecher, M. D., Loesche, P., Stoddard, P. K., & Medvin, M. B. (1989). Individual recognition by voice in swallows: Signal or perceptual adaptation? In R. J. Dooling & S. H. Hulse (Eds.), *Comparative psychology of audition: Perceiving complex sounds* (pp. 277–294). Hillsdale, NJ: Lawrence Erlbaum Associates. [16]

Beecher, M. D., Medvin, M. B., Stoddard, P. K., and Loesche, P. (1986). Acoustic adaptations for parent–offspring recognition in swallows. *Experimental Biology, 45,* 179–193. [16]

Beecher, M. D., & Stoddard, P. K. (in press). The role of bird song and calls in individual recognition: Field and laboratory perspectives. In M. Berkley & W. C. Stebbins (Eds.), *Comparative perception.* New York: John Wiley [16]

Beecher, M. D., Stoddard, P. K., & Loesche, P. (1985). Recognition of parents' voices by young cliff swallows. *Auk, 102,* 600–605. [16]

Beer, C. G. (1969). Laughing gull chicks: Recognition of their parents' voices. *Science, 166,* 1030–1032. [16]

Beer, C. G. (1979). Vocal communication between laughing gull parents and chicks. *Behaviour, 70,* 118–146. [16]

Bekoff, M. (1981). Mammalian sibling interactions. In D. J. Gubernick & P. H. Klopfer (Eds.), *Parental care in mammals* (pp. 307–346). New York: Plenum Press. [13]

Bent, A. C. (1964). *Life histories of North American jays, crows and titmice.* New York: Dover. [1]

Berger, P. J., & Negus, N. C. (1982). Stud male maintenance of pregnancy in *Microtus montanus. Journal of Mammalogy, 63,* 148–151. [6]

Berman, C. M. (1982). The social development of an orphaned rhesus infant on Cayo Santiago: Male care, foster mother–orphan interaction and peer interaction. *American Journal of Primatology, 3,* 131–141. [10]

Bertram, B. C. R. (1978). Living in groups: Predators and prey. In J. R. Krebs and N. B. Davies (Eds.), *Behavioural ecology* (pp. 64–96). Oxford: Blackwell Scientific Publications. [3]

Beyer, C., & Feder, H. H. (1987). Sex steroids and afferent input: Their roles in brain sexual differentiation. *Annual Review of Physiology, 49,* 349–364. [12]

Bielert, C. (1982). Experimental examination of baboon (*Papio ursinus*) sex stimuli. In C. T. Snowdon, C. H. Brown, and M. R. Petersen (Eds.), *Primate communication* (pp. 373–395). New York: Cambridge University Press. [10]

Birdsall, D. A., & Nash, D. (1973). Occurrence of successful multiple insemination of females in natural populations of deer mice (*Peromyscus maniculatus*). *Evolution, 27,* 106–110. [6]

Birke, L., & Sadler, D. (1987). Differences in maternal behavior of rats and the sociosexual development of the offspring. *Developmental Psychobiology, 20,* 85–99. [12]

Bitterman, M. E. (1965). Phyletic differences in learning. *American Psychologist, 20,* 396–410. [1]

Blanchard, B. (1941). The white-crowned sparrows (*Zonotrichia leucophrys*) of the Pacific seaboard: Environment and annual cycle. *University of California Publications in Zoology, 46,* 1–178. [15]

Blanchard, D. C., & Blanchard, R. J. (1984). Inadequacy of pain–aggression hypothesis revealed in naturalistic settings. *Aggressive Behavior, 10,* 33–46. [18]

Blanchard, D. C., & Blanchard, R. J. (1988). Ethoexperimental approaches to the biology of emotion. *Annual Review of Psychology, 39,* 43–68. [18]

Blanchard, D. C., Blanchard, R. J., & Rodgers, R. J. (in press). Defensive behaviors as a model for testing anxiolytic drugs. In P. F. Brain, S. Parmigiani, R. J. Blanchard, & D. Mainardi (Eds.), *The biopsychology of fear and defense.* [18]

Blanchard, D. C., Fukunaga-Stinson, C., Takahashi, L. K., Flannelly, K. J., & Blanchard, R. J. (1984). Dominance and aggression in social groups of male and female rats. *Behavioural Processes, 9,* 31–48. [18]

Blanchard, R. J., & Blanchard, D. C. (1977). Aggressive behavior in the rat. *Behavioral Biology, 21,* 197–224. [18]

Blanchard, R. J., & Blanchard, D. C. (1989). Anti-predator defensive behaviors in a visible burrow system. *Journal of Comparative Psychology, 103,* 70–82. [18]

Blanchard, R. J., Blanchard, D. C., & Flannelly, K. J. (1985). Social stress, mortality and aggression in colonies and burrowing habitats. *Behavioural Processes, 11,* 209–215. [18]

Blanchard, R. J., Blanchard, D. C., & Takahashi, L. K. (1977). Reflexive fighting in the albino rat: Aggressive or defensive behavior? *Aggressive Behavior, 3,* 145–155. [18]

Blanchard, R. J., Blanchard, D. C., & Takahashi, L. K. (1978). Pain and aggression in the rat. *Behavioral Biology, 23,* 291–305. [18]

Blanchard, R. J., Blanchard, D. C., Takahashi, T., & Kelley, M. J. (1977). Attack and defensive behaviour in the albino rat. *Animal Behaviour, 25,* 622–634. [18]

Blanchard, R. J., Flannelly, K. J., & Blanchard, D. C. (1988). Life span studies of dominance and aggression in established colonies of laboratory rats. *Physiology and Behavior, 43,* 1–7. [18]

Blanchard, R. J., Fukunaga, K., Blanchard, D. C., & Kelley, M. J. (1975). Conspecific aggression in the laboratory rat. *Journal of Comparative and Physiological Psychology, 88,* 81–88. [18]

Blanchard, R. J., Hori, K., & Blanchard, D. C. (1987). Social structure and ethanol consumption in the laboratory rat. *Pharmacology, Biochemistry, and Behavior, 28,* 437–442. [18]

Blanchard, R. J., Hori, K., & Blanchard, D. C. (1988). Social dominance and individual aggressiveness. *Aggressive Behavior, 14,* 195–204. [18]

Blanchard, R. J., Kleinschmidt, C. K., Flannelly, K. J., & Blanchard, D. C. (1984). Fear and aggression in the rat. *Aggressive Behavior, 10,* 309–315. [18]

Blanchard, R. J., Kleinschmidt, C. K., Fukunaga-Stinson, C., & Blanchard, D. C. (1980). Defensive attack behavior in male and female rats. *Animal Learning and Behavior, 8,* 177–183. [18]

Blanchard, R. J., Takahashi, L. K., & Blanchard, D. C. (1977). The development of intruder attack in colonies of laboratory rats. *Animal Learning and Behavior, 5,* 365–369. [18]

Blaustein, A. R., Bekoff, M., & Daniels, T. J. (1987). Kin recognition in vertebrates (excluding primates): Empirical evidence. In D. J. C. Fletcher & C. D. Michener (Eds.), *Kin recognition in animals* (pp. 287–331). New York: John Wiley & Sons. [13]

Blodgett, H. C. (1929). The effects of the introduction of reward upon the maze performance of rats. *University of California Publications in Psychology, 4,* 113–134. [2]

Blumer, L. S. (1979). Male parental care in the bony fishes. *Quarterly Review of Biology, 54,* 149–161. [9]

Boakes, R. A., Poli, M., Lockwood, M. J., & Goodall, G. (1978). A study of misbehavior: Token reinforcement in the rat. *Journal of the Experimental Analysis of Behavior, 29*, 115–134. [2]

Bock, W. J., Balda, R. P., & Vander Wall, S. B. (1973). Morphology of the sublingual pouch and tongue musculature in Clark's nutcracker. *Auk, 90*, 491–519. [1]

Boice, R. (1977). Burrows of wild and albino rats: Effects of domestication, outdoor raising, age, experience, and maternal state. *Journal of Comparative and Physiological Psychology, 91*, 649–661. [2]

Bolles, R. C. (1970). Species-specific defense reactions and avoidance learning. *Psychological Review, 77*, 32–48. [2]

Bolles, R. C. (1988). Nativism, naturalism, and niches. In R. C. Bolles & M. D. Beecher (Eds.), *Evolution and learning* (pp. 1–15). Hillsdale, NJ: Lawrence Erlbaum Associates. [9]

Bolles, R. C., & Fanselow, M. S. (1980). A perceptual–defensive–recuperative model of fear and pain. *Behavioral and Brain Sciences, 3*, 291–301. [2]

Bols, R. J., & Wong, R. (1973). Gerbils reared by rats: Effects on adult open-field and ventral marking activity. *Behavioral Biology, 9*, 741–748. [13]

Booth, J. E. (1977). Sexual behavior of neonatally castrated rats injected during infancy with estrogen and dihydrotestosterone. *Journal of Endocrinology, 72*, 135–141. [12]

Borgia, G., & Gore, M. (1986). Feather stealing in the satin bowerbird (*Ptilonorhynchus violaceus*): Male competition and the quality of display. *Animal Behaviour, 34*, 727–738. [8]

Boring, E. G. (1957). *A history of experimental psychology* (2nd ed.). New York: Appleton-Century-Crofts. [9]

Box, H. O. (1977). Quantitative data on the carrying of young captive monkeys (*Callithrix jacchus*) by other members of their family groups. *Primates, 18*, 475–484. [10]

Box, H. O., & Hubrecht, R. C. (1987). Long-term data on the reproduction and maintenance of a colony of common marmosets (*Callithrix jacchus jacchus*), 1972–1983. *Laboratory Animals, 21*, 249–260. [10]

Brain, P. F. (1988). The adaptiveness of house mouse aggression. In P. F. Brain & S. Parmigiani (Eds.), *House mouse aggression*. London: Gordon and Breach Science Publishers. [18]

Bramble, D. M., & Carrier, D. R. (1983). Running and breathing in mammals. *Science, 219*, 251–256. [4]

Brand, H. M., & Martin, R. D. (1983). The relationship between female urinary estrogen excretion and mating behavior in cotton-topped tamarins, *Saguinus oedipus oedipus*. *International Journal of Primatology, 4*, 275–290. [10]

Brant, D. H., & Kavanau, J. L. (1964). "Unrewarded" exploration and learning of complex mazes by wild and domestic mice. *Nature, 204*, 267–269. [2]

Breene, R. G., & Sweet, M. H. (1985). Evidence of insemination of multiple females by the male black widow spider, *Latrodectus mactans* (Araneae, Theridiidae). *Journal of Arachnology, 13*, 331–335. [7]

Breland, K., & Breland, M. (1961). The misbehavior of organisms. *American Psychologist, 16*, 681–684. [2]

Breland, K., & Breland, M. (1966). *Animal behavior*. New York: Acadmic Press. [2]

Bronson, F. H. (1973). Establishment of social rank among grouped male mice: Relative effects on circulating FSH, LH and corticosterone. *Physiology and Behavior, 10*, 947–951. [9]

Bronson, F. H. (1987). Environmental regulation of reproduction in rodents. In D. Crews (Ed.), *Psychobiology of reproductive behavior: An evolutionary perspective* (pp. 204–230). Englewood Cliffs, NJ: Prentice-Hall. [12]

Bronson, F. H., & Eleftheriou, B. E. (1963). Influence of strange males on implantation in the deermouse. *General and Comparative Endocrinology, 3*, 515–518. [6]

Bronstein, P. D. (1986). Socially mediated learning in male *Betta splendens*. *Journal of Comparative Psychology, 100*, 279–284. [9]

Brower, L. P. (1969). Ecological chemistry. *Scientific American, 220*, 22–29. [2]

Brown, K., & Mack, D. S. (1978). Food sharing among captive *Leontopithecus rosalia*. *Folia Primatologica, 29*, 268–290. [10]

Brown, P. L., & Jenkins, H. M. (1968). Auto-shaping of the pigeon's key-peck. *Journal of the Experimental Analysis of Behavior, 11*, 1–8. [2]

Brown, R. E. (1975). Object directed urine marking by male rats (*Rattus norvegicus*). *Behavioral Biology, 15*, 251–254. [2]

Brown, S. G. (1985). Mating behavior of the golden orb-weaving spider, *Nephila clavipes*: 2. Sperm capacitation, sperm competition, and fecundity. *Journal of Comparative Psychology, 99,* 167–175. [7]

Brown, S. G., Hill, E. M., Goist, K. C., Wenzl, P. A., & Christenson, T. (1985). Ecological and seasonal variation in a free-moving population of the golden-web spider, *Nephila clavipes*. *Bulletin of the British Arachnological Society, 6,* 313–319. [7]

Brown-Grant, K., Davidson, J. M., & Greig, F. (1978). Induced ovulation in albino rats exposed to constant light. *Journal of Endocrinology, 57,* 7–22. [12]

Brunswik, E. (1952). The conceptual framework of psychology. In *International encyclopedia of unified science* (Vol. 1). Chicago: University of Chicago Press. [15]

Brunswik, E. (1956). *Perception and the representative design of psychological experiments*. Berkeley: University of California Press. [15]

Bulger, J., & Hamilton, W. J. III (1988). Inbreeding and reproductive success in a natural chacma baboon, *Papio cynocephalus ursinus*, population. *Animal Behaviour, 36,* 574–578. [6]

Bull, J. J. (1983). *Evolution of sex determining mechanisms*. Menlo Park, CA: Benjamin-Cummings. [12]

Bunnell, B., Boland, B. D., & Dewsbury, D. A. (1977). Copulatory behavior of golden hamsters, *Mesocricetus auratus*. *Behaviour, 61,* 180–206. [17]

Burghardt, G. M. (1967). Chemical-cue preferences of inexperienced snakes: Comparative aspects. *Science, 157,* 718–721. [5]

Burghardt, G. M. (1969). Comparative prey-attack studies in newborn snakes of the genus *Thamnophis*. *Behaviour, 33,* 77–114. [5]

Burghardt, G. M. (1970). Chemical perception in reptiles. In F. W. Johnston, D. G. Moulton, & A. Turk (Eds.), *Communication by chemical signals* (pp. 241–308). New York: Appleton-Century-Crofts. [5]

Burghardt, G. M. (1988). Precocity, play, and the ectotherm–endotherm transition: Profound reorganization or superficial adaptation? In E. M. Blass (Ed.), *Handbook of behavioral neurobiology: Vol. 9. Developmental psychobiology and behavioral ecology* (pp. 107–148). New York: Plenum. [12]

Burley, N. (1979). The evolution of concealed ovulation. *American Naturalist, 114,* 835–858. [10]

Bushberg, D. M., & Holmes, W. G. (1985). Sexual maturation in male Belding's ground squirrels: Influence of body weight. *Biology of Reproduction, 33,* 302–308. [8]

Butler, C. G. (1967). A sex attractant acting as an aphrodisiac in the honey bee (*Apis mellifera* L.). *Proceedings of the Royal Entomological Society, London (A), 42,* 71–76. [17]

Butler, C. G. (1971). The mating behavior of the honeybee (*Apis mellifera* L.). *Journal of Entomology, 46,* 1–11. [17]

Buxton, C. E. (1985). Early sources and basic conceptions of functionalism. In C. E. Buxton (Ed.), *Points of view in the modern history of psychology* (pp. 85–111). Orlando, FL: Academic Press. [E]

Bykov, K. M. (1959). *The cerebral cortex and the internal organs*. Moscow: Foreign Languages Publishing House. [9]

Calder, W. A. III (1984). *Size, function and life history*. Cambridge, MA: Harvard University Press. [4]

Calhoun, J. B. (1962). *The ecology and sociology of the Norway rat*. Bethesda, MD: U.S. Department of Health, Education, and Welfare. [3]

Campbell, D. T., & Fiske, D. W. (1959). Convergent and discriminant validation by the multitrait–multimethod matrix. *Psychological Bulletin, 56,* 81–105. [15]

Canady, R. A., Kroodsma, D. E., & Nottebohm, F. (1984). Population differences in complexity of a learned skill are correlated with the brain space involved. *Proceedings of the National Academy of Sciences, 81,* 6232–6234. [14]

Capretta, P. J., & Rawls, L. H. III (1974). Establishment of flavor preference in rats: Importance of nursing and weaning experience. *Journal of Comparative and Physiological Psychology, 86,* 670–673. [3]

Carl, E. A. (1971). Population control in Arctic ground squirrels. *Ecology, 52,* 396–413. [8]

Cassone, V. M., & Moore, R. Y. (1987). Retinohypothalmic projection and suprachiasmatic nucleus of the house sparrow, *Passer domesticus*. *Journal of Comparative Neurology, 266,* 171–182. [11]

Catchpole, C. K., Dittami, J., & Leisler, B. (1984). Differential responses to male song repertoires in female song birds implanted with oestradiol. *Nature, 312,* 563–564. [14]

Charnov, E. L. (1976). Optimal foraging: The marginal value theorem. *Theoretical Population Biology, 9*, 129–136. [1]

Chiszar, D., Andren, C., Nilson, G., O'Connell, B., Mestas, J. S., Smith, H. M., & Radcliffe, C. W. (1982). Strike-induced chemosensory searching in old world vipers and new world pit vipers. *Animal Learning and Behavior, 10*, 121–125. [5]

Chiszar, D., Carrillo, D., Rand, P., Chiszar, J., & Smith, H. M. (1985). Nocturnal activity in captive brown tree snakes (*Boiga irregularis*). *Bulletin of the Maryland Herpteological Society, 21*, 115–118. [5]

Chiszar, D., & Kandler, K. (1986). Adjustment of brown tree snakes (*Boiga irregularis*) to a reversed light cycle. *Bulletin of the Maryland Herpetological Society, 22*, 171–174. [5]

Chiszar, D., Kandler, K., Lee, R., & Smith, H. M. (1988). Stimulus control of predatory attack in the brown tree snake (*Boiga irregularis*): 2. Use of chemical cues during foraging. *Amphibia-Reptilia, 9*, 77–88. [5]

Chiszar, D., Kandler, K., & Smith H. M. (1988). Stimulus control of predatory attack in the brown tree snake (*Boiga irregularis*): 1. Effects of visual cues arising from prey. *The Snake, 20*, 151–155. [5]

Chiszar, D., Radcliffe, C. W., O'Connell, B., & Smith, H. M. (1982). Analysis of the behavioral sequence emitted by rattlesnakes during feeding episodes: 2. Duration of stimuli-induced chemosensory searching in rattlesnakes (*Crotalus viridis, C. enyo*). *Behavioral and Neural Biology, 34*, 261–270. [5]

Chiszar, D., Radcliffe, C. W., Scudder, K. M., & Duvall, D. (1983). Strike-induced chemosensory searching by rattlesnakes: The role of envenomation-related chemical cues in the post-strike environment. In D. Müller-Schwarze & R. Silverstein (Eds.), *Chemical signals in vertebrates* (Vol. 3, pp. 1–24). New York: Plenum Press. [5]

Chiszar, D., Stimac, K., Poole, T., Miller, T., Radcliffe, C. W., & Smith, H. M. (1983). Strike-induced chemosensory searching in cobras (*Naja naja kaouthia, N. mossambica pallida*). *Zeitschrift für Tierpsychologie, 63*, 51–62. [5]

Chiszar, D., Taylor, S. V., Radcliffe, C. W., Smith, H. M., & O'Connell, B. (1981). Effects of chemical and visual stimuli upon chemosensory searching by garter snakes and rattlesnakes. *Journal of Herpetology, 15*, 415–424. [5]

Chivers, D. J. (1972). The siamang and gibbon in the Malay peninsula. *Gibbon and Siamang, 1*, 103–135. [10]

Christenson, T. E. (1984). Alternative reproductive tactics in spiders. *American Zoologist, 24*, 321–332. [7]

Christenson, T. E. (1989). Sperm depletion in the golden orbweaving spider, *Nephila clavipes*. *Journal of Arachnology, 17*, 115–118. [7]

Christenson, T. E., Brown, S. G., Wenzl, P. A., Hill, E. M., & Goist, K. C. (1985). Mating behavior of the golden orb-weaving spider, *Nephila clavipes*: 1. Female receptivity and male courtship. *Journal of Comparative Psychology, 99*, 160–166. [7]

Christenson, T. E., & Cohn, J. (1988). Male advantage for egg fertilization in the golden orbweaving spider, *Nephila clavipes*. *Journal of Comparative Psychology, 102*, 312–318. [7]

Christenson, T. E. & Goist, K. C. (1979). Costs and benefits of male–male competition in the orb weaving spider, *Nephila clavipes*. *Behavioral Ecology and Sociobiology, 5*, 87–92. [7]

Christenson, T. E., Schlosser, J., Cohn, J., & Myers, L. (1987). X-ray sterilization of male golden-web spiders, *Nephila clavipes* (Araneae). *Journal of Arachnology, 14*, 401–403. [7]

Christenson, T. E., & Wenzl, P. A. (1980). Egg laying of the golden silk spider, *Nephila clavipes*: Functional analysis of the egg sac. *Animal Behaviour, 28*, 1110–1118. [7]

Christenson, T., Wenzl, P., & Legum, P. (1979). Seasonal variation in egg hatching and certain egg parameters of the golden silk spider *Nephila clavipes*. *Psyche, 86*, 137–147. [7]

Clancy, A. N., Macrides, F., Singer, A. G., & Agosta, W. C. (1984). Male hamster copulatory responses to a high molecular weight fraction of vaginal discharge: Effects of vomeronasal organ removal. *Physiology and Behavior, 33*, 653–660. [17]

Clark, F. H. (1936). The estrous cycle of the deer-mouse, *Peromyscus maniculatus*. *Contributions from the Laboratory of Vertebrate Genetics, University of Michigan, 1*, 1–7. [6]

Clark, M. M., Bone, S., & Galef, B. G., Jr. (1989). Uterine positions and schedules of urination: Correlates of differential maternal anogenital stimulation. *Developmental Psychobiology, 22*, 389–400. [12]

Clark, M. M., & Galef., B. G., Jr. (1988). Effects of uterine position on rate of sexual development in female Mongolian gerbils. *Physiology and Behavior, 42*, 15–18. [13]

Clark, M. M., & Galef, B. G., Jr. (1989). Male rat pups are more hesitant to urinate in response to anogenital stimulation than are their female sibs. *Developmental Psychobiology, 22*, 81–85. [12]

Clemens, L. G. (1969). Experimental analysis of sexual behavior of the deermouse, *Peromyscus maniculatus gambeli*. *Behaviour, 34*, 267–285. [6]

Clemens, L. G., Gladue, B. A., & Coniglio, L. P. (1978). Prenatal endogenous androgenic influences on masculine sexual behavior and genital morphology in male and female rats. *Hormones and Behavior, 10*, 40–53. [12]

Cleveland, J., & Snowdon, C. T. (1982). The complex vocal repertoire of the adult cotton-top tamarin (*Saguinus oedipus oedipus*). *Zeitschrift für Tierpsychologie, 58*, 231–270. [10]

Cleveland, J., & Snowdon, C. T. (1984). Social development during the first twenty weeks in the cotton-top tamarin (*Saguinus o. oedipus*). *Animal Behaviour, 32*, 432–444. [10]

Cloues, R., Ramos, C., & Silver, R. (1988). Correlation between parental behavior and infundibular VIP-like immunoreactivity in dove. *Neuroscience Society Abstracts, 14*, No. 114.2. [11]

Clutton-Brock, T. H. (1983). Selection in relation to sex. In D. S. Bendall (Ed.), *Evolution from molecules to men* (pp. 457–481). Cambridge: Cambridge University Press. [8]

Clutton-Brock, T. H., Albon, S. D., & Harvey, P. H. (1980). Antlers, body size and breeding group size in the Cervidae. *Nature, 285*, 565–567. [4]

Clutton-Brock, T. H., & Harvey, P. H. (1983). The functional significance of variation in body size among mammals. In J. F. Eisenberg & D. G. Kleiman (Eds.), *Advances in the study of mammalian behavior* (pp. 632–663). Stillwater, OK: The American Society of Mammalogists. [4]

Clutton-Brock, T. H., & Harvey, P. H. (1984). Comparative approaches to investigating adaptation. In J. R. Krebs & N. B. Davies (Eds.), *Behavioural ecology: An evolutionary approach* (2nd ed., pp. 7–29). Oxford: Blackwell Scientific Publications. [4]

Coddington, J. A. (1988). Cladistic tests of adaptational hypotheses. *Cladistics, 4*, 3–22. [7]

Cohen, P. S., Looney, T. A., Campagnoni, F. R., & Lawler, C. P. (1985). A two-state model of reinforcer-induced motivation. In F. R. Brush & J. B. Overmier (Eds.), *Affect, conditioning, and cognition: Essays on the determinants of behavior* (pp. 281–297). Hillsdale, NJ: Lawrence Erlbaum Associates. [2]

Cohn, J. (1988). *Male morphology and reproductive success in the golden orbweaving spider*, Nephila clavipes. Unpublished doctoral dissertation, Tulane University, New Orleans. [7]

Cohn, J., Balding, F., & Christenson, T. (1988). In defense of *Nephila clavipes*: Pre-mate guarding by the male golden orb-weaving spider. *Journal of Comparative Psychology, 102*, 319–325. [7]

Cohn, J., & Christenson, T. (1987). Utilization of resources by the male golden orbweaving spider, *Nephila clavipes*. *Journal of Arachnology, 15*, 185–192. [7]

Colgan, P. (1983). *Comparative social recognition*. New York: John Wiley. [16]

Collier, G. H. (1983). Life in a closed economy: The ecology of learning and motivation. In M. D. Zeiler & P. Harzem (Eds.), *Advances in analysis of behavior: Vol. 3. Biological factors in learning* (pp. 223–274). Chichester, England: John Wiley & Sons. [2]

Commins, D., & Yahr, P. (1984). Lesions of the sexually dimorphic area disrupt mating and marking in male gerbils. *Brain Research Bulletin, 13*, 185–193. [12]

Cook, M., Mineka, S., Wolkenstein, B., & Laitsch, K. (1985). Observational conditioning of snake fear in unrelated rhesus monkeys. *Journal of Abnormal Psychology, 94*, 591–610. [3]

Cook, R. M., & Cockrell, B. J. (1978). Predator ingestion rate and its bearing on feeding time and the theory of optimal diets. *Journal of Animal Ecology, 46*, 115–125. [1]

Coon, D. W., & Arnold, K. A. (1977). Origins of brown-headed cowbird populations wintering in central Texas. *North American Bird Bander, 2*, 7–11. [14]

Cooper, A. J., & Cowley, J. (1976). Mother–infant interaction in mice bulbectomized early in life. *Physiology and Behavior, 16*, 453–459. [13]

Cooper, M. L., Pickard, G. E., & Silver, R. (1983). Retinohypothalamic pathway in the dove (*Streptopelia risoria*) demonstrated by anterograde HRP. *Brain Research Bulletin, 10*, 715–718. [11]

Cooper, W. E., Jr. (1988, August). Prey odor discrimination by lizards and snakes. Paper presented at the Symposium on Chemical Signals in Vertebrates, Oxford. [5]

Cooper, W. E., Jr. (in press). Strike induced chemosensory searching occurs in lizards. *Journal of Chemical Ecology*. [5]

Cooper, W. E., Jr., McDowell, S. G., & Ruffer, J. (in press). Strike induced chemosensory searching in the colubrid snakes *Elaphe g. guttata* and *Thamnophis sirtalis*. *Ethology*. [5]

Coopersmith, R., & Leon, M. (1988). The neurobiology of early olfactory learning. In E. M. Blass (Ed.), *Handbook of behavioral neurobiology: Vol. 9. Developmental psychobiology and behavioral ecology* (pp. 283–308). New York: Plenum. [12]

Coulehan, K. (1987). Powerless again. *Guam Business News*, January 13–15. [5]

Cowie, R. J. (1977). Optimal foraging in great tits (*Parus major*). *Nature, 268*, 137–139. [1]

Crabtree, J. M., & Moyer, K. E. (1972). *An analysis of measures of aggressive behavior in the rat induced by shock and morphine withdrawal*. Paper presented at the meeting of the Midwestern Psychological Association, Cleveland, OH. [18]

Crabtree, J. M., & Moyer, K. E. (1977). *Bibliography of aggressive behavior: A reader's guide to the research literature*. New York: Alan R. Liss. [18]

Craig, W. (1918). Appetites and aversions as constituents of instincts. *Biological Bulletin, 34*, 91–107. [2]

Crews, D. (1984). Gamete production, sex hormone secretion, and mating behavior uncoupled. *Hormones and Behavior, 18*, 22–28. [12]

Crews, D. (1985). Effects of early sex hormone treatment on courtship behavior and sexual attractivity in the red-sided garter snake, *Thamnophis sirtalis parietalis*. *Physiology and Behavior, 35*, 569–575. [12]

Cronbach, L. F., Gleser, G. C., Nanda, H., & Rajaratnam, N. (1972). *The dependability of behavioral measurements*. New York: Wiley. [15]

Cronbach, L. J., & Meehl, P. E. (1955). Construct validity in psychological tests. *Psychological Bulletin, 52*, 288–302. [15]

Cullen, E. (1957). Adaptations in the kittiwake to cliff-nesting. *Ibis, 99*, 275–303. [16]

Curio, E. (1976). *The ethology of predation*. New York: Springer-Verlag. [5]

Curio, E., Ernst, U., & Vieth, W. (1978). Cultural transmission of enemy recognition: One function of mobbing. *Science, 202*, 899–901. [3]

Daly, M. (1978). The cost of mating. *American Naturalist, 112*, 771–774. [9]

Darby, E. M., Devor, M., & Chorover, S. L. (1975). A presumptive sex pheromone in the hamster: some behavioral effects. *Journal of Comparative and Physiological Psychology, 88*, 496–502. [17]

Darwin, C. (1871). *The descent of man, and selection in relation to sex*. London: John Murray. [2, 6, 8]

Darwin, E. (1794). *Zoonomia, or the laws of organic life* (2 vols.) London. [2]

Davies, N. B., & Houston, A. I. (1984). Territory economics. In J. R. Krebs & N. B. Davies (Eds.), *Behavioural ecology: An evolutionary approach* (2nd ed., pp. 148–169). Oxford: Blackwell Scientific Publications. [9]

Davis, L. S. (1982). Copulatory behaviour of Richardson's ground squirrels (*Spermophilus richardsonii*) in the wild. *Canadian Journal of Zoology, 60*, 2953–2955. [8]

Davis, L. S. (1984). Alarm calling in Richardson's ground squirrels (*Spermophilus richardsonii*). *Zeitschrift für Tierpsychologie, 66*, 152–164. [13]

Davis, L. S., & Murie, J. O. (1985). Male territoriality and the mating system of Richardson's ground squirrels (*Spermophilus richardsonii*). *Journal of Mammalogy, 66*, 268–279. [8]

Dawkins, M. (1971). Shifts of "attention" in chicks during feeding. *Animal Behaviour, 19*, 575–582. [5]

Dawkins, R. (1976). *The selfish gene*. Oxford: Oxford University Press. [6]

Dawson, G. A. (1979). The use of time and space by Panamanian tamarins (*Saguinus oedipus*). *Folia Primatologica, 31*, 253–284. [10]

DeCoursey, P. J. (1960). Phase control of activity in a rodent. *Cold Spring Harbor Symposium on Quantitative Biology, 25*, 49–55. [11]

DeCoursey, P. J. (1986). Light-sampling behavior in photoentrainment of a rodent circadian rhythm. *Journal of Comparative Physiology, 159*, 161–169. [11]

DeGroot, P. (1980). Information transfer in a socially roosting weaver bird (*Quelea quelea*: Ploceinae): An experimental study. *Animal Behaviour, 28*, 1249–1254. [3]

Dember, W. N., & Earl, R. W. (1957). Analysis of exploratory, manipulative, and curiosity behavior. *Psychological Review, 64*, 91–96. [2]

Demski, L. S. (1987). Diversity in reproductive patterns and behavior in teleost fishes. In D. Crews (Ed.), *Psychobiology of reproductive behavior: An evolutionary perspective* (pp. 1–27). Englewood Cliffs, NJ: Prentice-Hall. [12]

Denenberg, V. H., Zarrow, M. Z., & Ross, S. (1969). The behaviour of rabbits. In E. S. E. Hafez (Ed.), *The behavior of domestic animals* (pp. 417–437). Baltimore: Williams & Wilkins. [13]

Denniston, R. H. (1957). Notes on breeding and size of young in the Richardson ground squirrel. *Journal of Mammalogy, 38*, 414–416. [8]

Depaulis, A., Bandler, R., & Vergnes, M. (in press). Midbrain localization of cell bodies involved in the mediation of intraspecific defensive reactions in the rat. In R. J. Blanchard, P. F. Brain, D. C. Blanchard, & S. Parmigiani (Eds.), *Ethoexperimental approaches to the study of behavior*. The Hague: Martinus Nijhoff. [18]

Devor, M., & Murphy, M. R. (1973). The effect of peripheral olfactory blockade on the social behavior of the male golden hamster. *Behavioral Biology, 9*, 31–42. [17]

DeWolfe, G. B., Baptista, L.F., & Petrinovich, L. (1989). Song development and territory establishment in Nuttall's white-crowned sparrows. *Condor, 91*, 397–407. [15]

Dewsbury, D. A. (1972). Patterns of copulatory behavior in male mammals. *Quarterly Review of Biology, 47*, 1–33. [6]

Dewsbury, D. A. (1974). The use of muroid rodents in the psychology laboratory. *Behavior Research Methods & Instrumentation, 6*, 301–308. [6]

Dewsbury, D. A. (1975a). Diversity and adaptation in rodent copulatory behavior. *Science, 190*, 947–954. [6]

Dewsbury, D. A. (1975b). The normal heterosexual pattern of copulatory behavior in male rats: effects of drugs that alter brain monoamine levels. In M. Sandler & G. L. Gessa (Eds.), *Sexual behavior: Pharmacology and biochemistry* (pp. 169–179). New York: Raven Press. [6]

Dewsbury, D. A. (1978a). *Comparative animal behavior*. New York: McGraw-Hill. [E]

Dewsbury, D. A. (1978b). The comparative method in studies of reproductive behavior. In T. E. McGill, D. A. Dewsbury, & B. D. Sachs (Eds.), *Sex and behavior: Status and prospectus* (pp. 83–112). New York: Plenum. [6]

Dewsbury, D. A. (1979a). Copulatory behavior of deer mice (*Peromyscus maniculatus*): 1. Normative data, subspecific differences, and effects of cross-fostering. *Journal of Comparative and Physiological Psychology, 93*, 151–160. [6]

Dewsbury, D. A. (1979b). Copulatory behavior of deer mice (*Peromyscus maniculatus*): 2. A study of some factors regulating the fine structure of behavior. *Journal of Comparative and Physiological Psychology, 93*, 161–177. [6]

Dewsbury, D. A. (1979c). Copulatory behavior of deer mice (*Peromyscu maniculatus*): 3. Effects on pregnancy initiation. *Journal of Comparative and Physiological Psychology, 93*, 178–188. [6]

Dewsbury, D. A. (1979d). Factor analyses of measures of copulatory behavior in three species of muroid rodents. *Journal of Comparative and Physiological Psychology, 93*, 868–878. [6]

Dewsbury, D. A. (1981a). Effects of novelty on copulatory behavior: The Coolidge effect and related phenomena. *Psychological Bulletin, 89*, 464–482. [6]

Dewsbury, D. A. (1981b). An exercise in the prediction of monogamy in the field from laboratory data on 42 species of muroid rodents. *Biologist, 63*, 138–162. [6, 10]

Dewsbury, D. A. (1981c). On the function of the multiple-intromission, multiple-ejaculation copulatory patterns of rodents. *Bulletin of the Psychonomic Society, 18*, 221–223. [6, 8]

Dewsbury, D. A. (1981d). Social dominance, copulatory behavior, and differential reproduction in deer mice (*Peromyscus maniculatus*). *Journal of Comparative and Physiological Psychology, 95*, 880–895. [6]

Dewsbury, D. A. (1982a). Avoidance of incestuous breeding between siblings in two species of *Peromyscus* mice. *Biology of Behaviour, 7*, 157–169. [6]

Dewsbury, D. A. (1982b). Dominance rank, copulatory behavior, and differential reproduction. *Quarterly Review of Biology, 57*, 135–159. [6, 8]

Dewsbury, D. A. (1982c). Ejaculate cost and male choice. *American Naturalist, 119*, 601–610. [6, 7, 8]

Dewsbury, D. A. (1982d). Pregnancy blockage following multiple-male copulation or exposure at the time of mating in deer mice, *Peromyscus maniculatus*. *Behavioral Ecology and Sociobiology, 11*, 37–42. [6]

Dewsbury, D. A. (1983). Recovery from sexual satiety in deer mice (*Peromyscus maniculatus bairdi*). *Journal of Comparative Psychology, 97*, 34–42. [6]

Dewsbury, D. A. (1984a). Aggression, copulation, and differential reproduction of deer mice (*Peromyscus maniculatus*) in a semi-natural enclosure. *Behaviour, 91*, 1–23. [6]

Dewsbury, D. A. (1984b). *Comparative psychology in the twentieth century*. Stroudsburg, PA: Hutchinson Ross. [I, E]

Dewsbury, D. A. (1984c). Muroid rodents as research animals. *ILAR News*, 28(1), 8–15. [6]

Dewsbury, D. A. (1984d). Sperm competition in muroid rodents. In R. L. Smith (Ed.), *Sperm competition and the evolution of animal mating systems* (pp. 547–571). Orlando, FL: Academic Press. [6, 7, 8, 12]

Dewsbury, D. A. (1985a). Interactions between males and their sperm during multi-male copulatory episodes of deer mice (*Peromyscus maniculatus*). *Animal Behaviour*, 33, 1266–1274. [6]

Dewsbury, D. A. (1985b). Paternal behavior in rodents. *American Zoologist*, 25, 841–852. [13]

Dewsbury, D. A. (1985c). Studies of pericopulatory pregnancy blockage and the gestation period in deer mice (*Peromyscus maniculatus*). *Hormones and Behavior*, 19, 164–173. [6, 13]

Dewsbury, D. A. (1985d). Studies of the effects of variation at the transferrin locus on reproductive processes in deer mice. *Acta Theriologica*, 30, 227–240. [6]

Dewsbury, D. A. (1987). *Experiences with the study of rodents in seminatural enclosures*. Paper presented at the Conference on Design and Use of Indoor Naturalistic Habitats for Behavior Research, State University of New York, Stony Brook. [2]

Dewsbury, D. A. (1988a). The comparative psychology of monogamy. In D. W. Leger (Ed.), *Comparative perspectives in modern psychology*. (Nebraska Symposium on Motivation, Vol. 35, pp. 1–50). Lincoln: University of Nebraska Press. [6, 10, 14]

Dewsbury, D. A. (1988b). Kin discrimination and reproductive behavior in muroid rodents. *Behavior Genetics*, 18, 525–536. [6, 13]

Dewsbury, D. A. (1988c). Kinship, familiarity, aggression, and dominance in deer mice (*Peromyscus maniculatus*) in seminatural enclosures. *Journal of Comparative Psychology*, 102, 124–128. [6]

Dewsbury, D. A. (1988d). Mating capacity of male deer mice (*Peromyscus maniculatus bairdi*) copulating with successive females. *Bulletin of the Psychonomic Society*, 26, 265–268. [6]

Dewsbury, D. A. (1988e). Sperm competition in deer mice (*Peromyscus maniculatus bairdi*): Effects of cycling versus postpartum estrus and delays between matings. *Behavioral Ecology and Sociobiology*, 22, 251–256. [6]

Dewsbury, D. A. (1988f). A test of the role of copulatory plugs in sperm competition in deer mice (*Peromyscus maniculatus*). *Journal of Mammalogy*, 69, 854–857. [6]

Dewsbury, D. A. (1989a). Tests of preferences of adult deer mice (*Peromyscus maniculatus bairdi*) for siblings versus nonsiblings. Unpublished manuscript. [6]

Dewsbury, D. A. (1989b). Tests of preferences of young deer mice (*Peromyscus maniculatus bairdi*) for siblings versus nonsiblings. Unpublished manuscript. [6]

Dewsbury, D. A., & Baumgardner, D. J. (1981). Studies of sperm competition in two species of muroid rodents. *Behavioral Ecology and Sociobiology*, 9, 121–133. [6]

Dewsbury, D. A., Baumgardner, D. J., Evans, R. L., & Webster, D. G. (1980). Sexual dimorphism for body mass in 13 taxa of muroid rodents under laboratory conditions. *Journal of Mammalogy*, 61, 146–149. [6]

Dewsbury, D. A., Ferguson, B., Hodges, A. W., & Taylor, S. A. (1986). Tests of preferences of deer mice (*Peromyscus maniculatus bairdi*) for individuals and their odors as a function of sex and estrous conditions. *Journal of Comparative Psychology*, 100, 117–127. [6]

Dewsbury, D. A., & Sawrey, D. K. (1984). Male capacity as related to sperm production, pregnancy initiation, and sperm competition in deer mice (*Peromyscus maniculatus*). *Behavioral Ecology and Sociobiology*, 16, 37–47. [6]

Dewsbury, D. A., Shapiro, L. E., & Taylor, S. A. (1987). Disruption of ejaculates by male copulation in deer mice (*Peromyscus maniculatus*). *Physiology and Behavior*, 41, 53–58. [6]

Dickinson, A. (1980). *Contemporary animal learning theory*. Cambridge: Cambridge University Press. [9]

Dickinson, J. L. (1986). Prolonged mating in the milkweed leaf beetle *Labidomera clivicollis clivicollis* (Coleoptera: Chrysomelidae): a test of the "sperm loading" hypothesis. *Behavioral Ecology and Sociobiology*, 18, 331–338. [6]

Dieterlen, F. (1959). Das Verhalten des syrischen Goldhamsters (*Mesocricetus auratus* Waterhouse). *Zeitschrift für Tierpsychologie*, 16, 47–103. [17]

Digby, K. (1664). *Two treatises. In one of which the nature of bodies; in the other, the nature of mans soule; is looked into*. Paris. [2]

Dixson, A. F., & George, L. (1982). Prolactin and parental behaviour in a male New World primate. *Nature, 29,* 551–553. [10]

Dixson, A. F., & Lunn, S. F. (1987). Post-partum changes in hormones and sexual behaviour in captive groups of marmosets (*Callithrix jacchus*). *Physiology and Behavior, 41,* 577–583. [10]

Dizinno, G., Whitney, G., & Nyby, J. (1978). Ultrasonic vocalizations by male mice (*Mus musculus*) to female sex pheromone: Experiential determinants. *Behavioral Biology, 22,* 104–113. [9]

Dobson, F. S. (1983). Agonism and territoriality in the California ground squirrel. *Journal of Mammalogy, 64,* 218–225. [8]

Dobson, F. S. (1984). Environmental influences on sciurid mating systems. In J. O. Murie & G. R. Michener (Eds.), *The biology of ground-dwelling squirrels* (pp. 227–249). Lincoln: University of Nebraska Press. [8]

Dodd, D. H., & Schultz, R. F. (1973). Computational procedures for estimating magnitudes of effect for some analysis of variance designs. *Psychological Bulletin, 79,* 391–395. [1]

Dohler, K. D., & Wuttke, W. (1975). Changes with age in levels of serum gonadotrophins, prolactin and gonadal steroids in prepubertal male and female rats. *Endocrinology, 97,* 898–907. [12]

Dollard, J., Doob, L., Miller, N. E., Mowrer, O., & Sears, R. (1939). *Frustration and aggression.* New Haven: Yale University Press. [18]

Dominey, W. J. (1980). Female mimicry in male bluegill sunfish—a genetic polymorphism? *Nature, 284,* 546–548. [12]

Domjan, M. (1987). Comparative psychology and the study of animal learning. *Journal of Comparative Psychology, 101,* 237–241. [4]

Domjan, M., & Galef, B. G., Jr. (1983). Biological constraints on instrumental and classical conditioning: Retrospect and prospect. *Animal Learning and Behavior, 11,* 151– 161. [3]

Domjan, M., & Hall, S. (1986). Sexual dimorphism in the social proximity of Japanese quail (*Coturnix coturnix japonica*). *Journal of Comparative Psychology, 100,* 68–71. [9]

Domjan, M., & Hollis, K. L. (1988). Reproductive behavior: A potential model system for adaptive specializations in learning. In R. C. Bolles & M. D. Beecher (Eds.), *Evolution and learning* (pp. 213–237). Hillsdale, NJ: Lawrence Erlbaum Associates. [9]

Domjan, M., Lyons, R., North, N. C., & Bruell, J. (1986). Sexual Pavlovian conditioned approach behavior in male Japanese quail (*Coturnix coturnix japonica*). *Journal of Comparative Psychology, 100,* 413–421. [9]

Draper, P. (1976). Social and economic constraints on child life among the !Kung. In R. B. Lee and I. DeVore (Eds.), *Kalahari hunter-gatherers* (pp. 218–245). Cambridge, MA: Harvard University Press. [10]

Dronzek, L. A., Savage, A., Snowdon, C. T., Whaling, C. S., & Ziegler, T. E. (1986). Techniques of handrearing and reintroducing rejected cotton-top tamarin infants. *Laboratory Animal Science, 36,* 243–247. [10]

Drummond, B. A. (1984). Multiple mating and sperm competition in the Lepidoptera. In R. L. Smith (Ed.), *Sperm competition and the evolution of animal mating systems* (pp. 291–370). New York: Academic Press. [7]

D'Udine, B., & Alleva, E. (1983). Early experience and sexual preferences in rodents. In P. Bateson (Ed.), *Mate choice* (pp. 311–327). Cambridge: Cambridge University Press. [12, 13]

Dunbar, R. I. M. (1982). Intraspecific variations in mating strategy. In P. P. G. Bateson & P. H. Klopfer (Eds.), *Perspectives in ethology: Vol. 5. Ontogeny* (pp. 385–431). New York: Plenum. [12]

Dunford, C. (1977). Social system of round-tailed ground squirrels. *Animal Behaviour, 25,* 885–906. [8]

Eastzer, D. H. (1988). Geographic variation in the song of the brown-headed cowbird (*Molothrus ater*). Unpublished doctoral dissertation, University of North Carolina, Chapel Hill. [14]

Eberhard, W. (1985). *Sexual selection and animal genitalia.* Cambridge, MA: Harvard University Press. [7]

Ebihara, S., & Kawamura, H. (1981). The role of the pineal organ and the suprachiasmatic nuclei in the control of the circadian locomotor rhythms in the the Java sparrow, *Padda orizivora. Journal of Comparative Physiology, 141,* 207–214. [11]

Economos, A. E. (1982). On the origin of biological similarity. *Journal of Theoretical Biology, 94,* 25–60. [4]

Edmunds, M. (1974). *Defense in animals.* Harlow, Essex, U.K.: Longman Group. [5]

Eibl-Eibesfeldt, I. (1953). Zur Ethologie des Hamsters (*Cricetus cricetus* L.). *Zeitschrift für Tierpsychologie, 10,* 204–254. [17]

Eibl-Eibesfeldt, I. (1958). The fighting behavior of animals. *Scientific American, 205,* 470–482. [18]

Eisenberg, J. F. (1981). *The mammalian radiations: An analysis of trends in evolution, adaptation, and behavior.* Chicago: University of Chicago Press. [4, 12, 13]

Eisenberg, J. F., & Kleiman, D. (1972). Olfactory communication in mammals. *Annual Review of Ecology and Systematics, 3,* 1–31. [17]

Eisenberg, J. F., & Wilson, D. E. (1978). Relative brain size and feeding strategies in the Chiroptera. *Evolution, 32(4),* 740–751. [4]

Elliott, L. (1978). Social behavior and foraging ecology of the Eastern chipmunk (*Tamias striatus*) in the Adirondack Mountains. *Smithsonian Contributions to Zoology, 265,* 1–107. [8]

Elliott, P. F. (1980). Evolution of promiscuity in the brown-headed cowbird. *Condor, 82,* 138–141. [14]

Elwood, R. W. (1983). Paternal care in rodents. In R. W. Elwood (Ed.), *Parental behaviour of rodents* (pp. 235–257). Chichester: John Wiley & Sons. [13]

Elwood, R. W., & Broom, D. M. (1978). The influence of litter size and parental behaviour on the development of Mongolian gerbil pups. *Animal Behaviour, 26,* 438–454. [13]

Emery, D. E., & Sachs, B. D. (1975). Ejaculatory pattern in female rats without androgen treatment. *Science, 190,* 484–486. [12]

Emlen, S. T. (1970). Celestial rotation: its importance in the development of migratory orientation. *Science, 170,* 1198–1201. [2]

Emlen, S. T., & Oring, L. W. (1977). Ecology, sexual selection, and the evolution of mating systems. *Science, 197,* 215–223. [7, 8, 9]

Engbring, J., & Fritts, T. H. (in press). Demise of an insular avifauna: The brown tree snake on Guam. *Transactions of the Western Section of the Wildlife Society.* [5]

Engbring, J., & Pratt, H. D. (1985). Endangered birds in Micronesia: Their history, status, and future prospects. *Bird Conservation, 2,* 71–105. [5]

Engbring, J., & Ramsey, F. L. (1984). *Distribution and abundance of the forest birds of Guam: Results of a 1981 survey* (FWS/OBS-84/20). Washington, DC: U. S. Fish and Wildlife Service. [5]

Epple, G. (1975). Parental behavior in *Saguinus fuscicollis* ssp. *Folia Primatologica, 24,* 221–238. [10]

Epple, G. (1977). Notes on the establishment and maintenance of the pair-bond in *Saguinus fuscicollis.* In D. G. Kleiman (Ed.), *The biology and conservation of the Callitrichidae* (pp. 231–238). Washington, DC: Smithsonian Institution Press. [10]

Epple, G. (1978). Reproductive and social behavior of marmosets with special reference to captive breeding. *Primates in Medicine, 10,* 50–62. [10]

Epple, G. (1986). Communication by chemical signals. In G. Mitchell (Ed.), *Comparative primate biology: Vol. 2A. Behavior conservation and ecology* (pp. 531–580). New York: Alan R. Liss. [10]

Epple, G., & Alverario, M. C. (1985). Social facilitation of agonistic responses to strangers in pairs of saddle-back tamarins (*Saguinus fuscicollis*). *American Journal of Primatology, 9,* 207–218. [10]

Epple, G., Alverario, M. C., & Katz, Y. (1982). The role of chemical communication in aggressive behavior and its gonadal control in the tamarin (*Saguinus fuscicollis*). In C. T. Snowdon, C. H. Brown, & M. R. Petersen (Eds.), *Primate communication* (pp. 279–302). New York: Cambridge University Press. [10]

Epple, G., & Katz, Y. (1980). Social influences on first reproductive success and related behaviors in the saddle-back tamarin (*Saguinus fuscicollis,* Callitrichidae). *International Journal of Primatology, 1,* 171–183. [10]

Epple, G., & Katz, Y. (1984). Social influences on estrogen excretion and ovarian cyclicity in the saddle-back tamarin (*Saguinus fuscicollis*). *American Journal of Primatology, 6,* 215–227. [10]

Epstein, A. N. (1967). Oropharyngeal factors in feeding and drinking. In C. F. Code (Ed.), *Handbook of physiology: Vol 1. Alimentary canal* (pp. 197–218). Washington, DC: American Physiological Society. [3]

Erwin, M. R. (1977). Foraging and breeding adaptations to different food regimes in three seabirds: The common tern, *Sterna hirundo,* royal tern, *Sterna maxima,* and black skimmer, *Rynchops niger. Ecology, 58,* 389–397. [3]

Evans, S. (1983). The pair-bond of the common marmoset, *Callithrix jacchus jacchus*: An experimental investigation. *Animal Behaviour, 31,* 651–658. [10]

Ewer, R. F. (1971). The biology and behaviour of a free-living population of black rats (*Rattus rattus*). *Animal Behavior Monographs, 4,* part 3. [18]

Fagen, R. (1982). Evolutionary issues in development of behavioral flexibility. In P. P. G. Bateson & P. H. Klopfer (Eds.), *Perspectives in ethology: Vol. 5. Ontogeny* (pp. 365–383). New York: Plenum. [12]

Fanselow, M. S., & Lester, L. S. (1988). A functional behavioristic approach to aversively motivated behavior: Predatory imminence as a determinant of the topography of defensive behavior. In R. C. Bolles & M. D. Beecher (Eds.), *Evolution and learning* (pp. 185–212). Hillsdale, NJ: Lawrence Erlbaum Associates. [2, 9]

Fantino, E. (1987). Operant conditioning simulations of foraging and the delay-reduction hypothesis. In A. C. Kamil, J. R. Krebs, & H. R. Pulliam (Eds.), *Foraging behavior* (pp. 193–214). New York: Plenum. [1]

Fantino, E., & Abarca, N. (1985). Choice, optimal foraging, and the delay-reduction hypothesis. *Behavioral and Brain Sciences, 8*, 315–330. [2]

Farentinos, R. C. (1972). Social dominance and mating activity in the tassel-eared squirrel (*Sciurus aberti ferreus*). *Animal Behaviour, 20*, 316–326. [8]

Farentinos, R. C. (1980). Sexual solicitation of subordinate males by female tassel-eared squirrels (*Sciurus aberti*). *Journal of Mammalogy, 61*, 337–341. [8]

Farr, J. A. (1976). Social behavior of the golden silk spider, *Nephila clavipes*. *Journal of Arachnology, 4*, 137–144. [7]

Farris, H. E. (1964). Behavioral development, social organization and conditioning of courting behavior in the Japanese quail, *Coturnix coturnix japonica*. *Dissertation Abstracts International, 25*, 7389. (University Microfilms No. 65-1738). [9]

Farris, H. E. (1967). Classical conditioning of courting behavior in the Japanese quail, *Coturnix coturnix japonica*. *Journal of the Experimental Analysis of Behavior, 10*, 213–217. [9]

Fedak, M. A., Heglund, N. C., & Taylor, C. R. (1982). Energetics and mechanics of terrestrial locomotion. *Journal of Experimental Biology, 79*, 23–40. [4]

Feistner, A. T. C., & Chamove, A. S. (1986). High motivation toward food increases food-sharing in cotton-top tamarins. *Developmental Psychobiology, 19*, 439–452. [10]

Fentress, J. C. (1983). Ethological models of hierarchy and patterning of species-specific behavior. In P. Teitelbaum & E. Satinoff (Eds.), *Handbook of behavioral neurobiology* (Vol. 6, pp. 185–234). New York: Plenum Press. [2]

Ferrari, S. F. (1987). Food transfer in a wild marmoset group. *Folia Primatologica, 48*, 203–206. [10]

Ferris, C. F., Albers, H. E., Wesolowski, S. M., Goldman, B. D., & Luman, S. E. (1984). Vasopressin injected into the hypothalamus triggers a stereotypic behavior in golden hamsters. *Science, 224*, 521–523. [17]

Ferris, C. F., Meenan, D. M., & Albers, H. E. (1986). Microinjection of kainic acid into the hypothalamus of golden hamsters prevents vasopressin-dependent flank marking behavior. *Neuroendocrinology, 44*, 112–116. [17]

Ferris, C. F., Pollock, J., Albers, H. E., & Luman, S. E. (1985). Inhibition of flank marking behavior in golden hamsters by microinjection of a vasopressin antagonist into the hypothalamus. *Neuroscience Letters, 55*, 239–243. [17]

Fillion, T. J., & Blass, E. M. (1986). Infantile experience with suckling odors determines adult sexual behavior in male rats. *Science, 34*, 123–133. [12]

Fishelson, L. (1970). Protogynous sex reversal in the fish *Anthias squamipinnis* (Teleostei, Anthiidae) regulated by the presence or absence of a male fish. *Nature, 227*, 90–91. [12]

Flannelly, K. J., Flannelly, L., & Blanchard, R. J. (1984). Adult experience and the expression of aggression. In K. J. Flannelly, R. J. Blanchard, & D. C. Blanchard (Eds.), *Biological perspectives on aggression* (pp. 207–259). New York: Alan R. Liss. [18]

Flannelly, K. J., Flannelly, L., & Lore, R. (1986). Post partum aggression against intruding male conspecifics in Sprague-Dawley rats. *Behavioural Processes, 13*, 279–286. [18]

Fleischer, S. F., & Turkewitz, G. (1979). Effect of neonatal stunting on development of rats: Large litter rearing. *Developmental Psychobiology, 12*, 137–149. [13]

Fletcher, D. J. C., & Michener, C. D. (1987). *Kin recognition in animals*. New York: John Wiley & Sons. [13]

Floody, O. R., & Pfaff, D. W. (1977a). Communication among hamsters by high-frequency acoustic signals: 1. Physical characteristics of hamster calls. *Journal of Comparative and Physiological Psychology, 91*, 794–806. [17]

Floody, O. R., & Pfaff, D. W. (1977b). Communication among hamsters by high-frequency acoustic signals: 3. Responses evoked by natural and synthetic ultrasounds. *Journal of Comparative and Physiological Psychology*, 91, 820–829. [17]

Floody, O. R., Pfaff, D. W., & Lewis, C. D. (1977). Communication among hamsters by high-frequency acoustic signals: 2. Determinants of calling by females and males. *Journal of Comparative and Physiological Psychology*, 91, 807–819. [17]

Foelix, R. F. (1982). *Biology of spiders*. Cambridge, MA: Harvard University Press. [7]

Foltz, D. W., & Hoogland, J. (1981). Analysis of the mating system in the black-tailed prairie dog (*Cynomys ludovicianus*) by likelihood of paternity. *Journal of Mammalogy*, 62, 706–712. [8]

Foltz, D. W., & Schwagmeyer, P. L. (1989). Sperm competition in the thirteen-lined ground squirrel: Differential fertilization success under field conditions. *American Naturalist*, 133, 257–265. [8]

Forselius, S. (1957). Studies of Anabantid fishes. *Zoologiska bidrag fran Uppsala*, 32, 93–597. [9]

French, J. A. (1982). The role of scent marking in social and sexual communication in tamarins (*Saguinus o. oedipus*). (Doctoral dissertation, University of Wisconsin, Madison.) *Dissertation Abstracts International*, DEP 82-24036. [10]

French, J. A., Abbott, D. H., Scheffler, G., Robinson, J. A., & Goy, R. W. (1983). Cyclic excretion of urinary oestrogens in female tamarins (*Saguinus oedipus*). *Journal of Reproduction and Fertility*, 67, 177–184. [10]

French, J. A., Abbott, D. H., & Snowdon, C. T. (1984). The effect of social environment on estrogen excretion, scent marking and sociosexual behavior in tamarins (*Saguinus oedipus*). *American Journal of Primatology*, 6, 155–167. [10]

French, J. A., & Cleveland, J. (1984). Scent marking in the tamarin, *Saguinus oedipus*: Sex differences and ontogeny. *Animal Behaviour*, 32, 615–621. [10]

French, J. A., & Inglett, B. J. (1989). Female–female aggression and male indifference in response to unfamiliar intruders in lion tamarins. *Animal Behaviour*, 37, 487–497. [10]

French, J. A., & Snowdon, C. T. (1981). Sexual dimorphism in response to unfamiliar intruders in the tamarin *Saguinus oedipus*. *Animal Behaviour*, 29, 822–829. [10]

French, J. A., & Stribley, J. A. (1987). Synchronization of ovarian cycles within and between social groups in golden lion tamarins (*Leontopithecus rosalia*). *American Journal of Primatology*, 12, 469–478. [10]

Freud, S. (1949). *An outline of psychoanalysis*. (J. Strachey, Trans.) New York: Norton. (Original work published 1940) [18]

Frey, K. (1978). *Behavioral responses of male hamsters to relatively volatile and involatile fractions of the vaginal secretion*. Unpublished master's thesis, Cornell University, Ithaca, NY. [17]

Friedman, M. I., Bruno, J. P., & Alberts, J. R. (1981). Physiological and behavioral consequences in rats of water recycling during lactation. *Journal of Comparative and Physiological Psychology*, 95, 26–35. [12]

Friedmann, H. (1929). *The cowbirds*. Springfield, IL: Charles C. Thomas. [14]

Frisch, K. von. (1967). *The dance language and orientation of bees*. Cambridge, MA: Belknap Press of Harvard University Press. [3]

Fritts, T. H. (1984). *The brown tree snake: An introduced species on Guam. An assessment of ecological and socioeconomic impacts of the species on Guam and threats to other Pacific Islands*. (Unpublished report submitted to the U. S. Fish and Wildlife Service, Region 1, Portland, Oregon.) [5]

Fritts, T. H. (1987). Movements of snakes via cargo in the Pacific region. *Elapaio*, 47, 17–18. [5]

Fritts, T. H., & Scott, N. J., Jr. (1985). *The brown tree snake on Guam: Studies of its ecology, control, and threats to other islands*. (Unpublished report submitted to the U. S. Fish and Wildlife Service, Region 1, Portland, Oregon.) [5]

Fritts, T. H., Scott, N. J., Jr., & Savidge, J. A. (1987). Activity of the arboreal brown tree snake (*Boiga irregularis*) on Guam as determined by electrical outages. *The Snake*, 19, 51–58. [5]

Fritts, T. H., Scott, N. J., Jr., & Smith, B. E. (in press). Trapping *Boiga irregularis* on Guam using bird odors. *Journal of Herpetology*. [5]

Fullenkamp, A. M., Fischer, R. B., & Vance, R. A. (1987). A lack of avoidance of flank gland secretions by male Syrian hamsters. *Physiology and Behavior*, 39, 73–76. [17]

Galef, B. G., Jr. (1970). Aggression and timidity: Responses to novelty in feral Norway rats. *Journal of Comparative and Physiological Psychology, 70,* 370–381. [3]

Galef, B. G., Jr. (1976). Mechanisms for the social transmission of acquired food preferences from adult to weanling rats. In L. M. Barker, M. R. Best, and M. Domjan (Eds.), *Learning mechanisms in food selection* (pp. 123–147). Waco, TX: Baylor University Press. [3]

Galef, B. G., Jr. (1986a). Olfactory communication among rats: Information concerning distant diets. In D. Duvall, D. Müller-Schwarze, & R. M. Silverstein (Eds.), *Chemical signals in vertebrates: Vol. 4. Ecology, evolution, and comparative biology* (pp. 487–506). New York: Plenum Press. [3]

Galef, B. G., Jr. (1986b). Social interaction modifies learned aversions, sodium appetite, and both palatability and handling-time induced dietary preference in rats *(Rattus norvegicus)*. *Journal of Comparative Psychology, 100,* 432–439. [3]

Galef, B. G., Jr. (1986c). Social identification of toxic diets by Norway rats. *Journal of Comparative Psychology, 100,* 331–334. [3]

Galef, B. G., Jr. (1988). Evolution and learning before Thorndike: A forgotten epoch in the history of behavioral research. In R. C. Bolles & M. D. Beecher (Eds.), *Evolution and Learning* (pp. 39–58). Hillsdale, NJ: Lawrence Erlbaum Associates. [2]

Galef, B. G., Jr. (in press). Enduring social enhancement of rats' preferences for the palatable and the piquant. *Appetite.* [3]

Galef, B. G., Jr. & Beck, M. (in press). Diet selection and poison avoidance by mammals individually and in social groups. In E. M. Stricker (Ed.), *Handbook of neurobiology* (Vol. 11). New York: Plenum Press. [3]

Galef, B. G., Jr., Kennett, D. J., & Stein, M. (1985). Demonstrator influence on observer diet preference: Effects of familiarity and exposure context in R. *norvegicus. Animal Learning & Behavior, 13,* 25–30. [3]

Galef, B. G., Jr., Kennett, D. J., & Wigmore, S. W. (1984). Transfer of information concerning distant food in rats: A robust phenomenon. *Animal Learning & Behavior, 12,* 292–296. [3]

Galef, B. G., Jr., & Mason, J. R. (1986). *Enhanced rodent edible with natural attractants.* Serial No. 922,185; filing date Oct. 23, 1986. U.S. Patent Office. [3]

Galef, B. G., Jr., Mason, J. R., Preti, G., & Bean, N. J. (1988). Carbon disulfide can mediate socially-induced diet choice in rats. *Physiology and Behavior, 42,* 119–124. [3]

Galef, B. G., Jr., Mischinger, A., & Malenfant, S. A. (1987). Hungry rats' following of conspecifics to food depends on the diets eaten by potential leaders. *Animal Behaviour, 35,* 1234–1239. [3]

Galef, B. G., Jr., & Stein, M. (1985). Demonstrator influence on observer diet preference: Analyses of critical social interactions and olfactory signals. *Animal Learning & Behavior, 13,* 131–138. [3]

Galef, B. G., Jr., & Wigmore, S. W. (1983). Transfer of information concerning distant foods: A laboratory investigation of the "information-centre" hypothesis. *Animal Behaviour, 31,* 748–758. [3]

Gallistel, C. R. (1980). *The organization of action: A new synthesis.* Hillsdale, NJ: Lawrence Erlbaum Associates. [2]

Gallup, G. (1965). Aggression in rats as a function of frustrative nonreward in a straight alley. *Psychonomic Science, 3,* 99–100. [18]

Gandelman, R., Saal, F. S. vom, & Reinisch, J. M. (1977). Contiguity to male foetuses affects morphology and behaviour of female mice. *Nature, 266,* 722–724. [13]

Gans, C. (1986). Locomotion of limbless vertebrates: Pattern and evolution. *Herpetologica, 42,* 33–46. [5]

Garcia, J., McGowan, B. K., & Green, K. F. (1972). Biological constraints on conditioning. In A. H. Black & W. F. Prokasy (Eds.), *Classical conditioning II: Current research and theory* (pp. 3–27). New York: Appleton-Century-Crofts. [2]

Gardner, R. A., & Gardner, B. T. (1988). Feedforward versus feedbackward: An ethological alternative to the law of effect. *Behavioral and Brain Sciences, 11,* 429–447. [2]

Garland, T., Jr. (1983). The relation between maximal running speed and body mass in terrestrial mammals. *Journal of Zoology, 199,* 157–170. [4]

Gary, N. E., & Marston, J. (1971). Mating behavior of drone honey bees with queen models *(Apis mellifera* L.). *Animal Behaviour, 19,* 299–304. [17]

Gaulin, S. J. C., & FitzGerald, R. W. (1986). Sex differences in spatial ability: An evolutionary hypothesis and test. *American Naturalist, 127,* 74–88. [8]

Geist, V. (1978a). *Life strategies, human evolution, environmental design*. New York: Springer-Verlag. [12]

Geist, V. (1978b). On weapons, combat, and ecology. In L. Krames, P. Pliner, & T. Alloway (Eds.), *Advances in the study of communication and affect: Vol. 4. Aggression, dominance, and individual spacing* (pp. 1–30). New York: Plenum Press. [18]

Gemberling, G. A. (1984). Ingestion of a novel flavor before exposure to pups injected with lithium chloride produces a taste aversion in mother rats (*Rattus norvegicus*). *Journal of Comparative Psychology, 98*, 285–301. [3]

Gerall, H. D., Ward, I. L., & Gerall, A. A. (1967). Disruption of the male rat's sexual behavior induced by social isolation. *Animal Behaviour, 15*, 54–58. [12]

Gerhardt, H. C., Daniel, R. E., Perrill, S. A., & Schram, S. (1987). Mating behaviour and male mating success in the green treefrog. *Animal Behaviour, 35*, 1490–1503. [12]

Ghiselin, M. T. (1974). *The economy of nature and the evolution of sex*. Berkeley: University of California Press. [12]

Gibb, J. A. (1960). Populations of tits and goldcrests and their food supply in pine plantations. *Ibis, 102*, 163–208. [1]

Gibb, J. A. (1962). L. Tinbergen's hypothesis of the role of specific search images. *Ibis, 104*, 106–111. [1]

Gibber, J. R., & Goy, R. W. (1985). Infant directed behavior in young rhesus monkeys: Sex differences and effects of prenatal androgens. *American Journal of Primatology, 8*, 225–237. [10]

Gibbon, J., Morrell, M., & Silver, R. (1984). Two kinds of timing in the circadian incubation rhythm of the ring dove. *American Journal of Physiology, 247*, R1083–R1087. [11]

Gill, F. B., & Wolf, L. L. (1977). Nonrandom foraging by sunbirds in a patchy environment. *Ecology, 58*, 1284–1296. [1]

Gillingham, J. C., & Clark, D. L. (1981). Snake tongue-flicking: Transfer mechanics to Jacobson's organ. *Canadian Journal of Zoology, 59*, 1651–1657. [5]

Glander, K. E. (1981). Feeding patterns in mantled howling monkeys. In A. C. Kamil & T. D. Sargent (Eds.), *Foraging behavior: Ecological, ethological, and psychological approaches* (pp. 231–264). New York: Garland Press. [1]

Goist, K. C. (1982). *Male–male competition in the orb weaving spider*, Nephila clavipes. Unpublished doctoral dissertation, Tulane University, New Orleans. [7]

Golan, L., Radcliffe, C. W., Miller, T., O'Connell, B., & Chiszar, D. (1982). Prey trailing by the prairie rattlesnake (*Crotalus viridis*). *Journal of Herpetology, 16*, 287–293. [5]

Goldenthal, P., Johnston, R. E., & Kraut, R. E. (1981). Smiling, appeasement, and the silent bared-teeth display. *Ethology and Sociobiology, 2*, 127–133. [17]

Goldizen, A. W. (1987). Facultative polyandry and the role of infant-carrying in wild saddle-back tamarins (*Saguinus fuscicollis*). *Behavioral Ecology and Sociobiology, 20*, 99–109. [10]

Gottlieb, G. (1971). Ontogenesis of sensory function in birds and mammals. In E. Tobach, L. R. Aronson, & E. Shaw (Eds.), *The biopsychology of development* (pp. 67–128). New York: Academic Press. [13]

Gould, S. J., (1966). Allometry and size in ontogeny and phylogeny. *Biological Reviews, 41*, 587–640. [4]

Gould, S. J. (1977). *Ontogeny and phylogeny*. Cambridge, MA: Belknap Press of Harvard University Press. [4, 12]

Gould, S. J., & Lewontin, R. C. (1979). The spandrels of San Marco and the Panglossian paradigm: a critique of the adaptationist program. *Proceedings of the Royal Society of London, B, 205*, 581–598. [3]

Goy, R. W., & McEwen, B. S. (1980). *Sexual differentiation of the brain*. Cambridge, MA: MIT Press. [12]

Grady, M., & Hoogland, J. L. (1986). Why do male black-tailed prairie dogs (*Cynomys ludovicianus*) give a mating call? *Animal Behaviour, 34*, 108–112. [8]

Graham, J. M., & Desjardins, C. (1980). Classical conditioning: Induction of luteinizing hormone and testosterone secretion in anticipation of sexual activity. *Science, 210*, 1039–1041. [9]

Grant, E. C. (1963). An analysis of the social behaviour of the male laboratory rat. *Behaviour, 21*, 260–281. [18]

Grant, E. C., & Chance, M. R. A. (1958). Rank order in caged rats. *Animal Behaviour, 6*, 183–194. [18]

Grant, E. C., & Mackintosh, J. H. (1963). A comparison of the social postures of some common laboratory rodents. *Behaviour, 21,* 246–259. [18]

Gray, R. (1987). Faith and foraging: A critique of the "paradigm argument from design." In A. C. Kamil, J. R. Krebs, & H. R. Pulliam (Eds.), *Foraging behavior* (pp. 69–140). New York: Plenum. [1]

Green, D. M., & Swets, J. A. (1966). *Signal detection theory and psychophysics.* New York: John Wiley. [16]

Green, R. (1987). Stochastic models of optimal foraging. In A. C. Kamil, J. R. Krebs, & H. R. Pulliam (Eds.), *Foraging behavior* (pp. 273–302). New York: Plenum. [1]

Greenberg, G., and Tobach, E. (Eds.) (1984). *Behavioral evolution and integrative levels.* Hillsdale, NJ: Lawrence Erlbaum Associates. [I]

Grinnell, J. (1909). A new cowbird of the genus *Molothrus*, with a note on the probable genetic relationships of the North American forms. *University of California Publications in Zoology, 5,* 275–281. [14]

Gross, M. R., & Charnov, E. L. (1980). Alternative male life histories in bluegill sunfish. *Proceedings of the National Academy of Sciences, 77,* 6937–6940. [12]

Gross, M. R., & Sargent, R. C. (1985). The evolution of male and female parental care in fishes. *American Zoologist, 25,* 807–822. [9]

Grosvenor, E. E., & Turner, C. W. (1960). Release and restoration of pituitary lactogen in response to nursing stimuli in lactating rats. *Endocrinology, 66,* 90–96. [12]

Grota, L. J. (1973). Effects of litter size, age of young, and parity on foster mother behaviour in *Rattus norvegicus. Animal Behaviour, 21,* 78–82. [13]

Grue, C. E. (1985). Pesticides and the decline of Guam's native birds. *Nature, 316,* 301. [5]

Gubernick, D. J., & Alberts, J. R. (1983). Maternal licking of young: Resource exchange and proximate controls. *Physiology and Behavior, 31,* 593–601. [12]

Guilford, T., & Dawkins, M. (1987). Search images not proven: A reappraisal of recent evidence. *Animal Behaviour, 35,* 1838–1845. [5]

Gurney, M., & Konishi, M. (1980). Hormone-induced sexual differentiation of brain and behavior in zebra finches. *Science, 208,* 1380–1383. [12]

Gustavson, C. R., Garcia, J., Hankins, W. J., & Rusiniak, K. I. (1974). Coyote predation: Control by aversive conditioning. *Science, 184,* 581–583. [2]

Gwinner, E. (1966). Periodicity of a circadian rhythm in birds by species-specific song cycles (Aves, Fringillidae: *Carduelis spinus, Serinus serinus*). *Experimentia, 22,* 765–766. [11]

Gwinner, E. (1978). Effects of pinealectomy on circadian locomotor activity rhythms in the European starling. *Journal of Comparative Physiology, 126,* 123–129. [11]

Hailman, J. P. (1967). The ontogeny of an instinct. *Behaviour* (Suppl. No. 15). [2]

Hailman, J. P. (1982). Evolution and behavior: an iconoclastic view. In H. C. Plotkin (Ed.), *Learning, development and culture* (pp. 205–254). Chichester: Wiley & Sons. [7]

Hainsworth, F. R., & Wolf, L. L. (1976). Nectar characteristics and food selection by hummingbirds. *Oecologia, 25,* 101–113. [1]

Hall, D. (1983). *String too short to be saved.* Boston: Nonpareil Press. [14]

Hall, G. S. (1885). The new psychology. *Andover Review, 3,* 120–135, 239–248. [E]

Hall, K. R. L. (1965). Behaviour and ecology of the wild patas monkey, *Erythrocebus patas,* in Uganda. *Journal of Zoology, 148,* 15–87. [10]

Hall, K. R. L., & DeVore, I. (1965). Baboon social behavior. In I. DeVore (Ed.), *Primate behavior: Field studies of monkeys and apes* (pp. 53–110). New York: Holt, Rinehart & Winston. [10]

Halliday, T. R. (1978). Sexual selection and mate choice. In J. R. Krebs & N. B. Davies (Eds.), *Behavioural ecology: An evolutionary approach* (pp. 180–213). Oxford: Blackwell Scientific Publications. [9]

Halliday, T. R., & Houston, A. (1978). The newt as an honest salesman. *Animal Behaviour, 26,* 1273–1281. [6]

Halpern, M., & Kubie, J. L. (1980). Chemical access to the vomeronasal organs of garter snakes. *Physiology and Behavior, 24,* 367–371. [5]

Halpin, Z. T. (1986). Individual odors among mammals: Origins and functions. *Advances in the Study of Behavior, 16,* 39–70. [17]

Hamilton, W. D. (1964). The genetical evolution of social behaviour: 1 and 2. *Journal of Theoretical Biology, 7,* 1–52. [6, 13]

Hammer, R. P., Hori, K. M., Cholvanich, P., Blanchard, D. C., & Blanchard, R. J. (in press). Opiate, serotonin and benzodiazepine receptor systems in rat brain defense circuits. In P. F. Brain, S. Parmigiani, R. J. Blanchard, & M. Mainardi (Eds.), *Psychobiology of fear and defense*. London: Gordon and Breach Science Publishers. [18]

Hammond, K. R. (1954). Representative vs. systematic design in clinical psychology. *Psychological Bulletin, 51,* 140–159. [15]

Hammond, K. R., Hamm, R. M., & Grassia, J. (1986). Generalizing over conditions by combining the multitrait–multimethod matrix and the representative design of experiments. *Psychological Bulletin, 100,* 257–269. [15]

Hanken, J., & Sherman, P. W. (1981). Multiple paternity in Belding's ground squirrel litters. *Science, 212,* 351–353. [8]

Hannes, R. P., Franck, D., & Liemann, F. (1984). Effects of rank-order fights on whole-body and blood-concentration of androgens and corticosteroids in the male swordtail (*Xiphophorus helleri*). *Zeitschrift für Tierpsychologie, 65,* 53–65. [9]

Harestad, A. S., & Bunnell, F. L. (1979). Home range and body weight—a reevaluation. *Ecology, 60,* 389–402. [4]

Harlow, H. F. (1965). Sexual behavior in rhesus monkeys. In F. A. Beach (Ed.), *Sex and behavior* (pp. 234–265). New York: Wiley. [12]

Harlow, H. F., Harlow, M. K., Dodsworth, R. O., & Arling, G. A. (1965). Maternal behavior of rhesus monkeys deprived of mothering and peer associations in infancy. *Proceedings of the American Philosophical Society, 110,* 58–66. [10]

Harris, M. A., & Murie, J. O. (1982). Responses to oral gland scents from different males in Columbian ground squirrels. *Animal Behaviour, 30,* 140–148. [8]

Hart, B. L. (1977). Neonatal dihydrotestosterone and estrogen stimulation: Effects on sexual behavior of male rats. *Hormones and Behavior, 8,* 192–201. [12]

Hart, B. L. (1983). Role of testosterone secretion and penile reflexes in sexual behavior and sperm competition in male rats: A theoretical contribution. *Physiology and Behavior, 31,* 823–827. [9]

Hart, B. L., & Melese-D'Hospital, P. Y. (1983). Penile mechanisms and the role of the striated penile muscles in penile reflexes. *Physiology and Behavior, 31,* 807–813. [12]

Hartung, T. G., & Dewsbury, D. A. (1978). A comparative analysis of copulatory plugs in muroid rodents and their relationship to copulatory behavior. *Journal of Mammalogy, 59,* 717–723. [6]

Hartung, T. G., & Dewsbury, D. A. (1979). Parental behavior in six species of muroid rodents. *Behavioral and Neural Biology, 26,* 466–478. [6]

Harvey, P. H., & Clutton-Brock, T. H. (1981). Primate home-range size and metabolic needs. *Behavioral Ecology and Sociobiology, 8,* 151–155. [4]

Harvey, P. H., & Clutton-Brock, T. H. (1983). The survival of the theory. *New Scientist, 5,* 313–315. [4]

Harvey, P. H., Clutton-Brock, T. H., & Mace, G. M. (1980). Brain size and ecology in small mammals and primates. *Proceedings of the National Academy of Sciences, 77,* 4387–4389. [4]

Harvey, P. H., & Harcourt, A. H. (1984). Sperm competition, testes size, and breeding systems in primates. In R. L. Smith (Ed.), *Sperm competition and the evolution of animal mating systems* (pp. 589–600). Orlando, FL: Academic Press. [8]

Hauser, H., & Gandelman, R. (1983). Contiguity to males in utero affects avoidance responding in adult female mice. *Science, 220,* 437–438. [13]

Heaney, L. R. (1984). Climatic influences on life-history tactics and behavior of North American tree squirrels. In J. O. Murie & G. R. Michener (Eds.), *The biology of ground-dwelling squirrels* (pp. 43–78). Lincoln: University of Nebraska Press. [8]

Hearst, E., & Franklin, S. R. (1977). Positive and negative relations between a signal and food: Approach–withdrawal behavior to the signal. *Journal of Experimental Psychology: Animal Behavior Processes, 3,* 37–52. [9]

Hearst, E., & Jenkins, H. M. (1974). *Sign tracking: The stimulus–reinforcer relation and directed action*. Austin, TX: Psychonomic Society. [9]

Hebb, D. O. (1951). The role of neurological ideas in psychology. *Journal of Personality, 20,* 39–55. [11]

Hebb, D. O. (1958). Alice in wonderland or psychology among the biological sciences. In H. F. Harlow & C. N. Woolsey (Eds.), *Biological and biochemical bases of behavior* (pp. 451–467). Madison: University of Wisconsin Press. [15]

Heglund, N. C., Cavagna, G. A., & Taylor, C. R. (1982). Energetics and mechanics of terrestrial locomotion. *Journal of Experimental Biology, 79,* 41–56. [4]

Heglund, N. C., Fedak, M. A., Taylor, C. R., & Cavagna, G. A. (1982). Energetics and mechanics of terrestrial locomotion. 4. Total mechanical energy changes as a function of speed and body size in birds and mammals. *Journal of Experimental Biology, 97,* 57–66. [4]

Hepper, P. G. (1986). Kin recognition: Functions and mechanisms. *Biological Reviews, 61,* 63–93. [6, 13]

Hewlett, B. S. (1987). Intimate fathers: Patterns of paternal holding among Aka pygmies. In M. E. Lamb (Ed.), *The father's role: Cross-cultural perspectives* (pp. 295–330). Hillsdale, NJ: Lawrence Erlbaum Associates. [10]

Heymann, E. W. (1987). A field observation of predation on a mustached tamarin (*Saguinus mystax*) by an anaconda. *International Journal of Primatology, 8,* 193–195. [10]

Hill, A. V. (1950). Science progress: The dimensions of animals and their muscular dynamics. *Science Progress, 38,* 209–230. [4]

Hill, E., & Christenson, T. (1988). Male residency on juvenile female *Nephila clavipes* (Araneae, Araneidae) webs. *Journal of Arachnology, 16,* 257–259. [7]

Hinde, R. A. (1966). *Animal behaviour.* New York: McGraw-Hill. [17]

Hinde, R. A., & Stevenson-Hinde, J. (Eds.). (1973). *Constraints on learning; Limitations and predispositions.* New York: Academic Press. [2, 9]

Hoage, R. J. (1977). Parental care in *Leontopithecus rosalia rosalia*: Sex and age differences in carrying behavior and the role of prior experience. In D. G. Kleiman (Ed.), *The biology and conservation of the Callitrichidae* (pp. 293–305). Washington, DC: Smithsonian Institution Press. [10]

Hodos, W., & Campbell, C. B. G. (1969). *Scala naturae*: Why there is no theory in comparative psychology. *Psychological Review, 76,* 337–350. [1]

Hofer, M. A. (1976). Olfactory denervation: Its biological and behavioral effects in infant rats. *Journal of Comparative and Physiological Psychology, 90,* 829–838. [13]

Hofer, M. A., & Shair, H. N. (1987). Isolation distress in two-week-old rats: Influence of home cage, social companions, and prior experience with littermates. *Developmental Psychobiology, 20,* 465–476. [13]

Hogan, J. A. (1988). Cause and function in the development of behavior systems. In E. M. Blass (Ed.), *Handbook of behavior and neurobiology* (Vol 9, pp. 63–106). New York: Plenum Press. [2]

Holley, A. J. F. (1984). Adoption, parent–chick recognition and maladaptation in the herring gull. *Zeitschrift für Tierpsychologie, 64,* 9–14. [16]

Holling, C. S. (1964). The analysis of complex population processes. *Canadian Entomologist, 96,* 335–347. [5]

Holling, C. S. (1965). The functional responses of predators to prey density and its role in mimicry and population regulation. *Memoirs of the Entomological Society of Canada, 45,* 1–60. [5]

Holling, C. S. (1966). The functional response of invertebrate predators to prey density. *Memoirs of the Entomological Society of Canada, 48,* 1–86. [5]

Hollis, K. L. (1982). Pavlovian conditioning of signal-centered action patterns and autonomic behavior: A biological analysis of function. *Advances in the Study of Behavior, 12,* 1–64. [2, 9]

Hollis, K. L. (1984a). The biological function of Pavlovian conditioning: The best defense is a good offense. *Journal of Experimental Psychology: Animal Behavior Processes, 10,* 413–425. [9]

Hollis, K. L. (1984b). Cause and function of animal learning processes. In P. Marler & H. S. Terrace (Eds.), *The biology of learning* (pp. 357–371). Berlin: Springer-Verlag. [9]

Hollis, K. L., Cadieux, E. L., & Colbert, M. M. (1989). The biological function of Pavlovian conditioning: A mechanism for mating success in the blue gourami (*Trichogaster trichopterus*). *Journal of Comparative Psychology, 103,* 115–121. [9]

Hollis, K. L., Martin, K. A., Cadieux, E. L., & Colbert, M. M. (1984). The biological function of Pavlovian conditioning: Learned inhibition of aggressive behavior in territorial fish. *Learning and Motivation, 15,* 459–478. [9]

Hollis, K. L., & Roberts, K. (1989). [Pavlovian conditional courtship responses and intersexual selection.] Unpublished raw data. [9]

Holmes, W. G. (1984). The ecological basis of monogamy in Alaskan hoary marmots. In J. O. Murie & G. R. Michener (Eds.), *The biology of ground-dwelling squirrels* (pp. 250–274). Lincoln: University of Nebraska Press. [8]

Hoogland, J. L. (1981). Nepotism and cooperative breeding in the black-tailed prairie dog (Sciuridae: *Cynomys ludovicianus*). In R. D. Alexander & D. W. Tinkle (Eds.), *Natural selection and social behavior* (pp. 283–310). New York: Chiron Press. [8]

Hoogland, J. L., & Foltz, D. W. (1982). Variance in male and female reproductive success in a harem-polygynous mammal, the black-tailed prairie dog (Sciuridae: *Cynomys ludovicianus*). *Behavioral Ecology and Sociobiology, 11,* 155–163. [8]

Hoogland, J. L., & Sherman, P. W. (1976). Advantages and disadvantages of bank swallow coloniality. *Ecological Monographs, 32,* 33–58. [16]

Hopp, S. L., & Timberlake, W. (1983). Odor cue determinants of urine marking in male rats (*Rattus norvegicus*). *Behavioral and Neural Biology, 37,* 162–172. [2]

Horwich, R. H. (1972). The ontogeny of social behavior in the gray squirrel (*Sciurus carolinensis*). *Advances in Ethology, 8,* 1–103. [8]

Houston, A., Kacelnik, A., & McNamara, J. (1982). Some learning rules for acquiring information. In D. J. McFarland (Ed.), *Functional ontogeny* (pp. 140–191). London: Plenum. [1]

Howard, W. E. (1949). Dispersal, amount of inbreeding, and longevity in a local population of prairie deermice on the George Reserve, southern Michigan. *Contributions from the Laboratory of Vertebrate Biology, 43,* 1–52. [6]

Hrdy, S. B. (1986, December). *Comparative primatology and the absence of estrus in* Homo sapiens. Paper presented to the American Anthropological Association, Philadelpha, PA. [10]

Hull, C. L. (1943). *Principles of behavior.* New York: Appleton-Century-Crofts. [2]

Hutchinson, G. E. (1959). Homage to Saint Rosalia or why there are so many kinds of animals. *American Naturalist, 93,* 145–159. [1]

Hutchinson, R. R. (1983). The pain–aggression relationship and its expression in naturalistic settings. *Aggressive Behavior, 9,* 229–243. [18]

Huxley, S. J. (1972). *Problems of relative growth.* New York: Dover Publications, Inc. (Original work published 1932) [4]

Hwang, C. P. (1987). The changing role of Swedish fathers. In M. E. Lamb (Ed.), *The father's role: Cross-cultural perspectives* (pp. 115–138). Hillsdale, NJ: Lawrence Erlbaum Associates. [10]

Ingram, J. C. (1977). Interactions between parents and infants and the development of independence in the common marmoset (*Callithrix jacchus*). *Animal Behaviour, 25,* 811–827. [10]

Innis, N. K., Simmelhag-Grant, V. L., & Staddon, J. E. R. (1983). Behavior induced by periodic food delivery: The effects of interfood interval. *Journal of the Experimental Analysis of Behavior, 39,* 309–322. [2]

Inouye, S. T., & Kawamura, H. (1979). Persistence of circadian rhythmicity in a mammalian hypothalmic "island" containing the suprachiasmatic nucleus. *Neurobiology, 76,* 5962–5966. [11]

Iwasa, Y., Higashi, M., & Yamamura, N. (1981). Prey distribution as a factor determining the choice of optimal foraging strategy. *American Naturalist, 117,* 710–723. [1]

Jackson, J. F. (1988). Crevice occupation by musk turtles: Taxonomic distribution and crevice attributes. *Animal Behaviour, 36,* 793–801. [5]

Jackson, R. R. (1979). Comparative studies of *Dictyna* and *Mallos* (Araneae, Dictynidae). 2. The relationship between courtship, mating, aggression and cannibalism in species with differing types of social organization. *Revue Arachnologique, 2,* 103–132. [7]

Jackson, R. R. (1980). The mating strategy of *Phidippus johnsoni* (Araneae, Salticidae): 2. Sperm competition and the function of copulation. *Journal of Arachnology, 8,* 217–240. [7]

Jacobson, M. (1970). *Developmental neurobiology.* New York: Holt, Rinehart & Winston. [12]

Jameson, E. W. (1953). Reproduction of deer mice (*Peromyscus maniculatus* and *P. boylei*) in the Sierra Nevada, California. *Journal of Mammalogy, 34,* 44–58. [6]

Jarman, P. (1983). Mating system and sexual dimorphism in large, terrestrial, mammalian herbivores. *Biological Review, 58,* 485–520. [4]

Jenkins, H. M., Barrera, F. J., Ireland, C., & Woodside, B. (1978). Signal-centered action patterns of dogs in appetitive classical conditioning. *Learning and Motivation, 9,* 272–296. [2]

Jenkins, J. M. (1983). *The native forest birds of Guam* (Ornithological Monograph No. 31). Washington, DC: American Ornithologists' Union. [5]

Jenkins, P. F. (1978). Cultural transmission of song patterns and dialect development in a free-living bird population. *Animal Behaviour, 25*, 50–78. [15]

Jenkins, S. H. (1981). Common patterns in home range–body size relationships of birds and mammals. *American Naturalist, 118*, 126–128. [4]

Jerison, H. J. (1973). *Evolution of the brain and intelligence*. New York: Academic Press. [4]

Johnson, K. (1981). Social organization in a colony of rock squirrels (*Spermophilus variegatus*, Sciuridae). *Southwestern Naturalist, 26*, 237–242. [8]

Johnson, R. P. (1973). Scent marking in mammals. *Animal Behaviour, 21*, 521–535. [17]

Johnston, R. E. (1970). *Scent marking, olfactory communication and social behavior in the golden hamster*, Mesocricetus auratus. (Doctoral dissertation, Rockefeller University, 1970). *Dissertation Abstracts International, 1972, 32*. (University Microfilms No. 72-12-666). [17]

Johnston, R. E. (1974). Sexual attraction function of golden hamster vaginal secretion. *Behavioral Biology, 12*, 111–117. [17]

Johnston, R. E. (1975a). Scent marking by male hamsters: 1. Effects of odors and social encounters. *Zeitschrift für Tierpsychologie, 37*, 75–98. [17]

Johnston, R. E. (1975b). Scent marking by male hamsters: 2. The role of flank gland odor in the causation of marking. *Zeitschrift für Tierpsychologie, 37*, 138–144. [17]

Johnston, R. E. (1975c). Scent marking by male hamsters: 3. Behavior in a semi-natural environment. *Zeitschrift für Tierpsychologie, 37*, 213–221. [17]

Johnston, R. E. (1975d). Sexual excitation function of hamster vaginal secretion. *Animal Learning & Behavior, 3*, 161–166. [17]

Johnston, R. E. (1977a). The causation of two scent marking behaviors in female golden hamsters. *Animal Behaviour, 25*, 317–327. [17]

Johnston, R. E. (1977b). Sex pheromones in golden hamsters. In D. Müller-Schwarze and M. M. Mozell (Eds.), *Chemical signals in vertebrates* (Vol. 1, pp. 225–249). New York: Plenum Press. [17]

Johnston, R. E. (1979). Olfactory preferences, scent marking and "proceptivity" in female hamsters. *Hormones and Behavior, 13*, 21–39. [17]

Johnston, R. E. (1980). Responses of male hamsters to the odors of females in different reproductive states. *Journal of Comparative and Physiological Psychology, 94*, 894–904. [17]

Johnston, R. E. (1981a). Attraction to odors in hamsters: An evaluation of methods. *Journal of Comparative and Physiological Psychology, 95*, 951–960. [17]

Johnston, R. E. (1981b). Testosterone dependence of scent marking by male hamsters (*Mesocricetus auratus*). *Behavioral and Neural Biology, 31*, 96–99. [17]

Johnston, R. E. (1983). Mechanisms of individual discrimination in hamsters. In D. Müller-Schwarze and R. M. Silverstein (Eds.), Chemical signals in vertebrates (Vol. 3, pp. 245–258). New York: Plenum Press. [17]

Johnston, R. E. (1985a). Communication. In H. I. Siegel (Ed.), *The hamster: Reproduction and behavior* (pp. 121–154). New York: Plenum Press. [17]

Johnston, R. E. (1985b). Olfactory and vomeronasal mechanisms of communication. In D. W. Pfaff (Ed.), *Taste, olfaction and the central nervous system* (pp. 322–346). New York: Rockefeller University Press. [17]

Johnston, R. E. (1986). Effects of female odors on the sexual behavior of male hamsters. *Behavioral and Neural Biology, 46*, 168–188. [17]

Johnston, R. E., & Brenner, D. (1982). Species specificity of scent marking in hamsters. *Behavioral and Neural Biology, 35*, 46–55. [17]

Johnston, R. E., & Coplin, B. (1979). Development of responses to vaginal secretion and other substances in golden hamsters. *Behavioral & Neural Biology, 25*, 473–489. [17]

Johnston, R. E., & Kwan, M. (1984). Effects of vaginal scent marking on ultrasonic calling, exploration and movement patterns of male hamsters. *Behavioral and Neural Biology, 42*, 158–168. [17]

Johnston, R. E., Pfeiffer, C., & Mueller, U. (1987). Roles of vomeronasal and olfactory systems in mediating hormonal responses and communicative behaviors in golden hamsters. *Chemical Senses, 12*, 668–669. [17]

Johnston, R. E., & Rasmussen, K. (1984). Individual recognition of female hamsters by males: Role of chemical cues and of the olfactory and vomeronasal systems. *Physiology and Behavior, 33,* 95–104. [17]

Johnston, R. E., & Schmidt, T. (1979). Responses of hamsters to scent marks of different ages. *Behavioral and Neural Biology, 26,* 64–75. [17]

Johnston, T. D. (1981). Contrasting approaches to a theory of learning. *Behavioral & Brain Sciences, 4,* 125–139. [2]

Johnston, T. D. (1985). Introduction: Conceptual issues in the ecological study of learning. In T. D. Johnston & A. T. Pietrewicz (Eds.), *Issues in the ecological study of learning* (pp. 1–24). Hillsdale, NJ: Lawrence Erlbaum Associates. [2]

Kahn, R. M. (1989). Photoperiodic control of incubation in ring doves. Doctoral dissertation, Columbia University, New York. [11]

Kahn, R. M., Fifer, W., & Silver, R. (1984). Automatic monitoring of temperature and/or location: A computer-controlled radiotelemetry system. *Behavior Research Methods, Instruments, and Computers, 16,* 533–537. [11]

Kamil, A. C. (1978). Systematic foraging by a nectar-feeding bird, the Amakihi (*Loxops virens*). *Journal of Comparative and Physiological Psychology, 92,* 388–396. [1]

Kamil, A. C. (1988a). Experimental design in ornithology. In R. F. Johnston (Ed.), *Current Ornithology* (Vol. 5, pp. 313–346). New York: Plenum. [1]

Kamil, A. C. (1988b). A synthetic approach to the study of animal intelligence. In D. W. Leger (Ed.), *Comparative perspectives in modern psychology*. (Nebraska Symposium on Motivation, Vol. 35, pp. 257–308). Lincoln: University of Nebraska Press. [1]

Kamil, A. C., & Balda, R. (1985). Cache recovery and spatial memory in Clark's nutcrackers (*Nucifraga columbiana*). *Journal of Experimental Psychology: Animal Behavior Processes, 11,* 95–111. [1, 2]

Kamil, A. C., Lindstrom, F., & Peters, J. (1985). Foraging for cryptic prey by blue jays. 1. The effects of travel time. *Animal Behaviour, 33,* 1068–1079. [1]

Kamil, A. C., & Yoerg, S. I. (1982). Learning and foraging behavior. In P. P. G. Bateson & P. H. Klopfer (Eds.), *Perspectives in ethology* (Vol. 5). New York: Plenum Press. [2]

Kamil, A. C., & Yoerg, S. I. (1985). Effects of prey depletion on patch choice by foraging blue jays (*Cyanocitta cristata*). *Animal Behaviour, 33,* 1089–1095. [1]

Kamil, A. C., Yoerg, S. I., & Clements, K. C. (1988). Rules to leave by: Patch departure in foraging blue jays. *Animal Behaviour, 36,* 843–853. [1]

Kardong, K. V. (1982). Comparative study of changes in prey capture behavior of the cottonmouth (*Agkistrodon piscivorus*) and Egyptian cobra (*Naje naje*). *Copeia,* 337–343. [5]

Kardong, K. V. (1986). Predatory strike behavior of the rattlesnake, *Crotalus viridis oreganus*. *Journal of Comparative Psychology, 100,* 304–314. [5]

Keeton, W. T. (1981). The ontogeny of bird orientation. In G. W. Barlow, L. Petrinovich, & M. Main (Eds.), *Behavioral development* (pp. 509–517). New York: Cambridge University Press. [2]

Kemble, E. D., Thornton, A. E., & Schultz, L. A. (1987). Some fear-potentiating effects of fluprazine hydrochloride in mice. *Aggressive Behavior, 13,* 269–280. [18]

Kenagy, G. J. (1987). Energy allocation for reproduction in the golden-mantled ground squirrel. *Symposia of the Zoological Society of London, 57,* 259–273. [8]

Kenagy, G. J., & Trombulak, S. C. (1986). Size and function of mammalian testes in relation to body size. *Journal of Mammalogy, 67,* 1–22. [8]

Kendrick, K. M., & Dixson, A. F. (1983). The effect of the ovarian cycle on the sexual behaviour of the common marmoset (*Callithrix jacchus*). *Physiology and Behavior, 30,* 735–740. [10]

Kendrick, K. M., & Dixson, A. F. (1985). Effects of oestradiol 17B, progesterone and testosterone upon proceptivity and receptivity in ovariectomized common marmosets (*Callithrix jacchus*). *Physiology and Behavior, 34,* 123–128. [10]

Kenney, A. M., Evans, R. L., & Dewsbury, D. A. (1977). Postimplantation pregnancy disruption in *Microtus ochrogaster, M. pennsylvanicus,* and *Peromyscus maniculatus*. *Journal of Reproduction and Fertility, 49,* 365–367. [6]

Killeen, P. R., Smith, J. P., & Hanson, S. J. (1981). Central place foraging in *Rattus norvegicus*. *Animal Behaviour, 29,* 64–70. [2]

King, A. P., & West, M. J. (1977). Species identification in the North American cowbird: Appropriate responses to abnormal song. *Science, 195,* 1002–1004. [14]

King, A. P., & West, M. J. (1983a). Dissecting cowbird song potency: Assessing a song's geographic identity and relative appeal. *Zeitschrift für Tierpsychologie, 63,* 37–50. [14]

King, A. P., & West, M. J. (1983b). Epigenesis of cowbird song: A joint endeavor of males and females. *Nature, 305,* 704–706. [14]

King, A. P., & West, M. J. (1983c). Female perception of cowbird song: A closed developmental program. *Developmental Psychobiology, 16,* 335–342. [14]

King, A. P., & West, M. J. (1984). Social metrics of vocal learning. *Learning & Motivation, 15,* 441–458. [2, 14]

King, A. P., & West, M. J. (1987). Different outcomes of synergy between song perception and song production in the same subspecies (*Molothrus ater ater*). *Developmental Psychobiology, 20,* 177–187. [14]

King, A. P., & West, M. J. (1989). The presence of females affect vocal imitation and improvisation in male cowbirds (*Molothrus ater ater*). *Journal of Comparative Psychology, 103,* 39–44. [14]

King, A. P., West, M. J., & Eastzer, D. H. (1980). Song structure and song development as potential contributors to reproductive isolation in cowbirds (*Molothrus ater*). *Journal of Comparative and Physiological Psychology, 94,* 1028–1039. [14]

King, A. P., West, M. J., & Eastzer, D. H. (1986). Female cowbird song perception: Evidence for different developmental systems within the same subspecies. *Zeitschrift für Tierpsychologie, 72,* 89–98. [14]

King, J. A. (1963). Maternal behavior in *Peromyscus.* In H. L. Rheingold (Ed.), *Maternal behavior in mammals* (pp. 58–93). New York: Wiley. [E]

Kleiman, D. G. (1977). Monogamy in mammals. *Quarterly Review of Biology, 52,* 39–69. [10]

Kleiman, D. G., & Malcolm, J. R. (1981). The evolution of male parental investment in mammals. In D. J. Gubernick and P. H. Klopfer (Eds.), *Parental care in mammals* (pp. 347–387). New York: Plenum. [10, 13]

Knudsen, B., & Evans, R. M. (1986). Parent–young recognition in herring gulls. *Animal Behaviour, 34,* 77–80. [16]

Koford, R. R. (1982). Mating system of a territorial tree squirrel (*Tamiasciurus douglasii*) in California. *Journal of Mammalogy, 63,* 274–283. [8]

Kon, S. K. (1931). 58. The self-selection of food constituents by the rat. *Biochemical Journal, 25,* 473–481. [3]

Konorski, J. (1948). *Conditioned reflexes and neuron organization.* Cambridge: Cambridge University Press. [9]

Kraut, R. E., & Johnston, R. E. (1979). Social and emotional messages of smiling: An ethological approach. *Journal of Personality and Social Psychology, 37,* 1539–1553. [17]

Krebs, J. R., & Davies, N. B. (1987). *An introduction to behavioural ecology* (2nd ed.). Oxford: Blackwell Scientific Publications. [9]

Krebs, J. R., Kacelnik, A., & Taylor, P. (1978). Test of optimal sampling by foraging great tits. *Nature, 275,* 27–31. [1]

Krebs, J. R., & Kroodsma, D. E. (1980). Repertoires and geographic variation in bird song. *Advances in the Study of Behavior, 11,* 143–177. [14]

Krebs, J. R., Ryan, J. C., & Charnov, E. L. (1974). Hunting by expectation or optimal foraging? A study of patch use by chickadees. *Animal Behaviour, 22,* 953–964. [1]

Krieger, M. S., & Barfield, R. J. (1976). Masculine sexual behavior: Pacing and ejaculatory patterns in female rats induced by electric shock. *Physiology and Behavior, 16,* 671–675. [12]

Kroodsma, D. E. (1974). Song learning, dialects and dispersal in the Bewick's wren. *Auk, 90,* 342–352. [15]

Kroodsma, D. E. (1982). Learning and the ontogeny of sound signals in birds. In D. E. Kroodsma & E. H. Miller (Eds.), *Acoustic communication in birds: Vol. 2. Song learning and its consequences* (pp. 1–24). New York: Academic Press. [14]

Kroodsma, D. E. (1983). The ecology of avian vocal learning. *BioScience, 33,* 165–171. [14]

Kroodsma, D. E. (1989). Suggested experimental designs for song playbacks. *Animal Behaviour, 37,* 600–609. [15]

Kruse, M. J., Overmier, J. B., Konz, W. A., & Rokke, E. (1983). Pavlovian conditioned stimulus effects upon instrumental choice behavior are reinforcer specific. *Learning and Motivation, 14,* 165–181. [9]

Kummer, H. (1967). Tripartite relations in Hamadryas baboons. In S. A. Altmann (Ed.), *Social communication among primates* (pp. 63–71). Chicago: University of Chicago Press. [10]

Kummer, H. (1968). *Social organization of hamadryas baboons.* Chicago: University of Chicago Press. [10]

Kuo, Z. Y. (1967). *The dynamics of behavior development.* New York: Random House. [2]

Kwan, M., & Johnston, R. E. (1980). The role of vaginal secretion in hamster sexual behavior: males' responses to normal and vaginectomized females and their odors. *Journal of Comparative and Physiological Psychology, 94,* 905–913. [17]

Lakoff, G., & Johnson, M. (1980) *Metaphors we live by.* Chicago: University of Chicago Press. [12]

Lamb, M. E. (1987). *The father's role: Cross-cultural perspectives.* Hillsdale, NJ: Lawrence Erlbaum Associates. [10]

Lancaster, J. B. (1985). Evolutionary perspectives on sex differences in the higher primates. In A. S. Rossi (Ed.), *Gender and the life course* (pp. 3–27). New York: Aldine. [10]

Langley, W. M. (1981). Failure of food aversion conditioning to suppress predatory attack of the grasshopper mouse, *Onychomys leucogaster. Behavioral and Neural Biology, 33,* 317–333. [2]

Lanier, D. L., Estep, D. Q., & Dewsbury, D. A. (1979). Role of prolonged copulatory behavior in facilitating reproductive success in a competitive mating situation in laboratory rats. *Journal of Comparative and Physiological Psychology, 93,* 781–792. [8]

Larsson, K. (1978). Experiential factors in the development of sexual behaviour. In J. B. Hutchison (Ed.), *Biological determinants of sexual behavior* (pp. 55–86). New York: Wiley. [12]

Leamy, L. (1981). The effect of litter size on fertility in *Peromyscus leucopus. Journal of Mammalogy, 62,* 692–697. [13]

Leavitt, W. W., & Blaha, G. C. (1970). Circulating progesterone levels in the golden hamster during the estrous cycle, pregnancy, and lactation. *Biology of Reproduction, 3,* 353–361. [17]

Leger, D. W. (Ed.) (1988). *Comparative perspectives in modern psychology.* (Nebraska Symposium on Motivation, Vol. 35.) Lincoln: University of Nebraska Press. [I]

Leger, D. W., Berney-Key, S. D., & Sherman, P. W. (1984). Vocalizations of Belding's ground squirrels (*Spermophilus beldingi*). *Animal Behaviour, 32,* 753–764. [8]

Lehman, M. N., Silver, R., Gladstone, W. R., Kahn, R. M., Gibson, M., & Bittman, E. L. (1987). Circadian rhythmicity restored by neural transplant. Immunocytochemical characterization of the graft and its integration with the host brain. *Journal of the Neurosciences, 7,* 1626–1638. [11]

Lehrman, D. S. (1970). Semantic and conceptual issues in the nature–nurture controversy. In L. R. Aronson, E. Tobach, D. S. Lehrman, & J. S. Rosenblatt, (Eds.), *Development and evolution of behavior* (pp. 53–74). San Francisco: W. H. Freeman [1]

Leibowitz, L. (1978). *Males, females and families.* North Scituate, MA: Duxbury Press. [10]

Leigh, H., & Hofer, M. (1973). Behavioral and physiologic effects of littermate removal on the remaining single pup and mother during the pre-weaning period in rats. *Psychosomatic Medicine, 35,* 497–508. [13]

Leonard, C. M. (1972). Effects of neonatal (day 10) olfactory bulb lesions on social behavior of female golden hamsters (*Mesocricetus auratus*). *Journal of Comparative and Physiological Psychology, 80,* 208–215. [17]

Leonard, C. M. (1975). Developmental changes in olfactory bulb projections revealed by degeneration argyrophilia. *Journal of Comparative Neurology, 162,* 467–486. [17]

Leutenegger, W. (1973). Maternal–fetal weight relationships in primates. *Folia Primatologica, 20,* 280–294. [10]

Levi, H. W. (1980). The orb-weaver genus *Mecynogea,* the subfamily Metinae and the genera *Pachygnatha, Glenognatha* and *Azilia* of the subfamily Tetragnathinae north of Mexico (Araneae: Araneidae). *Bulletin of the Museum of Comparative Zoology, 149,* 1–75. [7]

Lewis, C. (1986). *Becoming a father.* Milton Keynes: Open University Press. [10]

Lewontin, R. C. (1978). Adaptation. *Scientific American, 239*(3), 212–230. [3]

Leyhausen, P. (1979). *Cat behavior*. New York: Garland Press. [18]

Lima, S. (1983). Downy woodpecker foraging behavior: Foraging by expectation and energy intake rate. *Oecologia, 58*, 232–237. [1]

Linn, C. E., Campbell, M. G., & Roelofs, W. L. (1987). Pheromone components and active spaces: What do moths smell and where do they smell it? *Science, 237*, 650–652. [17]

Lisk, R. D., Ciaccio, L. A., & Catanzaro, C. (1983). Mating behavior of the golden hamster under seminatural conditions. *Animal Behaviour, 31*, 659–666. [17]

Lloyd, J. (1979). Sexual selection in luminescent beetles. In M. S. Blum & N. A. Blum (Eds.), *Sexual selection and reproductive competition in insects* (pp. 293–342). New York: Academic Press. [8]

Lockard, R. B. (1971). Reflections on the fall of comparative psychology: Is there a message for us all? *American Psychologist, 26*, 168–179. [2]

Lodder, J., & Zeilmaker, G. H. (1976). Effects of pelvic nerve and pudendal nerve transection on mating behavior in the male rat. *Physiology and Behavior, 16*, 745–751. [12]

Logue, A. W. (1979). Taste aversion and the generality of the laws of learning. *Psychological Bulletin, 86*, 276–296. [2]

Loher, W., & Rence, B. (1978). The mating behavior of *Teleogryllus commodus* (Walker) and its central and peripheral control. *Zeitschrift für Tierpsychologie, 46*, 225–259. [9]

Lopez, A. (1987). Glandular aspects of sexual biology. In W. Nentwig (Ed.), *Ecophysiology of spiders* (pp. 121–132). Berlin: Springer-Verlag. [7]

Lore, R. (1987). Maternal aggression and infanticide in rats. *Aggressive Behavior, 13*, 287. [18]

Lore, R., & Luciano, D. (1977). Attack stress induces gastrointestinal pathology in domesticated rats. *Physiology and Behavior, 18*, 743–745. [18]

Lorenz, K. Z. (1950). The comparative method in studying innate behaviour patterns. In *Symposia of the Society for Experimental Biology* (No. 4): *Physiological mechanisms in animal behaviour* (pp. 221–268). New York: Academic Press. [2, E]

Lorenz, K. Z. (1966). *On Aggression*. London: Methuen. [18]

Lorenz, K. Z. (1969). Innate bases of learning. In Pribram, K. H. (Ed.), *On the biology of learning* (pp. 13–93). New York: Harcourt, Brace & World. [2]

Lorenz, K. Z. (1970). The establishment of instinct concept. In K. Lorenz, *Studies in animal and human behavior* (Vol. 1, R. D. Martin, Trans.) Cambridge, MA: Harvard University Press. (Original work published 1937) [11]

Lorenz, K. Z. (1975). The fashionable fallacy of dispensing with description. In. R. I. Evans (Ed.), *Konrad Lorenz: The man and his ideas*. New York: Harcourt Brace Jovanovich. [5]

Lubbock, J. (1890). *Ants bees, and wasps*. New York: Appleton. [2]

Lucas, G. A., Timberlake, W., & Gawley, D. J. (1988). Adjunctive behavior of the rat under periodic food delivery in a 24-hr environment. *Animal Learning & Behavior, 16*, 19–30. [2]

Luciano, D., & Lore, R. (1975). Aggression and social experience in domesticated rats. *Journal of Comparative and Physiological Psychology, 88*, 917–923. [18]

McCarty, R., & Southwick, C. H. (1977). Cross-species fostering: Effects on the olfactory preference of *Onychomys torridus* and *Peromyscus leucopus*. *Behavioral Biology, 19*, 255–260. [13]

McConnell, P. B., & Snowdon, C. T. (1986). Vocal interactions between unfamiliar groups of captive cotton-top tamarins. *Behaviour, 97*, 273–296. [10]

McCracken, G. F. (1984). Communal nursing in Mexican free-tailed bat maternity colonies. *Science, 223*, 1090–1091. [16]

McCracken, G. F., & Gustin, M. F. (1987). Batmom's daily nightmare. *Natural History, 96*(10), 66–73. [16]

McDonald, D. L., & Forslund, L. G. (1978). The development of social preferences in the voles *Microtus montanus* and *Microtus canicaudus*: Effects of cross-fostering. *Behavioral Biology, 22*, 497–508. [13]

Mace, G. M., & Harvey, P. H. (1983). Energetic constraints on home-range size. *The American Naturalist, 121*, 120–132. [4]

McGregor, P. K., & Krebs, J. R. (1982). Song types in a population of great tits (*Parus major*). *Behaviour, 72*, 126–152. [15]

McGrew, W. C. (1988). Parental division of infant caretaking varies with family composition in cotton-top tamarins. *Animal Behaviour, 36*, 285–286. [10]

McGrew, W. C., & McLuckie, E. C. (1986). Philopatry and dispersion in the cotton-top tamarin, *Saguinus o. oedipus*: An attempted laboratory simulation. *International Journal of Primatology, 7*, 401–422. [10]

McGuire, M. R., & Getz, L. L. (1981). Incest taboo between sibling *Microtus ochrogaster*. *Journal of Mammalogy, 62*, 213–215. [13]

McKinney, F., Derrickson, S. R., & Mineau, P. (1983). Forced copulation in waterfowl. *Behaviour, 86*, 250–294. [12]

Mackintosh, N. J. (1983). *Conditioning and associative learning*. Oxford: Clarendon Press of Oxford University Press. [9]

McLean, I. G. (1982). The association of female kin in the Arctic ground squirrel *Spermophilus parryii*. *Behavioral Ecology and Sociobiology, 10*, 91–99. [8, 13]

McLean, I. G. (1983). Paternal behaviour and killing of young in Arctic ground squirrels. *Animal Behaviour, 31*, 32–44. [8]

McMahon, T. A., & Bonner, J. T. (1983). *On size and life*. New York: Scientific American Library. [4]

McNab, B. K. (1963). Bioenergetics and the determination of home range size. *American Naturalist, 97*, 133–140. [4]

McNamara, J. M. (1982). Optimal patch use in a stochastic environment. *Theoretical Population Biology, 21*, 269–288. [1]

Macrides, F., Bartke, A., Fernandez, F., & D'Angelo, W. (1974). Effects of exposure to vaginal odor and receptive females on plasma testosterone in the male hamster. *Neuroendocrinology, 15*, 355–364. [17]

Macrides, F., Johnson, P. A., & Schneider, S. P. (1977). Responses of the male golden hamster to vaginal secretion and dimethyl disulfide: Attraction versus sexual behavior. *Behavioral Biology, 20*, 377–386. [17]

Maier, N. R. F., & Schneirla, T. C. (1935). *Principles of animal psychology*. New York: McGraw-Hill. [2]

Manning, J. T. (1985). Choosy females and correlates of male age. *Journal of Theoretical Biology, 116*, 349–354. [4]

Marchlewska-Koj, A. (1983). Pregnancy blocking by pheromones. In J. G. Vandenbergh (Ed.), *Pheromones and reproduction in mammals* (pp. 151–174). New York: Academic Press. [6]

Marler, P. (1970). A comparative approach to vocal learning: song development in white-crowned sparrows. *Journal of Comparative and Physiological Psychology, 71*, 1–25. [15]

Marler, P. (1976). Sensory templates in species-specific behavior. In J. C. Fentress (Ed.), *Simpler networks and behavior* (pp. 314–329). Sunderland, MA: Sinauer Associates. [14]

Marler, P. (1987). Sensitive periods and the roles of specific and general sensory stimulation in birdsong learning. In J. F. Rauschecker & P. Marler (Eds.), *Imprinting and cortical plasticity* (pp. 99–135). New York: Wiley. [15]

Marler, P., & Hamilton, W. J. (1966). *Mechanisms of Animal Behavior*. New York: Wiley. [17]

Marler, P., & Peters, S. (1982). Subsong and plastic song: Their role in vocal learning process. In D. E. Kroodsma & E. H. Miller (Eds.), *Acoustic communication in birds: Vol. 2. Song learning and its consequences* (pp. 25–50). New York: Academic Press. [2]

Marler, P., & Tamura, M. (1964). Culturally transmitted patterns of vocal behavior in sparrows. *Science, 146*, 1483–1486. [3]

Martan, J., & Shepherd, B. A. (1976). The role of the copulatory plug in reproduction of the guinea pig. *Journal of Experimental Zoology, 196*, 79–84. [8]

Martin, R. D. (1974). Maternal behaviour and the effects of stress in tree shrews. *Nature, 251*, 309–311. [13]

Martin, R. F. (1980). Analysis of hybridization between the Hirundinid genera *Hirundo* and *Petrochelidon* in Texas. *Auk, 97*, 148–159. [16]

Mason, J. R., & Reidinger, R. F. (1982). Observational learning of food aversions in red-winged blackbirds (*Agelaius phoeniceus*). *Auk, 99*, 548–554. [3]

Mason, R. T., & Crews, D. (1985). Female mimicry in garter snakes. *Nature, 316*, 59–60. [12]

Mayfield, H. (1965). The brown-headed cowbird, with old and new hosts. *The Living Bird, 4*, 13–28. [14]

Maynard Smith, J. (1977). Parental investment: A prospective analysis. *Animal Behaviour, 25*, 1–9. [9]

Maynard Smith, J. (1982). *Evolution and the theory of games*. Cambridge: Cambridge University Press. [8]

Mayr, E. (1974). Behavior programs and evolutionary strategies. *American Scientist, 62*, 650–659. [2, 3, 14]

Mayr, E. (1982). *The growth of biological thought: Diversity, evolution and inheritance*. Cambridge, MA: Belknap Press of Harvard University Press. [4, 14]

Meaney, M. J., & Stewart, J. (1981). Neonatal androgens influence the social play of prepubescent rats. *Hormones and Behavior, 15*, 197–213. [12]

Medvin, M. B., & Beecher, M. D. (1986). Parent–offspring recognition in the barn swallow. *Animal Behaviour, 34*, 1627–1639. [16]

Meisel, R. L., & Ward, I. L. (1981). Fetal female rats are masculinized by male littermates located caudally in the uterus. *Science, 213*, 239–242. [13]

Melson, G. F., Fogel, A., & Toda, S. (1986). Children's ideas about infants and their care. *Child Development, 57*, 1519–1527. [10]

Menaker, M., & Binkley, S. (1981). Neural and endocrine control of circadian rhythms in the vertebrates. In J. Aschoff (Ed.), *Handbook of behavioral neurobiology: Vol. 4. Biological rhythms* (pp. 243–255). New York: Plenum Press. [11]

Menaker, M., & Eskin, A. (1966). Entrainment of circadian rhythms by sound in *Passer domesticus*. *Science, 154*, 1579–1581. [11]

Mendl, M. (1988a). The effects of litter size variation on mother–offspring relationships and behavioural and physical development in several mammalian species (principally rodents). *Journal of Zoology, 215*, 15–34. [13]

Mendl, M. (1988b). The effects of litter-size variation on the development of play behaviour in the domestic cat: litters of one and two. *Animal Behaviour, 36*, 20–34. [13]

Mendoza, S. P., & Mason, W. A. (1986). Contrasting responses to intruders and to involuntary separation by monogamous and polygynous New World monkeys. *Physiology and Behavior, 38*, 795–801. [10]

Meredith, M. (1980). The vomeronasal organ and accessory olfactory system in the hamster. In D. Müller-Schwarze and R. Silverstein (Eds.), *Chemical signals in vertebrates: Vol. 2. Vertebrates and aquatic invertebrates* (pp. 303–326). New York: Plenum Press. [17]

Meredith, M. (1983). Sensory physiology of pheromone communication. In J. G. Vandenbergh (Ed.), *Pheromones and Reproduction in Mammals* (pp. 199–252). New York: Academic Press. [17]

Michener, G. R. (1983a). Copulatory plugs in Richardson's ground squirrels. *Canadian Journal of Zoology, 62*, 267–270. [8]

Michener, G. R. (1983b). Spring emergence schedules and vernal behavior of Richardson's ground squirrels: Why do males emerge from hibernation before females? *Behavioral Ecology and Sociobiology, 14*, 29–38. [8]

Michener, G. R. (1984). Age, sex, and species differences in the annual cycles of ground-dwelling sciurids: Implications for sociality. In J. O. Murie & G. R. Michener (Eds.), *The biology of ground-dwelling squirrels* (pp. 79–107). Lincoln: University of Nebraska Press. [8]

Miczek, K. A. (1987). The psychopharmacology of aggression. In L. Iversen, S. D. Iversen, & S. H. Snyder (Eds.), *Handbook of Psychopharmacology* (Vol. 19, pp. 183–328). New York: Plenum Press. [18]

Militzer, K., & Reinhard, H.-J. (1982). Rank positions in rats and their relations to tissue parameters. *Physiological Psychology, 10*, 251–260. [9]

Miller, A. H. (1947). Panmixia and population size with reference to birds. *Evolution, 1*, 186–190. [15]

Miller, D. B. (1977). Roles of naturalistic observation in comparative psychology. *American Psychologist, 32*, 211–219. [2]

Miller, D. E., & Emlen, J. T., Jr. (1975). Individual chick recognition and family integrity in the ring-billed gull. *Behaviour, 52*, 124–144. [16]

Miller, R. J. (1964). Studies on the social behavior of the blue gourami, *Trichogaster trichopterus* (Pisces, Belontiidae). *Copeia, 3*, 469–496. [9]

Milton, K., & May, M. L. (1976). Body weight, diet and home range area in primates. *Nature, 259*, 459–462. [4]

Mink, J. W., & Adams, D. B. (1981). Why offense is reduced when rats are tested in a strange cage. *Physiology and Behavior, 26*, 567–573. [18]

Mitchell, G., & Brandt, E, M. (1972). Paternal behavior in primates. In F. E. Poirier (Ed.), *Primate socialization* (pp. 173–206). New York: Random House. [10]

Mock, D. W. (1984). Infanticide, siblicide, and avian nestling mortality. In G. Hausfater & S. Blaffer Hrdy (Eds.), *Infanticide* (pp. 3–30). New York: Aldine. [13]

Mondloch, C. J., & Timberlake, W. (1988). *The allocation and development of parental feeding in the pigeon (Columba livia)*. Unpublished manuscript, Indiana University, Bloomington. [2]

Mook, J. H., Mook, L. J., & Heikens, H. S. (1960). Further evidence for the role of "searching image" in the hunting behavior of titmice. *Archives Neerlandaises de Zoologie, 13*, 448–465. [1]

Moore, B. R. (1973). The role of directed Pavlovian reactions in simple instrumental learning in the pigeon. In R. A. Hinde & J. Stevenson-Hinde (Eds.), *Constraints on learning: Limitations and predispositions* (pp. 159–186). New York: Academic Press. [9]

Moore, C. L. (1982). Maternal behavior of rats is affected by hormonal condition of pups. *Journal of Comparative and Physiological Psychology, 96*, 123–129. [12]

Moore, C. L. (1984). Maternal contributions to the development of masculine sexual behavior in laboratory rats. *Developmental Psychobiology, 17*, 347–356. [12]

Moore, C. L. (1985a). Another psychobiological view of sexual differentiation. *Developmental Review, 5*, 18–55. [12]

Moore, C. L. (1985b). Development of mammalian sexual behavior. In E. S. Gollin (Ed.) *The comparative development of adaptive skills: Evolutionary implications* (pp. 19–55). Hillsdale, NJ: Lawrence Erlbaum Associates. [12]

Moore, C. L. (1985c). Sex differences in urinary odors produced by young laboratory rats (*Rattus norvegicus*). *Journal of Comparative Psychology, 99*, 336–341. [12]

Moore, C. L., & Chadwick-Dias, A.-M. (1986). Behavioral responses of infant rats to maternal licking: Variations with age and sex. *Developmental Psychobiology, 19*, 427–438. [12]

Moore, C. L., & Morelli, G. A. (1979). Mother rats interact differently with male and female offspring. *Journal of Comparative and Physiological Psychology, 93*, 677–684. [12]

Moore, C. L., & Rogers, S. (1984). Contribution of self-grooming to onset of puberty in male rats. *Developmental Psychobiology, 17*, 243–253. [12]

Moore, C. L., & Samonte, B. (1986). Preputial glands of infant rats (*Rattus norvegicus*) provide chemosignals for maternal discrimination of sex. *Journal of Comparative Psychology, 100*, 76–80. [12]

Moore, R. Y. (1973). Retinohypothalmic projection in animals: A comparative study. *Brain Research, 49*, 403–409. [11]

Moore, R. Y. (1979). The retinohypothalamic tract, suprachiasmatic hypothalamic nucleus and central neural mechanisms of circadian rhythm regulation. In M. Suda, O. Hayashi, & N. Nakagowa (Eds.), *Biological rhythms and their central mechanism* (pp. 343–354). Amsterdam: Elsevier North Holland. [11]

Moore, R. Y. (1983). Organization and function of central nervous system oscillator: the suprachiasmatic hypothalamic nucleus. *Federation Proceedings, 42*, 2783–2789. [11]

Moore, R. Y., & Lenn, N. J. (1972). A retinohypothalmic projection in the rat. *Journal of Comparative Neurology, 146*, 1–14. [11]

Moore-Ede, M. C., Sulzman, F. M., & Fuller, C. A. (1982). *The clocks that time us*. Cambridge, MA: Harvard University Press. [11]

Morgan, C. L. (1896). *Habit and instinct*. London: Arnold. [2]

Morgan, C. T. (1965). *Physiological psychology*. New York: McGraw-Hill. [17]

Morse, D. H. (1974). Niche breadth as a function of social dominance. *American Naturalist, 108*(964), 818–830. [4]

Morse, R. A., Gary, N. E., & Johansson, T. S. K. (1962) Mating of virgin queen honey bees (*Apis mellifera*) following mandibular gland extirpation. *Nature, 4828*, 605. [17]

Mos, J., Olivier, B., Oorschot, R. van, & Dijkstra, H. (1984). Different test situations for measuring offensive aggression in male rats do not result in the same wound pattern. *Physiology and Behavior, 32*, 453–456. [18]

Moyer, K. E. (1968). Kinds of aggression and their physiological basis. *Communications in Behavioral Biology, Part A*, 65–87. [18]

Mrosovsky, N., & Salmon, P. A. (1987). A behavioral method for accelerating re-entrainment of rhythms to new light–dark cycles. *Nature, 330*, 372–373. [11]

Murie, J. O., & Harris, M. A. (1978). Territoriality and dominance in male Columbian ground squirrels (*Spermophilus columbianus*). *Canadian Journal of Zoology, 56*, 2402–2412. [8]

Murie, J. O., & Harris, M. A. (1984). The history of individuals in a population of Columbian ground squirrels: Source, settlement, and site attachment. In J. O. Murie & G. R. Michener (Eds.), *The biology of ground-dwelling squirrels* (pp. 353–374). Lincoln: University of Nebraska Press. [8]

Murie, J. O., & McLean, I. G. (1980). Copulatory plugs in ground squirrels. *Journal of Mammalogy, 61,* 355–356. [8]

Murphy, M. R. (1971). Natural history of the Syrian golden hamster—a reconnaissance expedition. *American Zoologist, 11,* 632. [17]

Murphy, M. R. (1973). Effects of female hamster vaginal discharge on the behavior of male hamsters. *Behavioral Biology, 9,* 367–375. [17]

Murphy, M. R. (1977). Intraspecific sexual preferences of female hamsters. *Journal of Comparative and Physiological Psychology, 91,* 1337–1346. [17]

Murphy, M. R. (1978). Oestrous Turkish hamsters display lordosis toward conspecific males but attack heterospecific males. *Animal Behaviour, 26,* 311–312. [17]

Murphy, M. R. (1980). Sexual preferences of male hamsters: importance of preweaning and adult experience, vaginal secretion, and olfactory or vomeronasal sensation. *Behavioral and Neural Biology, 30,* 323–340. [17]

Murphy, M. R., & Schneider, G. E. (1970). Olfactory bulb removal eliminates mating behavior in the male golden hamster. *Science, 167,* 302–304. [17]

Myers, L., & Christenson, T. E. (1988). Transition from predatory juvenile male to mate-searching adult in the orb-weaving spider *Nephila clavipes. Journal of Arachnology, 16,* 260–262. [7]

New, R. S., & Benigni, L. (1987). Italian fathers and infants: Cultural constraints on paternal behavior. In Lamb, M. E. (Ed.), *The father's role: Cross-cultural perspectives* (pp. 139–167). Hillsdale, NJ: Lawrence Erlbaum Associates. [10]

Neyman, P. A. (1977). Aspects of the ecology and social organization of free-ranging cotton-top tamarins (*Saguinus oedipus*) and the conservation status of the species. In D. G. Kleiman (Ed.), *The biology and conservation of the Callitrichidae* (pp. 39–71). Washington, DC: Smithsonian Institution Press. [10]

Niebuhr, V., & McFarland, D. (1983). Nest-relief behavior in the herring gull. *Animal Behaviour, 31,* 701–707. [9]

Nieto, J. (1984). Transfer of conditioned inhibition across different aversive reinforcers in the rat. *Learning and Motivation, 15,* 37–57. [9]

Norberg, U. M. (1981). Allometry of bat wings and legs and comparison with bird wings. *Philosophical Transactions of the Royal Society of London: B. Biological Sciences, 292,* 359–398. [4]

Norgren, R. B., & Silver, R. (in press-a). A comparative study of retinohypothalnic projections in birds using horseradish peroxidase. *Brain Behavior and Evolution.* [11]

Norgren, R. B., & Silver, R. (in press-b). Distribution of VIP NP, and AChE in dove hypothalmus with an emphasis on the question of an avian SCN. *Cell and Tissue Research.* [11]

Norris, M. L., & Adams, C. E. (1979). Mating post partum, concurrent lactation and reproduction in the laboratory rat. *Laboratory Animal, 13,* 167–170. [13]

Nottebohm, F. (1969). The song of the chingolo, *Zonotrichia capensis* in Argentina: description and evaluation of a system of dialects. *Condor, 71,* 299–315. [15]

Nottebohm, F. (1972). The origins of vocal learning. *American Naturalist, 106,* 116–140. [2]

Nottebohm, F., Nottebohm, M. E., & Crane, L. (1986). Developmental and seasonal changes in canary song and their relation to changes in the anatomy of song-control nuclei. *Behavioural and Neural Biology, 46,* 445–471. [12]

Novak, M. A., & Harlow, H. F. (1975). Social recovery of monkeys isolated for the first year of life: 1. Rehabilitation and therapy. *Developmental Psychology, 11,* 453–465. [12]

Nyby, J., Whitney, G., Schmitz, S., & Dizinno, G. (1978). Post-pubertal experience establishes signal value of mammalian sex odor. *Behavioral Biology, 22,* 545–552. [9]

Oberholser, H. C. (1920). The migration of North American birds: 14. Cowbirds. *Bird Lore, 22,* 343–345. [14]

O'Connell, R. J., & Meredith, M. (1984). Effects of volatile and non-volatile chemical signals on male sex behaviors mediated by the main and accessory olfactory systems. *Behavioral Neuroscience, 98,* 1083–1093. [17]

O'Connell, R. J., Singer, A. G., Macrides, F., Pfaffmann, C., & Agosta, W. C. (1978). Responses of the male golden hamster to mixtures of odorants identified from vaginal discharge. *Behavioral Biology, 24,* 244–255. [17]

O'Connell, R. J., Singer, A. G., Pfaffmann, C., & Agosta, W. C. (1979). Pheromones of hamster vaginal discharge: Attraction to femtogram amounts of dimethyl disulfide and to mixtures of volatile components. *Journal of Chemical Ecology, 5,* 575–585. [17]

O'Connell, R. J., Singer, A. G., Stern, F. L., Jesmajian, S., & Agosta, W. C. (1981). Cyclic variations in the concentration of sex attractant pheromone in hamster vaginal discharge. *Behavioral and Neural Biology, 31,* 457–464. [17]

Oglesby, J. N., Lanier, D. L., & Dewsbury, D. A. (1981). The role of prolonged copulatory behavior in facilitating reproductive success in male Syrian golden hamsters (*Mesocricetus auratus*) in a competitive mating situation. *Behavioral Ecology and Sociobiology, 8,* 47–54. [9]

Olive, C. W. (1982). Sex pheromones in two orb-weaving spiders, (Araneae, Araneidae): An experimental field study. *Journal of Arachnology, 10,* 241–245. [7]

Oliver, J. (1958). *Snakes in fact and fiction.* New York: Macmillan Company. [5]

Olivier, B. (1981). Selective anti-aggressive properties of DU 27725: Ethological analyses of intermale and territorial aggression in the male rat. *Pharmacology, Biochemistry and Behavior, 14*(suppl. 1), 61–77. [18]

Olivier, B., Mos, J., Poel, A. M. van der, Krijzer, F. N. C., & Kruk, M. R. (1984). Effects of a new psychoactive drug (DU27716) on different models of rat agonistic behaviour and EEG. In K. J. Flannelly, R. J. Blanchard, & D. C. Blanchard (Eds.), *Biological perspectives on aggression* (pp. 261–279). New York: Alan R. Liss. [18]

Olson, D. J. (1989). *Comparative spatial memory in birds.* Unpublished doctoral dissertation, University of Massachusetts, Amherst. [1]

Olton, D. S., Handelman, G. E., & Walker, J. A. (1981). Spatial memory and food searching strategies. In A. C. Kamil & T. D. Sargent (Eds.), *Foraging behavior: Ecological, ethological, and psychological approaches* (pp. 333–354). New York: Garland Press. [2]

Orians, G. H. (1969). On the evolution of mating systems in birds and mammals. *American Naturalist, 103,* 589–603. [9]

Orsini, M. W. (1961). The external vaginal phenomena characterizing the stages of the estrous cycle, pregnancy, pseudopregnancy, lactation, and the anestrous hamster (*Mesocricetus auratus* Waterhouse). *Proceedings of the Animal Care Panel, 11,* 193–206. [17]

Ossa, J. de la, Moreno, G., & Segura, C. (1988). Anotaciones sobre el comportamiento agresivo en la conformacion de una colonia semicautiva de *Saguinus oedipus* (Linneaus, 1758) (Mammalia: Primates). *Trianea (Acta Cientifica y Tecnologica), 1,* 131–139. [10]

Owings, D. H., Borchert, M., & Virginia, R. (1977). The behaviour of California ground squirrels. *Animal Behaviour, 25,* 221–230. [8]

Oxnard, C. E. (1983). Sexual dimorphisms in the overall proportions of primates. *American Journal of Primatology, 4,* 1–22. [4]

Oxnard, C. E. (1984). *The order of man: A biomathematical anatomy of the primates.* New Haven: Yale University Press. [4]

Palametta, B., & Lefebvre, L. (1985). The social transmission of a food-finding technique in pigeons: What is learned? *Animal Behaviour, 33,* 892–896. [3]

Parke, R. D., & O'Leary, S. E. (1976). Father–mother–infant interaction in the newborn period: Some findings, some observations and some unresolved issues. In K. Riegel and J. Meacham (Eds.), *The developing individual in a changing world: Vol. 2. Social and environmental issues* (pp. 653–663). The Hague: Mouton. [10]

Parker, G. A. (1970a). Sperm competition and its evolutionary consequences in the insects. *Biological Reviews, 45,* 525–567. [6, 7, 8]

Parker, G. A. (1970b). Sperm competition and its evolutionary effect on copula duration in the fly *Scatophaga stercoraria.* *Journal of Insect Physiology, 16,* 1301–1328. [8]

Parker, G. A. (1974). Courtship persistence and female-guarding as male time investment strategies. *Behaviour, 48,* 157–184. [8]

Parker, G. A. (1978a). Evolution of competitive mate searching. *Annual Review of Entomology, 23,* 173–196. [8]

Parker, G. A. (1978b). Searching for mates. In J. Krebs & N. B. Davies (Eds.), *Behavioural ecology* (pp. 214–244). Oxford: Blackwell Scientific Publications. [8]

Parker, G. A. (1984a). Evolutionarily stable strategies. In J. Krebs & N. B. Davies (Eds.), *Behavioural ecology* (pp. 30–61). Oxford: Blackwell Scientific Publications. [8]

Parker, G. A. (1984b). Sperm competition and the evolution of animal mating strategies. In R. L. Smith (Ed.), *Sperm competition and the evolution of animal mating systems* (pp. 1–60). Orlando, FL: Academic Press. [7, 8]

Partridge, L., & Halliday, T. (1984). Mating patterns and mate choice. In J. R. Krebs & N. B. Davies (Eds.), *Behavioural ecology: An evolutionary approach* (pp. 222–250). Oxford: Blackwell Scientific Publications. [9]

Patterson, T. L., & Petrinovich, L. (1979). Field studies of habituation: 2. Effects of massed stimulus presentation. *Journal of Comparative and Physiological Psychology, 93,* 351–359. [15]

Pavlov, I. P. (1927). *Conditioned reflexes.* (G. V. Anrep, Trans.). London: Oxford University Press. [9]

Pavlov, I. P. (1941). *Lectures on conditioned reflexes* (Vol. 2, W. H. Gantt, Trans.). New York: International Publishers. [9]

Payne, R. B. (1973). *Behavior, mimetic songs and song dialects, and relationships of the parasitic indigobirds* (Vidua) *of Africa* (Ornithological Monographs, No. 11). Washington, DC: American Ornithologists Union. [15]

Payne, R. B. (1981). Song learning and social interaction in indigo buntings. *Animal Behaviour, 29,* 688–697. [15]

Payne, R. B. (1983). The social context of song mimicry: Song matching dialects in indigo buntings (*Passerina cyanea*). *Animal Behaviour, 31,* 35–47. [15]

Payne, R. B., Payne, L. L., & Doehler, S. M. (1987). Song, mate choice and the question of kin recognition in a migratory songbird. *Animal Behaviour, 35,* 35–47. [15]

Pearce, J. M., Montgomery, A., & Dickinson, A. (1981). Contralateral transfer of inhibition and excitatory eyelid conditioning in the rabbit. *Quarterly Journal of Experimental Psychology, 33B,* 45–61. [9]

Peden, B. F., & Timberlake, W. (1988). Environmental influences on flank and urine marking by male and female rats (*Rattus norvegicus*). Manuscript submitted for publication. [2]

Pedersen, P. E., & Blass, E. M. (1981). Olfactory control over suckling in albino rats. In R. N. Aslin, J. R. Alberts, & M. R. Petersen (Eds.), *Development of perception* (Vol. 1, pp. 359–387). New York: Academic Press. [3]

Pedersen, P. E., Williams, C. L., & Blass, E. M. (1982). Activation and odor conditioning of suckling behavior in 3-day-old albino rats. *Journal of Experimental Psychology: Animal Behavior Processes, 8,* 329–341. [12]

Peeke, H. V. S., & Peeke, S. C. (1973). Habituation in fish with special reference to intraspecific aggressive behavior. In H. V. S. Peeke & M. J. Herz (Eds.), *Habituation: Behavioral studies* (Vol. 1, pp. 59–83). New York: Academic Press. [9]

Peeke, H. V. S., & Peeke, S. C. (1982). Parental factors in the sensitization and habituation of territorial aggression in the convict cichlid (*Cichlasoma nigrofasciatum*). *Journal of Comparative and Physiological Psychology, 96,* 955–966. [9]

Pellis, S. M. (1988). Agonistic versus amicable targets of attack and defense: Consequences for the origin, function, and descriptive classification of play-fighting. *Aggressive Behavior, 14,* 85–104. [18]

Peters, R. H. (1983). *The ecological implications of body size.* New York: Cambridge University Press. [4]

Petrinovich, L. (1976). Molar reductionism. In L. Petrinovich & J. L. McGaugh (Eds.), *Knowing, thinking and believing* (pp. 11–27). New York: Plenum Press. [15]

Petrinovich, L. (1979). Probabilistic functionalism: A conception of research method. *American Psychologist, 34,* 373–390. [15]

Petrinovich, L. (1980). Brunswikian behavioral biology. In K. R. Hammond & N. E. Wascoe (Eds.), *Realizations of Brunswik's representative design: New directions for methodology of social and behavioral science* (Vol. 3, pp. 85–93). San Francisco: Jossey-Bass. [15]

Petrinovich, L. (1981). A method for the study of development. In K. Immelmann, G. Barlow, L. Petrinovich, & M. Main (Eds.), *Behavioral Development* (pp. 90–130). New York: Cambridge University Press. [15]

Petrinovich, L. (1984). A two-factor dual-process theory of habituation and sensitization. In H.V.S. Peeke & L. Petrinovich (Eds.), *Habituation, sensitization, and behavior* (pp. 17–55). New York: Academic Press. [15]

Petrinovich, L. (1985). Factors influencing song development in the white-crowned sparrow (*Zonotrichia leucophrys*). *Journal of Comparative Psychology*, 99, 15–29. [15]

Petrinovich, L. (1988a). Individual stability, local variability and the cultural transmission of song in white-crowned sparrows (*Zonotrichia leucophrys nuttalli*). *Behaviour*, 107, 208–240. [15]

Petrinovich, L. (1988b). The role of social factors in white-crowned sparrow song development. In T. R. Zentall & B. G. Galef, Jr. (Eds.), *Social learning: Psychological and biological perspectives* (pp. 255–278). Hillsdale, NJ: Lawrence Erlbaum Associates. [14, 15]

Petrinovich, L. (1989). *Field studies of habituation: 6. Individual differences*. Unpublished manuscript. [15]

Petrinovich, L. (in press). Representative design and the quality of generalization. In L. W. Poon, D. C. Rubin, & B. A. Wilson (Eds.), *Cognition in everyday life*. New York: Cambridge University Press. [15]

Petrinovich, L., & Baptista, L. F. (1984). Song dialects, mate selection, and breeding success in white-crowned sparrows. *Animal Behaviour*, 32, 1078–1088. [14, 15]

Petrinovich, L., & Baptista, L. F. (1987). Song development in the white-crowned sparrow: Social factors and sex differences. *Animal Behaviour*, 35, 961–974. [15]

Petrinovich, L., & Patterson, T. L. (1979). Field studies of habituation: 1. The effects of reproductive condition, number of trials, and different delay intervals on the responses of the white-crowned sparrow. *Journal of Comparative and Physiological Psychology*, 93, 337–350. [9, 15]

Petrinovich, L., & Patterson, T. L. (1982). The white-crowned sparrow: Stability, recruitment, and population structure in the Nuttall subspecies (1975–1980). *Auk*, 99, 1–14. [15]

Petrinovich, L., & Patterson, T. L. (1983). The white-crowned sparrow: Reproductive success (1975–1980). *Auk*, 100, 811–825. [15]

Petrinovich, L., & Widaman, K. F. (1984). An evaluation of statistical strategies to analyze repeated measures data. In H. V. S. Peeke & L. Petrinovich (Eds.), *Habituation, sensitization, and behavior* (pp. 155–201). New York: Academic Press. [15]

Pfeiffer, C. (1988). *Factors contributing to acute androgen surges in male golden hamsters: the role of olfaction and female cues*. Unpublished doctoral dissertation, Cornell University, Ithaca, NY. [17]

Pfeiffer, C., & Johnston, R. E. (1986). Role of olfaction in socially induced testosterone release in the male hamster. *Biology of Reproduction*, 34(Suppl. 1), 159. [17]

Picciolo, A. R. (1964). Sexual and nest discrimination in Anabantid fishes of the genera *Colisa* and *Trichogaster*. *Ecological Monographs*, 34, 53–77. [9]

Pietrewicz, A. T., & Kamil, A. C. (1977). Visual detection of cryptic prey by blue jays (*Cyanocitta cristata*). *Science*, 195, 580–582. [1]

Pietrewicz, A. T., & Kamil, A. C. (1979). Search image formation in the blue jay (*Cyanocitta cristata*). *Science*, 204, 1332–1333. [1, 2]

Pietrewicz, A. T., & Kamil, A. C. (1987). Search images and the detection of crypic prey: An operant approach. In A. C. Kamil, J. R. Krebs, & H. R. Pulliam (Eds.), *Foraging behavior* (pp. 311–331). New York: Plenum. [1]

Pittendrigh, C. S., & Bruce, V. G. (1957). An oscillator model for biological clocks. In D. Rudnik (Ed.), *Rhythmic and synthetic processes in growth* (pp. 75–109). Princeton, NJ: Princeton University Press. [11]

Plomin, R. (1986). *Development, genetics, and psychology*. Hillsdale, NJ: Lawrence Erlbaum Associates. [14]

Plomin, R., & Daniels, D. (1987). Why are children in the same family so different from one another? *Behavioral and Brain Sciences*, 10, 1–60. [14]

Poll, N. E. van de, Smeets, J., Oyen, H. G. van, & Zwan, S. M. van der (1982). Behavioral consequences of agonistic experience in rats: Sex differences and the effects of testosterone. *Journal of Comparative and Physiological Psychology*, 96, 893–903. [9]

Porter, R. H. (1986). Chemical signals and kin recognition in spiny mice (*Acomys cahirinus*). In D. Duvall, D. Müller-Schwarze, & R. M. Silverstein (Eds.), *Chemical signals in vertebrates: Vol. 4. Ecology, evolution, and comparative biology* (pp. 397–411). New York: Plenum Press. [13]

Porter, R. H. (1987). Kin recognition: Functions and mediating mechanisms. In C. B. Crawford, M. F. Smith., & D. L. Krebs (Eds.), *Sociobiology and psychology: Ideas, issues and findings* (pp. 175–203). Hillsdale, NJ: Lawrence Erlbaum Associates. [13]

Porter, R. H. (1988). The ontogeny of sibling recognition in rodents: Superfamily Muroidea. *Behavior Genetics*, 18, 483–494. [13]

Porter, R. H., Cavallaro, S. A., & Moore, J. D. (1980). Developmental parameters of mother–offspring interactions in *Acomys cahirinus*. *Zeitschrift für Tierpsychologie*, 53, 153–170. [13]

Porter, R. H., Cernoch, J. M., & Matochik, J. A. (1983). Littermate influences on behavioral development in *Acomys cahirinus* and *Mus musculus*. *Zeitschrift für Tierpsychologie*, 62, 93–104. [13]

Porter, R. H., Matochik, J. A., & Makin, J. W. (1983). Evidence for phenotype matching in spiny mice (*Acomys cahirinus*). *Animal Behaviour*, 31, 978–984. [13]

Porter, R. H., Matochik, J. A., & Makin, J. W. (1986). Discrimination between full-sibling spiny mice (*Acomys cahirinus*) by olfactory signatures. *Animal Behaviour*, 34, 1182–1188. [13]

Porter, R. H., Moore, J. D., & White, D. M. (1981). Food sharing by sibling vs. nonsibling spiny mice (*Acomys cahirinus*). *Behavioral Ecology and Sociobiology*, 8, 207–212. [13]

Porter, R. H., Sentell, S. W., & Makin, J. W. (1987). Effects of intranasal $ZnSO_4$ irrigation are mitigated by the presence of untreated littermates. *Physiology and Behavior*, 40, 97–102. [13]

Porter, R. H., Tepper, V. J., Baumeister, A. A., Cernoch, J. M., & Matochik, J. A. (1982). Interactions among unfamiliar spiny mouse (*Acomys cahirinus*) weanlings. *Behavioral and Neural Biology*, 34, 190–200. [13]

Porter, R. H., Tepper, V. J., & White, D. M. (1981). Experiential influences on the development of huddling preferences and "sibling" recognition in spiny mice. *Developmental Psychobiology*, 14, 375–382. [13]

Porter, R. H., & Wyrick, M. (1979). Sibling recognition in spiny mice (*Acomys cahirinus*): Influence of age and isolation. *Animal Behaviour*, 27, 761–766. [13]

Porter, R. H., Wyrick, M., & Pankey, J. (1978). Sibling recognition in spiny mice (*Acomys cahirinus*). *Behavioral Ecology and Sociobiology*, 3, 61–68. [13]

Posadas-Andrews, A., & Roper, T. J. (1983). Social transmission of food-preferences in adult rats. *Animal Behaviour*, 31, 265–271. [3]

Potter, E. F., & Whitehurst, G. T. (1981). Cowbirds in the Carolinas. *Chat*, 45, 57–67. [14]

Pough, F. H. (1988). Mimicry and related phenomena. In C. Gans & R. B. Huey (Eds.), *Biology of the Reptilia: Vol. 16. Ecology B: Defense and life history* (pp. 153–234). New York: Alan R. Liss. [5]

Pough, F. H., & Groves, J. D. (1983). Specializations of the body form and food habits of snakes. *American Zoologist*, 23, 443–454. [5]

Power, K. L., & Moore, C. L. (1986). Prenatal stress eliminates differential maternal attention to male offspring in Norway rats. *Physiology and Behavior*, 38, 667–671. [12]

Powers, J. B., Fields, R. B., & Winans, S. S. (1979). Olfactory and vomeronasal system participation in male hamsters' attraction to female vaginal secretions. *Physiology and Behavior*, 22, 77–84. [17]

Powers, J. B., & Winans, S. S. (1975). Vomeronasal organ: Critical role in mediating sexual behavior of the male hamster. *Science*, 187, 961–963. [17]

Price, J. L. (1987). The central olfactory and accessory olfactory systems. In T. E. Finger and W. L. Silva (Eds.), *Neurobiology of taste and smell* (pp. 179–203). New York: Wiley. [17]

Priestnall, R. (1972). Effects of litter size on the behaviour of lactating female mice (*Mus musculus*). *Animal Behaviour*, 20, 386–394. [13]

Prigogine, I. (1976). Order through fluctuation: Self-organization and social system. In E. Jantsch & C. H. Waddington (Eds.), *Evolution and consciousness: Human systems in transition* (pp. 93–133). Ontario: Addison-Wesley Publishing Co. [4]

Prothero, J. (1986). Methodological aspects of scaling in biology. *Journal of Theoretical Biology*, 118, 259–286. [4]

Quadagno, D. M., & Banks, E. M. (1970). The effects of reciprocal cross fostering on the behaviour of two species of rodents, *Mus musculus* and *Baiomys taylori ater*. *Animal Behaviour*, 18, 379–390. [13]

Rackham, D. W. (1971). *Conditioning of the pigeon's courtship and aggressive display*. Unpublished master's thesis, Dalhousie University, Halifax, Nova Scotia. [9]

Radcliffe, C. W., Estep, K., Boyer, T., & Chiszar, D. (1986). Stimulus control of predatory behavior in red spitting cobras (*Naja mossambica pallida*) and prairie rattlesnakes (*Crotalus v. viridis*). *Animal Behaviour*, 34, 804–814. [5]

Radcliffe, C. W., Stimac, K., Smith, H. M., & Chiszar, D. (1983). Effects of prey size on post-strike behavior of juvenile red spitting cobras (*Naja mossambica pallida*). *Transactions of the Kansas Academy of Science*, 87, 59–62. [5]

Raisman, G., & Field, P. M. (1971). Sexual dimorphism in the preoptic area of the rat. *Science, 173*, 731–733. [12]

Ralls, K. (1971). Mammalian scent marking. *Science, 171*, 443–449. [17]

Raskin, L. A. (1982). Effect of olfactory bulbectomy on reactivity to environmental stimuli in the preweanling rat. *Behavioral and Neural Biology, 34*, 307–318. [13]

Ratcliffe, L., & Weisman, R. (1987). Phrase order recognition in brown-headed cowbirds. *Animal Behaviour, 35*, 1260–1262. [14]

Reberg, D., Innis, N. K., Mann, B., & Eizenga, C. (1978). "Superstitious" behavior resulting from periodic response-independent presentations of food or water. *Animal Behaviour, 26*, 507–519. [2]

Redican, W. K. (1976). Adult male–infant interactions in nonhuman primates. In M. E. Lamb (Ed.), *The role of the father in child development* (pp. 345–385). New York: Wiley. [10]

Regal, P. J., & Connolly, M. S. (1980). Social influences on biological rhythms. *Behaviour, 72*, 3–4, 171–197. [11]

Reichman, O. J. (1981). Factors influencing foraging in desert rodents. In A. C. Kamil & T. D. Sargent (Eds.), *Foraging behavior: Ecological, ethological, and psychological approaches* (pp. 195–213). New York: Garland Press. [1]

Rescorla, R. A. (1979). Conditioned inhibition and extinction. In A. Dickinson & R. A. Boakes (Eds.), *Mechanisms of learning and motivation* (pp. 83–110). New York: Academic Press. [9]

Rescorla, R. A. (1988). Pavlovian conditioning: It's not what you think it is. *American Psychologist, 43*, 151–160. [1, 9]

Resko, J. A. (1985). Gonadal hormones during sexual differentiation in vertebrates. In N. Adler, D. Pfaff, & R. W. Goy (Eds.), *Handbook of behavioral neurobiology: Vol. 7. Reproduction* (pp. 21–42). New York: Plenum. [12]

Revusky, S. (1977). Learning as a general process with an emphasis on data from feeding experiments. In N. W. Milgram, I. Krames, & T. M. Alloway (Eds.), *Food aversion learning* (pp. 1–51). New York: Plenum Press. [2]

Rheingold, H. L. (1963). Maternal behavior in the dog. In H. L. Rheingold (Ed.), *Maternal behavior in mammals* (pp. 169–202). New York: John Wiley & Sons. [13]

Ridley, M. (1978). Paternal care. *Animal Behaviour, 26*, 904–932. [9]

Riechert, S. E. (1982). Spider interaction strategies: communication vs. coercion. In P. N. Witt & J. S. Rovner (Eds.), *Spider communication: Mechanisms and ecological significance* (pp. 281–315). Princeton, NJ: Princeton University Press. [7]

Riley, J. N., Card, J. P., & Moore, R. Y. (1981). A retinal projection to the lateral hypothalmus in the rat. *Cell and Tissue Research, 214*, 257–269. [11]

Robinson, M. H., & Robinson, B. (1973). Ecology and behavior of the giant wood spider *Nephila maculata* (Fabricius) in New Guinea. *Smithsonian Contributions to Zoology, 149*, 1–76. [7]

Robinson, M. H., & Robinson, B. (1980). *Comparative studies of the courtship and mating behavior of tropical araneid spiders* (Pacific Insects Monograph No. 36). Honolulu: Bishop Museum. [7]

Rohwer, S., & Spaw, C. D. (1988). Evolutionary lag versus bill-size constraints: a comparative study of acceptance of cowbird eggs by old hosts. *Evolutionary Ecology, 2*, 27–36. [16]

Roitblat, H. L. (1987). *Introduction to comparative cognition*. New York: Freeman. [I]

Roitblat, H. L., Bever, T. G., and Terrace, H. S. (1984). *Animal cognition*. Hillsdale, NJ: Lawrence Erlbaum Associates. [I]

Romanes, G. J. (1883). *Animal intelligence*. New York: Appleton. [2]

Rosenzweig, M. L. (1968). The strategy of body size in mammalian carnivores. *American Midland Naturalist, 80*, 299–315. [4]

Rothstein, S. I. (1982). Success and failures in avian and nestling recognition with comments on the utility of optimality reasoning. *American Zoologist, 22*, 547–560. [16]

Rothstein, S. I., & Fleischer, R. C. (1987). Brown-headed cowbirds learn flight whistles after the juvenile period. *Auk, 104*, 513–516. [14, 15]

Rothstein, S. I., Verner, J., & Stevens, E. (1980). Range expansion and diurnal changes in dispersion of the brown-headed cowbird in the Sierra Nevada. *Auk, 97*, 253–267. [14]

Rothstein, S. I., Verner, J., & Stevens, E. (1984). Radio-tracking confirms a unique diurnal pattern of spatial occurrence in the parasitic brown-headed cowbird. *Ecology, 65*, 77–88. [14]

Rothstein, S. I., Yokel, D. A., & Fleischer, R. C. (1986). Social dominance, mating, and spacing systems, female fecundity and vocal dialects in captive and free-ranging brown-headed cowbirds. *Current Ornithology, 3*, 127–185. [14]

Rothstein, S. I., Yokel, D. A., & Fleischer, R. C. (1988). The agonistic and sexual functions of vocalizations of male brown-headed cowbirds (*Molothrus ater*). *Animal Behaviour, 36*, 73–86. [14]

Rozin, P. (1984). The acquisition of food habits and preferences. In J. D. Matarazzo, S. M. Weiss, J. A. Herd, N. C. Miller, & S. M. Weiss (Eds.), *Behavioral health: A handbook of health enhancement and disease prevention* (pp. 590–607). New York: John Wiley & Sons. [3]

Rozin, P., Gruss, L., & Berk, G. (1979). Reversal of innate aversions: Attempts to induce a preference for chili peppers in rats. *Journal of Comparative and Physiological Psychology, 93*, 1001–1014. [3]

Rozin, P., & Kalat, J. W. (1971). Specific hungers and poison avoidance as adaptive specializations of learning. *Psychological Review, 78*, 459–486. [2]

Rubenstein, D. I. (1987). Alternative reproductive tactics in the spider *Meta segmentata. Behavioral Ecology and Sociobiology, 20*, 229–237. [7]

Ruckmich, C. A. (1913). The use of the term *function* in English textbooks of psychology. *American Journal of Psychology, 24*, 99–123. [E]

Rusak, B. (1979). Neural mechanisms for entrainment and generation of mammalian circadian rhythms. *Federation Proceedings, 38*, 2589–2595. [11]

Rusak, B. (1982). Circadian organization in mammals and birds: Role of the pineal gland. In R. Reiter (Ed.), *Pineal gland: Vol. 3. Extrareproductive effects* (pp. 27–51). Boca Raton, FL: CRC Press. [11]

Rushen, J., & Pajor, E. (1987). Offence and defence in fights between young pigs (*Sus scrofa*). *Aggressive Behavior, 13*, 329–346. [18]

Rypstra, A. L. (1985). Aggregations of *Nephila clavipes* in relation to prey availability. *Journal of Arachnology, 13*, 71–78. [7]

Saal, F. S. vom, & Bronson, F. H. (1980). Sexual characteristics of adult female mice are correlated with their blood testosterone levels during prenatal development. *Science, 208*, 597–599. [13]

Sachs, B. D., & Dewsbury, D. A. (1978). The temporal patterning of copulation in laboratory rats and other muroid rodents. In T. E. McGill, D. A. Dewsbury, & B. D. Sachs (Eds.), *Sex and behavior: Status and prospectus* (pp. 297–302). New York: Plenum. [12]

Sacks, R. A., Kamil, A. C., & Mack, R. (1972). The effects of fixed-ratio sample requirements on matching-to-sample in the pigeon. *Psychonomic Science, 17*, 483–488. [1]

Sargent, T. D. (1976). *Legion of night*. Amherst: University of Massachusetts Press. [1]

Saunders, D. S. (1977). Circadian rhythms: "Continuosly-consulted" clocks. In *An Introduction to Biological Rhythms* (Chapter 4). London: Blackie and Son. [11]

Savage, A., Ziegler, T. E., & Snowdon, C. T. (1988). Sociosexual development, pairbond formation and mechanisms of fertility suppression in female cotton-top tamarins (*Saguinus oedipus oedipus*). *American Journal of Primatology, 14*, 345–359. [10]

Savidge, J. A. (1986). *The role of disease and predation in the decline of Guam's avifauna*. Unpublished doctoral dissertation, University of Illinois, Urbana-Champaign. [5]

Savidge, J. A. (1987a). Extinction of an island forest avifauna by an introduced snake. *Ecology, 68*, 660–668. [5]

Savidge, J. A. (1987b). Death on an island. *The Living Bird Quarterly, 6*, 6–10. [5]

Sawaki, Y., Nihonmatsu, I., & Kawamura, H. (1984). Transplantation of the neonatal suprachiasmatic nuclei into rats with complete bilateral suprachiasmatic lesions. *Neuroscience Research, 1*, 67–71 [11]

Sawrey, D. K., & Dewsbury, D. A. (1981). Effects of space on the copulatory behavior of deer mice (*Peromyscus maniculatus*). *Bulletin of the Psychonomic Society, 17*, 249–251. [6]

Scalia, F., & Winans, S. S. (1975). The differential projections of the olfactory bulb and accessory olfactory bulb in mammals. *Journal of Comparative Neurology, 161*, 31–53. [17]

Scalia, F., & Winans, S. S. (1976). New perspectives on the morphology of the olfactory system: Olfactory and vomeronasal pathways in mammals. In R. L. Doty (Ed.), *Mammalian olfaction, reproductive processes and behavior* (pp. 8–28). New York: Academic Press. [17]

Schaffer, W. M., & Reed, C. A. (1972). The co-evolution of social behavior and cranial morphology in sheep and goats (Bovidae, Caprini). *Field Museum of Natural History, 61*, 1–88. [4]

Schmidt-Nielsen, K. (1984). *Scaling: Why is animal size so important?* New York: Cambridge University Press. [4]

Schneider, D. (1974). The sex-attractant receptor of moths. *Scientific American, 231*, 28–35. [17]

Schneirla, T. C. (1950). The relationship between observation and experimentation in the field study of behavior. *Annals of the New York Academy of Sciences, 51*, 1022–1044. [7]

Schneirla, T. C. (1966). Behavioral development and comparative psychology. *Quarterly Review of Biology, 41*, 283–302. [12]

Schoener, T. W. (1968). Sizes of feeding territories among birds. *Ecology, 49*, 123–141. [4]

Schoener, T. W. (1987). A brief history of optimal foraging ecology. In A. C. Kamil, J. R. Krebs, & H. R. Pulliam (Eds.), *Foraging behavior* (pp. 5–68). New York: Plenum. [1]

Schrier, A. M. (1969). *Rattus* revisited. *American Psychologist, 24*, 681–682. [I]

Schwagmeyer, P. L. (1980). Alarm calling behavior of the thirteen-lined ground squirrel, *Spermophilus tridecemlineatus*. *Behavioral Ecology and Sociobiology, 7*, 195–200. [13]

Schwagmeyer, P. L. (1988). Scramble-competition polygyny in an asocial mammal: Male mobility and mating success. *American Naturalist, 132*, 885–892. [8]

Schwagmeyer, P. L., & Brown, C. H. (1983). Factors affecting male–male competition in thirteen-lined ground squirrels. *Behavioral Ecology and Sociobiology, 13*, 1–6. [8]

Schwagmeyer, P. L., & Parker, G. A. (1987). Queuing for mates in thirteen-lined ground squirrels. *Animal Behaviour, 35*, 1015–1025. [8]

Schwagmeyer, P. L., & Woontner, S. J. (1985). Mating competition in an asocial ground squirrel, *Spermophilus tridecemlineatus*. *Behavioral Ecology and Sociobiology, 17*, 291–295. [8]

Schwagmeyer, P. L., & Woontner, S. J. (1986). Scramble competition polygyny in thirteen-lined ground squirrels: The relative contributions of overt conflict and competitive mate searching. *Behavioral Ecology and Sociobiology, 19*, 359–364. [8]

Schwalb, D. W., Imaizumi, N., & Nakazawa, J. (1987). The modern Japanese father: Roles and problems in a changing society. In Lamb, M. E. (Ed.), *The father's role: Cross-cultural perspectives* (pp. 247–269). Hillsdale, NJ: Lawrence Erlbaum Associates. [10]

Schwartz, O. A., & Armitage, K. B. (1980). Genetic variation in social mammals: The marmot model. *Science, 207*, 665–667. [8]

Scott, E. M., & Quint, E. (1946). Self-selection of diet: 4. Appetite for protein. *Journal of Nutrition, 32*, 293–301. [3]

Scott, E. M., Smith, S., & Verney, E. (1948). Self-selection of diet: 7. The effects of age and pregnancy on selection. *Journal of Nutrition, 35*, 281–286. [3]

Scott, J. P. (1958). *Animal behavior*. Chicago: University of Chicago Press. [2]

Seale, A. (1901). Report of a mission to Guam. *Occasional Papers of the Bernice P. Bishop Museum, 1*, 17–128. [5]

Searcy, W. A. (1984). Song repertoire size and female preferences in song sparrows. *Behavioral Ecology and Sociobiology, 14*, 281–286. [14]

Searcy, W. A., & Marler, P. (1981). A test for responsiveness to song structure and programming in female sparrows. *Science, 213*, 926–928. [14]

Searcy, W. A., & Marler, P. (1984). Interspecific differences in the response of female birds to song repertoires. *Zeitschrift für Tierpsychologie, 66*, 128–142. [14]

Searcy, W. A., Marler, P., & Peters, S. S. (1981). Species song discrimination in adult female song and swamp sparrows. *Animal Behaviour, 29*, 997–1003. [14]

Seitz, P. F. D. (1954). The effects of infantile experiences upon adult behavior in animal subjects: 1. Effects of litter size during infancy upon adult behavior in the rat. *American Journal of Psychiatry, 110*, 916–928. [13]

Seligman, M. E. P. (1970). On the generality of the laws of learning. *Psychological Review, 77*, 406–418. [2]

Sevenster, P. (1973). Incompatibility of response and reward. In R. A. Hinde & J. Stevenson-Hinde (Eds.), *Constraints on learning: Limitations and predispositions* (pp. 265–283). New York: Academic Press. [9]

Shannon, C. E., and Weaver, W. (1949). *The mathematical theory of communication*. Urbana: University of Illinois. [16]

Shapiro, D. Y. (1983). Distinguishing behavioral interactions from visual cues as causes of adult sex change in a coral reef fish. *Hormones and Behavior, 17*, 424–432. [12]

Sharma, G. P., & Gupta, B. L. (1956). Cytological studies on the male germ cells of the spider *Pardosa* sp., with observations under the phase contrast microscope. *Research Bulletin of the Punjab University, 84*, 5–19. [7]

Sherman, P. W. (1976). Natural selection among some group-living organisms. Unpublished doctoral dissertation, University of Michigan, Ann Arbor. [8]

Sherman, P. W. (1977). Nepotism and the evolution of alarm calls. *Science, 197*, 1246–1253. [13]

Sherman, P. W. (1980). The limits of ground squirrel nepotism. In G. W. Barlow & J. Silverberg (Eds.), *Sociobiology: Beyond nature/nurture?* (pp. 505–544). Boulder: Westview Press. [8]

Sherman, P. W. (1981). Kinship, demography, and Belding's ground squirrel nepotism. *Behavioral Ecology and Sociobiology, 8*, 251–259. [13]

Sherman, P. W., & Holmes, W. G. (1985). Kin recognition: Issues and evidence. In B. Hölldobler & M. Lindauer (Eds.), *Experimental behavioral ecology and sociobiology* (pp. 437–460). Sunderland, MA: Sinauer Associates. [13]

Sherman, P. W., & Morton, M. L. (1984). Demography of Belding's ground squirrels. *Ecology, 65*, 1617–1628. [8]

Sherry, D. F. (1987). Foraging for stored food. In M. L. Commons, A. Kacelnik, & S. J. Shettleworth (Eds.), *Quantitative analyses of behavior: Vol. 6. Foraging* (pp. 209–227). Hillsdale, NJ: Lawrence Erlbaum Associates. [2]

Sherry, D. F. (1988). Learning and adaptation in food-storing birds. In R. C. Bolles & M. D. Beecher (Eds.), *Evolution and learning* (pp. 79–96). Hillsdale, NJ: Lawrence Erlbaum Associates. [16]

Sherry, D. F., Krebs, J. R., & Cowie, R. J. (1981). Memory for the location of stored food in marsh tits. *Animal Behaviour, 24*, 1260–1266. [8]

Shettleworth, S. J. (1972). Constraints on learning. *Advances in the Study of Behavior, 4*, 1–68. [2, 9]

Shettleworth, S. J. (1983). Function and mechanism in learning. In M. D. Zeiler & P. Harzem (Eds.), *Advances in analysis of behavior: Vol. 3. Biological factors in learning* (pp. 1–38). Chichester, England: John Wiley & Sons. [1, 2]

Shettleworth, S. J., & Krebs, J. R. (1982). How marsh tits find their hoards: the idea of site preference and spatial memory. *Journal of Experimental Psychology: Animal Behavior Processes, 8*, 354–375. [2]

Shibata, S., & Moore, R. Y. (1988). Electrical and metabolic activity of suprachiasmatic nucleus neurons in hamster hypothalmic slices. *Brain Research, 438*, 374–378. [11]

Shine, R., & Schwaner, T. (1985). Prey constriction by venomous snakes: A review, and new data on Australian species. *Copeia*, 1067–1071. [5]

Shugart, G. W. (1977). The development of chick recognition by adult Caspian terns. *Proceedings of the Colonial Waterbird Group, 1*, 110–117. [16]

Shugart, G. W. (1987). Individual clutch recognition by Caspian terns, *Sterna caspia*. *Animal Behaviour, 35*, 1563–1565. [16]

Silver, R., & Bittman, E. L. (1984). Reproductive mechanisms: Interaction of circadian and interval timing. In L. Allen and J. Gibbon (Eds.), *Timing and time perception. Annals of the New York Academy of Sciences, 423*, 488–514. [11]

Silver, R., & Gibson, M. J. (1980). Termination of incubation in doves: Influence of egg fertility and absence of mate. *Hormones and Behavior, 14*, 93–106. [11]

Silver, R., & Norgren, R. (1987). Avian circadian rhythms and behavior. In D. Crews (Ed.), *Psychobiology of reproductive behavior: An evolutionary perspective* (pp. 120–147). Englewood Cliffs, NJ: Prentice-Hall. [11]

Silver, R., & Ramos, C. (1989). *Endocrine control of sex differences in timing of dove parental behavior*. Unpublished manuscript. [11]

Simpson, M. J. A. (1976). The study of animal play. In P. P. G. Bateson & R. A. Hinde (Eds.), *Growing points in ethology* (pp. 385–400). Cambridge: Cambridge University Press. [12]

Simpson, S. M., & Follett, B. K. (1981). Pineal and hypothalamic pacemakers: Their role in regulating circadian rhythmicity in the Japanese quail. *Journal of Comparative Physiology, 144*, 381–389. [11]

Singer, A. G., Agosta, W. C., Clancy, A. N., & Macrides, F. (1987). The chemistry of vomeronasally detected pheromones: Characterization of an aphrodisiac protein. *Annals of the New York Academy of Sciences, 519*, 287–298. [17]

Singer, A. G., Agosta, W. C., O'Connell, R. J., Pfaffmann, C., Bowen, D. V., & Field, F. H. (1976). Dimethyl disulfide: An attractant pheromone in hamster vaginal secretion. *Science, 191*, 948–950. [17]

Singer, A. G., Clancy, A. N., Macrides, F., & Agosta, W. C. (1984). Chemical studies of hamster vaginal discharge: Male behavioral responses to a high molecular weight fraction require physical contact. *Physiology and Behavior, 33,* 645–651. [17]

Singer, A. G., Macrides, F., & Agosta, W. C. (1980). Chemical studies of hamster reproductive pheromones. In D. Müller-Schwarze and R. M. Silverstein (Eds.) *Chemical signals in vertebrates: Vol. 2. Vertebrates and aquatic invertebrates* (pp. 365–375). New York: Plenum Press. [3]

Singer, A. G., Macrides, F., Clancy, A. N., & Agosta, W. C. (1986). Purification and analysis of a proteinaceous aphrodisiac pheromone from hamster vaginal discharge. *Journal of Biological Chemistry, 261,* 13323–13326. [17]

Skinner, B. F. (1938). *The behavior of organisms.* New York: Appleton-Century-Crofts. [2]

Skinner, B. F. (1948). "Superstition" in the pigeon. *Journal of Experimental Psychology, 38,* 168–172. [2]

Small, W. S. (1900). An experimental study of the mental processes of the rat. *American Journal of Psychology, 11,* 131–165. [2]

Smith, A. P., & Alcock, J. (1980). A comparative study of the mating systems of Australian eumenid wasps (Hymenoptera). *Zeitschrift für Tierpsychologie, 53,* 41–60. [8]

Smith, C. C. (1968). The adaptive nature of social organization in the genus of three (sic) squirrels *Tamiasciurus. Ecological Monographs, 38,* 31–63. [8]

Smith, R. J. (1984). Allometric scaling in comparative biology: Problems of concept and method. *American Journal of Physiology, 246,* 152–160. [4]

Snowdon, C. T., Savage, A., & McConnell, P. B. (1985). A breeding colony of cotton-top tamarins (*Saguinus oedipus*). *Laboratory Animal Science, 35,* 477–480. [10]

Snowdon, C. T., & Suomi, S. J. (1982). Paternal behavior in infants. In H. E. Fitzgerald, J. A. Mullins, & P. Gage (Eds.), *Child nurturance: Volume 3. Studies of development in nonhuman primates* (pp. 63–108). New York: Plenum. [10]

Sohn, D. (1976). Two concepts of adaptation: Darwin's and psychology's. *Journal of the History of the Behavioral Sciences, 12,* 367–375. [E]

Sokal, R. R., & Rohlf, F. J. (1981). *Biometry* (2nd ed.). San Francisco: W. H. Freeman. [16]

Spalding, D. A. (1875). Instinct and acquisition. *Nature, 12,* 507–508. [2]

Speh, J. C., & Moore, R. Y. (1988). Development of the retinohypothalamic tract in the rat. *Society for Neuroscience Abstracts, 14,* 24.5. [11]

Staddon, J. E. R. (1977). Schedule-induced behavior. In W. K. Honig & J. E. R. Staddon (Eds.), *Handbook of operant behavior* (pp. 125–152). New York: Prentice-Hall. [2]

Staddon, J. E. R. (1983). *Adaptive behavior and learning.* Cambridge: Cambridge University Press. [9]

Staddon, J. E. R., & Simmelhag, V. L. (1971). The "superstition" experiment: A reexamination of its implications for the principles of adaptive behavior. *Psychological Review, 78,* 3–43. [2]

Stebbins, W. C. (1970). *Animal Psychophysics.* New York: Appleton-Century-Crofts. [16]

Steel, E., & Keverne, E. B. (1985). Effect of female odor on male hamsters mediated by the vomeronasal organ. *Physiology and Behavior, 35,* 195–200. [17]

Stephens, D. W. (in press). Risk and incomplete information in behavioral ecology. In E. Cashdan (Ed.), *Risk and uncertainty in tribal and peasant economies.* Boulder, CO: Westview Press. [1]

Stephens, D. W., & Krebs, J. R. (1986). *Foraging theory.* Princeton, NJ: Princeton University Press. [1, 9]

Stoddard, P. K., & Beecher, M. D. (1983). Parental recognition of offspring in the cliff swallow. *Auk, 100,* 795–799. [16]

Stribley, J. A., French, J. A., & Inglett, B. J. (1987). Mating patterns in the golden lion tamarin (*Leontopithecus rosalia*): Continuous receptivity and concealed estrus. *Folia Primatologica, 49,* 137–150. [10]

Strupp, B. J., & Levitsky, D. A. (1984). Social transmission of food preferences in adult hooded rats (*Rattus norvegicus*). *Journal of Comparative Psychology, 98,* 257–266. [3]

Sussman, R. W., & Garber, P. A. (1987). A new interpretation of the social organization and mating system of the Callitrichidae. *International Journal of Primatology, 8,* 73–92. [10]

Sutcliffe, A. G., & Poole, T. B. (1978). Scent marking and associated behaviour in captive common marmosets (*Callithrix jacchus*) with a description of the histology of the scent gland. *Journal of Zoology, London, 185,* 45–56. [10]

Sutcliffe, A. G., & Poole, T. B. (1984). An experimental analysis of social interactions in the common marmoset (*Callithrix jacchus jacchus*). *International Journal of Primatology, 5,* 591–607. [10]

Takahashi, J. S., & Menaker, M. (1979). Brain mechanisms in avian circadian systems. *Federation Proceedings, 38*, 2583–2588. [11]

Takahashi, J. S., & Menaker, M. (1984). Multiple redundant circadian oscillators within the avian pineal gland. *Journal of Comparative Physiology, 154*, 435–440. [11]

Takahashi, L. K., & Blanchard, R. J. (1978). Shock and defensive fighting in the rat. *Bulletin of the Psychonomic Society, 12*, 211–213. [18]

Takahashi, L. K., & Blanchard, R. J. (1982). Attack and defense in laboratory and wild Norway and black rats. *Behavioural Processes, 7*, 49–62. [18]

Takahashi, L. K., & Lisk, R. D. (1985). Estrogen action in anterior and ventromedial hypothalamus and the modulation of heterosexual behavior in female golden hamsters. *Physiology and Behavior, 34*, 233–239. [17]

Takahashi, L. K., Lisk, R. D., & Burnett, A. L. (1985). Dual estradiol action in diencephalon and the regulation of sociosexual behavior in female golden hamsters. *Brain Research, 359*, 194–207. [17]

Tardif, S. D. (1984). Social influences on sexual maturation of female *Saguinus oedipus oedipus*. *American Journal of Primatology, 6*, 199–209. [10]

Tardif, S. D., Carson, R. L., & Gangaware, B. L. (1986). Comparison of infant care in family groups of the common marmoset (*Callithrix jacchus*) and the cotton-top tamarin (*Saguinus oedipus*). *American Journal of Primatology, 11*, 103–110. [10]

Tardif, S. D., Richter, C. B., & Carson, R. L. (1984). Effects of sibling rearing experience on future reproductive success in two species of Callitrichidae. *American Journal of Primatology, 6*, 377–380. [10]

Taub, D. M. (1984). *Primate paternalism*. New York: Van Nostrand Reinhold, 1984. [10]

Taylor, C. R. (1977). The energetics of terrestrial locomotion and body size in vertebrates. In T. J. Pedley (Ed.), *Scale effects in animal locomotion* (pp. 127–141). London: Academic Press. [4]

Taylor, C. R., & Heglund, N. C. (1982). Energetics and mechanics of terrestrial locomotion. *Annual Review of Physiology, 44*, 97–107. [4]

Taylor, C. R., Heglund, N. C., & Maloiy, G. M. O. (1982). Energetics and mechanics of terrestrial locomotion: 1. Metabolic energy consumption as a function of speed and body size in birds and mammals. *Journal of Experimental Biology, 97*, 1–21. [4]

Taylor, C. S. (1985). Use of genetic size-scaling in evaluation of animal growth. *Journal of Animal Science, 61*, 118–143. [4]

Taylor, R. J. (1974). Role of learning in insect parasitism. *Ecological Monographs, 44*, 89–104. [5]

Taylor, R. J. (1984). *Predation* (pp. 1–166). New York: Chapman and Hall. [5]

Telle, H. J. (1966). Beitrag zur Kenntnis der Verhaltensweise von Ratten, vergleichend dargestellt bei *Rattus norvegicus* und *Rattus rattus*. *Zeitschift für Angewandte Zoologie, 53*, 129–196. [3]

Terborgh, J., & Goldizen, A. W. (1985). On the mating system of the cooperatively breeding saddle-backed tamarin (*Saguinus fuscicollis*). *Behavioral Ecology and Sociobiology, 16*, 293–299. [10]

Terrace, H. S. (1984). Animal learning, ethology, and biological constraints. In P. Marler & H. S. Terrace (Eds.), *The biology of learning* (pp. 15–45). Berlin: Springer-Verlag. [9]

Thierry, B., & Anderson, J. R. (1986). Adoption in anthropoid primates. *International Journal of Primatology, 7*, 191–216. [10]

Thiessen, D. D., & Rice, M. (1976). Mammalian scent gland marking and social behavior. *Psychological Bulletin, 83*, 505–539. [17]

Thompson, D. C. (1977). Reproductive behavior of the grey squirrel. *Canadian Journal of Zoology, 55*, 1176–1184. [8]

Thompson, T. (1966). Operant and classically conditioned aggressive behavior in Siamese fighting fish. *American Zoologist, 6*, 629–641. [9]

Thompson, T., & Sturm, T. (1965). Classical conditioning of aggressive display in Siamese fighting fish. *Journal of the Experimental Analysis of Behavior, 8*, 397–403. [9]

Thorndike, E. L. (1898). Animal intelligence: An experimental study of the associative processes in animals. *Psychological Review Monographs, 2* (Whole No. 8). [2]

Thorndike, E. L. (1900). Instinct. *Woods Hole Marine Biology Laboratory Biological Lectures, 7*, 57–67. [E]

Thornhill, R. (1979). Adaptive female-mimicking behavior in a scorpionfly. *Science, 205*, 412–414. [8]

Thornhill, R. (1984). Alternative hypotheses for traits believed to have been evolved by sperm competition. In R. L. Smith (Ed.), *Sperm competition and the evolution of animal mating systems* (pp. 151–179). Orlando, FL: Academic Press. [7]

Thornhill, R., & Alcock, J. (1983). *The evolution of insect mating systems*. Cambridge, MA: Harvard University Press. [8]

Tietjen, W. J., & Rovner, J. S. (1982). Chemical communication in lycosids and other spiders. In P. N. Witt & J. S. Rovner (Eds.), *Spider communication: Mechanisms and ecological significance* (pp. 249–279). Princeton, NJ: Princeton University Press. [7]

Timberlake, W. (1983a). Appetitive structure and straight alley running. In R. L. Mellgren (Ed.), *Animal cognition and behavior* (pp. 165–222). Amsterdam: North Holland Press. [2]

Timberlake, W. (1983b). The functional organization of appetitive behavior: Behavior systems and learning. In M. D. Zeiler & P. Harzem (Eds.), *Advances in analysis of behavior: Vol. 3. Biological factors in learning* (pp. 177–221). Chichester, England: John Wiley & Sons. [2, 9]

Timberlake, W. (1983c). Rat's responses to a moving object related to food or water: A behavior-systems analysis. *Animal Learning & Behavior, 11*, 309–320. [2]

Timberlake, W., Gawley, D. J., & Lucas, G. A. (1987). Time horizons in rats foraging for food in temporally separated patches. *Journal of Experimental Psychology: Animal Behavior Processes, 13*, 302–309. [2]

Timberlake, W., & Grant, D. L. (1975). Autoshaping in rats to the presentation of another rat predicting food. *Science, 190*, 690–692. [2]

Timberlake, W., & Lucas, G. A. (1985). The basis of superstitious behavior: Chance contingency, stimulus substitution, or appetitive behavior? *Journal of the Experimental Analysis of Behavior, 44*, 279–299. [2]

Timberlake, W., & Lucas, G. A. (in press). Behavior systems and learning: From misbehavior to general laws. In S. B. Klein & R. R. Mowrer (Eds.), *Contemporary learning theories: Instrumental conditioning theory and the impact of biological constraints on learning*. Hillsdale, NJ: Lawrence Erlbaum Associates. [2]

Timberlake, W., & Melcer, T. (1988). Effects of poisoning on predatory and ingestive behavior toward artificial prey in rats (*Rattus norvegicus*). *Journal of Comparative Psychology, 102*, 182–187. [2]

Timberlake, W., Wahl, G., & King, D. (1982). Stimulus and response contingencies in the misbehavior of rats. *Journal of Experimental Psychology: Animal Behavior Processes, 8*, 62–85. [2]

Timberlake, W., & Washburne, D. L. (1989). Feeding ecology and laboratory predatory behavior toward live and artificial moving prey in seven rodent species. *Animal Learning & Behavior, 17*, 2–11. [2]

Timberlake, W., & White, W. (1989). *Winning isn't everything: Food deprivation but not food reward is required to traverse the radial arm maze efficiently*. Unpublished manuscript, Indiana University, Bloomington.

Tinbergen, L. (1960). The natural control of insects in pinewoods. 1. Factors influencing the intensity of predation by songbirds. *Archives Néerlandaises de Zoologie, 13*, 266–343. [1, 5]

Tinbergen, N. (1951). *The study of instinct*. Oxford: Clarendon Press of Oxford University Press. [2, 5, 9, 10, 17, E]

Tinbergen, N. (1960). *The herring gull's world*. New York: Harper & Row. [9]

Tinbergen, N. (1963). On aims and methods of ethology. *Zeitschrift für Tierpsychologie, 20*, 410–429. [I, 5, 6, E]

Tinbergen, N., & Perdeck, A. C. (1950). On the stimulus situation releasing the begging response in the newly hatched herring gull chick (*Larus argentatus argentatus* Pont). *Behaviour, 3*, 1–39. [2]

Tomback, D. (1980). How nutcrackers find their seed stores. *Condor, 82*, 10–19. [1]

Tondat, L. M., & Daly, H. B. (1972). The combined effects of frustrative non-reward and shock on aggression between rats. *Psychonomic Science, 28*, 25–28. [18]

Tribe, D. (1954). The self-selection of purified food constituents by the rat during growth, pregnancy, and lactation. *Journal of Physiology, 124*, 64. [3]

Tribe, D. (1955). Choice of diet by rats: The choice of purified food constituents during growth, pregnancy, and lactation. *British Journal of Nutrition, 9*, 103–109. [3]

Trivers, R. L. (1972). Parental investment and sexual selection. In B. Campbell (Ed.), *Sexual selection and the descent of man 1871–1971* (pp. 136–179). Chicago: Aldine. [6, 7, 8, 9, 10]

Turek, F. W., Swann, J., & Earnest, D. (1984). Role of the circadian system in reproductive phenomena. In *Recent Progress in Hormone Research: Vol. 40*. New York: Academic Press. [11]

Turek, F. W., & Van Reeth, O. (1988a). Altering the mammalian circadian clock with the short-acting benzodiazepine, triazolam. *Trends in Neuroscience, 11,* 535–541. [11]

Turek, F. W., & Van Reeth, O. (1988b). Daily injections of triazolam induce long-term changes in the period of the circadian activity rhythm of golden hamsters. *Society for Neuroscience Abstracts, 14,* 366.4. [11]

Uetz, G. W. (1988). Risk sensitivity and foraging in colonial spiders. In C. N. Slobodchikoff (Ed.), *The ecology of social behavior* (pp. 353–377). New York: Academic Press. [7]

Ulrich, R. E., & Azrin, N. H. (1962). Reflexive fighting in response to aversive stimulation. *Journal of the Experimental Analysis of Behavior, 5,* 511–520. [18]

Vandenbergh, J. G. (1973). Effects of gonadal hormones on the flank gland of the golden hamster. *Hormone Research, 4,* 28–33. [17]

Vandenbergh, J. G. (Ed.) (1983). *Pheromones and reproduction in mammals.* New York: Academic Press. [6]

Vander Wall, S. B. (1982). An experimental analysis of cache recovery in Clark's nutcracker. *Animal Behaviour, 30,* 84–94. [1]

Vander Wall, S. B., & Hutchins, H. E. (1983). Dependence of Clark's nutcracker (*Nucifraga columbiana*) on conifer seeds during the postfledgling period. *Canadian Field Naturalist, 97,* 208–214. [1]

Vehrencamp, S. L., & Bradbury, J. W. (1984). Mating systems and ecology. In J. R. Krebs & N. B. Davies (Eds.), *Behavioural ecology: An evolutionary approach* (pp. 251–278). Oxford: Blackwell Scientific Publications. [9]

Vogt, R. C., & Bull, J. J. (1984). Ecology of hatchling sex ratio in map turtles. *Ecology, 65,* 582–587. [12]

Vollrath, F. (1980a). Male body size and fitness in the web-building spider *Nephila clavipes. Zeitschrift für Tierpsychologie, 53,* 61–78. [7]

Vollrath, F. (1980b). Why are some males small? A discussion including observations on *Nephila clavipes. Proceedings of the Eighth International Arachnological Congress* (pp. 165–169). Wien: Verlag Egerman. [7]

Vollrath, F. (1987). Growth, foraging, and reproductive success. In W. Nentwig (Ed.), *Ecophysiology of spiders* (pp. 357–370). Berlin: Springer-Verlag. [7]

Voss, R. (1979). Male accessory glands and the evolution of copulatory plugs in rodents. *Occasional Papers, Museum of Zoology, University of Michigan, 689,* 1–27. [8]

Waage, J. K. (1979). Dual function of the damselfly penis: Sperm removal and transfer. *Science, 203,* 916–918. [8]

Waldman, B. (1982). Sibling association among schooling toad tadpoles: field evidence and implications. *Animal Behaviour, 30,* 700–713. [13]

Waldman, B. (1987). Mechanisms of kin recognition. *Journal of Theoretical Biology, 128,* 159–185. [13]

Wallman, J., Grabon, M. B., & Silver, R. (1979). What determines the pattern of sharing incubation and brooding in ring doves? *Journal of Comparative Physiological Psychology, 93,* 481–492. [11]

Waltz, E. C. (1982). Resource characteristics and the evolution of information centers. *American Naturalist, 119,* 73–90. [3]

Ward, I. L. (1972). Prenatal stress feminizes and demasculinizes the behavior of males. *Science, 175,* 82–84. [12]

Ward, P., & Zahavi, A. (1973). The importance of certain assemblages of birds as "information-centres" for food finding. *Ibis, 115,* 517–534. [3]

Warren, R. P., & Pfaffmann, C. (1959). Early experience and taste aversion. *Journal of Comparative and Physiological Psychology, 52,* 263–266. [3]

Washburn, M. F. (1908). *The animal mind: A text-book of comparative psychology.* New York: Macmillan. [E]

Watson, J. B. (1925). *Behaviorism.* New York: Norton. [9]

Webb, P. W. (1978). Fast-start performance and body form in seven species of teleost fish. *Journal of Experimental Biology, 74,* 211–226. [4]

Webb, P. W. (1984a). Body form, locomotion and foraging in aquatic vertebrates. *American Zoologist, 24,* 107–120. [4]

Webb, P. W. (1984b). Form and function in fish swimming. *Scientific American, 251(1)*, 72–82. [4]

Weisz, J., & Ward, I. L. (1980). Plasma testosterone and progesterone titers of pregnant rats, their male and female fetuses, and neonatal offspring. *Endocrinology, 106*, 306–316. [12]

Wells, K. (1977). The social behaviour of anuran amphibians. *Animal Behaviour, 25*, 666–693. [8]

Wenner, A. M. (1971). *The language controversy*. Boulder, CO: Educational Programs Improvement Corp. [3]

Wenzl, P. (1980). *Mating behavior and egg productivity in the orb weaving spider*, Nephila clavipes. Unpublished masters thesis, Tulane University, New Orleans. [7]

Werner, Y. L. (1983). Behavioural triangulation of the head in three boigine snakes: A possible case of mimicry. *Israel Journal of Zoology, 32*, 205–228. [5]

Werner, Y. L. (1985). Similarities of the colubrid snakes *Spalerosophis* and *Pythonodipsas* to vipers: An additional hypothesis. *Copeia*, 266–268. [5]

Werner, Y. L. (1986). Evolutionary complications of occasional (non-mimetic) behavioral triangulation of the head in snakes (*Coluber rhodorhachis* and *Malpolon monspessulanus*). *The Snake, 18*, 37–41. [5]

Werner, Y. L., & Frankenberg, E. (1982). Head triangulation in the colubrine snakes: Probably behavioural reinforcement of Batesian mimicry. *Israel Journal of Zoology, 31*, 137–150. [5]

West, M. J., & King, A. P. (1980). Enriching cowbird song by social deprivation. *Journal of Comparative and Physiological Psychology, 93*, 263–270. [14]

West, M. J., & King, A. P. (1985). Social guidance of vocal learning by female cowbirds: Validating its functional significance. *Zeitschrift für Tierpsychologie, 70*, 225–235. [14]

West, M. J., & King, A. P. (1986). Song repertoire development in male cowbirds (*Molothrus ater*): Its relationship to female discrimination of song potency. *Journal of Comparative Psychology, 100*, 296–303. [14]

West, M. J., & King, A. P. (1987). Settling nature and nurture into an ontogenetic niche. *Developmental Psychobiology, 20*, 549–562. [13, 14]

West, M. J., & King, A. P. (1988a). Ontogenetic programs underlying geographic variation in cowbird song. In Ouellet, H. (Ed.), *Acta 19 Congressus Internationalis Ornithologici* (Vol. 1, pp. 1598–1605). Ottawa: University of Ottawa Press. [14]

West, M. J., & King, A. P. (1988b). Visual displays by female cowbirds affect the development of song in males. *Nature, 334*, 244–246. [14]

West, M. J., & King, A. P. (1988c). Vocalizations of juvenile cowbirds (*Molothrus ater ater*) evoke copulatory responses from females. *Developmental Psychobiology, 21*, 543–552. [14]

West, M. J., & King, A. P. (1989). Cowbird song. *Nature, 339*, 21–22. [14]

West, M. J., King, A. P., & Eastzer, D. H. (1981). Validating the female bioassay of cowbird song: Relating differences in song potency to mating success. *Animal Behaviour, 29*, 490–501. [14]

West, M. J., King, A. P., & Harrocks, T. J. (1983). Cultural transmission of cowbird song (*Molothrus ater*): Measuring its development and outcome. *Journal of Comparative Psychology, 97*, 327–337. [3, 14]

West-Eberhard, M. J. (1983). Sexual selection, social competition, and speciation. *Quarterly Review of Biology, 58*, 155–183. [14]

Whitsett, J. M. (1975). The development of aggressive and marking behavior in intact and castrated male hamsters. *Hormones and Behavior, 6*, 47–57. [17]

Whitten, W. K. (1966). Pheromones and mammalian reproduction. *Advances in Reproductive Physiology, 1*, 155–177. [17]

Wiehle, H. (1961). Der embolus des männlichen spinnentasters. *Zoologischer Anzeiger* (Suppl. 24), 457–480. [7]

Williams, G. C. (1966). *Adaptation and natural selection: A critique of some current evolutionary thought*. Princeton, NJ: Princeton University Press. [1, 3, 6, 7, 16]

Williams, G. C. (1975). *Sex and evolution*. Princeton, NJ: Princeton University Press. [12]

Wilson, E. O. (1975). *Sociobiology: The new synthesis*. Cambridge, MA: Belknap Press of Harvard University Press. [5, 9, 10, 18]

Wilson, E. O., & Bossert, W. H. (1963). Chemical communication among animals. *Recent Progress in Hormone Research, 19*, 673–710. [17]

Winans, S. S., & Powers, J. B. (1977). Olfactory and vomeronasal deafferentation of male hamsters: Histological and behavioral analyses. *Brain Research, 126*, 325–344. [17]

496 LITERATURE CITED

Winans, S. S., & Scalia, F. (1970). Amygdaloid nucleus: New afferent input from the vomeronasal organ. *Science, 170,* 330–332. [17]

Witschi, E. (1961). Sex and secondary sexual characters. In A. J. Marshall (Ed.), *Biology and comparative physiology of birds* (Vol. 2, pp. 115–168). New York: Academic Press. [12]

Wolff, J. O., Freeberg, M. H., & Dueser, R. D. (1983). Interspecific territoriality in two sympatric species of *Peromyscus* (Rodentia: Cricetidae). *Behavioral Ecology and Sociobiology, 12,* 237–242. [6]

Woolfenden, G. E., & Fitzpatrick, J. W. (1984). *The Florida scrub jay: Demography of a cooperatively breeding bird.* Princeton, NJ: Princeton University Press. [10]

Wright, P. C. (1986). Ecological correlates of monogamy in *Aotus* and *Callicebus.* In J. Else & P. Lee (Eds.), *Primate ecology and conservation* (pp. 159–167). Cambridge: Cambridge University Press. [10]

Wright, S. (1943). Isolation by distance. *Genetics, 28,* 114–138. [15]

Wysocki, C. J. (1979). Neurobehavioral evidence for the involvement of the vomeronasal system in mammalian reproduction. *Neuroscience and Biobehavioral Reviews, 3,* 301–341. [17]

Yahr, P. (1988). Sexual differentiation of behavior in the context of developmental psychobiology. In E. M. Blass (Ed.), *Handbook of behavioral neurobiology: Vol. 9. Developmental psychobiology and behavioral ecology* (pp. 197–243.) New York: Plenum. [12]

Yamada, S., Mikami, S., & Yanaihara, N. (1982). Immunohistochemical localization of vasoactive intestinal polypeptide (VIP)-containing neurons in the hypothalamus of the Japanese quail, *Coturnix coturnix. Cell and Tissue Research, 226,* 13–26. [11]

Yoerg, S. I., Clements, K. C., & Kamil, A. C. (1989). *Effects of variable patch quality on departure rules in blue jays.* Unpublished manuscript. [1]

Yokel, D. A. (1986). Monogamy and brood parasitism: an unlikely pair. *Animal Behaviour, 34,* 1348–1358. [14]

Zamble, E., Hadad, G. M., Mitchell, J. B., & Cutmore, T. R. H. (1985). Pavlovian conditioning of sexual arousal: First- and second-order effects. *Journal of Experimental Psychology: Animal Behavior Processes, 11,* 598–610. [9]

Ziegler, T. E., Bridson, W. E., Snowdon, C. T., & Eman, S. (1987). Urinary gonadotropin and estrogen excretion during the postpartum estrus, conception and pregnancy in the cotton-top tamarin (*Saguinus oedipus oedipus*). *American Journal of Primatology, 12,* 127–140. [10]

Ziegler, T. E., Savage, A., Scheffler, G., & Snowdon, C. T. (1987). The endocrinology of puberty and reproductive functioning in female cotton-top tamarins (*Saguinus oedipus*) under varying social conditions. *Biology of Reproduction, 37,* 618–627. [10]

Ziegler, T. E., Sholl, S., Scheffler, G., Haggerty, M. A., & Lasley, B. L. (1989). Excretion of estrone, estradiol and progesterone in the urine and feces of the female cotton-top tamarin (*Saguinus oedipus oedipus*). *American Journal of Primatology, 17,* 185–195. [10]

Zimmerman, N. H., & Menaker, M. (1975). Neural connections of sparrow pineal: Role in circadian control of activity. *Science, 190,* 477–490. [11]

Zucker, I. (1980). Light, behavior, and biologic rhythms. In D. T. Krieger and J. C. Hughes (Eds.), *Neuroendocrinology* (pp. 93–101). Sunderland, MA: Sinauer Associates. [11]

Index

Acomys cahirinus, *see* Spiny mice
Adaptation, 433, 434, 437, 443–446
    allometry and, 80, 81, 85, 88, 89, 91, 94, 96
    communication and, 319
    feeding and, 3, 4
    foraging and, 7, 25, 29
    ground squirrel and, 188, 190
    mating and, 127, 128
    monkeys and, 228, 229, 246, 248
    Norway rats and, 55–79
    Pavlovian conditioning and, 198, 211,
        216–219
    song development and, 343, 345, 351, 358
    species-typical behavior and, 321, 338
    spiny mice and, 314
    swallows and, 360–363, 372, 373, 377–380
    vertebrate sexual behavior and, 280, 286
Adjunctive behavior
    feeding and, 3
    laboratory paradigms and, 42–44
Adoption, monkeys and, 248
Aggregation sites, Norway rats and, 58
Aggression, 436, 439, 442, 444, 445
    colony model and, 410–414, 419–430
    communication and, 320
    deer mice and, 142, 143, 145, 146
    golden hamster and, 382, 384, 387, 388,
        390, 395, 408
    ground squirrel and, 175, 178, 181, 183,
        192, 193, 196
    laboratory paradigms and, 37
    mating and, 128
    monkeys and, 227, 229–231, 239, 242, 246,
        247, 251
    orb-weaving spider and, 150, 162
    Pavlovian conditioning and, 199–215, 218,
        219
    song development and, 345
    spiny mice and, 313
Alarm calling, ground squirrel and, 175
Albino rats, laboratory paradigms and, 33
Allometry, 81–100, 436, 437, 439, 443
    feeding and, 4
    vertebrate sexual behavior and, 286
Alouatta seniculus, 230, 250
Amphibians, brown tree snake and, 109
Anthias squamipinnis, 280
Anticipatory response, 197, 198, 210, 216–218
Anxiety, species-typical behavior and, 339
Aotus trivirgatus, 249

Aphelocoma coerulescens, *see* Scrub jay
Appetitive structure, 34–36, 38, 40, 44, 48,
    51–54
Artificial settings, 31–33, 36–38
Aspect ratio, 93–96
Association, laboratory paradigms and, 32
Assortative mating, 351, 352
Attack, 412, 413, 416–420, 423, 424, 427–430,
    442
Autoshaping
    feeding and, 3
    laboratory paradigms and, 44–52
Avian species, *see* Birds
Avoidance
    colony model and, 424
    doves and, 266
    ground squirrel and, 188–190
    laboratory paradigms and, 36
    mating and, 125
    Norway rats and, 76, 78, 79
    Pavlovian conditioning and, 197, 207

Baboon, monogamy and, 235, 248
Bank swallows, 365–369, 371, 372, 376,
    378–380
Barn swallows, 365–367, 369–372, 375–378,
    380
Bats
    allometry and, 93–96, 100
    brown tree snake and, 122
    recognition and, 362
Begging
    laboratory paradigms and, 41, 42
    monkeys and, 245
    swallows and, 369
Behavior system approach, 34–36
Behavioral biology, 343, 344
Behavioral ecology, 198, 199, 219
Betta splendens, 200, 207
Bias
    foraging and, 23
    Norway rats and, 58
Biological timing, doves and, *see* Doves,
    parental care and
Biology
    allometry and, 82, 83
    colony model and, 419
    communication and, 318, 320
    deer mice and, 129
    foraging and, 25, 29

laboratory paradigms and, 33, 34
Pavlovian conditioning and, 198, 199, 207
song development and, 342–344
Bird song development, 340, 341, 356–359
design, 343–349
reductionism, 341–343
white-crowned sparrow, 349–356
Birds, 437–439, 441, 445, 447, 448, see also
specific bird
allometry and, 89, 90, 94, 96, 100
biological timing and, 262, 275–277
brown tree snake and, 102, 103, 109, 110,
114, 118, 119, 122
communication and, 317–319
feeding and, 1, 5
foraging and, 9, 25
ground squirrel and, 188
laboratory paradigms and, 32
monkeys and, 227
Norway rats and, 58, 59, 78
parental care and, 222
Pavlovian conditioning and, 218
species-typical behavior and, 321, 322, 335,
336, 338
vertebrate sexual behavior and, 286, 287
Black-tailed prairie dog, 179, 182, 189, 192,
193, 195
Blackbird, 78
Blue gourami, 437, 438, 440
Pavlovian conditioning and, 199–201,
210–212, 215–219
Blue jay, 438, 439
foraging and, 10, 11, 13–25, 29, 30
laboratory paradigms and, 32
Bluegill sunfish, 283
Body care, laboratory paradigms and, 34
Body size, 443
allometry and, 81, 85, 87–89, 91, 93,
96–99
ground squirrel and, 184, 185
Pavlovian conditioning and, 200
vertebrate sexual behavior and, 286
Boiga irregularis, see Brown tree snake
Brain size, 80, 81, 91, 93, 94, 97
Brown tree snake, 101, 102, 121–123, 438,
440, 441, 444, 448
feeding and, 5
locomotion, 116–121
predation, 106–116
problems, 102, 103
starting, 103–106
Brunswik, E., 343, 344, 347, 441
Buffalo, 326

Cache, 437, 438, 440, 445
foraging and, 25–30
ground squirrel and, 188

Callicebus moloch, 230
Callithrix jacchus, see Marmoset
Callitrichids, 232, 241, 242
Canary, 284
Carbon disulfide
feeding and, 3
Norway rats and, 70–72
Carbon sulfide, Norway rats and, 70
Cascades
parental care and, 223
vertebrate sexual behavior and, 289–295,
298, 299
Caspian tern, 369
Catastrophic depletion, 13
Catocala, 11
Causation
brown tree snake and, 105
monkeys and, 226, 247
Cebuella pygmaea, see Pygmy marmoset
Cercopithecus neglectus, 227
Chacma baboons, 235
Chemical communication in golden hamster,
see Golden hamster
Chicken
brown tree snake and, 103
doves and, 267, 274
vertebrate sexual behavior and, 285
Chimpanzee
allometry and, 86
laboratory paradigms and, 37
Chiropteran species, 93, 94
Cichlasoma nigrofasciatum, 212
Circadian clock, doves and, 253–255, 259–272,
274–277
Circadian control, parental care and, 222
Cliff swallows, 365, 366, 369, 371, 372,
375–380
Closed developmental programs, Norway rats
and, 56, 57
Cobra, 114
Cognition
allometry and, 80, 91
golden hamster and, 381, 408
Colony model of aggression and defense,
410–412, 428–430, 445
intraspecific attack, 412–418
neural studies, 428
offense–defense model, 420–427
offensive attack, 418–420
pharmacology, 427, 428
Colubridae, 112
Communication, 317–320, 436, 438, 442, 445,
447
in golden hamster, see Golden hamster
species-typical behavior and, 321, 322, 324,
332, 333, 335, 336, 339

Competition, 440, 444
  brown tree snake and, 105
  deer mice and, 131, 135–139, 145, 147
  doves and, 266
  golden hamster and, 388, 408
  ground squirrel and, 179–185, 187–194,
    196
  mating and, 126, 127
  monkeys and, 225
  orb-weaving spider and, 150, 162, 166, 169,
    174
  parental care and, 223
  Pavlovian conditioning and, 211, 214, 215,
    218
  species-typical behavior and, 323
  spiny mice and, 301, 302, 304, 305, 312
  vertebrate sexual behavior and, 283, 294
Conditioning, 442
  feeding and, 3
  foraging and, 10–24
  laboratory paradigms and, 32, 33, 36, 40,
    43, 46–52, 54
  mating and, 128
  Pavlovian, see Pavlovian conditioning
Conflict, ground squirrel and, 182–186, 195
Conservation, brown tree snake and, 101, 102
Conspecifics, 444
  colony model and, 411, 418, 422–424, 429
  communication and, 317
  deer mice and, 141
  doves and, 266
  feeding and, 3, 4
  golden hamster and, 385, 387, 393, 402,
    403, 405, 408
  mating and, 125
  monkeys and, 227, 230
  Norway rats and, 58, 66, 70, 73, 78, 79
  Pavlovian conditioning and, 199, 217
  species-typical behavior and, 322, 323, 338
  spiny mice and, 302, 304, 307, 310–312,
    314
  swallows and, 366, 368, 372
  vertebrate sexual behavior and, 288, 297
Constraint
  doves and, 266
  laboratory paradigms and, 32, 52, 53
  Pavlovian conditioning and, 198
Context, 444, 445
  golden hamster and, 389, 390, 404
  monkeys and, 231
  Norway rats and, 66–72, 79
  Pavlovian conditioning and, 207, 210
  song development and, 341, 343, 344, 346,
    347
  species-typical behavior and, 323
  swallows and, 368, 377
  vertebrate sexual behavior and, 288

Contingency, laboratory paradigms and, 41, 51,
    52
Control, laboratory paradigms and, 34
Convict cichlid, 212
Copulation
  deer mice and, 130–134, 137, 139, 143,
    145–147
  golden hamster and, 382, 383, 395–400,
    402, 409
  ground squirrel and, 175, 180, 181, 184,
    186, 188–196
  mating and, 125
  monkeys and, 232, 235
  orb-weaving spider and, 149, 150, 153–160,
    162–164, 169–173
  Pavlovian conditioning and, 215
  song development and, 349
  species-typical behavior and, 322–324,
    331–334, 336
  spiny mice and, 304
  vertebrate sexual behavior and, 281, 283,
    284, 292, 298
Coral reef fish, 280
Cotton-top tamarin, 225–227, 229–232, 234,
    235, 237, 241, 242, 244–247, 250, 439,
    444, 448
Cowbird, 436, 438, 439, 442, 444, 445, 447
  communication and, 317
  recognition and, 368
  species-typical behavior and, 322–333,
    336–339
Coyote, 48
Cricetus cricetus, 384
Cricket, 46, 52
Cross-fostering experiments, swallows and,
    366–369, 372
Crow, 25
Cued response, 38
Cues, 440, 445
  brown tree snake and, 107, 108, 114, 123
  deer mice and, 141
  doves and, 254, 255, 260, 263, 266, 268,
    270, 271, 273, 276, 277
  feeding and, 3, 5
  foraging and, 20, 23, 26, 29
  golden hamster and, 308, 383, 387, 389,
    396–398, 400
  monkeys and, 228, 238, 239, 241
  Norway rats and, 57, 63–68, 70
  orb-weaving spider and, 162
  Pavlovian conditioning and, 207, 210
  song development and, 347
  species-typical behavior and, 333, 336, 337
  spiny mice and, 304, 310
  swallows and, 363, 364, 368, 370, 379
  vertebrate sexual behavior and, 280, 289
Cyanocitta cristata, see Blue jay

Cynomys ludovicianus, 179, 182, 189, 192, 193, 195

Darwin, C., 432, 433
  deer mice and, 129
  laboratory paradigms and, 31
  Norway rats and, 55
DeBrazza's monkey, 227
Deer mice, 129–131, 147, 148, 439, 442, 443
  allometry and, 82
  complex social situations, 142–146
  copulation, 131–133
  ejaculate disruption, 137–139
  littermates and, 302
  male capacity, 139
  mating and, 125, 127
  natural selection, 129, 130
  parental behavior, 146
  pregnancy, 133–135, 137, 138
  social discrimination, 140–142
  sperm competition, 135–137
Defense, 442, 445
  colony model and, 413, 414, 416–430
  communication and, 320
  golden hamster and, 389, 390
  ground squirrel and, 178, 179, 181, 188, 195
  laboratory paradigms and, 34
  monkeys and, 226, 229
  orb-weaving spider and, 153, 161, 165, 166, 173
  Pavlovian conditioning and, 200, 202–208
  vertebrate sexual behavior and, 287
Demonstrator
  feeding and, 3
  Norway rats and, 59–72, 75
Density, song development and, 348
Desert rodents, foraging and, 8, 25
Developmental programs, Norway rats and, 57, 79
Diet
  allometry and, 91, 99
  brown tree snake and, 109, 110
  Norway rats and, 55, 58–73, 75–78
  swallows and, 367
  vertebrate sexual behavior and, 286
Discrimination, 443
  communication and, 320
  deer mice and, 140–142, 147, 148
  golden hamster and, 387, 389, 405–407
  parental care and, 223
  Pavlovian conditioning and, 207
  species-typical behavior and, 323, 325, 329, 339
  spiny mice and, 302, 311, 314
  swallows and, 363, 364, 366, 369, 372, 377, 378

Diversity, 330–332, 334, 337, 339, 438
Dominance, 432, 440, 445
  colony model and, 411–414, 419, 421–427, 430
  communication and, 320
  deer mice and, 133, 136, 142, 143, 145, 147
  ground squirrel and, 178–180, 182–185, 194, 195
  monkeys and, 231
  species-typical behavior and, 323
Doves
  brown tree snake and, 118
  laboratory paradigms and, 42
Doves, parental care and, 252–254, 276, 277
  circadian oscillations, 274–276
  circadian rhythms, 259–272
  physiology of timekeeping, 272–274
  timekeeping, 254–259
Drosophila, 263
Ducklings, 32
Ducks, 283
Duration, Norway rats and, 61

Ecological release, 105
Ecology, 437, 441
  allometry and, 80–82, 88, 96, 97, 100
  brown tree snake and, 102, 108, 122
  colony model and, 423
  communication and, 318
  feeding and, 3, 5
  foraging and, 7, 10, 23, 24, 28, 30
  golden hamster and, 384
  ground squirrel and, 180–182
  laboratory paradigms and, 31–34, 46–52, 54
  orb-weaving spider and, 164, 166, 173, 174
  Pavlovian conditioning and, 198, 199, 211, 219
  song development and, 340, 358
  species-typical behavior and, 327, 329, 330, 336–339
  spiny mice and, 314
  swallows and, 361, 362
  vertebrate sexual behavior and, 285, 286, 289, 298
Ejaculation
  deer mice and, 131–136, 138–140, 147, 148
  ground squirrel and, 181, 189, 190
  monkeys and, 234
  orb-weaving spider and, 150, 156
  Pavlovian conditioning and, 214
  vertebrate sexual behavior and, 290–292, 298
Emotion, laboratory paradigms and, 31
Endocrinology
  colony model and, 411
  doves and, 277

golden hamster and, 390
mating and, 128
parental care and, 221
song development and, 358
Entrainment, doves and, 261, 262, 266, 268, 273
Environment, 433, 434, 440, 441, 444, 446, 448
allometry and, 83, 88, 90, 93, 94
brown tree snake and, 102
deer mice and, 140
doves and, 252, 254, 259, 262, 263, 266, 270–273, 277
feeding and, 2–5
foraging and, 10, 17, 18, 24
golden hamster and, 384, 385, 387, 390, 394, 407, 408
laboratory paradigms and, 33, 34, 36–40, 43, 52, 54
mating and, 126, 128
monkeys and, 229, 230, 237, 243, 250
Norway rats and, 56–58, 72, 75, 76, 78, 79
parental care and, 223
Pavlovian conditioning and, 211
species-typical behavior and, 322, 330, 338
spiny mice and, 300, 302, 311, 312, 314
swallows and, 367
vertebrate sexual behavior and, 280, 287, 294
Escalated aggression, 192, 193, 196
Escape, laboratory paradigms and, 36, 47
Ethology, 432–434, 441
brown tree snake and, 101, 106, 122
foraging and, 30
golden hamster and, 381–383, 407
laboratory paradigms and, 32, 37
song development and, 356
European hamster, 384
Evolution, 432, 434, 436–438
allometry and, 80, 96
brown tree snake and, 105, 110, 111, 122
communication and, 319
deer mice and, 129
feeding and, 5
foraging and, 29
golden hamster and, 398, 408
ground squirrel and, 180, 188
laboratory paradigms and, 34, 40
mating and, 125
Norway rats and, 56, 58
orb-weaving spider and, 149, 174
Pavlovian conditioning and, 198, 211
song development and, 342, 357, 358
species-typical behavior and, 327, 330, 337, 339
spiny mice and, 301

swallows and, 362, 365, 379, 380
vertebrate sexual behavior and, 278, 287, 298
Evolutionary Stable Strategy, 191–193
Exposure
laboratory paradigms and, 38–40
Norway rats and, 61
External validity, foraging and, 10
Extinction, brown tree snake and, 102

Facial expression, golden hamster and, 382
Facilitation, laboratory paradigms and, 39
Familiarity
colony model and, 419
deer mice and, 142, 145
Norway rats and, 65, 66
parental care and, 223
spiny mice and, 311, 315
Fear, laboratory paradigms and, 39
Feedback
doves and, 253
species-typical behavior and, 323, 324
Feeding, 1–5, 439
brown tree snake and, 104, 114
laboratory paradigms and, 34, 35, 39–44, 48, 51, 52
song development and, 344
swallows and, 369, 377
Female flexibility, species-typical behavior and, 329, 330
Finches, foraging and, 25
Fish, 438, *see also* specific fish
allometry and, 91, 93, 96, 99, 100
laboratory paradigms and, 32
mating and, 125, 128
Pavlovian conditioning and, 199–202, 207, 209, 213, 218
vertebrate sexual behavior and, 280
Fixed intervals, laboratory paradigms and, 41
Flank marking, 383–389, 400, 403, 407, 408, 438
Food, 440, 445
allometry and, 88, 89, 91, 93, 94, 96
colony model and, 423
deer mice and, 140
doves and, 252, 254, 259, 260, 263, 266
golden hamster and, 389
mating and, 125
monkeys and, 229, 233, 245, 249
Norway rats and, 55, 56, 58–61, 65, 66, 73–79
orb-weaving spider and, 151, 164, 165
parental care and, 223
Pavlovian conditioning and, 198, 207
species-typical behavior and, 336
spiny mice and, 301, 309, 312–314

Foraging, 7, 29, 30, 436, 438, 440, 441
  allometry and, 85, 86, 89–91, 93, 94, 96, 100
  brown tree snake and, 106–109, 119, 122
  doves and, 254, 255
  feeding and, 1, 3–5
  laboratory paradigms and, 32, 36, 40, 42, 43
  Norway rats and, 55, 58–61, 73, 75–77, 79
  orb-weaving spider and, 166
  patch, 7–10
  patch depletion, 10–24
  Pavlovian conditioning and, 208
  species differences, 24–29
  swallows and, 365
Frogs
  spiny mice and, 301
  vertebrate sexual behavior and, 283
Frontinella pyramitela, 157, 162
Frustration, colony model and, 410

Galapagos finches, 25
Geese, 283
Generalization, song development and, 341, 343, 348, 349, 352, 356
Genetic fitness, 130
Genetics
  allometry and, 96, 99, 100
  deer mice and, 135, 140, 142, 143, 145
  golden hamster and, 405, 407
  mating and, 125
  monkeys and, 247
  orb-weaving spider and, 164, 173
  parental care and, 223
  song development and, 353
  species-typical behavior and, 322, 336, 337
  spiny mice and, 311, 314
  vertebrate sexual behavior and, 278, 280, 285
Genotype
  deer mice and, 129
  Norway rats and, 57
  orb-weaving spider and, 174
  spiny mice and, 311
Gerbils
  laboratory paradigms and, 37
  spiny mice and, 302, 304–306
Gibbons, 232
Golden hamster, 381–384, 407–409, 438, 439, 441
  communication and, 319
  deer mice and, 131, 139
  flank marking, 384–391
  mediation, 398–407
  vaginal marking, 391–398
Grasshopper mice, 49
Ground squirrel, 175, 176, 195, 196, 437, 439, 440

interspecific diversity, 176–182
  reproduction, 191–195
  sexually selected traits, 183–190
Gull chicks, 32
Gymnorhinus cyanocephalus, *see* Pinyon jay

Habitat
  allometry and, 90, 91
  brown tree snake and, 104, 105, 116, 119
  colony model and, 414, 424, 427
  deer mice and, 144
  ground squirrel and, 177
  mating and, 126
  monkeys and, 226, 249
  Norway rats and, 56, 77
  parental care and, 222
  Pavlovian conditioning and, 210, 211
  species-typical behavior and, 339
  swallows and, 367
Habituation
  golden hamster and, 389
  Pavlovian conditioning and, 212
  song development and, 340, 341, 344, 345, 347
Hamadryas baboons, 232, 235
Hamsters, 436, 442
  biological timing and, 260, 261, 266, 267, 276, 277
  laboratory paradigms and, 45, 46
Herring gulls, 361
Hierarchy, 445
  allometry and, 91
  colony model and, 412, 413, 427, 430
  communication and, 320
  feeding and, 2
  laboratory paradigms and, 34, 36, 54
Hirundo pyrrhonota, *see* Cliff swallows
Hirundo rustica, *see* Barn swallows
Hoary marmots, 177, 178, 185, 192
Home range, 89–93, 96, 97, 440
Homeostasis, allometry and, 85, 90
Honeybees
  biological timing and, 254
  golden hamster and, 383, 396
  laboratory paradigms and, 37
  Norway rats and, 58, 78
  species-typical behavior and, 335
Hormones, 442
  doves and, 255–259, 271, 277
  golden hamster and, 387, 393, 395, 398, 400, 401, 407, 409
  monkeys and, 226, 233, 234, 236, 237, 239, 241–243, 247
  parental care and, 223
  song development and, 342, 359
  vertebrate sexual behavior and, 281, 282, 284, 288, 294, 298

Huddling, spiny mice and, 303, 304, 314, 315
Hull, C. L., laboratory paradigms and, 32
Hummingbirds, foraging and, 8
Hypothalamus
    doves and, 274–277
    golden hamster and, 388, 395
    vertebrate sexual behavior and, 297

Imitation, species-typical behavior and, 325, 326
Inclusive fitness, deer mice and, 130
Incubation
    doves and, 255–259, 269–271, 274, 276, 277
    song development and, 344
    species-typical behavior and, 322, 335
Inherited niches, 336, 337, 339, 437
Inhibition
    golden hamster and, 395
    Pavlovian conditioning and, 202–208
    spiny mice and, 313
Innate releasing mechanism, golden hamster and, 382, 383
Insects, see also specific insect
    brown tree snake and, 122
    golden hamster and, 396
    monkeys and, 230
    Pavlovian conditioning and, 216
Instinct, laboratory paradigms and, 31, 38
Intelligence, allometry and, 81
Internal validity, 10
Intersexual selection, 214–216, 218
Intertrial interval, 11
Intrasexual aggression, 230, 231
Intrasexual selection, 211–214, 218

Japanese quail, 214, 216–218, 437

Kin selection
    deer mice and, 130, 140, 141
    parental care and, 223
Kinship, ground squirrel and, 175
Kittiwakes, recognition and, 361
Komodo dragon, 111

Laboratory paradigms, natural learning in, 31, 32, 52–54, 439
    behavior system approach, 34–36
    deterring factors, 33
    ecological analysis, 38–52
    ecological considerations, 36–38
Language, 381, 382, 448
Lateral hypothalamic retinorecipient region, 275, 276
Learning, 431, 432, 435, 436, 439, 442–446, 448
    allometry and, 85
    foraging and, 7–30

mating and, 128
natural, laboratory paradigms and, see Laboratory paradigms
Norway rats and, 56–58, 72, 77
Pavlovian conditioning and, 198, 199, 202–208, 211, 216–219
song development and, 352, 353, 357
species-typical behavior and, 325, 330, 339
swallows and, 363, 379
Leontopithecus rosalia, 229
Lesions
    doves and, 276, 277
    golden hamster and, 382, 399, 400, 402, 404, 406
Linyphia litigiosa, 157, 162
Littermates, spiny mice and, 300–315
Lizards, 103, 110, 111, 122
Locomotion
    allometry and, 85–89, 91–93, 96, 99
    brown tree snake and, 104–106, 116–121
    doves and, 267, 268, 273, 274
    laboratory paradigms and, 43
    spiny mice and, 307, 309
Logarithmic transformations, 83
Lorenz, K., 436
    brown tree snake and, 105
    doves and, 255
    laboratory paradigms and, 32

Macaca mulatta, 235, 249
Marginal value theorem, 8, 9
Marmosets
    monogamy and, 225, 227, 229–232, 234, 241–246, 248, 250
    parental care and, 221
Marmota caligata, 177, 178, 185, 192
Marmota flaviventris, 179, 182, 189
Mating, 125–128, 437, 444, 445
    golden hamster and, 389, 393, 395, 397, 399
    ground squirrel and, 175–177, 180–195
    monkeys and, 228, 235, 236, 241
    orb-weaving spider and, 149–166, 169–173
    parental care and, 221
    Pavlovian conditioning and, 216, 218
    species-typical behavior and, 323, 329, 336
    spiny mice and, 310
    swallows and, 362
    vertebrate sexual behavior and, 278, 283–285, 288, 294
Mazes
    feeding and, 3
    golden hamster and, 394
    laboratory paradigms and, 38–40
    Norway rats and, 73, 74
Medial hypothalamic nucleus, 275, 276
Megachiropteran species, 93

Memory, 445, 446
  foraging and, 7–30
  ground squirrel and, 188
  laboratory paradigms and, 32
  species-typical behavior and, 335
Meriones unguiculatus, 52, 53
Mesocricetus auratus, *see* Golden hamster
Mesocricetus brandti, 387, 393
Mesocricetus neutoni, 384, 389
Metabolism
  allometry and, 81, 82, 86, 89, 90, 96, 99, 100
  colony model and, 420
  doves and, 252, 274, 276
  vertebrate sexual behavior and, 286
Mice, *see also* specific mice
  biological timing and, 267
  Pavlovian conditioning and, 209
Microchiropteran species, 93, 94
Midsong element, 327, 331
Migration
  song development and, 349, 351
  species-typical behavior and, 336
Mimicry
  brown tree snake and, 113
  vertebrate sexual behavior and, 283, 284
Misbehavior, laboratory paradigms and, 51–53
Mobility, ground squirrel and, 186, 187
Mode
  feeding and, 2
  laboratory paradigms and, 34, 35
Mollusks, 37
Molothrus ater, *see* Cowbird
Monarch butterflies, 32
Mongolian gerbil
  littermates and, 306
  vertebrate sexual behavior and, 290, 294, 298
Monkeys, *see also* specific monkey
  foraging and, 8
  Norway rats and, 78
  vertebrate sexual behavior and, 288, 289
Monkeys, monogamy in, 225–229, 250, 251, 444
  characteristics, 230–245
  integration, 245–248
  natural history, 229, 230
  paternal care, 248–250
Monogamy in monkeys, *see* Monkeys, monogamy in
Montane voles, 139
Morality, laboratory paradigms and, 31
Morphology
  allometry and, 84, 88
  brown tree snake and, 112
  doves and, 255
  foraging and, 27, 29

ground squirrel and, 176, 190
  monkeys and, 232
  orb-weaving spider and, 164
  Pavlovian conditioning and, 212
  species-typical behavior and, 326
  vertebrate sexual behavior and, 279–281, 283, 284, 286, 290, 291
Mortality
  colony model and, 425, 426
  spiny mice and, 308
Moth
  foraging and, 11, 13
  laboratory paradigms and, 32
Motivation
  allometry and, 85
  colony model and, 413, 422
  golden hamster and, 382, 385, 388
  laboratory paradigms and, 34, 35, 39, 51, 54
  orb-weaving spider and, 174
  species-typical behavior and, 335
  vertebrate sexual behavior and, 288
Mus musculus, 307, 308
Mustelids, 230

Natural learning in laboratory paradigms and, *see* Laboratory paradigms
Natural selection, 432, 443
  allometry and, 80, 81, 96
  communication and, 319
  deer mice and, 129, 130, 139, 147, 148
  feeding and, 2
  foraging and, 29
  mating and, 125, 126
  Norway rats and, 57
  orb-weaving spider and, 149, 150, 173, 174
  Pavlovian conditioning and, 200
  species-typical behavior and, 321
  swallows and, 360–364, 371, 372, 377
  vertebrate sexual behavior and, 286
Neo-Darwinism, 198, 199, 218
Nephila clavipes, *see* Orb-weaving spider
Nepotism, spiny mice and, 310–313, 315
Neurobiology, communication and, 320
Neuroendocrinology
  Pavlovian conditioning and, 199, 209, 210, 214, 219
  vertebrate sexual behavior and, 286, 292, 296
Niche, 437
  communication and, 318
  species-typical behavior and, 336–338
Night monkeys, 249
Norway rat, 55, 56, 77–79
  adaptation, 56–58
  colony model and, 411, 414, 416
  deer mice and, 131
  diet, 65–72

feeding and, 3
foraging, 58–61
messages, 61–65
relevance to outside world, 72–77
vertebrate sexual behavior and, 279, 285, 288, 289, 299
Novelty
deer mice and, 139
golden hamster and, 389, 406
laboratory paradigms and, 35, 49, 51
monkeys and, 231
spiny mice and, 302, 309, 312
Nucifraga, 25
Nutcracker, 25–30, 438, 439
Nuttall subspecies, 349, 350, 352, 354

Observers
feeding and, 3
Norway rats and, 58, 60–72
Offensive behavior, 413, 414, 416, 418–430, 442
Olfaction, 436, 438, 442
communication and, 319, 320
deer mice and, 141
feeding and, 3, 4
golden hamster and, 384, 391, 397–407, 409
monkeys and, 238, 239
Norway rats and, 56, 58, 61–67
spiny mice and, 308, 309, 311, 315
Ontogeny
allometry and, 81–83, 87, 100
brown tree snake and, 105, 106
monkeys and, 225, 226, 242, 247, 248, 250
Norway rats and, 56, 57
song development and, 356, 444
species-typical behavior and, 322, 326, 330–332, 337, 338
spiny mice and, 301, 302, 305, 311
vertebrate sexual behavior and, 279, 281, 288–290, 294, 295, 298
Onychomys leucogaster, 52, 53
Operant conditioning, 442
feeding and, 3
laboratory paradigms and, 36, 51, 52, 54
Operant simulation of patch depletion, 10–24
Optimality, foraging and, 8, 18, 20
Orb-weaving spider, 149, 150, 172–174, 438, 439, 444, 447
copulation, 153–155
mating, 160–165
methods, 152, 153
oviposition, 166, 167
postcopulatory behavior, 165, 166
reproduction, 156–160, 167–172
species, 150–152
Oscillation, doves and, 268, 273–276

Overmarking, 387
Oviposition
orb-weaving spider and, 150, 152, 157, 160, 166
spiny mice and, 301
Ovulation
monkeys and, 227, 228, 232–239, 241, 242, 245–247
parental care and, 222
Oxygen, allometry and, 86, 87

Pain-elicited aggression, 320, 420–422
Pairings, laboratory paradigms and, 41, 47
Papio cynocephalus, 235, 248
Papio hamadryas, 232, 235
Papio ursinus, 235
Parasitism
communication and, 317
species-typical behavior and, 325, 336
Parent–offspring recognition in swallows, *see* Swallows, recognition and
Parental care, 221–223
deer mice and, 146, 148
doves and, *see* Doves, parental care and
monkeys and, 226, 242–246, 248, 250, 251
spiny mice and, 300, 301
swallows and, 360
vertebrate sexual behavior and, 286, 287
Parid, foraging and, 29
Patch, 444
depletion, 435, 438
feeding and, 2
foraging and, 7–25
species-typical behavior and, 321, 339
Paternal care, 226–229, 248–251, 447, 448
Pavlov, I., 445
laboratory paradigms and, 32, 33, 36, 51
mating and, 127, 128
Pavlovian conditioning, 197–199, 218, 219
reproduction, 210–218
territorial behavior, 199–210
Perception
allometry and, 85
golden hamster and, 382, 398, 409
ground squirrel and, 186–188
swallows and, 364, 372, 376–380
Perceptual–motor module
feeding and, 2
laboratory paradigms and, 34, 36
Periodicity, parental care and, 222
Peromyscus, 39, 52, 53, 438
Peromyscus leucopus, 302
Peromyscus maniculatus, *see* Deer mice
Personality, species-typical behavior and, 335, 337
Pesticides, 103

Pharmacology, 427, 428
Phase shift, doves and, 261–266, 268
Phenotypes
    allometry and, 80
    deer mice and, 129, 130
    golden hamster and, 407
    ground squirrel and, 176, 183–190
    Norway rats and, 56–58, 79
    orb-weaving spider and, 149, 173, 174
    spiny mice and, 310, 311, 315
Pheromones, golden hamster and, 383,
    396–398, 407
Phidippus johnsoni, 157
Phylogeny, 435
    allometry and, 81–83, 99, 100
    brown tree snake and, 116
    foraging and, 25
    monkeys and, 225–227, 246, 247
    parental care and, 221
    Pavlovian conditioning and, 209
    species-typical behavior and, 337
    vertebrate sexual behavior and, 285, 298
Pigeons, 438
    biological timing and, 255
    laboratory paradigms and, 32, 38, 40–42
    Pavlovian conditioning and, 214
Pigs, 51
Pineal gland
    doves and, 267, 274
    parental care and, 222
Pinyon jay, 27, 28
Pisaura mirabilis, 163
Plasticity, 446, 447
    feeding and, 1, 5
    song development and, 352
    vertebrate sexual behavior and, 282, 284,
        285, 298
Poisson distribution, foraging and, 14
Polarization, colony model and, 413, 427
Polydipsia, laboratory paradigms and, 42, 53
Polygyny
    ground squirrel and, 176, 178–183, 188,
        195
    monkeys and, 228, 230, 232, 235, 248–250
    Pavlovian conditioning and, 211, 214, 218
    vertebrate sexual behavior and, 283
Population, 436, 438
    allometry and, 99, 100
    brown tree snake and, 102–105
    communication and, 317, 318
    deer mice and, 129
    feeding and, 5
    ground squirrel and, 177, 178, 182, 184,
        190, 192, 195
    song development and, 340, 351, 357
    species-typical behavior and, 322, 323,
        327–331, 333–339

Postcopulatory behavior
    ground squirrel and, 181, 189, 191–193,
        196
    orb-weaving spider and, 150, 160, 165,
        166, 173
Prairie voles, 142
Predation
    brown tree snake and, 105–116, 123
    colony model and, 411, 419, 423
    doves and, 252, 266
    feeding and, 1, 3, 5
    ground squirrel and, 175, 194
    laboratory paradigms and, 34, 39, 46–48
    mating and, 125, 126
    monkeys and, 230, 249
    orb-weaving spider and, 151, 162
    Pavlovian conditioning and, 211, 215
    song development and, 342
    vertebrate sexual behavior and, 287
Predisposition, laboratory paradigms and, 52, 53
Pregnancy
    deer mice and, 133–135, 137, 138, 147
    golden hamster and, 393
    ground squirrel and, 175
    mating and, 125
    monkeys and, 228, 234, 238, 242, 247
    vertebrate sexual behavior and, 292, 294
Principle of similitude, allometry and, 84, 85
Protein
    golden hamster and, 395, 396, 408, 409
    monkeys and, 230
    Norway rats and, 76
    Pavlovian conditioning and, 211
Proximate causation, 434, 435
    deer mice and, 130
    mating and, 128
    parental care and, 222
Proximate effects, swallows and, 365, 372
Proximate mechanisms
    communication and, 319, 320
    Pavlovian conditioning and, 200
    song development and, 341, 342, 352, 353,
        356, 358
    species-typical behavior and, 330
Proximity
    feeding and, 2
    Pavlovian conditioning and, 216
    species-typical behavior and, 329, 332
Pteropus mariannus, 103
Pygmy marmoset, 229, 232, 242, 247
Pythons, 111

Rabbits, 301
Raccoon, 51, 52
Raptors, 230
Rats, 436, 438–440, 442, 445, *see also* specific
    rat

biological timing and, 267, 274–277
brown tree snake and, 111
colony model and, 411–414, 418, 419, 421, 423, 424, 427, 429
deer mice and, 139
feeding and, 3, 4
laboratory paradigms and, 33, 34, 37–40, 43–47
littermates and, 302, 305, 308
Pavlovian conditioning and, 214
vertebrate sexual behavior and, 285, 288, 291–298
Rattus norvegicus, *see* Norway rat
Rattus rattus, colony model and, 414
Recognition, 443
communication and, 318, 319
golden hamster and, 404, 405, 407–409
parental care and, 223
spiny mice and, 310, 311, 315
swallows and, *see* Swallows
Red howler monkeys, 230, 250
Reductionism, song development and, 341–343
Reinforcement
feeding and, 3
foraging and, 14
Reproduction, 433, 435, 443, 445, 447
allometry and, 89, 90, 99
brown tree snake and, 104, 105, 108
communication and, 317, 319
deer mice and, 130, 133–137, 140, 144, 146, 147
doves and, 255, 274, 276
feeding and, 3
golden hamster and, 408, 409
ground squirrel and, 175, 176, 181, 183–185, 190–196
laboratory paradigms and, 34
mating and, 125–127
monkeys and, 227, 228, 232, 235–239, 242, 245–248, 251
Norway rats and, 57
orb-weaving spider and, 149, 150, 156–160, 162–173
parental care and, 222
Pavlovian conditioning and, 197, 199, 200, 210–219
song development and, 340, 342, 345–347, 357
species-typical behavior and, 323
spiny mice and, 304, 310
swallows and, 360, 365
vertebrate sexual behavior and, 278, 279, 281–283, 285–287, 292, 298
Reptiles
brown tree snake and, 109
vertebrate sexual behavior and, 286

Response-dependent reward, laboratory paradigms and, 38, 51
Responsiveness
colony model and, 419
golden hamster and, 394, 409
song development and, 347
species-typical behavior and, 332–335, 339
Retention interval, foraging and, 26, 28
Retina, doves and, 275
Retino-hypothalamic tract, parental care and, 222
Retrieval, laboratory paradigms and, 46, 47
Rhesus macaques, 235, 249
Rhesus monkey
monogamy and, 248
vertebrate sexual behavior and, 288
Ring doves, 222, 254, 255, 440
Riparia riparia, *see* Bank swallows
Rodents, *see also* specific rodent
allometry and, 91
brown tree snake and, 107, 109, 114–116
foraging and, 8
laboratory paradigms and, 39, 52
littermates and, 300, 302, 309, 312
monogamy and, 227
species-typical behavior and, 335
vertebrate sexual behavior and, 285, 298
Rough-winged swallows, 365–372, 375, 376, 379, 380
Roumanian hamster, 384, 389
Run of bad luck
feeding and, 2
foraging and, 9, 15, 18–23, 29

Saguinus oedipus, *see* Cotton-top tamarin
Saimiri sciureus, 230
Sampling, foraging and, 15
Sciurus, 189, 192, 194
Scramble competition, 180, 182, 183, 195, 440
Scrub jay
foraging and, 27–29
monogamy and, 246
Sea bass, 283
Search routines, feeding and, 3
Semiochemicals, Norway rats and, 70–72
Sensory gating, song development and, 353, 357
Sequence, laboratory paradigms and, 36, 54
Serranus subligarius, 283
Sex determination, 279, 280, 288
Sexual dimorphism
allometry and, 91, 99
deer mice and, 131
golden hamster and, 390, 398
ground squirrel and, 183, 185
monkeys and, 227, 231, 232
Sexual selection
deer mice and, 139

ground squirrel and, 176, 183–190
Pavlovian conditioning and, 216
Siamangs, 227
Sigmodon hispidus, 52, 53
Signals
    golden hamster and, 382, 407–409
    Pavlovian conditioning and, 197, 198, 200, 208, 210, 213, 214, 219
    species-typical behavior and, 331, 335
    spiny mice and, 304
    swallows and, 364, 372, 373, 379
    vertebrate sexual behavior and, 283
Signature call, 372, 376, 378–380
Similitude, allometry and, 84, 85
Simple exposure, 38–40
Simple familiarity hypothesis, 65, 66
Skinner, B. F., 32, 37, 40, 42
Snakes, *see also* specific snake
    monogamy and, 230
    vertebrate sexual behavior and, 283
Social discrimination, 140–142, 147, 148
Social interaction, 175
Social learning
    feeding and, 1, 3
    Norway rats and, 56–58, 72, 77
Sociobiology, 435, 443
Song, 438, 441, 445, 447, 448
    communication and, 317, 318
    development, *see* Bird song development
    laboratory paradigms and, 31, 32, 36
    species-typical behavior and, 321–334, 336–339
Sparrow, doves and, 276
Spatial ability, ground squirrel and, 186, 188
Species differentiation, foraging and, 24–29
Species-typical behavior, 321, 322, 339
    coastal perspectives, 332, 333
    communicative profiles, 335, 336
    cowbirds, 322–328
    ecological clocks, 337–339
    female flexibility, 329, 330
    inherited niches, 336, 337
    responsiveness, 333–335
    subspecies border, 330–332
Sperm
    orb-weaving spider and, 156–160, 162–164, 169–173
    vertebrate sexual behavior and, 278, 292
Sperm competition, 440
    deer mice and, 135–137, 139, 145, 147
    ground squirrel and, 181, 188–192, 195, 196
Spermophilus, *see* Ground squirrel
Spiders, mating and, 125–127
Spiny mice, 52, 53, 439
Spiny mice, littermates and, 300–302, 313–315
    characteristics, 305–309

feeding competition, 304, 305
huddling, 303, 304
recognition, 310–313
Squirrel monkeys, 230
Squirrels
    biological timing and, 263, 265–267
    mating and, 125, 126, 128
Starling
    biological timing and, 274
    recognition and, 377
Stelgidopteryx serripennis, *see* Rough-winged swallows
Strawberry finch, 352, 353
Stress, 446
    colony model and, 412, 423–427, 430
    communication and, 320
Strike-induced chemosensory searching, 114–116
Sturnus vulgaris, 377
Subpatch, 13
Subspecies
    song development and, 349, 350, 352–354
    species-typical behavior and, 327, 329–332
Subsystem
    feeding and, 2
    laboratory paradigms and, 34
Sulfur, Norway rats and, 70
Superstition
    feeding and, 3
    laboratory paradigms and, 40–42, 53
Suprachiasmatic nucleus
    doves and, 272–277
    parental care and, 222
Survival, 433
    allometry and, 89, 90
    brown tree snake and, 105
    colony model and, 423
    communication and, 317
    deer mice and, 130, 133
    doves and, 252, 253
    feeding and, 1, 5
    mating and, 125
    Norway rats and, 55, 57
    orb-weaving spider and, 150, 167, 173
    song development and, 342
    spiny mice and, 302, 308, 310
Swallows, 319, 435, 437, 439
Swallows, recognition and, 360, 361, 363–365, 379, 380
    cross-fostering experiments, 366–369
    field studies, 371, 372
    information analysis, 372–376
    natural observation, 366
    perceptual studies, 376–378
    playback experiments, 369–371
Swordtail fish, 209

System
  feeding and, 2
  laboratory paradigms and, 34

Tamarins, 439, 440
  monogamy and, 225–227, 229–235, 238,
    241–248
  parental care and, 221
Tamias striatus, 194
Tamiasciurus douglasii, 194
Taste aversion, 32, 51
Temporal organization, 222
Territory, 440, 445
  colony model and, 414
  deer mice and, 140
  golden hamster and, 388
  ground squirrel and, 178, 180, 182, 185
  laboratory paradigms and, 32
  mating and, 128
  monkeys and, 226, 229, 230, 232, 245,
    246, 251
  parental care and, 221
  Pavlovian conditioning and, 199–215, 218
  song development and, 340, 344, 345, 347,
    349–351, 353, 356
  vertebrate sexual behavior and, 283, 284
Testosterone
  communication and, 320
  golden hamster and, 387, 395, 400, 407,
    408
  song development and, 351, 355
  spiny mice and, 306
  vertebrate sexual behavior and, 289–295,
    297, 299
Timed response, laboratory paradigms and, 38,
    40–44
Timing
  doves and, *see* Doves, parental care and
  species-typical behavior and, 338
Tinbergen, N. 434–436
  brown tree snake and, 105, 106
  deer mice and, 130
  laboratory paradigms and, 32, 34, 37
  monkeys and, 226, 227, 245, 248
  parental care and, 221
  Pavlovian conditioning and, 198
Titi monkeys, 230, 250
Titmice, 8, 9
Toads
  spiny mice and, 301
  vertebrate sexual behavior and, 283
Tokens
  feeding and, 3
  laboratory paradigms and, 46, 51, 52
Traits
  allometry and, 82, 85, 88, 96, 100
  ground squirrel and, 176, 183–190

  swallows and, 364
Tree shrews, 301
Triazolam, 266
Trichogaster trichopterus, *see* Blue gourami
Tselesoobraznost, 197–199, 219
Tuning, laboratory paradigms and, 37, 38
Turkish hamster, 387, 393
Tutors, 353–356, 359, 444

Ultimate causation, 434, 435
Ultimate mechanisms, 342

Vaginal marking, golden hamster and, 384,
    386, 389, 391–398, 400, 402, 403, 405,
    407–409
Vasoactive intestinal polypeptide, 276
Vasopressin
  doves and, 276
  golden hamster and, 388
Vertebrate sexual behavior, 278, 279, 298, 299
  alternative patterns, 282–286
  behavioral complexity, 287, 288
  cascades, 289–295
  length of developments, 286, 287
  sex determination, 279, 280
  sexual differentiation, 280, 281
  social contributions, 288, 289
  webs, 295–298
Viper, 111–114, 116
Vomeronasal system, golden hamster and, 384,
    396, 397, 400, 401, 403–407, 409

Waterboatmen, 8
Webs, 446, 447
  parental care and, 223
  vertebrate sexual behavior and, 289,
    295–299
White-crowned sparrow, 438, 444, 445
  song development and, 340, 341, 349–356,
    358
Wing stroking, 442, 444
  communication and, 317
  species-typical behavior and, 324, 325, 334
Withdrawal, laboratory paradigms and, 43
Wound sites, 414–416, 424, 426

Xiphophorus helleri, 209

Yellow-bellied marmot, 179, 182, 189

Zebra finches, 284, 290
Zinc sulfate, 442
  golden hamster and, 400, 403
  spiny mice and, 308, 311
Zonotrichia leucophrys nuttalli, *see* White-
    crowned sparrow